A Charlton Standard Catalogue

Canadian Collector Coins
Royal Canadian Mint Issues
Volume Two

TENTH EDITION

2020

Mark Drake
Publisher

The Charlton Press

TORONTO, ONTARIO, CANADA

Library and Archives Canada Cataloguing in Publication

Canadian Coins (Charlton Press)
    Canadian Collector Coins: a Charlton Standard Catalogue. Volume Two:
    Royal Canadian Mint Issues

Annual
Canadian Collector Coins: a Charlton Standard Catalogue
ISSN 1928-8816
ISBN 978-0-88968-418-8

    1. Coins, Canadian--Catalogs. 2. Coins, Canadian--Prices--Periodicals.
and collecting. I. Title

CJ18610.S82 59- 2005-   737.4971'029   C2005-902187-X

**Printed in Canada
in the Province of Quebec**

EDITORIAL

Editor	Todd Sandham
Graphic Technician	Mary-Anne Luzba
Cover Photography	Royal Canadian Mint

SPECIAL MENTION

We would like to thank the Royal Canadian Mint for their help providing assistance with the 2019-2020 images and content. We would also like to thank all past contributors for submitting prices, answering requests or supplying information which assisted in building the many past editions of this catalogue.

CONTRIBUTORS TO THE TENTH EDITION

We would like to thank the following for their contributions to the 10th Edition of *Canadian Coins, Volume Two*: **Christie Paquet**, Senior Engraver, Royal Canadian Mint, Ottawa; **Jess Henrichs, Trevor Bishop, Kirk Parsons, Douglas Hawkes.**

COVER ILLUSTRATION:

6 oz. Pure Silver Gold-Plated Coin - Antique Carousel RCM Item #166265

A WORLD'S FIRST! Re-live the magic of an antique carousel with a MOVABLE miniature!

Round and round it goes! A fixture of regional fairs, travelling midways and amusement parks, the sights and sounds of a carousel (or merry-go-round) never fail to charm the young and young at heart. Rarer still is an antique carousel, whose lights, musical ambiance and fanciful décor are a beautiful invitation to step out of time and connect with a bygone age. From the "galloping" steeds to the old-time music, Canada's antique carousels have a rare ability to create a sense of magic and wonder that stays with us forever. Your pure silver coin allows you to re-live that enchantment through the selectively gold-plated reverse that typifies the carousel's fanciful décor. But atop the art of yester-year sits an extraordinary interactive feature that sets this coin apart: your very own miniature carousel.

The Charlton Press

Editorial Office
P.O. Box 414, Station F
Toronto, Ontario M4Y 2L8
Tel.: (416) 962-2665 • Toll Free: 1-866-663-8827
www.charltonpress.com email: chpress@charltonpress.com

APPLICATION FOR RCNA MEMBERSHIP / DEMANDE D'ADHÉSION À L' ARNC

Application for membership in **The Royal Canadian Numismatic Association** may be made by any reputable party upon payment of the required dues.
Les demandes d'adhésion à **l'Association royale de numismatique du Canada** peuvent être faites par une partie de bonne réputation sur paiement des frais exigés.

❑ Mr. / M.   ❑ Mrs. / Mme   ❑ Ms. / Mlle
❑ Renewal / Renouvèlement   ❑ Reinstatement / Réintégration *previous #_____*

Full Name / Nom   *for family membership include name of spouse / pour une adhésion familiale, inclure le nom du conjoint*

Mailing Address / Adresse postale complète

City / Ville   Province / State / État   Country / Pays   Postal Code/Zip

Phone / N° de téléphone   Email / Courriel

Signature of Applicant / Signature du demandeur   Sponsored By / Commandité par

Junior applicants (under age 18), state birth date / pour une adhésion junior (moins de 18 ans), inclure la date de naissance: _____

My numismatic speciality / spécialité numismatique (*optional/optionnel*): _____

❑ *I would like to be contacted by a mentor who also has my speciality. J'aimerais être mis en contact avec un mentor qui partage mes intérêt numismatiques.*

Membership Types: *Check only one* Types d'adhésion: *cochez une seule option*	Standard		Digital*	
	1 year	2 year	1 year	2 year
Regular: Canada and USA residents, age 18+ **Régulier:** adresses **Canadiennes et aux États-unis** (18 ans et plus)	❑ $45.00	❑ $88.00	❑ $34.00	❑ $66.00
Regular: Foreign (non-USA) **Régulier: étranger** (autre que les États-unis)	❑ $85.00	❑ $168.00	❑ $34.00	❑ $66.00
Junior: Applicants under age 18 *must be sponsored by a parent or guardian* *Les membres de moins de 18 ans doivent être commandités par un parent ou un gardien*	❑ $27.50	❑ $53.00	❑ $18.50	❑ $35.00
Family: Canada and USA residents. Member, spouse and children under age 18, (one printed and mailed *CN Journal* only) **Familial:** membre, époux (se) et enfants de moins de 18 ans. Un seul Journal	❑ $50.00	❑ $98.00	❑ $34.00	❑ $66.00
Corporate / Entreprises: Clubs, Societies / Sociétés, Libraries / Librairies and non-profit organizations / et autres organisations sans but lucratif	❑ $45.00	❑ $88.00	N.A.	N.A.
Life Membership / Adhésion à Vie:**	❑ $1,195.00		❑ $895.00	
Life Membership Senior: (65+) **Adhésion à Vie Aîné:**** (65 ans et plus)	❑ $895.00		❑ $695.00	
Life Membership Foreign: Adhésion à Vie Etranger:	❑ $2,195.00		❑ $895.00	

Dues shown are in Canadian$ to Canadian addresses and US$ to all international addresses and are exempt from Canadian sales taxes.

*   (A Digital Membership includes all of the benefits of membership except a printed copy of *The CN Journal*.)

**   (After one year of regular membership. Details of payment plan available on request.) Mail completed application with dues to:

Les cotisations sont indiquées en dollars canadiens à des adresses canadiennes, ou en dollars américains à toutes les autres adresses. Les cotisations sont exonérées de taxes sur les ventes domestiques.

*   (Adhésions numériques comprennent tous les avantages de l'adhésion, sauf une copie imprimée de *Le Journal canadien de numismatique*.)

**   (Après un an comme membre régulier. Détails du plan de paiement disponibles sur demande.) Envoyez la demande d'adhésion dûment complétée et le paiement à :

The Royal Canadian Numismatic Association
l'Association royale de numismatique du Canada

5694 Highway #7 East, Suite 432, Markham ON Canada L3P 1B4

Phone / Tel: 647-401-4014 Fax / Télécopie: 905-472-9645 Email / Courriel: *info@rcna.ca*

Apply online at: www.rcna.ca/paydues.php   01/01/2015

TABLE OF CONTENTS

INTRODUCTION xvi

ONE CENT... 2

      One Cent Derivatives 7

THREE CENTS 7

FIVE CENTS 8

      Five Cent Derivatives 10

TEN CENTS 14

      Ten Cent Derivatives 18

TWENTY-FIVE CENTS 19

      Twenty-Five Cent Derivatives 60

FIFTY CENTS 62

      Fifty Cent Derivatives 89

ONE DOLLAR ISSUES

      Silver Dollar Issues, 1971-2019 90

      Cased Nickel Dollar Issues, 1968-1984 117

      Nickel-Bronze Dollar Proof Issues, 1987-1995 121

      Nickel-Bronze Dollar Specimen Issues, The Bird Series, 1997-2019 122

      Nickel-Bronze Dollar Proof Issues, 2002-2012 124

      Loon Style Nickel Dollar Issues, 2008-2010 126

      Loon Style Sterling and Fine Silver Dollar Proof Issues, 2004-2019 129

      Three-Ply Brass-Plated Steel Dollar Issues, 2014-2019 132

      One Dollar Derivatives 135

TWO DOLLARS 136

      Two Dollar Derivatives 145

THREE DOLLARS 146

FOUR DOLLARS 161

FIVE DOLLARS 163

      Five Dollar Derivatives 179

FIVE AND TEN DOLLARS 180

EIGHT DOLLARS 189

      Eight Dollar Derivatives 195

TEN DOLLARS 196

      Ten Dollar Derivatives 226

FIFTEEN DOLLARS 227

TWENTY DOLLARS 242

      Twenty Dollar Derivatives 341

TWENTY FIVE DOLLARS 342

THIRTY DOLLARS 357

FIFTY DOLLARS 372

ONE HUNDRED DOLLARS 387

ONE HUNDRED TWENTY-FIVE DOLLARS 394

TWO HUNDRED DOLLARS 396

TWO HUNDRED FIFTY DOLLARS 397

FIVE HUNDRED DOLLARS 407

SILVER SPECIAL ISSUE SETS 409

GOLD COINS

ONE CENT 410

TWENTY-FIVE CENTS 410

FIFTY CENTS 412

ONE DOLLAR 415

FIVE DOLLARS 416

FIVE AND TEN DOLLARS 419

TEN DOLLARS 420

TWENTY DOLLARS 422

TWENTY-FIVE DOLLARS 423

FIFTY DOLLARS 424

SEVENTY-FIVE DOLLARS 426

ONE HUNDRED DOLLARS 429

ONE HUNDRED FIFTY DOLLARS 435

ONE HUNDRED SEVENTY-FIVE DOLLARS 438

TWO HUNDRED DOLLARS 439

TWO HUNDRED FIFTY DOLLARS 454

THREE HUNDRED DOLLARS 458

THREE HUNDRED FIFTY DOLLARS 465

FIVE HUNDRED DOLLARS 468

ONE THOUSAND DOLLARS 472

ONE THOUSAND TWO HUNDRED FIFTY DOLLARS 472

TWO THOUSAND FIVE HUNDRED DOLLARS 473

ONE HUNDRED THOUSAND DOLLAR GOLD COIN 480

GOLD AND SILVER SETS 481

PALLADIUM COINS

FIFTY DOLLARS 482

PLATINUM COINS

FIVE DOLLARS 483

THREE HUNDRED DOLLARS 484

COLLECTOR SETS

SPECIAL RCM WRAPPED ROLLS OF COINS 486

FIRST AND LAST DAY OF ISSUE CARDS 488

BOOKMARKS 489

COLLECTOR CARDS FOR CIRCULATION COINAGE, 2004-2018 490

PROOF-LIKE SETS, 1954-1967
    Six Coin Silver Proof-Like Sets, 1954-1960 492
    Six Coin Silver Proof-Like Sets, 1961-1967 493

BRILLIANT UNCIRCULATED AND UNCIRCULATED SETS, 1968-2006
    Six Coin Nickel Brilliant Uncirculated Sets, 1968-1987 494
    Six Coin Nickel Brilliant Uncirculated Sets, 1988-1996 496
    Seven Coin Nickel Brilliant Uncirculated Sets with Specimen Finish, 1997 496
    Seven Coin Nickel Brilliant Uncirculated Sets, 1998-2000 497
    Five Coin Multi-Ply Plated Steel Test Set for 1999 497
    Seven Coin Multi-Ply Plated Steel Brilliant Uncirculated Sets,
        "P" Composition Mark, 2001-2006 497

SPECIAL EDITION BRILLIANT UNCIRCULATED SETS, 2002-2010
    Queen Elizabeth II, Diademed Portrait, Golden Jubilee, 1952-2002 498
    Queen Elizabeth II, Mature Portrait, 2003..498
    Centenaries of Alberta and Saskatchewan, 2005..499
    10th Anniversary of the Two Dollar Coin, RCM Logo, 2006......................................499
    Seven Coin Multi-Ply Plated Steel Brilliant Uncirculated Sets,
        Maple Leaf Logo, 2007-2010 500
    Seven Coin Multi-Ply Plated Steel Uncirculated Sets,
        Maple Leaf Logo, 2011-2012 500
    Vancouver 2010 Winter Olympic Games, 2007-2008..501
    Vanvouver 2010 Winter Olympic Games, 2009-2010...502

SPECIAL EDITION UNCIRCULATED SETS, 2010-2019
    Special Edition Uncirculated Set, 2010..502
    Special Edition Uncirculated Sets, 2011-2012..503
    Special Edition Uncirulated Sets, 2012-2013
        The War of 1812 503
    Special Edition Uncirculated Sets, 2013-2014..504
    Special Edition Uncirculated Sets, 2015-2017..504
    Six Coin Multi-Ply Plated Steel Uncirculated Sets,
        Maple Leaf Logo, 2013-2019 505

TEST TOKEN SETS 505

MISCELLANEOUS GIFT SETS, 1983-2019 506

CONGRATULATIONS / GRADUATION GIFT SETS, 2004-2008 507

NHL TEAM GIFT SETS, 2006-2009 508

OH! CANADA! GIFT SETS, 1994-2019 509

BABY GIFT SETS, 1995-2019 511

HOLIDAY GIFT SETS, 2004-2018 513

WEDDING GIFTS SETS, 2004-2019 514

BIRTHDAY GIFT SETS, 2004-2019 515

VANCOUVER 2010 WINTER OLYMPIC AND PARALYMPIC GAMES
    Coin and Stamp Sets, 2010 516

COMMEMORATIVE CANADIAN COIN, TOKEN, OR MEDAL SETS, 2010-2013 517

SEVEN COIN NICKEL CUSTOM SETS, 1971-1975 518

SPECIMEN SETS, 1970-2019
    Six Coin Nickel Specimen Set, 1970 519
    Seven Coin Nickel Custom Specimen Sets, 1976-1980 519
    Six Coin Nickel Specimen Sets, 1981-1996 520
    Seven Coin Nickel Specimen Sets, 1997-2000 520
    Six or Seven Coin Multi-Ply Plated Steel
       Specimen Sets, 2001-2019...521

SPECIAL EDITION SPECIMEN SETS, 1967 AND 2010-2015
    100th Anniversary of Confederation, 1867-1967 522
    Special Edition "Young Wildlife" Specimen Sets, 2010-2015..522
    Special Edition "Canadian Arctic Expedition" Specimen Set, 2013 522

PRESTIGE SETS, 1971-1980
    Seven Coin Prestige Sets, 1971-1980...523

PROOF SETS, 1981-2019
    Seven Standard Coins, 1981-1995 524
    Seven Coin Set with Four Sterling Silver Coins, 1996 524
    Eight Coin Set with Five Sterling Silver Coins, 1997-2012 525
    Premium Proof Sets, 2012-2019..526
    Proof Sets, 2014-2019 526

SPECIAL ISSUE PROOF SETS, 1994-2011
    Special Limited Edition Proof Sets, 1994-1995...527
    90th Anniversary of the Royal Canadian Mint, 1908-1998...527
    Special Limited Edition Proof Sets, 2002-2003..528
    Premium Gift Baby and Wedding Sterling Silver Proof Sets, 2006-2008 528
    Special Limited Edition Proof Set, 2010..529
    Special Limited Edition Proof Set, 1911-2011 529

SPECIAL ISSUE COIN SETS, 2017-2019
    Royal Canadian Mint Coin Lore Series, 2017-2019...530

PROOF GOLD SET, 2012
    Year of the Dragon, 2012..535

PROOF PLATINUM SETS
    Canadian Wildlife Series, 1990-1994 536
    Endangered Wildlife Series, 1995-2004 538

Note: 1. For some sets the mintage was pre-announced as a maximum number of sets to be issued. In other cases the mintage was open-ended with the issue period a function of time. In the pricing tables for sets the mintage number denotes the number of sets sold. The final number is usually only available after a second year of RCM Reports.

2. Within the set listings are sets with different finishes and compositions. Currently the four main finish categories are Uncirculated, Brilliant Uncirculated, Specimen and Proof. Usually, these sets contain exact design copies of the circulating business strike coins, but there are a few exceptions when commemorative coins are involved.

3. For a complete explanation on finishes, see pages xvi-xvii in the introduction.

MAPLE LEAF BULLION COINS

GOLD MAPLE LEAFS   542

PLATINUM MAPLE LEAFS   562

PALLADIUM MAPLE LEAFS   567

SILVER MAPLE LEAFS   568

SILVER MAPLE LEAF DERIVATIVES   592

INTRODUCTION

The first non-circulating legal tender coin (NCLT) struck in Canada was a 1908 Edward VII gold sovereign. This coin was struck at the Ottawa Branch Mint in specimen quality along with specimen examples of the other five denominations (one cent, five cents, ten cents, twenty-five cents and fifty cents) that made up the circulating coins of the day. The difference between the five subsidiary coins and the gold sovereign was that the latter, being struck only in specimen quality, had no circulating counterpart. While the 1908 gold sovereign was not a commemorative issue, the current thinking is that it was struck to establish a series. There are still a few questions regarding this NCLT coin that have yet to be answered. One is "How was it distributed?"

Modern Canadian NCLT coinage began with the issue of the 1967 centennial anniversary specimen gold set. This set contained seven coins, the most important being a $20 gold coin. This coin was similar to the 1908 sovereign in that there was no circulating counterpart. This coin also set the stage for the next forty years. The Royal Canadian Mint sold 334,288 gold sets in 1967, creating a production bottleneck that was not cleared until well into 1968. The sales volume of 1967 collector coins was not lost on the organising officials of the Montreal 1976 Olympics games, for 1972 saw the beginning of the greatest issue of NCLT coins in Canadian history.

Canadian Collector Coins, Volume Two: Collector Issues, 2020, tenth edition, records and lists over forty years of non-circulating legal tender coins issued by the Royal Canadian Mint in Canada.

COMMEMORATIVE COINS

Commemorative coins are issued to commemorate a particular personage, event, either historic or current, or a place. Such coins have a distinct design with reference to the occasion for which they are issued. Many coins of this category are collector items only, but a great number were issued for circulation to promote a major national event, such as the Vancouver 2010 Olympic Winter Games.

Vast numbers of thematic coins highlighting monuments, sites, historical personalities, endangered species, or just wild species common to a specific area, are now being inserted into this commemorative mix. The line between commemorative and thematic coins is blurred, and probably intentionally so.

Types of Commemoratives

We shall include thematic coins among the commemoratives. Commemorative/thematic coins can be divided into two categories:

1. Commemorative/thematic legal tender circulating issues.

These are the everyday coins used in commerce which bear a design commemorating an event. They are issued at face value, without a premium, within a certain time frame. Usually, the concept is centred on one denomination, but may encompass all denominations for an event of outstanding national significance such as the Centennial of Confederation. This category of commemorative is issued in "business strike" or circulation finish.

2. Non circulating legal tender commemorative/thematic issues.

NCLT coins are deemed legal tender by a mint, but there is no expectation that they will be released into circulation. In theory, they may be used in commerce to purchase goods and services, but their recognition as a medium of exchange, and their acceptance by the modern day public, is questionable. In this category we will find single coins and sets, depending on how the issuing authorities developed their marketing strategies. The selling price has no relationship either to the face value or the intrinsic value. The selling price, intrinsic value and face value diminish in that order. The issuing authorities generally have no intention ever to redeem commemorative or thematic issues.

The earlier issues may command a substantial market price increase over the original issue price because of the increased intrinsic value of precious metals. Modern commemorative coins usually need time and additional increases in intrinsic value to return a profit.

FINISHES

Sales of modern collector coins are basically driven by the finish on the coins. The Royal Canadian Mint currently uses nine different finishes. See the next page for an outline of the different finishes used. A collector should be well versed in the different finishes as they will, at times, greatly affect the value of the issue.

SETS VS. SERIES

Coins with themes issued in a single year have been designated as sets. Coins with themes issued over multiple years have been designated as series.

FRATERNAL AFFILIATION

Over the years, coin clubs have sprung up in many Canadian communities. In addition, both Canada and the United States have national organisations which hold annual conventions. Coin clubs constitute one of the most attractive features of present-day collecting. They offer beginning collectors the opportunity for good fellowship and the encouragement and knowledge of more experienced collectors. The larger groups maintain lending libraries and publish a journal or newsletter on a regular basis.

Memberships and other information can be obtained from:

Royal Canadian Numismatic Association
5694 Highway # 7 East, Suite 432
Markham, Ontario
Canada L3P 1B4
Tel.: (647) 401-4014 Fax: (905) 472-9645
Email: info@rcna.ca

Ontario Numismatic Association
P.O. Box 40033, Waterloo Sq. P.O.
75 King Street South
Waterloo, Ontario
Canada N2J 4V1
www.ontario-numismatic.org/index.html

COLLECTOR COINS
Finishes 1953 to 2020

Introduction: A coin finish simply means the surface quality imparted to a blank during the striking process. At the striking stage the main factors influencing the quality of the finish are: (1) the quality of the blanks, (2) the finish of the dies, (3) the speed and pressure of the press, and (4) the number of times the blank is struck.

Circulation Finish: *Brilliant Relief Against a Satin Background.* This is the most common finish found on all business strikes, from the one cent to the two dollar coins. These are production coins struck at the rate of 700 to 800 per minute. They are allowed to tumble into waiting hoppers, then put through counting and wrapping machines before being sent to the banks.

Uncirculated Finish: *Brilliant Relief Against a Satin Background.* This process is very similar to the circulation finish above with common dies being used, but with slower striking speeds and definitely more care in the loading and unloading of the press. There are far fewer handling marks than the circulation variety, but still marks may be found.

The Uncirculated finish is used by the Numismatic Department of the Mint on singles and sets offered to collectors, or sold into the giftware market.

Proof-Like Finish: *Frosted to Semi-Mirror Relief Against a Semi-Mirror Background.* These coins are produced on a slow moving press with reasonably high pressure. The planchets and dies are polished with each coin being removed from the press individually. Large coins may be struck more than once.

The following die states are found on proof-like coins:

(1) **Ultra Heavy Cameo:** Full frosting across the relief of the coin, both effigy and legend, when viewed from all directions under full lighting conditions.

(2) **Heavy Cameo:** The frosting is neither full nor evenly applied across the relief of the coin. In fact, some areas may appear bright when viewed under full lighting conditions.

(3) **Cameo:** Touches of frosting may appear on the relief of the coin. There will be bright areas when the coin is viewed under full lighting conditions.

(4) **No Cameo:** No frosting, all relief areas will appear bright. There is no difference in contrast between the bright field and a bright relief. The majority of coins are from this die state.

Nickel has a hardness higher than silver making the striking of coins more difficult. In 1968 with the change from silver to nickel coinage came the need for a new finish on numismatic items. That finish is:

SP-68 / PR-69   This price is based on the item still being in the original package as issued by the Mint.

SP-69 / PR-70   This price is based on the item being graded by a reputable third-party grading company.

Brilliant Uncirculated Finish: *Brilliant Design, Legends and Dates Against a Brilliant Background.* Coins are struck by a slow moving press using high pressure, and polished dies. Blanks are inserted, and coins removed by hand. This finish was used on all packaged singles and sets offered by the Mint from 1968 to 2004. In 2004 production of sets was divided between Uncirculated and Brilliant Uncirculated.

Specimen Finish: From 1968 to 2020 there have been six different modifications used by the Mint on specimen coinage.

1858-1881:	**A Brilliant Relief Against a Brilliant Background.**
1902-1938:	**A Frosted Relief against a Frosted Background.**
1937-1967:	**A Brilliant Relief against a Brilliant Background.**
1968-1995:	**A Brilliant Relief against a Brilliant Background**
1996-2009:	**A Brilliant Relief, Frosted Legends and Date against a Lined Background**
2010-2020:	**A Brilliant Relief, Frosted Legends and Date against a Laser Lined Background**

Proof Finish: Frosted Relief Against a Mirror Field. This is the highest quality finish used by the Royal Canadian Mint on Canadian coinage. By definition, all coins with this finish are designated Ultra Heavy Cameo (UHC). They are identified in the pricing tables by PR.

Reverse Proof Finish: Mirror Relief Against a Frosted Background. This type of finish is at times called "satin matte" because of the background texture. All elements of the design that are in relief have a highly reflective finish.

Bullion Finish: Brilliant Relief Against a Parallel Lined Background. This finish was first used in 1979 on gold maple leafs for the bullion program. The finish is found on gold, platinum, palladium and silver maples. As this finish is the standard used on the maple leaf issues the grading designation is Mint State (MS). Starting in 2014, a new finish was introduced with brilliant relief against a radiating lined background. This was done to provide advanced visual security.

Bullion-Specimen (Reverse Proof): Brilliant Relief Against a Satin Background. A finish not often used, it can be found on special edition bullion singles and sets.

Bullion-Proof: Frosted Relief Against a Mirror Background. This finish is the same as that found on all numismatic proof issues.

ONE CENT

ONE CENT, ROUND, ELIZABETH II PROOF, 1997-2012.

From 1997 to 2012 the composition of the one cent coin included in the Standard Proof Set fluctuated between bronze and copper. The one cent coin in the Premium Proof Set for 2012 was struck on a fine silver planchet.

The last bronze cent issued for circulation was struck in 1996. It was a 12-sided coin and is listed in *Canadian Coins, Numismatic Issues, Volume One.*

| Obverse
1997-2003 | Obverse
2004-2006
Without Mint Logo | Obverse
2007-2012
With Mint Logo | Reverse
1997-2012 |

Designers:

Obv.:	1997-2003:	Dora de Pédery-Hunt
	2004-2012:	Susanna Blunt
Rev.:	1997-2012:	G. E. Kruger-Gray

Engravers:

Obv.:	1997-2003:	Dora de Pédery-Hunt
	2004-2012:	Susan Taylor
Rev.:	1997-2012:	Thomas Shingles

	Bronze	**Copper**	**Silver**
Composition:	98.0% Cu, 0.5% Sn, 0.15% Zn	1.00% Cu	99.99% Ag, Selectively gold plated
Silver content:			3.0 g, 0.096 tr oz
Weight:	2.5 g	2.5 g	3.05 g
Diameter:	19.1 mm	19.1 mm	19.05 mm
Thickness:	1.45 mm	1.45 mm	1.3 mm
Edge:	Plain	Plain	Plain
Die Axis:	↑↑	↑↑	↑↑
Finish:	Proof	Proof	Proof
Case of Issue:	Included in Proof Sets, see page 529		

DATE	DESCRIPTION	COMP.	QUANTITY SOLD	ISSUE PRICE	FINISH	PR-69	PR-70
1997	Diademed Portrait / Maple Twig	Bronze	113,647	N.I.I.	Proof	10.	—
1998		Bronze	93,632	N.I.I.	Proof	10.	—
1999		Bronze	95,113	N.I.I.	Proof	10.	—
2000		Bronze	90,921	N.I.I.	Proof	10.	—
2001		Bronze	74,194	N.I.I.	Proof	10.	—
2002		Bronze	65,315	N.I.I.	Proof	15.	—
2003		Bronze	62,007	N.I.I.	Proof	15.	—
2004	Uncrowned Portrait / Maple Twig	Copper	57,614	N.I.I.	Proof	15.	—
2005		Copper	63,562	N.I.I.	Proof	15.	—
2006		Bronze	53,822	N.I.I.	Proof	15.	—
2007	Uncrowned Portrait, Mint Logo / Maple Twig	Copper	37,413	N.I.I.	Proof	15.	—
2008		Copper	38,630	N.I.I.	Proof	15.	—
2009		Bronze	27,549	N.I.I.	Proof	15.	—
2010		Copper	32,342	N.I.I.	Proof	15.	—
2011		Copper	32,910	N.I.I.	Proof	15.	—
2012		Copper	27,254	N.I.I.	Proof	15.	—
2012	Premium Proof Set, Selectively gold plated	Silver	19,789	N.I.I.	Proof	60.	—

ONE CENT, 90TH ANNIVERSARY OF THE ROYAL CANADIAN MINT, 1908-1998.

To commemorate the opening of the Royal Canadian Mint in 1908 a five-coin set was issued featuring the original reverse designs that appeared on the 1908 coins, except the coins now feature the double date 1908-1998. The set was issued in two finishes, matte and mirror proof. The matte set cent does not carry the country of origin "Canada". This error was corrected on the mirror proof issues.

Matte Proof Issue
Without "CANADA"
on Obverse

Mirror Proof Issue
Reverse

Mirror Proof Issue
With "CANADA"
on Obverse

Designers and Engravers:
Obv.: Dora de Pédery-Hunt
Rev.: Ago Aarand, G. W. DeSaulles
Composition: 92.5% Ag, 7.5% Cu, Copper plate
Silver content: 5.24 g, 0.169 tr oz
Weight: 5.67 g
Diameter: 25.4 mm
Thickness: 1.5 mm   **Die Axis:** ↑↑
Edge: Plain   **Finish:** See below
Case of Issue: See Special Issue Proof Sets, page 529

DATE	DESCRIPTION	QUANTITY SOLD	ISSUE PRICE	FINISH	PR-68	PR-69
1998 (1908-)	Matte proof, Without "CANADA"	18,376	N.I.I.	Matte Proof	35.	—
1998 (1908-)	Mirror proof, With "CANADA"	24,893	N.I.I.	Mirror Proof	25.	—

ONE CENT, 50TH ANNIVERSARY OF THE CORONATION OF QUEEN ELIZABETH II, 1953-2003.

This one cent coin which carries the double date 1953-2003 is from the Special Edition Proof Set issued in 2003 to commemorate the 50th anniversary of the Coronation of Queen Elizabeth II.

Designers and Engravers:
Obv.: Mary Gillick, Dora de Pédery-Hunt
Rev.: G. E. Kruger-Gray Edge: Plain
Composition: Copper
Weight: 2.5 g
Case of Issue: See Special Issue Proof Sets, page 528

Diameter: 19.05 mm
Thickness: 1.25 mm

Die Axis: ↑↑
Finish: Proof

DATE	DESCRIPTION	QUANTITY SOLD	ISSUE PRICE	FINISH	PR-69	PR-70
2003 (1953-)	50th Anniv. Coronation Queen Elizabeth II	21,537	N.I.I.	Proof	25.	—

ONE CENT, ROYAL CANADIAN MINT ANNUAL REPORT, SELECTIVELY GOLD PLATED, 2003.

This one cent coin is the first in a series of six coins, one of which was to be included each year with the Annual Mint Report, leading up to the Royal Canadian Mint's centennial in 2008. However, this series was discontinued with the issue of the 2006 Annual Mint Report. See the One Cent Derivatives listed on page 7.

Designers and Engravers:
Obv.: Dora de Pédery-Hunt, Ago Aarand
Rev.: G. E. Kruger-Gray
Composition: Copper plated zinc, Selectively gold plated
Weight: 2.25 g   **Edge:** Plain
Diameter: 19.05 mm   **Die Axis:** ↑↑
Thickness: 1.45 mm   **Finish:** Proof
Case of Issue: See Derivatives, page 7

DATE	DESCRIPTION	QUANTITY SOLD	ISSUE PRICE	FINISH	PR-69	PR-70
2003	Copper plated zinc, Selectively gold plated	7,746	N.I.I.	Proof	50.	—

ONE CENT, 75TH ANNIVERSARY OF THE VOYAGEUR DOLLAR PROOF SET, 1935-2010.

This one cent coin is from the Special Limited Edition Proof Set issued in 2010 to commemorate Emanuel Hahn's classic voyageur design which first appeared on the 1935 silver dollar.

Designers and Engravers:

Obv.:	Sir. E. B. MacKennal
Rev.:	Fred Lewis
Composition:	Copper
Weight:	2.5 g
Diameter:	19.05 mm
Thickness:	1.45 mm
Case of Issue:	See Special Issue Proof Sets, page 529

Edge:	Plain
Die Axis:	↑↑
Finish:	Proof

DATE	DESCRIPTION	RCM ITEM #	QUANTITY SOLD	ISSUE PRICE	FINISH	PR-69	PR-70
2010 (1935-)	75th Anniv. Voyageur Silver Dollar Proof Set	111020	4,996	N.I.I.	Proof	25.	—

ONE CENT, 100TH ANNIVERSARY OF THE STRIKING OF CANADA'S 1911 SILVER DOLLAR, 1911-2011.

This one cent coin which carries the double date 1911-2011 is from the Special Edition Proof Set issued in 2011 to commemorate the 100th anniversary of the striking of Canada's 1911 silver dollar.

Designers and Engravers:

Obv.:	Sir E. B. MacKennal
Rev.:	Original design by L. C. Wyon, Modified by W. H. J. Blakemore
Composition:	Copper
Weight:	5.67 g
Diameter:	25.4 mm
Thickness:	1.6 mm
Edge:	Plain
Case of Issue:	See Special Issue Proof Sets, page 529

Die Axis:	↑↑
Finish:	Proof

DATE	DESCRIPTION	RCM ITEM #	QUANTITY SOLD	ISSUE PRICE	FINISH	PR-68	PR-69
2011 (1911-)	100th Anniv. Canada's 1911 Silver Dollar	114121	5,952	N.I.I.	Proof	40.	—

ONE CENT, FAREWELL TO THE PENNY, SELECTIVELY GOLD PLATED, 2012.

The last one cent coin was struck at the Royal Canadian Mint on May 4th, 2012. This half-ounce silver one cent coin was issued to mark the end of production of Canada's one-cent piece.

Designers and Engravers:

Obv.:	Susanna Blunt, Susan Taylor
Rev.:	G. E. Kruger-Gray, RCM Staff
Composition:	99.99% Ag, Selectively gold plated
Silver content:	15.87 g, 0.5 tr oz
Weight:	15.87 g
Diameter:	34.0 mm
Thickness:	2.2 mm
Finish:	Proof
Case of Issue:	Maroon leatherette clam style case, black flocked insert, encapsulated coin, COA, custom box

Edge:	Reeded
Die Axis:	↑↑

DATE	DESCRIPTION	RCM ITEM #	QUANTITY SOLD	ISSUE PRICE	FINISH	PR-69	PR-70
2012	Fine silver, (½ oz), Selectively gold plated	121186	29,998	54.95	Proof	65.	—

ONE CENT, FINE SILVER, 2012.

These coins are from the five-coin "Farewell to the Penny" special limited edition proof set issued in 2012.

Edward VII / Small Leaves Design

George V / Small Leaves Design

George V / Two Maples Leaves Design

George W. DeSaulles	George W. DeSaulles	Sir E.B. MacKennal
W. H. J. Blakemore	Sir E. B. MacKennal	Fred Lewis

Elizabeth II / Centennial Design

Elizabeth II / Maple Twig Design

Arnold Machin	Alex Colville	Susanna Blunt	G. E. Kruger-Gray

Designers:
| Obv.: | See obverse illustrations |
| Rev.: | See reverse illustrations |

Composition: 99.99% Ag
Silver content: 14.7 g, 0.473 (per set)
Weight: 2.94 g (per coin); 14.7 (set)
Diameter: 19.1
Thickness: 1.25 mm
Case of Issue: See Special Issue Proof Sets, page 554

Engravers:
| Obv.: | Susan Taylor |
| Rev.: | Samantha Strath |

Edge: Plain
Die Axis: ↑↑
Finish: Proof

DATE	DESCRIPTION	RCM ITEM #	QUANTITY SOLD	ISSUE PRICE	FINISH	PR-69	PR-70
2012	Edward VII / Small Leaves Design	N/A	N/A	N.I.I.	Proof	80.	—
2012	George V / Small Leaves Design with CANADA	N/A	N/A	N.I.I.	Proof	80.	—
2012	George V / Two Maple Leaves Design	N/A	N/A	N.I.I.	Proof	80.	—
2012	Elizabeth II / Centennial Design	N/A	N/A	N.I.I.	Proof	80.	—
2012	Elizabeth II /Maple Twig Design	N/A	N/A	N.I.I.	Proof	80.	—
2012	Farwell to the Penny 5-coin set	121188	5,001	149.95	Proof	375.	

ONE CENT, THE PENNY, FIVE OUNCE SILVER COIN, 2012.

This five-ounce silver one cent coin was issued to mark the end of production of Canada's one cent piece.

Designers and Engravers:
| Obv.: | Susanna Blunt, Susan Taylor |
| Rev.: | G. E. Kruger-Gray, RCM Staff |

Composition: 99.99% Ag
Silver content: 157.6 g, 5.06 tr oz
Weight: 157.6 g
Diameter: 65.0 mm
Thickness: N/A
Case of Issue: Maroon leatherette clam style case, black flocked insert, encapsulated coin, COA, custom box

Edge: Reeded
Die Axis: ↑↑
Finish: Proof

DATE	DESCRIPTION	RCM ITEM #	QUANTITY SOLD	ISSUE PRICE	FINISH	PR-69	PR-70
2012	Fine silver, (5 oz), The Penny	122053	1,499	495.95	Proof	600.	—

Note: Coin illustrated smaller than actual size.

ONE CENT, THE LEGACY OF THE PENNY, 2017.

This 5-coin set commemorates the 5th anniversary of the end of the penny's production.

Small leaves design (1908)
Designer and Engraver: George W. DeSaulles

Small leaves design (1911)
Designer: W.H.J. Blakemore Obverse: Sir E.B. MacKennal

Two maple leaves design (1920)
Designer: Fred Lewis
Engraver: Sir E.B. MacKennal

Centennial design (1967)
Designer: Alex Colville
Engraver: Arnold Machin

Maple twig design (1982)
Designer: G.E. Kruger-Gray
Engraver: Arnold Machin

Designers:
  Obv.:   See illustrations
  Rev.:   See illustrations

Engravers:
  Obv.:   See illustrations
  Rev.:   See illustrations

Composition: 99.99% Ag, selective rose gold plating
Silver content: 157.6 g, 5.06 tr oz

	Small leaves design (1908)	Small leaves design (1911)	Two maple leaves design (1920)	Centennial design (1967)	Maple twig design (1982)
Weight:	62.67 g	62.67 g	31.39 g	31.39 g	31.39 g
Diameter:	54.0 mm	54.0 mm	38.0 mm	38.0 mm	38.0 mm
Thickness:	N/A				
Edge:	Reeded				
Die Axis:	↑↑				
Finish:	Proof				
Case of Issue:	Wooden collector's case with black beauty box. COA				

DATE	DESCRIPTION	RCM ITEM #	QUANTITY SOLD	ISSUE PRICE	FINISH	PR-69	PR-70
2017	Legacy of the Penny Set, Fine silver	158117	1,946	709.95	Proof	550.	—

SPECIAL NOTE ON FINISHES

It is very important to understand the different finishes the Royal Canadian Mint uses on their various issues. These finishes are altered from time-to-time as the Mint develops new products.

For example, the brilliant relief against a parallel lined background finish first used on bullion coins was carried forward in 1996 to be used on the coins contained in the specimen set.

In 2006 this finish was used on giftware coins such as the twenty-five cent coin issued to celebrate the 80th birthday of Queen Elizabeth II.

In 2010 a new specimen finish, brilliant relief against a laser-lined background, was used for the coins contained in the specimen set. There are now two different specimen finishes being utilised on Canadian coinage.

Circulation and Brilliant Uncirculated (proof-like) finishes are another very confusing mixture of finishes, see pages xvi-xvii for a further explanation.

BIG COIN SERIES

ONE CENT, THE PENNY, FIVE OUNCE SILVER COIN – BIG COIN SERIES, 2017-2018.

The 1957 Canadian Centennial circulation coins recall a momentous anniverary, these iconic coin designs make their return once more in this stunning Big Coin series, beginning with one-cent coin designed by Alex Colville. Other coins in the set include a 5¢ coin (page 12), 10¢ coin (page 17), 25¢ coin (page 57), 50¢ coin (page 89), $1 coin (page 131) and a $2 coin (page 145).

Designers and Engravers:
Obv.:	Susanna Blunt, Susan Taylor
Rev.:	2017: Alex Colville
	2018: G.E. Kruger-Gray

Silver content: 157.58 g, 5.06 tr oz
Weight: 157.6 g
Diameter: 65.25 mm
Thickness: N/A
Case of Issue: Maroon clam style case, black flocked insert, encapsulated coin, COA, custom box

Composition:
2017:	99.99% Ag, Selectively gold plated
2018:	99.99% Ag, Selectively rose gold-plated

Edge: Reeded
Die Axis: ↑↑
Finish: Proof

DATE	DESCRIPTION	RCM ITEM #	MINTAGE	ISSUE PRICE	FINISH	PR-69	PR-70
2017	Big Coin, The Penny	154729	2,150	559.95	Proof	600.	—
2018	Big Coin, One-Cent	164542	1,434	559.95	Proof	560.	—

ONE CENT DERIVATIVES

DATE	DESCRIPTION	QUANTITY SOLD	ISSUE PRICE	ISSUER	FINISH	MARKET VALUE
2003	**2003 Annual Mint Report**, One cent coin, selectively gold plated	7,746	19.95	RCM	PR-69	50.
2003	**Coronation Coin and Stamp Set**, two one cent coins, 1953 and 2003; two fifty cent coins, 2002 Jubilee and 2003 Uncrowned Portrait; two mint and two cancelled stamps of Her Majesty's Jubilee and Coronation; Presentation Case	14,743	22.95	RCM, CP	MS-65	25.

THREE CENTS

THREE CENTS, 150TH ANNIVERSARY OF CANADA'S FIRST POSTAGE STAMP, 2001.

Sir Sandford Fleming's (1851) Three Pence Beaver was Canada's first postage stamp and a symbol of the transfer of postal authority from Britain to Canada.

Designers and Engravers:
Obv.:	Dora de Pédery-Hunt
Rev.:	Sir Sandford Fleming, Cosme Saffioti

Composition: 92.5% Ag, 7.5% Cu, 24-karat gold plate
Silver content: 4.95 g, 0.159 tr oz
Weight: 5.35 g
Diameter: 21.3 mm
Thickness: 1.9 mm
Case of Issue: See Derivatives below

Edge: Plain
Die Axis: ↑↑
Finish: Proof

DATE	DESCRIPTION	QUANTITY SOLD	ISSUE PRICE	FINISH	PR-69	PR-70
2001	Three Cent Beaver	59,573	N.I.I.	Proof	25.	—

THREE CENT DERIVATIVES

DATE	DESCRIPTION	QUANTITY SOLD	ISSUE PRICE	FINISH	PR-69	PR-70
2001	Three Cents, Medallion, Stamp set, Maroon leatherette case, COA	59,573	39.95	RCM, CP	25.	—

FIVE CENTS

FIVE CENTS, ELIZABETH II PROOF, 1996-2019.

Starting in 1996 the five-cent coin issued in the proof set, previously struck from cupronickel, was now struck on a sterling silver planchet. The use of sterling silver planchets was discontinued in 2011.

The year 2012 saw the introduction of the Premium Proof Set in which all coins were struck on fine silver planchets.

Standard Proof Sets were issued for 2012, 2014-2019. The five-cent coin in these sets was struck on a nickel planchet.

| Obverse 1996-2003 | Obverse 2004-2006, 2015-2019 Without Mint Logo | Obverse 2007-2014 With Mint Logo | Obverse 2017 With Canada 150 Logo | Reverse 1996-2019 Reverse | 2017 Living Traditions |

Designers:
Obv.:   1996-2003:   Dora de Pédery-Hunt
        2004-2019:   Susanna Blunt
Rev.:   1996-2016:   G. E. Kruger-Gray
        2017:   Gerald Gloade

Engravers:
Obv.:   1996-2003:   Dora de Pédery-Hunt
        2004-2019:   Susan Taylor
Rev.:   1996-2016:   Thomas Shingles

	Sterling Silver	Nickel	Fine Silver
Composition:	92.5% Ag, 7.5% Cu	100.% Ni	99.99% Ag
Silver content:	4.9 g, 0.158 tr oz	—	5.5 g, 0.177 tr oz
Weight:	5.35 g	3.95 g	5.5 g
Diameter:	21.3 mm	21.2 mm	21.0 mm
Thickness:	1.85 mm	1.85 mm	1.85 mm
Edge:	Plain	Plain	Plain
Die Axis:	↑↑	↑↑	↑↑
Finish:	Proof	Proof	Proof
Case of Issue:	Included in Proof Sets, see pages 524-526		

DATE	DESCRIPTION	COMP.	QUANTITY SOLD	ISSUE PRICE	FINISH	PR-69	PR-70
1996	Diademed Portrait / Beaver	Sterling	112,835	N.I.I.	Proof	15.	—
1997		Sterling	113,647	N.I.I.	Proof	15.	—
1998		Sterling	93,632	N.I.I.	Proof	15.	—
1999		Sterling	95,113	N.I.I.	Proof	15.	—
2000		Sterling	90,921	N.I.I.	Proof	18.	—
2001		Sterling	74,194	N.I.I.	Proof	20.	—
2002		Sterling	65,315	N.I.I.	Proof	20.	—
2003		Sterling	62,007	N.I.I.	Proof	20.	—
2004	Uncrowned Portrait / Beaver	Sterling	57,614	N.I.I.	Proof	20.	—
2005		Sterling	63,562	N.I.I.	Proof	20.	—
2006		Sterling	53,822	N.I.I.	Proof	20.	—
2007	Uncrowned Portrait, Mint Logo / Beaver	Sterling	37,413	N.I.I.	Proof	20.	—
2008		Sterling	38,630	N.I.I.	Proof	20.	—
2009		Sterling	27,549	N.I.I.	Proof	20.	—
2010		Sterling	32,342	N.I.I.	Proof	25.	—
2011		Sterling	32,910	N.I.I.	Proof	25.	—
2012		Nickel	27,254	N.I.I.	Proof	15.	—
2012	Premium Proof Set	Fine Silver	19,789	N.I.I.	Proof	25.	—
2013	Premium Proof Set	Fine Silver	20,182	N.I.I.	Proof	25.	—
2014		Nickel	11,251	N.I.I.	Proof	15.	—
2014	Premium Proof Set	Fine Silver	13,416	N.I.I.	Proof	25.	—
2015	Premium Proof Set	Fine Silver	20,000	N.I.I.	Proof	25.	—
2015		Nickel	20,000	N.I.I.	Proof	15.	—
2016	Premium Proof Set	Fine Silver	20,000	N.I.I.	Proof	25.	—
2016		Nickel	12,500	N.I.I.	Proof	15.	—
2017	Premium Proof Set, Beaver	Fine Silver	20,000	N.I.I.	Proof	25.	—
2017	Premium Proof Set, Living Traditions	Fine Silver	20,000	N.I.I.	Proof	25.	—
2017	Proof Set, Living Traditions	Nickel	25,000	N.I.I.	Proof	15.	—
2017	Premium Proof Set 1967-2017	Fine Silver	20,000	N.I.I.	Proof	25.	—
2018	Premium Proof Set	Fine Silver	20,000	N.I.I.	Proof	25.	—
2018		Nickel	25,000	N.I.I.	Proof	15.	—
2019	Premium Proof Set	Fine Silver	15,000	N.I.I.	Proof	25.	—
2019		Nickel	15,000	N.I.I.	Proof	15.	—

Note: Quantity sold figures are identical to those listed for Proof Sets sold.

FIVE CENTS, 90TH ANNIVERSARY OF THE ROYAL CANADIAN MINT, 1908-1998.

To commemorate the opening of the Royal Canadian Mint in 1908 a five-coin set was issued featuring the original reverse designs that appeared on the 1908 coins, except the coins now feature the double date 1908-1998. The set was issued in two finishes, matte and mirror proof. The matte set cent does not carry the country of origin "Canada." This error was corrected on the mirror proof issues.

Designers and Engravers:	
Obv.:	Dora de Pédery-Hunt
Rev.:	Ago Aarand, G. W. DeSaulles
Composition:	92.5% Ag, 7.5% Cu
Silver content:	1.08 g, 0.035 tr oz
Finish:	Matte Proof, Mirror Proof
Case of Issue:	See Special Issue Proof Sets, page 527

Weight:	1.167 g
Diameter:	15.5 mm
Thickness:	1.0 mm
Edge:	Reeded
Die Axis:	↑↑

DATE	DESCRIPTION	QUANTITY SOLD	ISSUE PRICE	FINISH	PR-68	PR-69
1998 (1908-)	90th Anniv. Royal Canadian Mint, Matte Proof	18,376	N.I.I.	Proof	18.	—
1998 (1908-)	90th Anniv. Royal Canadian Mint, Mirror Proof	24,893	N.I.I.	Proof	18.	—

FIVE CENTS, LES VOLTIGEURS DE QUEBEC, 2000.

Les Voltigeurs regiment was formed in March 1862, and was headquartered in Quebec. In 1942 it provided an armoured regiment for the Canadian Forces in World War II.

Designers and Engravers:	
Obv.:	Dora de Pédery-Hunt
Rev.:	Susan Taylor
Composition:	92.5% Ag, 7.5% Cu
Silver content:	4.9 g, 0.158 tr oz
Finish:	Proof
Case of Issue:	Black leatherette clam style case, green insert and sleeve, encapsulated coin

Weight:	5.3 g
Diameter:	Round: 21.3 mm
Thickness:	1.85 mm
Edge:	Reeded
Die Axis:	↑↑

DATE	DESCRIPTION	QUANTITY SOLD	ISSUE PRICE	FINISH	PR-68	PR-69
2000	Les Voltigeurs de Québec	34,024	16.95	Proof	8.	—

FIVE CENTS, ROYAL MILITARY COLLEGE OF CANADA, 2001.

The Royal Military College was established by an act of Parliament on May 26th, 1874. The college is located in Kingston, Ontario.

Designers and Engravers:	
Obv.:	Dora de Pédery-Hunt
Rev.:	G. T. Locklin, Susan Taylor
Composition:	92.5% Ag, 7.5% Cu
Silver content:	4.9 g, 0.158 tr oz
Finish:	Proof
Case of Issue:	Black leatherette clam style case, green insert, encapsulated coin, multicoloured sleeve

Weight:	5.3 g
Diameter:	Round: 21.3 mm
Thickness:	1.85 mm
Edge:	Plain
Die Axis:	↑↑

DATE	DESCRIPTION	QUANTITY SOLD	ISSUE PRICE	FINISH	PR-68	PR-69
2001	Royal Military College of Canada	25,834	16.95	Proof	12.	—

FIVE CENTS, 85TH ANNIVERSARY, BATTLE FOR VIMY RIDGE, 2002.

Vimy Ridge, France was the location of one of the major battles of World War I. It was taken and held by Canadian troops from April 9th to 12th, 1917.

Designers and Engravers:	
Obv.:	Dora de Pédery-Hunt
Rev.:	S. A. Allward, Susan Taylor
Composition:	92.5% Ag, 7.5% Cu
Silver content:	4.9 g, 0.158 tr oz
Finish:	Proof
Case of Issue:	Black leatherette clam style case; maroon insert, encapsulated coin, multicoloured sleeve

Weight:	5.3 g
Diameter:	Round: 21.3 mm
Thickness:	1.85 mm
Edge:	Plain
Die Axis:	↑↑

DATE	DESCRIPTION	QUANTITY SOLD	ISSUE PRICE	FINISH	PR-68	PR-69
2002	85th Anniv. Battle for Vimy Ridge	22,646	16.95	Proof	26.	—

FIVE CENTS, 50TH ANNIVERSARY OF THE CORONATION OF QUEEN ELIZABETH II, 1953-2003.

Elizabeth II was crowned Queen on June 2nd, 1953, in Westminster Abbey, London, England.

Designers and Engravers:		
Obv.:	M. Gillick, D. de Pédery-Hunt	
Rev.:	G. E. Kruger-Gray, T. Shingles	
Composition:	92.5% Ag, 7.5% Cu	
Silver content:	4.9 g, 0.158 tr oz	
Finish:	Proof	
Case of Issue:	See Special Issue Proof Sets, page 528	

Weight:	5.3 g	
Diameter:	12-sided: 21.3 mm	
Thickness:	1.85 mm	
Edge:	Plain	
Die Axis:	↑↑	

DATE	DESCRIPTION	QUANTITY SOLD	ISSUE PRICE	FINISH	PR-69	PR-70
2003 (1953-)	50th Anniv. Coronation Queen Elizabeth II	21,537	N.I.I.	Proof	25.	—

FIVE CENTS, 60TH ANNIVERSARY, D-DAY LANDING, 1944-2004.

On June 6th, 1944, over 175,000 troops landed on the beaches of Normandy, along a fifty-mile front. Originally came in 2004 D-Day Nickel & Medallion with CD Rom.

Designers and Engravers:		
Obv.:	Susanna Blunt, Susan Taylor	
Rev.:	Thomas Shingles, Christie Paquet	
Composition:	92.5% Ag, 7.5% Cu	
Silver content:	4.9 g, 0.158 tr oz	
Finish:	Proof	
Case of Issue:	See Derivatives below	

Weight:	5.3 g	
Diameter:	12-sided: 21.3 mm	
Thickness:	1.85 mm	
Edge:	Plain	
Die Axis:	↑↑	

DATE	DESCRIPTION	QUANTITY SOLD	ISSUE PRICE	FINISH	PR-69	PR-70
2004 (1944-)	60th Anniv. D-Day, 1944-2004	20,019	N.I.I.	Proof	30.	—

FIVE CENTS, 60TH ANNIVERSARY OF VE-DAY, 1945-2005.

These coins were issued to celebrate the 60th anniversary of the victory over Nazi Germany in Europe. Peace was declared May 8th, 1945.

The selectively gold plated Victory five cent coin was issued in conjunction with the 2005 Annual Mint Report. This is the third coin in what was to be an annual series ending in 2008. The series was discontinued with the issue of the 2006 annual report. See the Five Cent Derivatives, page 13.

Common	**1945-2005**	**1945-2005**
Obverse	**Victory**	**Victory**
		Gold plated

Designers and Engravers:		
Obv.:	T. H. Paget, Thomas Shingles	
Rev.:	Thomas Shingles, Christie Paquet	
Composition:	92.5% Ag, 7.5% Cu	
Silver content:	4.9 g, 0.158 tr oz	
Weight:	5.3 g	
Diameter:	12-sided: 21.3 mm	
Thickness:	1.85 mm	**Die Axis:** ↑↑
Edge:	Plain	**Finish:** Proof
Case of Issue:	See Derivatives below	

DATE	DESCRIPTION	QUANTITY SOLD	ISSUE PRICE	FINISH	PR-69	PR-70
2005 (1945-)	60th Anniv. VE-Day, 1945-2005	42,792	N.I.I.	Proof	15.	—
2005 (1945-)	60th Anniv. VE-Day, Selectively gold plated	6,065	N.I.I.	Proof	60.	—

FIVE CENT DERIVATIVES

DATE	DESCRIPTION	QUANTITY SOLD	ISSUE PRICE	ISSUER	FINISH	MARKET PRICE
2004 (1944-)	**D-Day Five Cents**, 1944-2004; Bronze medallion, CD, Folder	20,019	29.95	RCM	PR-69	30.
2005 (1945-)	VE-Day Five Cents, 1945-2005; Bronze medallion, Booklet	42,792	29.95	RCM	PR-69	15.
2005 (1945-)	2005 Annual Mint Report, Five cent coin, selectively gold plated		24.95	RCM	PR-69	
	English	5,213				65.
	French	852				65.

FIVE CENTS, GEORGE V, STERLING SILVER, PROOF, 1935-2010.

This five-cent coin is from the Special Limited Edition Proof Set issued in 2010 to commemorate Emanuel Hahn's classic voyageur design which first appeared on the 1935 silver dollar.

Designers and Engravers:		Weight:	5.35 g
Obv.:	Sir. E. B. MacKennal, RCM Staff	Diameter:	21.2 mm
Rev.:	W. H. J. Blakemore, RCM Staff	Thickness:	1.85 mm
Composition:	92.5% Ag, 7.5% Cu	Edge:	Plain
Silver content:	4.95 g, 0.195 tr oz	Die Axis:	↑↑
Finish:	Proof		
Case of Issue:	See Special Issue Proof Sets, page 529		

DATE	DESCRIPTION	RCM ITEM #	QUANTITY SOLD	ISSUE PRICE	FINISH	PR-69	PR-70
2010 (1935-)	George V, Sterling Silver	111020	4,996	N.I.I.	Proof	25.	—

FIVE CENTS, GEORGE V, STERLING SILVER, PROOF, 1911-2011.

This five-cent coin which carries the double date 1911-2011 is from the Special Edition Proof Set issued in 2011 to commemorate the 100th anniversary of the striking of Canada's 1911 silver dollar.

Designers and Engravers:		Weight:	1.559 g
Obv.:	Sir E. B. MacKennal, RCM Staff	Diameter:	15.5 mm
Rev.:	Original design by L. C. Wyon,	Thickness:	1.0 mm
	Modified by W. H. J. Blakemore	Edge:	Reeded
Composition:	92.5% Ag, 7.5% Cu	Die Axis:	↑↑
Silver content:	1.442 g, 0.046 tr oz	Finish:	Proof
Case of Issue:	See Special Issue Proof Sets, page 529		

DATE	DESCRIPTION	RCM ITEM #	QUANTITY SOLD	ISSUE PRICE	FINISH	PR-69	PR-70
2011 (1911-)	George V (1911), Sterling Silver	114121	5,952	N.I.I.	Proof	25.	—

NOTE TO COLLECTORS

When the initials N.I.I. appear in the pricing table it indicates the coin was part of a set issued by the Royal Canadian Mint, and not issued individually. Coin designs that are found only in sets offered by the Royal Canadian Mint are listed individually by denomination and date in Volume Two.

BIG COIN SERIES

FIVE CENTS, BIG COIN SET, 2015-2019.

This five-cent coin, which is part of the Big Coin Set started in 2015, features G.E. Kruger-Gray's enduring beaver design that first appeared on the 1937 Canadian five-cent piece, with the 2017 coin having the reverse design by Alex Colville. Other coins in the set include a 1¢ coin (page 7), 10¢ coin (page 17), 25¢ coin (page 57), 50¢ coin (page 87), $1 coin (page 131) and a $2 coin (page 145).

Designers and Engravers:

Obv.:	Susanna Blunt, Susan Taylor
Rev.:	2015-2016:G.E. Kruger-Gray
	2017: Alex Colville
	2018-2019: G.E. Kruger-Gray

Silver content: 157.58 g, 5.06 tr oz
Weight: 157.6 g
Diameter: 65.25 mm
Thickness: N/A
Case of Issue: Maroon clam style case, black flocked insert, encapsulated coin, COA, custom box

Composition:

2015:	99.99% Ag, Selectively gold plated
2016:	99.99% Ag, Selectively coloured
2017:	99.99% Ag, Selectively gold plated
2018:	99.99% Ag, Selectively rose gold-plated
2019:	99.99% Ag. Reverse gold plating

Edge: Reeded
Die Axis: ↑↑
Finish: Proof

DATE	DESCRIPTION	RCM ITEM #	QUANTITY SOLD	ISSUE PRICE	FINISH	PR-69	PR-70
2015	5¢ Big Coin	134867	1,500	549.95	Proof	500.	—
2016	5¢ Big Coin	151547	1,496	519.95	Proof	550.	—
2017	5¢ Big Coin	156446	2,150	559.95	Proof	550.	—
2018	5¢ Big Coin	163832	1,500	559.95	Proof	550.	—
2019	5¢ Big Coin	170836	1,250	569.95	Proof	570.	—

Note: Coins illustrated smaller than actual size.

LEGACY OF THE CANADIAN NICKEL

FIVE CENTS, LEGACY OF THE CANADIAN NICKEL, 2015.

This six coin set celebrates the history of the Canadian five-cent piece that was first minted in Canada after the Ottawa branch of the Royal Mint opened in 1908. Prior to that, Canadian coins were struck at the Royal Mint in England or the Birmingham Mint in Birmingham, England. Featuring the effigies of reigning monarchs at the time, the coins are larger than their original size. From originally containing sterling silver, to silver's removal from the coin in 1922, to an entirely-nickel composition, and a later tombac alloy due to the war's need for nickel in the 1940s, the five cent coin's current plated steel composition has changed through the years.

Obverse: King George V	The Crossed Maple Boughs	The Two Maple Leaves	Obverse: King George VI	The Victory	The Identification of Nickel
Designer: E.B. MacKennal	Designer: W.H.J. Blakemore	Designer: W.H.J. Blakemore	Designer: T.H. Paget	Designer & Engraver: Thomas Shingles	Des.: Stephan Trenka
Engraver: RCM Staff	Engraver: RCM Staff	Engraver: RCM Staff	Engraver: Thomas Shingles		Engraver: Thomas Shingles

Obverse: Elizabeth II	The Centennial Five Cents	Obverse: Elizabeth II	The Beaver
Designer: Arnold Machin	Designer: Alex Colville	Designer: Susanna Blunt	Designer: G.E. Kruger-Gray
Engraver: RCM Staff	Engraver: Myron Cook	Engraver: Susan Taylor	Engraver: RCM Staff

Designers:
Obv.:   See obverse illustrations
Rev.:   See reverse illustrations
Composition: 99.99% Ag, Selectively gold plated
Silver Content: 31.83 g, 1.02 tr oz
Weight: 31.83 g
Diameter: 40.0 mm
Thickness: N/A

Engravers:
Obv.:   See obverse illustrations
Rev.:   See reverse illustrations

Edge: Reeded
Die Axis: ↑↑
Finish: Proof

Case of Issue: Singly: Maroon leatherette clam style case, black flocked insert, encapsulated coin, COA
Subscription: Six-hole wooden case, black flocked insert, encapsulated coins, COA

DATE	DESCRIPTION	RCM ITEM #	QUANTITY SOLD	ISSUE PRICE	FINISH	PR-69	PR-70
2015	The Crossed Maple Boughs	135338	6,690	109.95	Proof	90.	—
2015	The Two Maple Leaves	135339	6,243	109.95	Proof	90.	—
2015	The Victory	135340	6,251	109.95	Proof	90.	—
2015	The Identification of Nickel	135342	5,595	109.95	Proof	90.	—
2015	The Centennial Five Cents	134341	5,993	109.95	Proof	90.	—
2015	The Beaver	134343	5,682	109.95	Proof	90.	—

TEN CENTS

TEN CENTS, ELIZABETH II PROOF, 1996-2019.

Starting in 1996 the ten-cent coin issued in the proof set, previously struck from cupronickel, was now struck on a sterling silver planchet. The use of sterling silver planchets was discontinued in 2011.

The year 2012 saw the introduction of the Premium Proof Set in which all coins were struck on fine silver planchets.

Standard Proof Sets were issued for 2012-2019. The ten-cent coin in these sets was struck on a nickel planchet.

| Obverse 1996-2003 | Obverse 2004-2006, 2015-2019 Without Mint Logo | Obverse 2007-2014, 2018-2019 With Mint Logo | Obverse 2017 With Canada 150 Logo | Reverse 1996-2019 | Reverse 2017 Wings of Peace |

Designers:

			Engravers:		
Obv.:	1996-2003:	Dora de Pédery-Hunt	Obv.:	1996-2003:	Dora de Pédery-Hunt
	2004-2019:	Susanna Blunt		2004-2019:	Susan Taylor
Rev.:		Emanuel Hahn	Rev.:		Emanuel Hahn
	2017:	Amy Choi			

	Sterling Silver	Nickel	Fine Silver
Composition:	92.5% Ag, 7.5% Cu	100.% Ni	99.99% Ag
Silver content:	2.15 g, 0.069 tr oz	—	2.5 g, 0.08 tr oz
Weight:	2.32 g	1.75 g	2.5 g
Diameter:	18.03 mm	18.05 mm	18.0 mm
Thickness:	1.7 mm	1.2 mm	1.2 mm
Edge:	Reeded	Reeded	Reeded
Die Axis:	↑↑	↑↑	↑↑
Finish:	Proof	Proof	Proof
Case of Issue:	Included in Proof Sets, see pages 524-526		

DATE	DESCRIPTION	COMP.	QUANTITY SOLD	ISSUE PRICE	FINISH	PR-69	PR-70
1996	Diademed Portrait / Bluenose	Sterling	112,835	N.I.I.	Proof	10.	—
1997		Sterling	113,647	N.I.I.	Proof	10.	—
1998		Sterling	93,632	N.I.I.	Proof	10.	—
1999		Sterling	95,113	N.I.I.	Proof	10.	—
2000		Sterling	90,921	N.I.I.	Proof	10.	—
2001		Sterling	74,194	N.I.I.	Proof	10.	—
2002		Sterling	65,315	N.I.I.	Proof	10.	—
2003		Sterling	62,007	N.I.I.	Proof	10.	—
2004	Uncrowned Portrait / Bluenose	Sterling	57,614	N.I.I.	Proof	10.	—
2005		Sterling	63,562	N.I.I.	Proof	10.	—
2006		Sterling	53,822	N.I.I.	Proof	10.	—
2007	Uncrowned Portrait, Mint Logo / Bluenose	Sterling	37,413	N.I.I.	Proof	10.	—
2008		Sterling	38,630	N.I.I.	Proof	10.	—
2009		Sterling	27,549	N.I.I.	Proof	10.	—
2010		Sterling	32,342	N.I.I.	Proof	20.	—
2011		Sterling	32,910	N.I.I.	Proof	20.	—
2012		Nickel	27,254	N.I.I.	Proof	20.	—
2012	Premium Proof Set	Fine Silver	19,789	N.I.I.	Proof	20.	—
2013	Premium Proof Set	Fine Silver	20,182	N.I.I.	Proof	20.	—
2014		Nickel	11,251	N.I.I.	Proof	10.	—
2014	Premium Proof Set	Fine Silver	13,416	N.I.I.	Proof	20.	—
2015	Premium Proof Set	Fine Silver	20,000	N.I.I.	Proof	20.	—
2015		Nickel	20,000	N.I.I.	Proof	10.	—
2016	Premium Proof Set	Fine Silver	20,000	N.I.I.	Proof	20.	—
2016		Nickel	12,500	N.I.I.	Proof	10.	—
2017	Premium Proof Set, Schooner	Fine Silver	20,000	N.I.I.	Proof	20.	—
2017	Premium Proof Set, Wings of Peace	Fine Silver	20,000	N.I.I.	Proof	20.	—
2017	Proof Set, Wings of Peace	Nickel	25,000	N.I.I.	Proof	10.	—
2017	Premium Proof Set, 1967-2017	Fine Silver	20,000	N.I.I.	Proof	20.	—
2018	Premium Proof Set,	Fine Silver	20,000	N.I.I.	Proof	20.	—
2018		Nickel	25,000	N.I.I	Proof	10.	—
2019	Premium Proof Set	Fine Silver	15,000	N.I.I.	Proof	20.	—
2019		Nickel	15,000	N.I.I.	Proof	10.	—

Note: Quantity sold figures are identical to those listed for Proof Sets sold.

TEN CENTS, 500TH ANNIVERSARY OF CABOTO'S FIRST TRANSATLANTIC VOYAGE, 1997.

Giovanni Caboto (c.1450-c.1508) was an Italian navigator and explorer whose 1497 discovery of North America is commonly held to be the first voyage to the continent since those of the Vikings.

Designers and Engravers:			**Weight:**	2.4 g
Obv.:	Dora de Pédery-Hunt		**Diameter:**	18.0 mm
Rev.:	Donald H. Curley, Stan Witten		**Thickness:**	1.2 mm
Composition:	92.5% Ag, 7.5% Cu		**Edge:**	Reeded
Silver content:	2.22 g, 0.071 tr oz		**Die Axis:**	↑↑
Finish:	Proof			
Case of Issue:	Clear plastic case with black insert, white sleeve. See Derivatives, page 18			

DATE	DESCRIPTION	QUANTITY SOLD	ISSUE PRICE	FINISH	PR-69	PR-70
1997	500th Anniv. of Caboto's Voyage	49,848	10.95	Proof	12.	—

TEN CENTS, 90TH ANNIVERSARY OF THE ROYAL CANADIAN MINT, 1908-1998.

First opened on January 2nd, 1908, the Ottawa Branch of the Royal Mint became the Royal Canadian Mint in 1931.

Designers and Engravers:			**Weight:**	2.32 g
Obv.:	Dora de Pédery-Hunt		**Diameter:**	18.03 mm
Rev.:	G. W. DeSaulles, RCM Staff		**Thickness:**	1.7 mm
Composition:	92.5% Ag, 7.5% Cu		**Edge:**	Reeded
Silver content:	2.15 g, 0.069 tr oz		**Die Axis:**	↑↑
Finish:	Matte Proof, Mirror Proof			
Case of Issue:	See Special Issue Proof Sets, page 527			

DATE	DESCRIPTION	QUANTITY SOLD	ISSUE PRICE	FINISH	PR-69	PR-70
1998 (1908-)	Sterling silver, Matte Proof	18,376	N.I.I.	Proof	15.	—
1998 (1908-)	Sterling silver, Mirror Proof	24,893	N.I.I.	Proof	15.	—

TEN CENTS, 100TH ANNIVERSARY OF THE BIRTH OF THE CREDIT UNIONS IN NORTH AMERICA, 2000.

The first credit union in North America, The Caisse Populaire de Lévis in Quebec, began operation on January 23rd, 1901, with a ten-cent deposit.

Designers and Engravers:			**Weight:**	2.4 g
Obv.:	Dora de Pédery-Hunt		**Diameter:**	18.0 mm
Rev.:	Jean-Guy Lebel, W. Woodruff		**Thickness:**	1.2 mm
Composition:	92.5% Ag, 7.5% Cu		**Edge:**	Reeded
Silver content:	2.22 g, 0.071 tr oz		**Die Axis:**	↑↑
Finish:	Proof			
Case of Issue:	Green printed card folder with encapsulated coin			

DATE	DESCRIPTION	QUANTITY SOLD	ISSUE PRICE	FINISH	PR-69	PR-70
2000	100th Anniv. Birth of Credit Unions in N.A.	69,791	9.95	Proof	8.	—

TEN CENTS, INTERNATIONAL YEAR OF THE VOLUNTEERS, 2001.

The United Nations declaration of International Year of the Volunteers gave cause for celebration for more than 7.5 million Canadian volunteers.

Designers and Engravers:			**Weight:**	2.4 g
Obv.:	Dora de Pédery-Hunt		**Diameter:**	18.0 mm
Rev.:	RCM Design, Stan Witten		**Thickness:**	1.2 mm
Composition:	92.5% Ag, 7.5% Cu		**Edge:**	Reeded
Silver content:	2.22 g, 0.071 tr oz		**Die Axis:**	↑↑
Finish:	Proof			
Case of Issue:	Multicoloured printed card folder with encapsulated coin			

DATE	DESCRIPTION	QUANTITY SOLD	ISSUE PRICE	FINISH	PR-69	PR-70
2001	International Year of the Volunteers	40,634	14.95	Proof	8.	—

Note: 1. For the ten cent font varieties of 2007 (Curved and Straight 7) see page 500.
   2. For the ten cent Finish variety from the 2010 Special Edition Specimen Set, see page 522.

TEN CENTS, 50TH ANNIVERSARY OF THE CORONATION OF QUEEN ELIZABETH II, 1953-2003.

Elizabeth II was crowned Queen June 2nd, 1953; her 50th anniversary was June 2nd, 2003.

Designers and Engravers:
Obv.: Dora de Pédery-Hunt
Rev.: Emanuel Hahn
Composition: 92.5% Ag, 7.5% Cu
Silver content: 2.15 g, 0.069 tr oz
Finish: Mirror Proof
Case of Issue: See Special Issue Proof Sets, page 528

Weight: 2.32 g
Diameter: 18.0 mm
Thickness: 1.7 mm
Edge: Reeded
Die Axis: ↑↑

DATE	DESCRIPTION	QUANTITY SOLD	ISSUE PRICE	FINISH	PR-69	PR-70
2003 (1953-)	50th Anniv. Coronation Queen Elizabeth II	21,537	N.I.I.	Proof	15.	—

TEN CENTS, 100TH ANNIVERSARY OF THE CANADIAN OPEN GOLF CHAMPIONSHIP, 2004.

The Canadian Open Golf Tournament was first played on the Royal Montreal Golf Club course in 1904. The tournament was won by the English player, John H. Oke.

Designers and Engravers:
Obv.: Susanna Blunt, Susan Taylor
Rev.: Cosme Saffioti
Composition: Nickel plated steel
Weight: 1.75 g
Case of Issue: See Derivatives, page 18

Diameter: 18.03 mm
Thickness: 1.2 mm
Edge: Reeded
Die Axis: ↑↑
Finish: Circulation

DATE	DESCRIPTION	QUANTITY SOLD	ISSUE PRICE	FINISH	MS-65 NC	MS-66 NC	MS-67 NC
2004	100th Anniv. of Canadian Open Golf Championship	39,486	N.I.I.	Circulation	12.	25.	—

TEN CENTS, GEORGE V, STERLING SILVER, PROOF, 1935-2010.

This ten-cent coin is from the Special Limited Edition Proof Set issued in 2010 to commemorate Emanuel Hahn's classic voyageur design which first appeared on the 1935 silver dollar.

Designers and Engravers:
Obv.: Sir E. B. MacKennal
Rev.: Original design by L. C. Wyon,
Modified by W. H. J. Blakemore
Composition: 92.5% Ag, 7.5% Cu
Silver content: 2.22 g, 0.071 tr oz
Case of Issue: See Special Issue Proof Sets, page 529

Weight: 2.4 g
Diameter: 18.1 mm
Thickness: 1.1 mm
Edge: Reeded
Die Axis: ↑↑
Finish: Proof

DATE	DESCRIPTION	RCM ITEM #	QUANTITY SOLD	ISSUE PRICE	FINISH	PR-69	PR-70
2010 (1935-)	George V, Sterling Silver	111020	4,996	N.I.I.	Proof	20.	—

TEN CENTS, GEORGE V, STERLING SILVER, PROOF, 1911-2011.

This ten-cent coin which carries the double date 1911-2011 is from the Special Edition Proof Set issued in 2011 to commemorate the 100th anniversary of the striking of Canada's 1911 silver dollar.

Designers and Engravers:
Obv.: Sir E. B. MacKennal
Rev.: Original design by L. C. Wyon,
Modified by W. H. J. Blakemore
Composition: 92.5% Ag, 7.5% Cu
Silver content: 2.22 g, 0.071 tr oz
Case of Issue: See Special Issue Proof Sets, page 529

Weight: 2.4 g
Diameter: 18.1 mm
Thickness: 1.1 mm
Edge: Reeded
Die Axis: ↑↑
Finish: Proof

DATE	DESCRIPTION	RCM ITEM #	QUANTITY SOLD	ISSUE PRICE	FINISH	PR-69	PR-70
2011 (1911-)	George V, Sterling Silver	114121	5,952	N.I.I.	Proof	35.	—

BIG COIN SERIES

TEN CENTS, BIG COIN SET, 2015-2019.

The Big Coin Series started in 2015, features the classic Bluenose design for 2015, 2016, 2018 and 2019, which first appeared on the 1937 Canadian ten-cent coin designed by Emanuel Hahn, and Alex Colville's 1967 design for the 2017 coin. Other coins in the set include a 1¢ coin (page 7, 5¢ coin (page 12), 25¢ coin (page 57), 50¢ coin (page 87), $1 coin (page 131) and a $2 coin (page 145).

Designers and Engravers:

Obv.:	Susanna Blunt, Susan Taylor
Rev.:	Emanuel Hahn, Myron Cook,
	Alex Colville
	Emanuel Hahn

Composition:

2015:	99.99% Ag, Selectively gold plated
2016:	99.99% Ag, Selectively coloured on reverse
2017:	99.99% Ag, Selectively gold plated
2018:	99.99% Ag, Selectively rose gold-plated
2019:	99.99% Ag, Reverse gold plating

Silver content: 157.6 g, 5.06 tr oz
Weight: 157.6 g
Diameter: 65.25 mm
Thickness: N/A
Case of Issue: Maroon clam style case, black flocked insert, encapsulated coin, COA, custom box

Edge: Reeded
Die Axis: ↑↑
Finish: Proof

DATE	DESCRIPTION	RCM ITEM #	QUANTITY SOLD	ISSUE PRICE	FINISH	PR-69	PR-70
2015	10¢ Big Coin	134869	1,483	549.95	Proof	500.	—
2016	10¢ Big Coin	151545	1,489	519.95	Proof	500.	—
2017	10¢ Big Coin	156072	2,150	559.95	Proof	560.	—
2018	10¢ Big Coin	163712	1,500	559.95	Proof	560.	—
2019	10¢ Big Coin	170228	1,250	569.95	Proof	570.	

Note: Coins illustrated smaller than actual size.

TEN CENTS, LEGACY OF THE DIME, 2018.

The Legacy of the Dime set is a uique retrospective look at Canada's 10-cent circulation coin through the years, as struck by the Royal Canadian Mint.

1936 Dot
Reverse: W.H.J. Blakemore Obv.: Sir E.B. MacKennal

1947 Maple Leaf
Reverse: Emanuel Hahn Obverse: T.H. Paget

1967 Centennial
Reverse: Alex Colville
Obverse: Arnold Machin

2001 Year of the Volunteer
Reverse: RCM Staff
Obverse: Dora de Pédery-Hunt

2017 Wing of Peace)
Reverse: Amy Choi
Obverse: Susanna Blunt

Designers:		**Engravers:**	
Obv.:	See illustrations	Obv.:	See illustrations
Rev.:	See illustrations	Rev.:	See illustrations

Composition: 99.99% Ag, selective gold plating
Silver content: 157.6 g, 5.06 tr oz

	1936 Dot	**1947 Maple Leaf**	**1967 Centennial**	**2001 Year of the Volunteer**	**2017 Wing of Peace**
Weight:	62.67 g	62.67 g	31.39 g	31.39 g	31.39 g
Diameter:	54.0 mm	54.0 mm	38.0 mm	38.0 mm	38.0 mm
Thickness:	N/A				
Edge:	Reeded				
Die Axis:	↑↑				
Finish:	Proof				
Case of Issue:	Wooden collector's case with black beauty box. COA				

DATE	DESCRIPTION	RCM ITEM #	QUANTITY SOLD	ISSUE PRICE	FINISH	PR-69	PR-70
2018	Legacy of the Dime Set, Fine silver	164046	3,000	709.95	Proof	710.	—

TEN CENT DERIVATIVES

DATE	DESCRIPTION	QUANTITY SOLD	ISSUE PRICE	ISSUER	FINISH	MARKET PRICE
1997	**John Caboto Ten Cents,** Sterling;. Canada 45¢ stamp; Italy 1300 Lira stamp; Set in multicoloured card folder	15,000	19.95	RCM, CP	PR-69	20
2000	**Bluenose Ten Cents,** Sterling; Two 46¢ stamps; Blue presentation case	15,000	19.95	RCM, CP	PR-69	20.
2001	**International Year of the Volunteers Ten Cents,** Thank You card and envelope	N/A	N/A	RCM	MS-65	10.
2004	**Ten Cent and Five Dollar Coins,** (100th Anniv. Canadian Open Golf Championship); Framed with two 48¢ circular stamps	18,750	49.95	RCM, CP	MS-65, PR-69	45.
2004	**Canadian Open Championship Ten Cents,** Framed with two circular commemorative stamps, and a divot repair tool	20,736	21.49	RCM, CP	MS-65	20.
2004	**Canadian Open Championship Ten Cents,** Canister also contains four commemorative stamps, a divot repair tool, three golf balls, five golf tees and a T-shirt	N/A	39.95	RCM, CP	MS-65	35.

TWENTY-FIVE CENTS

TWENTY-FIVE CENTS, ELIZABETH II PROOF, 1996-2019.

Starting in 1996 the twenty-five-cent coin issued in the proof set, previously struck from cupronickel, was now struck on a sterling silver planchet. The use of sterling silver planchets was discontinued in 2011.

The year 2012 saw the introduction of the Premium Proof Set in which all coins were struck on fine silver planchets.

Standard Proof Sets were issued for 2012, 2014-2019. The twenty-five cent coin in these sets was struck on a nickel planchet.

Obverse
1996-2003

Obverse
2004-2006, 2015-2019
Without Mint Logo

Obverse
2007-2014, 2019
With Mint Logo

Obverse 2018
With Canada 150
Logo

Reverse
1996-2019

Reverse
2017
Greener Future

Designers:
Obv.:	1996-2003:	Dora de Pédery-Hunt
	2004-2019:	Susanna Blunt
Rev.:		Emanuel Hahn
	2017:	Joelle Wong

Engravers:
Obv.:	1996-2003:	Dora de Pédery-Hunt
	2004-2019:	Susan Taylor
Rev.:	2017	Emanuel Hahn

Reverse
2017 Colour
Greener Future

	Sterling Silver	Nickel	Fine Silver
Composition:	92.5% Ag, 7.5% Cu	100.%	99.99% Ag
Silver content:	5.458 g, 0.175 tr oz	—	6.0 g, 0.193 tr oz
Weight:	5.9 g	4.4 g	6.0 g
Diameter:	23.9 mm	23.88 mm	23.9 mm
Thickness:	1.6 mm	1.62 mm	1.7 mm
Edge:	Reeded	Reeded	Reeded
Die Axis:	↑↑	↑↑	↑↑
Finish:	Proof	Proof	Proof
Case of Issue:	Included in Proof Sets, see pages 524-526		

DATE	DESCRIPTION	COMP.	QUANTITY SOLD	ISSUE PRICE	FINISH	PR-69	PR-70
1996	Diademed Portrait / Caribou	Sterling	112,835	N.I.I.	Proof	12.	—
1997		Sterling	113,647	N.I.I.	Proof	12.	—
1998		Sterling	93,632	N.I.I.	Proof	15.	—
1999		Sterling	95,113	N.I.I.	Proof	15.	—
2000		Sterling	90,921	N.I.I.	Proof	15.	—
2001		Sterling	74,194	N.I.I.	Proof	15.	—
2002		Sterling	65,315	N.I.I.	Proof	15.	—
2003		Sterling	62,007	N.I.I.	Proof	15.	—
2004	Uncrowned Portrait / Caribou	Sterling	57,614	N.I.I.	Proof	15.	—
2005		Sterling	63,562	N.I.I.	Proof	15.	—
2006		Sterling	53,822	N.I.I.	Proof	15.	—
2007	Uncrowned Portrait, Mint Logo / Caribou	Sterling	37,413	N.I.I.	Proof	15.	—
2008		Sterling	38,630	N.I.I.	Proof	15.	—
2009		Sterling	27,549	N.I.I.	Proof	15.	—
2010		Sterling	32,342	N.I.I.	Proof	20.	—
2011		Sterling	32,910	N.I.I.	Proof	20.	—
2012		Nickel	27,254	N.I.I.	Proof	20.	—
2012	Premium Proof Set	Fine Silver	19,789	N.I.I.	Proof	20.	—
2013	Premium Proof Set	Fine Silver	20,182	N.I.I.	Proof	20.	—
2014		Nickel	11,251	N.I.I.	Proof	15.	—
2014	Premium Proof Set	Fine Silver	13,416	N.I.I.	Proof	20.	—
2015	Premium Proof Set	Fine Silver	20,000	N.I.I.	Proof	20.	—
2015		Nickel	20,000	N.I.I.	Proof	15.	—
2016	Premium Proof Set	Fine Silver	20,000	N.I.I.	Proof	20.	—
2016		Nickel	12,500	N.I.I.	Proof	15.	—
2017	Premium Proof Set, Caribou	Fine Silver	20,000	N.I.I.	Proof	20.	—
2017	Premium Proof Set, Greener Future	Fine Silver	20,000	N.I.I.	Proof	20.	—
2017	Proof Set, Greener Future, Colour	Nickel	25,000	N.I.I.	Proof	15.	—
2017	Premium Proof Set 1967-2017	Fine Silver	20,000	N.I.I.	Proof	20.	—
2018	Premium Proof Set,	Fine Silver	20,000	N.I.I.	Proof	20.	—
2018		Nickel	25,000	N.I.I.	Proof	15.	—
2019	Premium Proof Set	Fine Silver	15,000	N.I.I.	Proof	20.	—
2019		Nickel	15,000	N.I.I.	Proof	15.	—

Note: Quantity sold figures are identical to those listed for Proof Sets sold.

125TH ANNIVERSARY OF CANADA, SILVER PROOF AND NICKEL UNCIRCULATED SETS, 1992.

Issued by the Royal Canadian Mint, in silver and nickel, the twelve different designs represent a familiar scene from each of the twelve provinces and territories of Canada. This is the first issue of sterling silver twenty-five cent coins since 1919.

Also, a collection of nickel brilliant uncirculated coins mounted in a coloured map of Canada, with each twenty-five-cent coin placed in the province or territory commemorated by its design was released October 7th, 1992. The Canada Day dollar which is the central point of a compass is listed on page 121.

1867-1992
Obverse

Designers and Engravers:			
Obv.:	Dora de Pédery-Hunt, Ago Aarand		
Rev.:	See reverse illustrations		
Composition:	Silver	Nickel	
Silver content:	5.458 g	—	
	0.175 tr oz	—	
Weight:	5.9 g	5.05 g	
Diameter:	23.8 mm	23.9 mm	
Thickness:	1.7 mm	1.6 mm	
Edge:	Reeded	Reeded	
Die Axis:	↑↑	↑↑	
Finish:	Proof	Circulation	

Issue Price:	
Individual proof silver:	$9.95
13-coin proof silver set:	$129.45
13 coin nickel set, "Map" holder:	$17.25
Quantity: Total individual silver coins:	651,812
Sold: Total silver sets:	84,397
Nickel sets, "Map" holder:	448,178

Case of Issue: (A) Royal blue flocked single coin case
(B) Royal blue flocked case, 13 coins. Twelve 25¢ coins; one $1.00 coin

New Brunswick	Northwest	Newfoundland	Manitoba	Yukon	Alberta
January 9, 1992	Territories	March 5, 1992	April 7, 1992	May 7, 1992	June 4, 1992
Ronald Lambert	February 6, 1992	Christopher	Muriel Hope	Libby Dulac	Mel Heath
Sheldon Beveridge	Beth McEachen	Newhook	Ago Aarand	William Woodruff	William Woodruff

Prince Edward	Ontario	Nova Scotia	Quebec	Saskatchewan	British Columbia
Island	August 6, 1992	September 9, 1992	October 1, 1992	November 5, 1992	November 9, 1992
July 7, 1992	Greg Salmela	Bruce Wood	R. Bukauskas	Brian Cobb	Carla Egan
N. Roe, S. Beveridge	Susan Taylor	Terry Smith	Stan Witten	Terry Smith	Sheldon Beveridge

DATE	DESCRIPTION	PROOF STERLING SILVER		UNCIRCULATED NICKEL		
		PR-68	PR-69	MS-65 NC	MS-66 NC	MS-67 NC
1992	New Brunswick	15.	—	5.	10.	—
1992	Northwest Territories	15.	—	5.	10.	—
1992	Newfoundland	15.	—	5.	10.	—
1992	Manitoba	15.	—	5.	10.	—
1992	Yukon	15.	—	5.	10.	—
1992	Alberta	15.	—	5.	10.	—.
1992	Prince Edward Island	15.	—	5.	10.	—
1992	Ontario	15.	—	5.	10.	—
1992	Nova Scotia	15.	—	5.	10.	—
1992	Quebec	15.	—	5.	10.	—
1992	Saskatchewan	15.	—	5.	10.	—
1992	British Columbia	15.	—	5.	10.	—
1992	13 Coin Silver Proof Set	90.	—	*	*	*
1992	13 Coin Nickel Set with "Map" Holder	*	*	15.	—	—

TWENTY-FIVE CENTS, 125TH ANNIVERSARY MULE, 1867-1992.

A 1867-1992 obverse is muled with a Caribou reverse. The coin was reportedly issued in a Brilliant Uncirculated set of 1993.

Designers and Engravers:

Obv.:	Dora de Pédery-Hunt
Rev.:	Emanuel Hahn
Composition:	Nickel
Weight:	5.05 g
Diameter:	23.9 mm
Thickness:	1.6 mm	Edge:	Reeded
Die Axis:	↑↑	Finish:	Circulation

DATE	DESCRIPTION	MS-65
1992 (1867-)	Mule	Only two known

TWENTY-FIVE CENTS, 90TH ANNIVERSARY OF THE ROYAL CANADIAN MINT, 1908-1998.

Issued to commemorate the opening of the Branch Mint in Ottawa, a five-coin set was struck featuring the same reverse designs as the original 1908 coins, except for the double date 1908-1998. The set was issued in two finishes, matte and mirror proof.

Designers and Engravers:

Obv.:	Dora de Pédery-Hunt
Rev.:	Ago Aarand, W. H. J. Blakemore
Composition:	92.5% Ag, 7.5% Cu
Silver content:	5.374 g, 0.173 tr oz
Weight:	5.89 g	Edge:	Reeded
Diameter:	23.6 mm	Die Axis:	↑↑
Thickness:	1.7 mm	Finish:	See below
Case of Issue:	See Special Issue Proof Sets, page 527	

DATE	DESCRIPTION	QUANTITY SOLD	ISSUE PRICE	FINISH	PR-69	PR-70
1998 (1908-)	90th Anniv. R.C. Mint, Matte Proof	18,376	N.I.I.	Matte Proof	25.	—
1998 (1908-)	90th Anniv. R.C. Mint, Mirror Proof	24,893	N.I.I.	Mirror Proof	25.	—

MILLENNIUM SILVER PROOF AND NICKEL UNCIRCULATED COMMEMORATIVE SETS, 1999.

The twelve 25-cent nickel coins (circulation finish) of 1999 were issued along with a 1999 millennium medallion, inserted in a replica of a 1785 map of Canada. Two different medallions were issued, one with a maple leaf obverse, the other carried the Nestlé logo; both have the common Royal Mint logo reverse. They were only available in the millennium set. The set of twelve coins was also issued in sterling silver with a proof finish.

1999 Obverse

Designers and Engravers:

Obv.:	Dora de Pédery-Hunt
	Ago Aarand
Rev.:	See reverse illustrations

Composition:	Silver	Nickel
Silver content:	5.458 g	—
	0.175 tr oz	—
Weight:	5.9 g	5.05 g
Diameter:	23.88 mm	23.9 mm
Thickness:	1.7 mm	1.6 mm
Edge:	Reeded	Reeded
Die Axis:	↑↑	↑↑
Finish:	Proof	Circulation

Issue Price:

Individual proof silver:	$14.95
12 coin proof silver set:	$149.45
12 coin unc. nickel / RCM set:	$24.95
12 coin unc. nickel / Nestlé set:	$24.95

Quantity:	Total individual silver coins:	111,414
Sold:	Total silver sets:	60,245
	Total nickel sets:	1,499,973
Case of Issue:	(A)	Gold plastic single hole, oval case, royal blue flocked insert
	(B)	Gold plastic 12-hole, oval case, royal blue flocked insert

January	February	March	April	May	June
P. Ka-Kin Poon	L. Springer	M. Lavoie	Ken Ojnak Ashevac	S. Minenok	G. Ho
Cosme Saffioti	José Osio	Stan Witten	Sheldon Beveridge	William Woodruff	William Woodruff

MILLENNIUM SILVER PROOF AND NICKEL UNCIRCULATED COMMEMORATIVE SETS, 1999 (cont.).

July	August	September	October	November	December
M. H. Sarkany	A. Botelho	C. Bertrand	J. E. Read	B. R. Bacon	J. L. P. Provencher
Stan Witten	Cosme Saffioti	Stan Witten	Sheldon Beveridge	Stan Witten	Stan Witten

DATE	DESCRIPTION	PROOF STERLING SILVER		UNCIRCULATED NICKEL		
		PR-68	PR-69	MS-65 NC	MS-66 NC	MS-67 NC
1999	January, A Country Unfolds	15.	—	5.	10.	—
1999	February, Etched in Stone	15.	—	5.	10.	—
1999	March, The Log Drive	15.	—	5.	10.	—
1999	April, Our Northern Heritage	15.	—	5.	10.	—
1999	May, The Voyageurs	15.	—	5.	10.	—
1999	June, From Coast to Coast	15.	—	5.	10.	—
1999	July, A Nation of People	15.	—	5.	10.	—
1999	August, The Pioneer Spirit	15.	—	5.	10.	—
1999	September, Canada Through a Child's Eye	15.	—	5.	10.	—
1999	October, A Tribute to the First Nation	15.	—	5.	10.	—
1999	November, The Airplane Opens the North	15.	—	5.	10.	—
1999	December, This is Canada	15.	—	5.	10.	—
1999	12 Coin Silver Proof Set plus RCM Medallion	90.	—	*	*	*
1999	12 Coin Nickel Set plus RCM Medallion	*	*	12.	—	—
1999	12 Coin Nickel Set plus "Nestlé" Medallion	*	*	20.	—	—

TWENTY-FIVE CENT MILLENNIUM MULES OF 1999.

It is in the 1999 millennium nickel set that the "No Denomination" coins of September and November are found. During the Fall of 1999, a Queen Elizabeth II obverse die became paired with the reverse dies of September and November millennium twenty-five cents coins creating two mules. The interesting result of these pairings is that for the first time Canada has a non denominated legal tender coin.

Queen Elizabeth II	1999 September	1999 November
No denomination	Reverse Mule	Reverse Mule
Obverse		

DATE	DESCRIPTION	MS-63 NC	MS-64 NC	MS-65 NC	MS-66 NC
1999	September, no denomination, Mule	100.	125.	175.	225.
1999	November, no denomination, Mule	100.	125.	175.	225.

TWENTY-FIVE CENT SOUVENIR MEDALLIONS OF 1999.

Along with the nickel souvenir sets two different medallions were issued: A Royal Canadian Mint medallion and a Nestlé Canada Inc. medallion.

| 1999 RCM Medallion Obv. | 1999 RCM Medallion Rev. | | 1999 Nestlé Medallion Obv. | 1999 RCM Medallion Rev. |

DATE	DESCRIPTION	QUANTITY SOLD	ISSUE PRICE	FINISH	MS-65 NC	MS-66 NC	MS-67 NC
1999	RCM Medallion	N/A	N.I.I.	Uncirculated	6.	10.	—
1999	Nestlé Medallion	N/A	N.I.I.	Uncirculated	12.	15.	—

TWENTY-FIVE CENT STERLING SILVER SOUVENIR MEDALLION OF 1999-2000.

The 24-coin sterling silver set which was issued for the Chinese market in Hong Kong contains a 1999-2000 sterling silver medallion.

DATE	DESCRIPTION	QUANTITY SOLD	ISSUE PRICE	FINISH	PR-68	PR-69
1999-2000	Sterling Silver Medallion	N/A	N.I.I.	Proof	75.	—

MILLENNIUM SILVER PROOF AND NICKEL UNCIRCULATED COMMEMORATIVE SETS, 2000.

The 2000 Souvenir set was issued in sterling silver with a proof finish and in nickel with a circulation finish. The nickel set features 12 coins plus the 2000 commemorative medallion which was only issued with the souvenir set. The coins are displayed on an easel featuring an aerial photograph of Canada.

2000 Obverse

	Designers and Engravers:			**Issue Price:**	
Obv.:	Dora de Pédery-Hunt			Individual proof silver:	$14.95
	Ago Aarand			12 coin proof silver set:	$149.45
Rev.:	See reverse illustrations			12 coin unc. nickel/RCM set:	$24.95
Composition:	Silver	Nickel		12 coin unc. nickel set/plastic case:	$49.55
Silver content:	5.458 g	—	**Quantity:**	Total silver sets:	37,940
	0.175 tr oz	—	**Sold:**	Total nickel sets:	876,041
Weight:	5.9 g	5.05 g			
Diameter:	23.9 mm	23.9 mm			
Thickness:	1.7 mm	1.6 mm			
Edge:	Reeded	Reeded			
Die Axis:	↑↑	↑↑			
Finish:	Proof	Uncirculated			

Case of Issue: **Silver:**
(A)   Black plastic single-hole, oval case, royal blue flocked insert
(B)   Black plastic 12-hole, oval case, royal blue flocked insert
(C)   Red plush presentation case, light brown insert, 24 coins, a 1999 and 2000 medallion. Issued for the Chinese market.

Nickel: (A)   13 hole, Map of Canada. (B) 13 hole, plastic case

January	February	March	April	May	June
Donald F. Warkentin	John Jaciw	Daryl Dorosz	Annie Wassef	Randy Trantau	Haver Demirer
José Osio	William Woodruff	Stan Witten	Stan Witten	José Osio	José Osio

MILLENNIUM SILVER PROOF AND NICKEL UNCIRCULATED COMMEMORATIVE SETS, 2000 (cont.).

July	August	September	October	November	December
Laura Paxton	W. S. Baker	Cezar Serbanescu	Jerik (Kong Tat) Hui	Kathy Vinish	Michelle Thibodeau
Stan Witten	Susan Taylor	Cosme Saffioti	Susan Taylor	William Woodruff	José Osio

DATE	DESCRIPTION	PROOF STERLING SILVER		UNCIRCULATED NICKEL		
		PR-69	PR-70	MS-65 NC	MS-66 NC	MS-67 NC
2000	January, Pride	15.	—	5.	10.	—
2000	February, Ingenuity	15.	—	5.	10.	—
2000	March, Achievement	15.	—	5.	10.	—
2000	April, Health	15.	—	5.	10.	—
2000	May, Natural Legacy	15.	—	5.	10.	—
2000	June, Harmony	15.	—	5.	10.	—
2000	July, Celebration	15.	—	5.	10.	—
2000	August, Family	15.	—	5.	10.	—
2000	September, Wisdom	15.	—	5.	10.	—
2000	October, Creativity	15.	—	5.	10.	—
2000	November, Freedom	15.	—	5.	10.	—
2000	December, Community	15.	—	5.	10.	—
2000	12 Coin Silver Proof Set	90.	—	*	*	*
2000	12 Coin Nickel Set, RCM Medallion	*	*	10.	—	—
2000	12 Coin Nickel Set, Nestlé Medallion	*	*	15.	—	—

TWENTY-FIVE CENT SOUVENIR MEDALLIONS OF 2000.

Again in 2000 the nickel souvenir sets contained souvenir medallions. Two types were issued: The Royal Canadian Mint and Nestlé Canada Inc.

2000 Royal Canadian Mint Medallion   **2000 Nestle Medallion**

TWENTY-FIVE CENT MEDALLION MULE OF 2000.

In 2000 two dies were mismatched creating a mule. The obverse die of the February twenty-five cents is paired with the obverse die of the 2000 medallion. The mule is found in the Medallion position of the 13-hole, Map of Canada Brilliant Uncirculated Set of 2000.

  Mule

February Reverse   **February Obverse**   **Medallion Obverse**   **Medallion Reverse**

DATE	DESCRIPTION	QUANTITY SOLD	ISSUE PRICE	FINISH	MS-63 NC	MS-64 NC	MS-65 NC	MS-66 NC	MS-67 NC
2000	RCM Medallion	N.I.I.	—	Uncirculated	—	—	5.	8.	—
2000	Nestlé Medallion	N.I.I.	—	Uncirculated	—	—	8.	15.	—
2000	Coin / Medallion Mule	N.I.I.	—	Uncirculated	300.	500.	700.	—	—

TWENTY-FIVE CENTS, CANADA'S FIRST COLOURISED COIN, 2000.

Issued to celebrate the year 2000, this was the first colourised coin issued by the Royal Canadian Mint.

Designers and Engravers:

Obv.:	Dora de Pédery-Hunt
Rev.:	Donald F. Warkentin, José Osio

Composition: Nickel
Weight: 5.05 g   **Edge:** Reeded
Diameter: 23.9 mm   **Die Axis:** ↑↑
Thickness: 1.6 mm
Finish: Circulation, Colourised
Case of Issue: Blister packed on information card.

DATE	DESCRIPTION	QUANTITY SOLD	ISSUE PRICE	FINISH	MS-65 NC	MS-66 NC	MS-67 NC
2000	January, Pride, Colourised	49,719	8.95	Circulation	10.	18.	—

TWENTY-FIVE CENTS, CANADA DAY SERIES, 2000-2008.

The following series of twenty-five cent coins was issued to celebrate the Canada Day celebrations that took place during the last week of June, leading up to July 1st.

In 2004, four thousand six hundred and fifteen "Moose" coins were given to new Canadians during Canada Week Celebrations June 25th to July 1st. Of the initial offering of 27,000, only 16,028 were sold in a "walking bundle" (see page 60).

Years:	2000	2001 to 2008
Composition:	1.00 nickel, Painted	Nickel plated steel, Painted
Weight:	5.05 g	4.4 g
Diameter:	23.9 mm	23.9 mm
Thickness:	1.6 mm	1.6 mm
Edge:	Reeded	Reeded
Die Axis:	↑↑	↑↑
Finish:	Uncirculated	2001 to 2008: Circulation
		2004: Circulation
Case of Issue:	2000: Blister packed on information card.	
	2001: Encapsulated coin fastened to an information card	
	2002 to 2008: Folder	
	2004: See Derivatives, page 60-61	

2000

Designers and Engravers:

Obv.:	Dora de Pédery-Hunt
Rev.:	Laura Paxton, Stan Witten

2001

Designers and Engravers:

Obv.:	Dora de Pédery-Hunt
Rev.:	Silke Ware, William Woodruff

2003

Designers and Engravers:

Obv.:	Dora de Pédery-Hunt, Ago Aarand
Rev.:	Jade Pearen, Stan Witten

2004

Designers and Engravers:

Obv.:	Susanna Blunt, Susan Taylor
Rev.:	Cosme Saffiotti, Stan Witten

TWENTY-FIVE CENTS, CANADA DAY SERIES, 2000-2008 (cont.).

2002

Designers and Engravers:
    Obv.:   Dora de Pédery-Hunt, Ago Aarand
    Rev.:   Judith Chartier, Stan Witten

2004

Designers and Engravers:
    Obv.:   Susanna Blunt, Susan Taylor
    Rev.:   Nick Wooster, William Woodruff

2005

Designers and Engravers:
    Obv.:   Susanna Blunt, Susan Taylor
    Rev.:   Stan Witten, Stan Witten

2007

Designers and Engravers:
    Obv.:   Susanna Blunt, Susan Taylor
    Rev.:   José Osio

2006

Designers and Engravers:
    Obv.:   Susanna Blunt, Susan Taylor
    Rev.:   Stan Witten, Stan Witten

2008

Designers and Engravers:
    Obv.:   Susanna Blunt, Susan Taylor
    Rev.:   Stan Witten, Stan Witten

DATE/ COMP. MARK	DESCRIPTION	QUANTITY SOLD	ISSUE PRICE	FINISH	MS-65 NC
2000	Canada Day, Colourised, Celebration	26,106	8.95	Uncirculated	40.
2001P	Canada Day, Colourised	96,352	9.95	Uncirculated	8.
2002P (1952-)	Canada Day, Colourised	49,901	9.95	Uncirculated	12.
2003P	Canada Day, Colourised	63,511	9.95	Uncirculated	12.
2004P	Canada Day, Colourised	44,752	9.95	Uncirculated	12.
2004P	Canada Day, Citizenship/Moose	16,028	N.I.I.	Uncirculated	20.
2005P	Canada Day, Colourised	58,370	9.95	Uncirculated	12.
2006P	Canada Day, Colourised	30,328	9.95	Uncirculated	12.
2007	Canada Day, Colourised	27,743	9.95	Uncirculated	15.
2008	Canada Day, Colourised	11,538	9.95	Uncirculated	15.

TWENTY-FIVE CENTS, 50TH ANNIVERSARY OF THE CORONATION OF QUEEN ELIZABETH II, 1953-2003.

This twenty-five-cent coin is from the Special Edition Proof Set issued in 2003 to commemorate the 50th anniversary of the Coronation of Queen Elizabeth II.

Designers and Engravers:
Obv.: Mary Gillick, Thomas Shingles
Rev.: Emanuel Hahn, Thomas Shingles
Composition: 92.5% Ag, 7.5% Cu
Silver content: 5.458 g, 0.175 tr oz
Weight: 5.9 g Edge: Reeded
Diameter: 23.9 mm Die Axis: ↑↑
Thickness: 1.6 mm Finish: Proof
Case of Issue: See Special Issue Proof Sets, page 528

DATE	DESCRIPTION	QUANTITY SOLD	ISSUE PRICE	FINISH	PR-69	PR-70
2003 (1953-)	50th Anniv. Coronation Queen Elizabeth II	21,537	N.I.I.	Proof	20.	—

TWENTY-FIVE CENTS, CANADA DAY, 2009, (GIFTWARE).

In 2009 the Royal Canadian Mint discontinued the standard Canada Day colourised twenty-five cent piece, changing it to a crown size coin, with no relation to the standard twenty-five-cent denomination.

Designers and Engravers:
Obv.: Susanna Blunt, Susan Taylor
Rev.: RCM Staff
Composition: Nickel plated steel, Painted
Weight: 12.59 g
Diameter: 35.0 mm
Thickness: 2.0 mm
Edge: Plain
Die Axis: ↑↑
Finish: Specimen
Case of Issue: Folder

DATE	DESCRIPTION	RCM ITEM #	QUANTITY SOLD	ISSUE PRICE	FINISH	MS-65 NC
2009	Canada Day, Churchill	105512	11,091	14.95	Specimen	20.

TWENTY-FIVE CENTS, CHRISTMAS DAY SERIES, COLOURISED, 2004-2010.

The twenty-five cents Christmas Day coins are issued as part of the Holiday Gift Set series, see page 513. The quantity sold figures shown are from the number of Holiday Sets sold for that year. The last colourised twenty-five-cent coin in the Christmas Series was issued in 2010. The Holiday Gift Sets continued in 2011, however, the twenty-five-cent coin was no longer coloured, see pages 34-35.

Obverse With Mint Mark "P" 2004-2006	Obverse With RCM Logo 2007-2009	Obverse Without RCM Logo 2010	2004 Santa Claus José Osio	2005 Christmas Stocking José Osio

2006 Santa in Sleigh and Reindeer M. Hallam, J. Osio	2007 Christmas Tree RCM Staff	2008 Santa RCM Staff	2009 Santa Claus and Maple Leaves RCM Staff	2010 Santa Claus and Christmas Tree RCM Staff

TWENTY-FIVE CENTS, CHRISTMAS DAY SERIES, COLOURISED, 2004-2010 (cont.).

Designers and Engravers:

Obv.: Susanna Blunt, Susan Taylor
Rev.: See reverse illustrations
Composition: Nickel plated steel, Decal
Weight: 4.4 g
Finish: Circulation

Diameter: 23.9 mm
Edge: Reeded
Thickness: 1.6 mm
Die Axis: ↑↑
Case of Issue: See Holiday Gift Sets page 513

DATE/ COMP. MARK	DESCRIPTION	SOURCE	QUANTITY SOLD	ISSUE PRICE	FINISH	MS-65 NC
2004P	Santa Claus		62,777	N.I.I.	Uncirculated	25.
2005P	Christmas Stocking	Available only from Holiday Gift Sets	72,831	N.I.I.	Uncirculated	12.
2006P	Santa in Sleigh and Reindeer		99,258	N.I.I.	Uncirculated	12.
2007	Christmas Tree		66,267	N.I.I.	Uncirculated	15.
2008	Santa		42,344	N.I.I.	Uncirculated	15.
2009	Santa Claus and Maple Leaves		32,967	N.I.I.	Uncirculated	15.
2010	Santa Claus and Christmas Tree		10,870	N.I.I.	Uncirculated	15.

TWENTY-FIVE CENTS, SILVER POPPY, ROYAL CANADIAN MINT ANNUAL REPORT, SELECTIVELY GOLD PLATED, 2004.

This coin is the second in the Royal Canadian Mint Annual Report series. This series was cancelled in 2006.

Designers and Engravers:

Obv.: Susanna Blunt, Susan Taylor
Rev.: Cosme Saffioti, Stan Witten
Composition: 92.5% Ag, 7.5% Cu, Selectively gold plated
Silver content: 5.458 g, 0.175 tr oz
Weight: 5.9 g   **Edge:** Reeded
Diameter: 23.9 mm   **Die Axis:** ↑↑
Thickness: 1.7 mm   **Finish:** Proof
Case of Issue: See Derivatives, page 60-61

DATE	DESCRIPTION	QUANTITY SOLD	ISSUE PRICE	FINISH	PR-69	PR-70
2004	Poppy, selectively gold plated	12,677	N.I.I.	Proof	25.	—

TWENTY-FIVE CENTS, REMEMBRANCE DAY POPPY, COLOURISED, 2005 AND 2008, (GIFTWARE).

These twenty-five-cent coins were issued to commemorate Remembrance Day 2005 and 2008. They are encased in plastic bookmarks.

Designers and Engravers:

Obv.: Susanna Blunt, Susan Taylor
Rev.: Cosme Saffioti, Stan Witten
Composition: Nickel plated steel, Colourised
Weight: 4.4 g   **Edge:** Reeded
Diameter: 23.9 mm   **Die Axis:** ↑↑
Thickness: 1.6 mm   **Finish:** Circulation
Case of Issue: See Derivatives, page 60-61

2005   2008

DATE/ COMP. MARK	DESCRIPTION	SOURCE	QUANTITY SOLD	ISSUE PRICE	FINISH	MS-65 NC
2005P	Remembrance Day Poppy, Colourised	Bookmark	29,975	N.I.I.	Uncirculated	25.
2008	Remembrance Day Poppy, Colourised	Bookmark	489	12.95	Uncirculated	20.

Note: A colourised circulation Poppy coin was issued in 2004 to commemorate Remembrance Day 2004. See *Canadian Coins, Numismatic Issues, Volume One*.

TWENTY-FIVE CENTS, 60TH ANNIVERSARY OF THE LIBERATION OF THE NETHERLANDS, 2005.

The Canadian Armed Forces played a leading role in the liberation of the Netherlands that was completed May 5th, 1945. This coin was issued in an eight-coin, Brilliant Uncirculated set, by the Netherlands Mint.

Designers and Engravers:

Obv.:	Susanna Blunt, Susan Taylor
Rev.:	Peter Mossman, José Osio

Composition:	92.5% Ag, 7.5% Cu		
Silver content:	5.458 g, 0.175 tr oz		
Weight:	5.9 g	**Edge:**	Reeded
Diameter:	23.9 mm	**Die Axis:** ↑↑	
Thickness:	1.7 mm	**Finish:**	Specimen
Case of Issue:	See Derivatives, page 60-61		

DATE	DESCRIPTION	QUANTITY SOLD	ISSUE PRICE	FINISH	SP-68	SP-69
2005	60th Year of Liberation	3,500	N.I.I.	Specimen	40.	—

TWENTY-FIVE CENTS, QUEBEC WINTER CARNIVAL, 2006 (GIFTWARE).

The Quebec Winter Carnival, the largest in North America, is held each year in Quebec City, Quebec.

Designers and Engravers:

Obv.:	Susanna Blunt, Susan Taylor
Rev.:	RCM Staff, Cecily Mok

Composition:	Nickel plated steel, Painted		
Weight:	4.4 g		
Diameter:	23.9 mm	**Edge:**	Reeded
Thickness:	1.6 mm	**Die Axis:** ↑↑	
Finish:	Circulation		
Case of Issue:	See Miscellaneous Gift Sets, page 506		

DATE/ COMP. MARK	DESCRIPTION	SOURCE	QUANTITY SOLD	ISSUE PRICE	FINISH	MS-65 NC
2006P	Quebec Winter Carnival, Painted	Promo Gift Set	8,200	N.I.I.	Uncirculated	20.

TWENTY-FIVE CENTS, BREAST CANCER AWARENESS, 2006 (GIFTWARE).

This coin was issued to promote awareness for breast cancer. It is identical to the circulation issue, except the three outer ribbons and the central ribbon are painted pink. This variety was issued encased in a plastic bookmark. Removal of the coin from the encased plastic is very difficult and may result in the Awareness ribbons being damaged.

Designers and Engravers:

Obv.:	Susanna Blunt, Susan Taylor
Rev.:	C. Saffioti, S. Witten, K. Wachelko

Composition:	Nickel plated steel, Painted		
Weight:	4.4 g		
Diameter:	23.9 mm	**Edge:**	Reeded
Thickness:	1.6 mm	**Die Axis:** ↑↑	
Finish:	Circulation		
Case of Issue:	See Derivatives, page 60-61		

DATE/ COMP. MARK	DESCRIPTION	SOURCE	QUANTITY SOLD	ISSUE PRICE	FINISH	MS-65 NC
2006P	Breast Cancer Awareness, Painted	Bookmark	40,911	N.I.I.	Uncirculated	40.

TWENTY-FIVE CENTS, QUEEN ELIZABETH II COMMEMORATIVES, 2006-2007 (GIFTWARE).

2006	2006	2007	2007
Obverse	80th Birthday	Obverse	60th Wedding Anniv.
	Queen Elizabeth II		Elizabeth II / Prince Philip
	Designer: Cosme Saffioti		Designer: R. R. Carmichael
	Engraver: Cecily Mok		Engraver: Cecily Mok

Designers:
Obv.:   Susanna Blunt
Rev.:   See reverse illustrations
Composition: Nickel plated steel, Decal
Weight: 12.61 g
Diameter: 35.0 mm
Finish: Specimen

Engravers:
Obv.:   Susan Taylor
Rev.:   See reverse illustrations
Thickness: 3.4 mm
Edge: Plain
Die Axis: ↑↑
Case of Issue: Blistered packed on information card

DATE	DESCRIPTION	QUANTITY SOLD	ISSUE PRICE	FINISH	SP-68	SP-69
2006 (1926-)	80th Birthday of Queen Elizabeth II	24,977	19.95	Specimen	18.	—
2007 (1947-)	60th Wedding Anniversary Elizabeth II and Prince Philip	15,235	21.95	Specimen	20.	—

TWENTY-FIVE CENTS, NHL HOCKEY SERIES (GIFTWARE), 2006-2007.

The nine coloured twenty-five cent coins listed below are found in the NHL Team Gift Sets of 2006 and 2007, see page 508.

Designers:
Obv.:   Susanna Blunt
Rev.:   RCM Staff
Composition: Nickel plated steel, Decal
Weight: 4.4 g
Diameter: 23.9 mm
Finish: Circulation
Case of Issue: See NHL Team Gift Sets, page 508

Engravers:
Obv.:   Susan Taylor
Rev.:   RCM Staff
Thickness: 1.6 mm
Edge: Reeded
Die Axis: ↑↑

2006   HOCKEY SEASON, 2005-2006

Common Obverse	Montreal Canadiens	Ottawa Senators	Toronto Maple Leafs

DATE/ COMP. MARK	DESCRIPTION	SOURCE	QUANTITY SOLD	ISSUE PRICE	FINISH	MS-65 NC
2006P	Montreal Canadiens Logo	NHL Team	11,765	N.I.I.	Uncirculated	15.
2006P	Ottawa Senators Logo	Gift	Included	N.I.I.	Uncirculated	15.
2006P	Toronto Maple Leafs Logo	Sets	Included	N.I.I.	Uncirculated	15.

TWENTY-FIVE CENTS, NHL HOCKEY SERIES (GIFTWARE), 2006-2007 (cont.).

2007   HOCKEY SEASON, 2006-2007

Common Obverse

Calgary Flames

Edmonton Oilers

Montreal Canadiens

Ottawa Senators

Toronto Maple Leafs

Vancouver Canucks

DATE/ COMP. MARK	DESCRIPTION	SOURCE	QUANTITY SOLD	ISSUE PRICE	FINISH	MS-65 NC
2007	Calgary Flames Logo	Available only from NHL Team Gift Sets	1,082	N.I.I.	Uncirculated	15.
2007	Edmonton Oilers Logo		2,214	N.I.I.	Uncirculated	15.
2007	Montreal Canadiens Logo		4,091	N.I.I.	Uncirculated	25.
2007	Ottawa Senators Logo		2,474	N.I.I.	Uncirculated	15.
2007	Toronto Maple Leafs Logo		5,365	N.I.I.	Uncirculated	15.
2007	Vancouver Canucks Logo		1,526	N.I.I.	Uncirculated	15.

OCCASIONS SERIES

TWENTY-FIVE CENTS, OCCASIONS SETS, 2007-2013 (GIFTWARE).

In 2007 the Royal Canadian Mint continued their expansion into the giftware market with an issue of three new Occasion Gift Sets. The sets contain seven circulation finish coins with the Caribou twenty-five cent coin being replaced with a coloured twenty-five-cent coin representing the occasion.

Common Obverse
2007-2008

Designers and Engravers:
Obv.:	Susanna Blunt, Susan Taylor
Rev.:	RCM Staff
Composition:	Nickel plated steel, Decal
Weight:	4.4 g
Diameter:	23.9 mm
Thickness:	1.6 mm
Case of Issue:	See Gift Sets, pages 509-515

Edge:	Reeded
Die Axis:	↑↑
Finish:	Circulation

OCCASIONS - 2007

Balloons
Birthday Set

Bouquet
Wedding Set

Fireworks
Congratulations Set

Maple Leaf
Oh! Canada Set

Rattle
Baby Set

TWENTY-FIVE CENTS, OCCASIONS SETS, 2007 (GIFTWARE) PRICING TABLE.

DATE/ COMP. MARK	DESCRIPTION	SOURCE	QUANTITY SOLD	ISSUE PRICE	FINISH	MS-65 NC
2007	Balloons, Birthday Gift Set	Available only from Occasions Gift Sets	13,423	N.I.I.	Uncirculated	20.
2007	Bouquet, Wedding Gift Set		10,687	N.I.I.	Uncirculated	20.
2007	Fireworks, Congratulations Gift Set		9,671	N.I.I.	Uncirculated	30.
2007	Maple Leaf, Oh! Canada Gift Set		24,096	N.I.I.	Uncirculated	25.
2007	Rattle, Baby Gift Set		30,090	N.I.I.	Uncirculated	120.

OCCASIONS - 2008

Cake	Canadian Flag	Party Hat	Teddy Bear	Trophy
Wedding Set	Oh! Canada Set	Birthday Set	Baby Set	Congratulations Set

DATE/ COMP. MARK	DESCRIPTION	SOURCE	RCM ITEM #	QUANTITY SOLD	ISSUE PRICE	FINISH	MS-65 NC
2008	Cake, Wedding	Available only from Occasions Gift Sets	6260808	7,404	N.I.I.	Uncirculated	40.
2008	Canadian Flag, Oh! Canada		6260508	30,567	N.I.I.	Uncirculated	30.
2008	Party Hat, Birthday		100514	11,376	N.I.I.	Uncirculated	45.
2008	Teddy Bear, Baby		6260608	29,819	N.I.I.	Uncirculated	90.
2008	Trophy, Congratulations		100521	6,821	N.I.I.	Uncirculated	60.

OCCASIONS - 2009

Common Obverse With RCM Logo   **Four Maple Leaves Oh! Canada Set**   **Teddy Bear Baby Set**

DATE/ COMP. MARK	DESCRIPTION	SOURCE	RCM ITEM #	QUANTITY SOLD	ISSUE PRICE	FINISH	MS-65 NC
2009	4 Maple Leaves, Oh! Canada	Occasions Gift Sets	103353	14,451	N.I.I.	Uncirculated	30.
2009	Teddy Bear, Baby		103354	25,182	N.I.I.	Uncirculated	100.

In 2009 only the Oh! Canada! and Baby giftware sets were issued. The other twenty-five cent Occasions coins were incorporated into gift cards, see page 34-35.

OCCASIONS - 2010

For 2010, the Wedding Occasion twenty-five cent coin was moved back to the Wedding Gift Set series.

Common Obverse	Carriage	Heart and Roses	Three Maple Leaves
Without RCM Logo	Baby Set	Wedding Set	Oh! Canada Set

DATE/ COMP. MARK	DESCRIPTION	SOURCE	RCM ITEM #	QUANTITY SOLD	ISSUE PRICE	FINISH	MS-65 NC
2010	Carriage, Baby	Occasions Gift Sets	105801	27,048	N.I.I.	Uncirculated	30.
2010	Heart and Roses, Wedding		107023	8,194	N.I.I.	Uncirculated	20.
2010	Maple Leaves, Oh! Canada		105802	19,769	N.I.I.	Uncirculated	20.

OCCASIONS SERIES (cont.).

TWENTY-FIVE CENTS, OCCASIONS SETS, 2007-2013 (GIFTWARE) [cont.].

Beginning in 2011, the reverse designs on the twenty-five-cent coins contained in the Occasions Sets are die struck rather than illustrated with a decal.

Common Obverse
2011-2012

Designers:
Obv.: Susanna Blunt
Rev.: Gary Taxali
Composition: Nickel plated steel
Weight: 4.4 g
Diameter: 23.6 mm
Finish: Circulation
Case of Issue: See Gift Sets, pages 509-515

Engravers:
Obv.: Susan Taylor
Rev.: See reverse illustrations
Thickness: 1.6 mm
Edge: Reeded
Die Axis: ↑↑

OCCASIONS - 2011

Baby's Feet	Four Balloons	Maple Leaf	Wedding Rings	Snowflake
Baby Set	Birthday Set	O Canada Set	Wedding Set	Holiday Set
Engr.: Matt Bowen	Engr.: Stan Witten	Engr.: Cecily Mok	Engr.: Stan Witten	Engr.: C. Paquet

DATE/ COMP. MARK	DESCRIPTION	SOURCE	RCM ITEM #	QUANTITY SOLD	ISSUE PRICE	FINISH	MS-65 NC
2011	Baby's Feet, Baby		111600	38,576	N.I.I.	Uncirculated	100.
2011	Four Balloons, Birthday	Occasions	111601	21,173	N.I.I.	Uncirculated	15.
2011	Maple Leaf, O Canada	Gift	111599	22,475	N.I.I.	Uncirculated	15.
2011	Wedding Rings, Wedding	Sets	111602	20,461	N.I.I.	Uncirculated	15.
2011	Snowflake, Holiday		111605	41,666	N.I.I.	Uncirculated	15.

OCCASIONS - 2012

The Occasions Sets issued in 2012 contain six coins (1¢, 5¢, 10¢, 25¢, $1 and $2). The use of the fifty-cent coin was discontinued.

Mobiles	Ice Cream Cone	Stylized Maple	Wedding Rings	Christmas Tree
Baby Gift Set	and Balloons	Leaves	and Heart	Ornaments
Engr.: C. Paquet	Birthday Gift Set	O Canada Set	Wedding Set	Holiday Set
	Engr.: C. Paquet	Engr.: C. Paquet	Engr.: C. Paquet	Engr.: C. Paquet

DATE/ COMP. MARK	DESCRIPTION	SOURCE	RCM ITEM #	QUANTITY SOLD	ISSUE PRICE	FINISH	MS-65 NC
2012	Mobiles, Baby		117368	38,576	N.I.I.	Uncirculated	110.
2012	Ice Cream Cone & Balloons, Birthday	Occasions	117370	21,173	N.I.I.	Uncirculated	15.
2012	Stylized Maple Leaves, O Canada	Gift	117367	22,475	N.I.I.	Uncirculated	15.
2012	Wedding Rings & Heart, Wedding	Sets	119369	20,461	N.I.I.	Uncirculated	15.
2012	Christmas Tree Ornaments, Holiday		117371	41,666	N.I.I.	Uncirculated	15.

OCCASIONS SERIES (cont.).

TWENTY-FIVE CENTS, OCCASIONS SETS, 2007-2013 (GIFTWARE) [cont.].

The Occasions Sets issued in 2013 contain five coins (5¢, 10¢, 25¢, $1 and $2). The one-cent coin was discontinued in 2012.

Common Obverse

Designers:			Engravers:	
Obv.:	Susanna Blunt		Obv.:	Susan Taylor
Rev.:	Martin Coté		Rev.:	See reverse illustrations
Composition:	Nickel plated steel		Thickness:	1.6 mm
Weight:	4.4 g		Edge:	Reeded
Diameter:	23.9 mm		Die Axis:	↑↑
Finish:	Circulation			
Case of Issue:	See Gift Sets, pages 509-515			

OCCASIONS - 2013

Baby's Feet	Slice Birthday Cake	Maple Leaf	Wedding Rings	Holly Wreath
Baby Set	Birthday Set	O Canada Set	Wedding Set	Holiday Set
Engr.: Matt Bowen	Engr.: Stan Witten	Engr.: Stan Witten	Engr.: Matt Bowen	Engr.: Matt Bowen

DATE/ COMP. MARK	DESCRIPTION	SOURCE	RCM ITEM #	QUANTITY SOLD	ISSUE PRICE	FINISH	MS-65 NC
2013	Baby's Feet, Baby		121967	53,708	N.I.I.	Uncirculated	45.
2013	Slice of Birthday Cake, Birthday	Occasions	121968	22,678	N.I.I.	Uncirculated	15.
2013	Maple Leaf, O Canada	Gift	121966	26,068	N.I.I.	Uncirculated	15.
2013	Intertwined Wedding Rings, Wedding	Sets	121969	20,317	N.I.I.	Uncirculated	15.
2013	Holly Wreath, Holiday		121970	N/A	N.I.I.	Uncirculated	15.

OCCASIONS CARDS WITH COINS

TWENTY-FIVE CENTS, CARDS WITH COINS, 2009-2010 (GIFTWARE).

In 2009 a series of four cards incorporating twenty-five cent Occasions (decal) coins was released into the gift market. The Cards With Coins series was discontinued in 2010.

Designers:			Engravers:	
Obv.:	Susanna Blunt		Obv.:	Susan Taylor
Rev.:	RCM Staff		Rev.:	RCM Staff
Composition:	Nickel plated steel, Decal		Thickness:	1.6 mm
Weight:	4.4 g		Edge:	Reeded
Diameter:	23.9 mm		Die Axis:	↑↑
Finish:	Circulation			
Case of Issue:	Folder			

CARDS WITH COINS - 2009

Common Obverse	Balloons, Streamers	Doves and Rings	Fireworks	Stylized Flower
With RCM Logo	Birthday Card	Wedding Card	Congratulation Card	Thank You Card

TWENTY-FIVE CENTS, CARDS WITH COINS, 2009 PRICING TABLE.

DATE	DESCRIPTION	RCM ITEM #	QUANTITY SOLD	ISSUE PRICE	FINISH	MS-65 NC
2009	Balloons and Streamers, Birthday Card	103355	9,663	9.95	Uncirculated	15.
2009	Doves and Rings, Wedding Card	103356	7,571	9.95	Uncirculated	20.
2009	Fireworks, Congratulations Card	103357	4,126	9.95	Uncirculated	15.
2009	Stylized Flower, Thank You Card	103358	4,415	9.95	Uncirculated	15.

CARDS WITH COINS - 2010

| Common Obverse Without RCM Logo | Flowers Thank You Card | Gift Box Birthday Card | Stars Congratulations Card |

DATE	DESCRIPTION	RCM ITEM #	QUANTITY SOLD	ISSUE PRICE	FINISH	MS-65 NC
2010	Flowers, Thank You Card	107025	5,932	9.95	Uncirculated	10.
2010	Gift Box, Birthday Card	107022	8,751	9.95	Uncirculated	10.
2010	Stars, Congratulations Card	107024	5,693	9.95	Uncirculated	10.

TOOTH FAIRY GIFT CARDS

TWENTY-FIVE CENTS, TOOTH FAIRY GIFT CARDS, 2011-2012 (GIFTWARE).

In 2011 a new gift card theme was introduced. The Tooth Fairy Gift Card contains a "ready-to-fill" money envelope to place under a child's pillow to make the trade for the tooth.

Designers:
  Obv.: Susanna Blunt
  Rev.: 2011: RCM Staff
       2012: Gary Taxali
Composition: Nickel plated steel
Weight: 4.4 g
Diameter: 23.9 mm
Finish: Circulation
Case of Issue: Folder

Engravers:
  Obv.: Susan Taylor
  Rev.: 2011: Marcos Hallam
       2012: Christie Paquet
Thickness: 1.6 mm
Edge: Reeded
Die Axis: ↑↑

| Common Obverse | 2011 | 2012 |

DATE	DESCRIPTION	RCM ITEM #	QUANTITY SOLD	ISSUE PRICE	FINISH	MS-65 NC
2011	Fairy	112505	38,200	9.95	Uncirculated	15.
2012	Stylized Fairy	117372	20,359	9.95	Uncirculated	15.

ISSUES OF THE VANCOUVER 2010 OLYMPIC WINTER GAMES

TWENTY-FIVE CENTS, VANCOUVER 2010 WINTER OLYMPIC GAMES, 2007-2008.

The painted maple leaf outlined twenty-five cent coins were co-issued with Petro Canada and encased in a collector card format. The coins are listed in issue date order. The Collector Cards though numbered 1 to 15 do not necessarily correspond to the issue date order. The Alpine Skiing painted reverse was issued with a 2007 and 2008 dated obverse.

2007 Obverse
Olympic Games

2010
Olympic
Logo

Designers and Engravers:

Obv.:	Susanna Blunt, Susan Taylor
Rev.:	See reverse illustrations
Composition:	Nickel plated steel, Painted
Weight:	4.4 g
Diameter:	23.9 mm
Thickness:	1.6 mm
Edge:	Reeded
Die Axis:	↑↑
Finish:	Circulation

Ice Hockey
Bookmark and
Lapel Pin

Curling
Des.: Glen Green
Engr.: C. Mok

Ice Hockey
Des.: Glen Green
Engr.: K. Wachelko

Biathlon
Des.: Glen Green
Engr.: K. Wachelko

Alpine Skiing
Des.: Glen Green
Engr.: RCM Staff

Collector Card No. 4
2007 Alpine Skiing

DATE	DESCRIPTION	QUANTITY SOLD	ISSUE PRICE	FINISH	MARKET VALUE
2007	Curling, Sport Card, Painted leaf	90,756	7.95	Circulation	15.
2007	Curling, Bookmark and Lapel Pin	5,332	9.95	Circulation	10.
2007	Ice Hockey, Sport Card, Painted leaf	100,839	7.95	Circulation	15.
2007	Ice Hockey, Bookmark and Lapel Pin	9,062	9.95	Circulation	10.
2007	Biathlon, Sport Card, Painted leaf	30,279	7.95	Circulation	15.
2007	Biathlon, Bookmark and Lapel Pin	Not issued	—	—	—
2007	Alpine Skiing, Sport Card, Painted leaf dated 2007	919	7.95	Circulation	30.
2007	Alpine Skiing, Bookmark and Lapel Pin	6,172	9.95	Circulation	10.
2008	Alpine Skiing, Sport Card, Painted leaf dated 2008	40,470	7.95	Circulation	15.

ISSUES OF THE VANCOUVER 2010 OLYMPIC WINTER GAMES (cont.).

TWENTY-FIVE CENTS, VANCOUVER 2010 WINTER OLYMPIC GAMES, 2008-2009.

**2008 Obverse
Olympic Games**

**Snowboarding
Des.: Glen Green
Engr.: K. Wachelko**

**2010
Olympic
Logo**

Designers and Engravers:

Obv.:	Susanna Blunt, Susan Taylor
Rev.:	See reverse illustrations
Composition:	Nickel plated steel, Painted
Weight:	4.4 g
Diameter:	23.9 mm
Thickness:	1.6 mm
Edge:	Reeded
Die Axis:	↑↑
Finish:	Circulation

**Freestyle Skiing
Des.: Glen Green
Engr.: C. Mok**

**Figure Skating
Des.: Glen Green
Engr.: C. Mok**

**Bobsleigh
Des.: Glen Green
Engr.: RCM Staff**

**Cross Country Skiing
Des.: Glen Green
Engr.: RCM Staff**

**Speed Skating
Des.: Glen Green
Engr.: K. Wachelko**

**Collector Card No. 6
Snowboarding**

**Snowboarding
Bookmark and
Lapel Pin**

DATE	DESCRIPTION	RCM ITEM #	QUANTITY SOLD	ISSUE PRICE	FINISH	MARKET VALUE
2008	Snowboarding, Sport Card, Painted leaf	628408	40,771	7.95	Circulation	15.
2008	Snowboarding, Bookmark and Lapel Pin	N/A	5,150	9.95	Circulation	10.
2008	Freestyle Skiing, Sport Card, Painted leaf	628418	35,447	7.95	Circulation	15.
2008	Freestyle Skiing, Bookmark and Lapel Pin	N/A	Not Issued	—	—	—
2008	Figure Skating, Sport Card, Painted leaf	628428	16,479	7.95	Circulation	15.
2008	Figure Skating, Bookmark and Lapel Pin	N/A	6,047	9.95	Circulation	10.
2008	Bobsleigh, Sport Card, Painted leaf	628438	1,383	7.95	Circulation	15.
2008	Bobsleigh, Bookmark and Lapel Pin	N/A	Not Issued	—	—	—
2009	Cross Country Skiing, Sport Card, Painted leaf	628419	261	7.95	Circulation	15.
2009	Cross Country Skiing, Bookmark and Lapel Pin	N/A	Not Issued	—	—	—
2009	Speed Skating, Sport Card, Painted leaf	628409	309	7.95	Circulation	15.
2009	Speed Skating, Bookmark and Lapel Pin	N/A	3,529	9.95	Circulation	10.

ISSUES OF THE VANCOUVER 2010 OLYMPIC WINTER GAMES (cont.).

TWENTY-FIVE CENTS, GOLDEN MOMENTS OLYMPIC COMMEMORATIVES, 2009.

The Golden Moments twenty-five cent coins were issued to commemorate the gold medals won at the Salt Lake City Winter Olympic Games by the Canadian men's and women's hockey teams in 2002, and the gold medal won by Cindy Klassen at the 2006 Turin Winter Olympic Games.

While three different commemorative designs are present, there are also three different major finish varieties within each design, making a total of nine major varieties in this series. Adding to the complication are two minor varieties within the Men's Ice Hockey colourised coins that of a raised and incused 2, making the grand total ten varieties.

Seven varieties are listed in Canadian Coins, 70th edition, Volume One, and six are listed here in Volume Two. The overlapping colourised varieties are duplicated in each volume.

The Men's Ice Hockey, colourised, raised 2 variety is NOT found in Petro Canada Sport Cards.

DESIGNS	FINISH VARIETIES	DIE VARIETIES
Men's Ice Hockey	Circulation	Raised 2 (See Volume One)
	Colourised	Incused 2
	Painted	Incused 2
Women's Ice Hockey	Circulation	None
	Colourised	None
	Painted	None
Cindy Klassen	Circulation	None
	Colourised	None
	Painted	None

Collector Card No. 12
Canadian Men's Ice Hockey Team

Collector Card No. 13
Canadian Women's Ice Hockey Team

Collector Card No. 14
Cindy Klassen Speed Skating

ISSUES OF THE VANCOUVER 2010 OLYMPIC WINTER GAMES (cont.).

TWENTY-FIVE CENTS, GOLDEN MOMENTS OLYMPIC COMMEMORATIVES, 2009 (cont.).

Obverse
2009

Designers and Engravers:
Obv.:	Susanna Blunt, Susan Taylor
Rev.:	Jason Bouwman, Susan Taylor

Composition: Nickel plated steel
Weight: 4.4 g   **Edge:** Reeded
Diameter: 23.9 mm   **Die Axis:** ↑↑
Thickness: 1.6 mm
Finish:
  1. Circulation, Colourised
  2. Brilliant Uncirculated, Painted

Men's Ice Hockey
Colourised Red

Colourised Leaf
Incused 2

Men's Ice Hockey
Painted Red

Painted Leaf
Incused 2

Women's Ice Hockey
Colourised Red

Colourised Leaf

Women's Ice Hockey
Painted Red

Painted Leaf

Cindy Klassen
Speed Skating
Colourised Red

Colourised Leaf

Cindy Klassen
Speed Skating
Painted Red

Painted Leaf

DATE	DESCRIPTION	SOURCE	QUANTITY SOLD	ISSUE PRICE	FINISH	MS-65
2009	Men's Ice Hockey, Incused "2", Colourised	Sport Card	N/A	7.95	Circulation	8.
2009	Men's Ice Hockey, Incused "2", Painted	Spec. Ed. Set	8,564	N.I.I.	PL	10.
2009	Women's Ice Hockey, Colourised	Sport Card	N/A	7.95	Circulation	8.
2009	Women's Ice Hockey, Painted	Sp. Ed. Set	8,564	N.I.I.	PL	10.
2009	Cindy Klassen, Speed Skating, Colourised	Sport Card	N/A	7.95	Circulation	8.
2009	Cindy Klassen, Speed Skating, Painted	Spec. Ed. Set	8,564	N.I.I.	PL	10.

ISSUES OF THE VANCOUVER 2010 PARALYMPIC WINTER GAMES

TWENTY-FIVE CENTS, VANCOUVER 2010 PARALYMPIC WINTER GAMES SPORT CARDS, 2007 AND 2009.

**2007 Obverse
Paralympic Games**

**2010
Paralympic
Logo**

Designers and Engravers:

Obv.:	Susanna Blunt, Susan Taylor
Rev.:	See reverse illustrations
Composition:	Nickel plated steel, Painted
Weight:	4.4 g
Diameter:	23.9 mm
Thickness:	1.6 mm
Edge:	Reeded
Die Axis:	↑↑
Finish:	Circulation

**Wheelchair Curling
Painted Leaf
Des.: Glen Green
Engr.: C. Mok**

Ice Sledge Hockey
**Painted Leaf
Des.: Glen Green
Engr.: RCM Staff**

25¢ Wheelchair Curling Mule

The Vancouver Olympic obverse was paired with the Paralympic Wheelchair Curling reverse to create a mule. This coin was not issued for circulation, but is found in the Vancouver 2010 Brilliant Uncirculated Sets of 2007, which were assembled in Ottawa. See page 501 for the set listing.

**Collector Card No. 3
Wheelchair Curling**

**2007 Obverse with
Olympic Logo**

**2007 Reverse
Wheelchair Curling
Des.: Glen Green
Engr.: C. Mok**

DATE	DESCRIPTION	QUANTITY SOLD	ISSUE PRICE	FINISH	MARKET VALUE
2007	Wheelchair Curling, Sport Card, Painted leaf	34,956	7.95	Circulation	15.
2007	Wheelchair Curling, Mule	N/A	N.I.I.	PL	550.
2009	Ice Sledge Hockey Sport Card, Painted leaf	N/A	7.95	Circulation	15.

NOTE ON TWENTY-FIVE CENT ISSUES

The Petro Canada sport card twenty-five cent issues of 2007, 2008 and 2009 have a painted outline of a maple leaf supporting a central design. There are twelve different designs. The painted coins were inserted into sport cards and bookmarks which were encased in a plastic film. This film is all but impossible to remove without removing the painted outline from the coin.

ISSUES OF THE VANCOUVER 2010 OLYMPIC AND PARALYMPIC WINTER GAMES

TWENTY-FIVE CENTS, VANCOUVER 2010 OLYMPIC AND PARALYMPIC WINTER GAMES, SILVER PROOF SET, 2007-2009.

The twenty-five cent silver proof coins were issued in a presentation case. The set contains twelve coins and a one ounce sterling silver bar. Single proof coins may only be obtained from a break up of this set.

Designers:		Engravers:	
Obv.:	Susanna Blunt	Obv.:	Susan Taylor
Rev.:	Glen Green	Rev.:	RCM Staff
Composition:	92.5% Ag, 7.5% Cu		
Silver content:	Single Coin: 5.365 g, 0.172 tr oz		
	Bar: 28.77 g, 0.925 tr oz	**Thickness:**	1.7 mm
	Set: 93.15 g, 3.0 tr oz	**Edge:**	Reeded
Weight:	5.8 g	**Die Axis:**	↑↑
Diameter:	23.6 mm	**Finish:**	Proof
Case of Issue:	Black leatherette clam case, 13-hole flocked insert, encapsulated coins, COA		

DATE	DESCRIPTION	QUANTITY SOLD	ISSUE PRICE	FINISH	PR-69	PR-70
2007	Curling	N.I.I.	—	Proof	20.	—
2007	Ice Hockey	N.I.I.	—	Proof	20.	—
2007	Wheelchair Curling	N.I.I.	—	Proof	20.	—
2007	Biathlon	N.I.I.	—	Proof	20.	—
2007	Alpine Skiing,	N.I.I.	—	Proof	20.	—
2008	Snowboarding	N.I.I.	—	Proof	20.	—
2008	Free Style Skiing	N.I.I.	—	Proof	20.	—
2008	Bobsleigh	N.I.I.	—	Proof	20.	—
2008	Figure Skating	N.I.I.	—	Proof	20.	—
2009	Cross Country Skiing	N.I.I.	—	Proof	20.	—
2009	Speed Skating	N.I.I.	—	Proof	20.	—
2009	Ice Sledge Hockey	N.I.I.	—	Proof	20.	—
—	Complete Set, 12 coins, 1 one ounce silver bar	3,172	199.95	Proof	200.	—

TWENTY-FIVE CENTS, VANCOUVER 2010 OLYMPIC WINTER GAMES MASCOTS, 2008, (GIFTWARE).

The three mascots, Miga and Quatchi for the Olympic Winter Games, and Sumi for the Paralympic Winter Games, appear on many souvenirs for the Vancouver Winter Games.

Common Obverse

Miga

Quatchi

Sumi

Sumi Introduction Folder
"Meet The Vancouver 2010 Mascots!"

Designers:
Obv.:	Susanna Blunt
Rev.:	Design Team of the Vancouver Organising Committee for the 2010 Olympic and Paralympic Games

Composition: Nickel plated steel, Decal
Weight: 4.4 g
Diameter: 23.9 mm
Finish: Circulation
Case of Issue: Introduction Folder "Meet The Vancouver 2010 Mascots!"

Engravers:
Rev.:	Susan Taylor
Rev.:	RCM Staff

Thickness: 1.6 mm
Edge: Reeded
Die Axis: ↑↑

DATE	DESCRIPTION	QUANTITY SOLD	ISSUE PRICE	FINISH	MARKET VALUE
2008	Miga	14,654	10.95	Uncirculated	25.
2008	Quatchi	15,310	10.95	Uncirculated	25.
2008	Sumi	15,333	10.95	Uncirculated	25.

TWENTY-FIVE CENT DERIVATIVES OF THE VANCOUVER 2010 OLYMPIC AND PARALYMPIC WINTER GAMES

DATE	DESCRIPTION	QUANTITY SOLD	ISSUE PRICE	FINISH	MARKET VALUE
2007	**Vancouver 2010 Coin Collector Card** (card only)	104,400	4.95	—	5.
2007	**Magnetic lapel pin**, Curling	3,118	9.95	Circulation	10.
2007	**Magnetic lapel pin**, Ice Hockey	3,158	9.95	Circulation	10.
2007	**Magnetic lapel pin**, Alpine Skiing	3,013	9.95	Circulation	10.
2008	**Magnetic lapel pin**, Snowboarding	6,095	9.95	Circulation	10.
2008	**Alpine Skiing**, Twenty-five cents, Painted and lapel pin	3,350	9.95	Circulation	10.
2008	**Snowboarding**, Twenty-five cents, Painted and lapel pin	2,922	9.95	Circulation	10.
2007-2010	**Magnetic Lapel Pin** for interchangeable sport coin	RCM	9.95	Circulation	10.
2007-2010	**Green See Through Tin Can**, Magnetic lapel pin, 5 twenty-five cent coins of various sports	RCM	14.95	Circulation	15.
2007-2010	**Green Tin Can** to hold the 15 Petro Canada Collector Cards	RCM	5.95	—	6.

BIRDS OF CANADA SERIES

TWENTY-FIVE CENTS, COLOURISED BIRDS OF CANADA SERIES, 2007-2014 (GIFTWARE).

This series features popular Canadian birds as depicted by artists Arnold Nogy, Trevor Tennant and Tony Bianco.

2007 Common Obverse
With RCM Logo

Ruby-Throated Hummingbird

Red-Breasted Nuthatch

2008 Common Obverse
With RCM Logo

Downy Woodpecker

Northern Cardinal

2010 Common Obverse
Without RCM Logo

Goldfinch

Blue Jay

Designers:		**Engravers:**	
Obv.:	Susanna Blunt	Obv.:	Susan Taylor
Rev.:	Arnold Nogy	Rev.:	RCM Staff
Composition:	Nickel plated steel, Decal	**Thickness:**	2.0 mm
Weight:	12.61 to 13.0 g	**Edge:**	Plain
Diameter:	35.0 mm	**Die Axis:**	↑↑
Finish:	Specimen		
Case of Issue:	Maroon leatherette clam style case, black flocked insert, encapsulated coin, COA		

DATE	DESCRIPTION	RCM ITEM #	QUANTITY SOLD	ISSUE PRICE	FINISH	SP-68	SP-69
2007	Ruby-Throated Hummingbird	627107	17,174	24.95	Specimen	80.	—
2007	Red-Breasted Nuthatch	N/A	11,909	24.95	Specimen	250.	—
2008	Downy Woodpecker	100459	14,282	24.95	Specimen	130.	—
2008	Northern Cardinal	100771	11,604	24.95	Specimen	200.	—
2010	Goldfinch	108058	13,991	24.95	Specimen	100.	—
2010	Blue Jay	109964	13,965	24.95	Specimen	75.	—

TWENTY-FIVE CENTS, COLOURISED BIRDS OF CANADA SERIES, 2007-2014 (GIFTWARE) [cont.].

**2011-2014 Common Obverse
Without RCM Logo**

**Black-capped Chickadee
Des.: Arnold Nogy**

**Barn Swallow
Des.: Arnold Nogy**

**Rose-Breasted Grosbeak
Des.: Arnold Nogy**

**Evening Grosbeak
Des.: Arnold Nogy**

**American Robin
Des.: Trevor Tennant**

**Barn Owl
Des.: Trevor Tennant**

**Eastern Meadowlark
Des.: Tony Bianco**

**Scarlet Tanager
Des.: Pierre Leduc**

Designers:		Engravers:	
Obv.:	Susanna Blunt	Obv.:	Susan Taylor
Rev.:	See reverse illustrations	Rev.:	RCM Staff
Composition:	2011: Nickel plated steel, Decal	**Thickness:**	2.0 mm
	2012-2014: Cupronickel, Decal	**Edge:**	Plain
Weight:	12.61 to 13.0 g	**Die Axis:**	↑↑
Diameter:	35.0 mm	**Finish:**	Specimen
Case of Issue:	Maroon leatherette clam style case, black flocked insert, encapsulated coin, COA		

DATE	DESCRIPTION	RCM ITEM #	QUANTITY SOLD	ISSUE PRICE	FINISH	SP-68	SP-69
2011	Black-capped Chickadee	113230	13,947	25.95	Specimen	40.	—
2011	Barn Swallow	113224	14,000	25.95	Specimen	40.	—
2012	Rose-Breasted Grosbeak	117753	19,897	29.95	Specimen	22.	—
2012	Evening Grosbeak	118003	19,985	29.95	Specimen	22.	—
2013	American Robin	121254	17,493	29.95	Specimen	25.	—
2013	Barn Owl	122415	15,166	29.95	Specimen	25.	—
2014	Eastern Meadowlark	127976	17,474	29.95	Specimen	25.	—
2014	Scarlet Tanager	130582	12,182	29.95	Specimen	25.	—

TWENTY-FIVE CENTS, 90TH ANNIVERSARY OF THE END OF WORLD WAR I SET, 2008 (GIFTWARE).

These two twenty-five-cent pieces were issued in a 2008 commemorative set to mark the ninetieth anniversary of the end of WorldWar One. The 35 mm crown-size coin depicts the Tomb of the Unknown Soldier at the NationalWar Memorial in Ottawa.

The standard 25-cent colourised Poppy coin was released into circulation during 2008. It was also incorporated into a bookmark that sold in the gift market. A donation of $1.00 per bookmark sold was given to the Legion's Dominion Command Fund.

2008   TOMB OF THE UNKNOWN SOLDIER

Designers and Engravers:
Obv.:	Susanna Blunt, Susan Taylor
Rev.:	David Craig, Cecily Mok

Composition: Nickel plated steel
Weight: 12.61 g
Diameter: 35.0 mm
Thickness: 3.4 mm
Edge: Plain
Die Axis: ↑↑
Finish: Specimen

2008   COLOURISED POPPY

Specifications: See 2005 Colourised Poppy, page 28
Case of Issue:
(A)   Illustrated folder: Two coins, Serialised
(B)   Bookmark: Twenty-five cent coin only

DATE	DESCRIPTION	SOURCE	RCM ITEM #	QUANTITY SOLD	ISSUE PRICE	FINISH	SP-68	MS-65 NC
2008	Tomb of the Unknown Soldier and Poppy	Folder	N/A	Incl. below	N.I.I.	Specimen	25.	—
2008	Poppy "Remembrance"	Folder	N/A	Incl. below	N.I.I.	Circulation	—	5.
2008	Set of Two Coins	Folder	103204	10,167	24.95	—	—	25.
2008	Poppy, Bookmark	Bookmark	N/A	489	12.95	Circulation	—	15.

Note: 1. While the finish on the Tomb of the Unknown Soldier, large size twenty-five cent coin, is listed by the Royal Canadian Mint as specimen, it certainly is not a specimen finish when compared with coins of their specimen set issues of 1996 to 2009.

2. The "quantity sold" figure is understated. The 2008 RCM Report omitted the quantity sold number for that year. That number should have been added to the 489 from the RCM Report for 2009.

TWENTY-FIVE CENTS, 100TH ANNIVERSARY OF ANNE OF GREEN GABLES©, 1908-2008 (GIFTWARE).

This coin was issued to commemorate the 100th anniversary of Anne of Green Gables©, which was first published in 1908.

Designers and Engravers:
Obv.:	Susanna Blunt, Susan Taylor
Rev.:	Ben Stahl

Composition: Nickel plated steel, Decal
Weight: 12.61 g
Diameter: 35.0 mm
Thickness: 2.0 mm
Edge: Plain
Die Axis: ↑↑
Finish: Specimen
Case of Issue: Illustrated folder, Serialised

DATE	DESCRIPTION	RCM ITEM #	QUANTITY SOLD	ISSUE PRICE	FINISH	SP-68	SP-69
2008 (1908-)	Anne of Green Gables©	100638	32,795	19.95	Specimen	25.	—

TWENTY-FIVE CENTS, NOTRE-DAME-DU-SAGUENAY, 2009 (GIFTWARE).

The Lady of the Saguenay Fjord sits high on Cape Trinité in the majestic Saguenay Fjord, three hundred metres above sea level. The solid wooden statue was designed by Louis Jobin in 1881.

Designers and Engravers:

Obv.:	Susanna Blunt, Susan Taylor
Rev.:	Promotion Saguenay, Susan Taylor
Composition:	Nickel plated steel, Decal
Weight:	11.7 g
Diameter:	35.0 mm
Thickness:	2.0 mm
Edge:	Plain
Die Axis:	↑↑
Finish:	Specimen
Case of Issue:	Coloured card

DATE	DESCRIPTION	RCM ITEM #	QUANTITY SOLD	ISSUE PRICE	FINISH	SP-68	SP-69
2009	Notre-Dame-Du-Saguenay	105230	16,653	14.95	Specimen	25.	—

TWENTY-FIVE CENTS, REMEMBRANCE DAY POPPIES, 2010 (GIFTWARE).

This twenty-five-cent coin is included in the Remembrance Day Collector Card. The card also has two die-cut holes to house the 2004 and 2008 "Poppy" coins.

Designers and Engravers:

Obv.:	Susanna Blunt, Susan Taylor		
Rev.:	Cosme Saffioti, Stan Witten		
Composition:	Nickel plated steel, Colourised		
Weight:	4.4 g		
Diameter:	23.9 mm	Edge:	Reeded
Thickness:	1.6 mm	Die Axis:	↑↑
Finish:	Circulation		
Case of Issue:	See Derivatives, page 60-61		

DATE	DESCRIPTION	RCM ITEM #	QUANTITY SOLD	ISSUE PRICE	FINISH	MS-65	MS-66	MS-67
2010	Remembrance Day Poppies, colourised	113637	21,738	N.I.I.	Uncirculated	5.	10.	—

TWENTY-FIVE CENTS, GEORGE V, STERLING SILVER, PROOF, 1935-2010.

This twenty-five-cent coin is from the Special Limited Edition Proof Set issued in 2010 to commemorate Emanuel Hahn's classic voyageur design which first appeared on the 1935 silver dollar.

Designers and Engravers:

Obv.:	Sir. E. B. MacKennal		
Rev.:	L. C. Wyon		
Composition:	92.5% Ag, 7.5% Cu		
Silver content:	5.458 g, 0.175 tr oz		
Weight:	5.9 g	Edge:	Reeded
Diameter:	23.9 mm	Die Axis:	↑↑
Thickness:	1.7 mm	Finish:	Proof
Case of Issue:	See Special Issue Proof Sets, page 529		

DATE	DESCRIPTION	RCM ITEM #	QUANTITY SOLD	ISSUE PRICE	FINISH	PR-69	PR-70
2010 (1935-)	George V, Sterling Silver	111020	4,996	N.I.I.	Proof	30.	—

CANADIAN MYTHICAL CREATURES SET

TWENTY-FIVE CENTS, CANADIAN MYTHICAL CREATURES SET, 2011 (GIFTWARE).
This set features mythical Canadian animals as depicted by artist Emily S. Damstra.

| Common Obverse | Sasquatch | Memphré | Mishepishu |

Designers:
  Obv.:   Susanna Blunt
  Rev.:   Emily S. Damstra
Composition: Nickel plated steel, Decal
Weight: 12.61 to 13.0 g
Diameter: 35.0 mm
Finish: Specimen

Engravers:
  Obv.:   Susan Taylor
  Rev.:   RCM Staff
Thickness: 2.0 mm
Edge: Plain
Die Axis: ↑↑
Case of Issue: Coloured folder

DATE	DESCRIPTION	RCM ITEM #	QUANTITY SOLD	ISSUE PRICE	FINISH	SP-68	SP-69
2011	Sasquatch	113832	12,321	24.95	Specimen	20.	—
2011	Memphré	113826	5,811	24.95	Specimen	20.	—
2011	Mishepishu	113838	5,831	24.95	Specimen	20.	—

TWENTY-FIVE CENTS, THE WEDDING CELEBRATION, HRH PRINCE WILLIAM AND MISS CATHERINE MIDDLETON, 2011 (GIFTWARE).
This coin was issued to commemorate the marriage of HRH Prince William and Miss Catherine Middleton on April 29th, 2011.

Designers and Engravers:
  Obv.:   Susanna Blunt, Susan Taylor
  Rev.:   José Osio
Composition: Nickel plated steel, Decal
Weight: 12.61 g
Diameter: 35.0 mm
Thickness: 2.0 mm
Edge: Reeded
Die Axis: ↑↑
Finish: Specimen
Case of Issue: Illustrated folder

DATE	DESCRIPTION	RCM ITEM #	QUANTITY SOLD	ISSUE PRICE	FINISH	SP-68	SP-69
2011	HRH Prince William and Miss Catherine Middleton	114642	59,585	25.95	Specimen	20.	—

CANADA'S FLORA AND FAUNA SERIES

TWENTY-FIVE CENTS, CANADA'S FLORA AND FAUNA SERIES, 2011-2014 (GIFTWARE).

This series of coins is based on the flora and fauna of Canada's natural landscape. For similar series, see pages 263 and 455.

| Common obverse | Tulip with Ladybug
Designer: Cosme Saffioti
Engraver: RCM Staff | Aster with Bumble Bee
Designer: Maurice Gervais
Engraver: Cecily Mok | Purple Coneflower and
Eastern Tailed Blue Butterfly
Designer: Maurice Gervais
Engraver: RCM Staff | Water-lily and Leopard Frog
Designer: Maurice Gervais
Engraver: RCM Staff |

Designers:
- Obv.: Susanna Blunt
- Rev.: See reverse illustrations

Composition: 2011: Nickel plated steel, Decal
2012-2014: Cupronickel, Decal

Weight: 12.61 g
Diameter: 35.0 mm
Thickness: 1.9 to 2.0 mm

Engravers:
- Obv.: Susan Taylor
- Rev.: See reverse illustrations

Edge: Plain
Die Axis: ↑↑
Finish: Specimen

Case of Issue: 2011: Illustrated folder; 2012-2014: Maroon leatherette clam style case, black flocked insert, encapsulated coin, COA

DATE	DESCRIPTION	RCM ITEM #	QUANTITY SOLD	ISSUE PRICE	FINISH	SP-68	SP-69
2011	Tulip with Ladybug	114346	15,777	24.95	Specimen	35.	—
2012	Aster with Bumble Bee	118104	16,005	29.95	Specimen	25.	—
2013	Purple Coneflower and Eastern Tailed Blue Butterfly	121913	14,459	29.95	Specimen	25.	—
2014	Water-lily and Leopard Frog	129871	11,199	29.95	Specimen	25.	—

TWENTY-FIVE CENTS, 75TH ANNIVERSARY OF CANADIAN BROADCASTING CORPORATION / RADIO-CANADA, 2011 (GIFTWARE).

Radio Canada's first broadcast was on November 2nd, 1936. The microphone depicted on the reverse of the coin was created by CBC/Radio-Canada for the Royal Tour of King George VI and Queen Elizabeth in 1939. It was designed for outside broadcasts. Its special wind-resisting device represented a major technological advance of the time.

Designers and Engravers:
- Obv.: Susanna Blunt, Susan Taylor
- Rev.: Konrad Wachelko, Nick Martin

Composition: Cupronickel
Weight: 12.61 g
Diameter: 35.0 mm
Thickness: 1.58 mm
Case of Issue: Illustrated folder

Edge: Reeded
Die Axis: ↑↑
Finish: Specimen

DATE	DESCRIPTION	RCM ITEM #	QUANTITY SOLD	ISSUE PRICE	FINISH	SP-68	SP-69
2011	75th Anniversary of CBC/Radio-Canada	115949	7,777	29.95	Specimen	15.	—

TWENTY-FIVE CENTS, WAYNE GRETZKY, 2011 (GIFTWARE).

Wayne Gretzky "The Great One", whose hockey jersey bore the number 99, is commemorated on this coin.

Designers and Engravers:

Obv.:	Susanna Blunt, Susan Taylor
Rev.:	Glen Green, RCM Staff
Composition:	Copper plated steel, Decal
Weight:	12.5 g **Edge:** Plain
Diameter:	35.0 mm **Die Axis:** ↑↑
Thickness:	1.9 mm **Finish:** Specimen
Case of Issue:	Illustrated folder

DATE	DESCRIPTION	RCM ITEM #	QUANTITY SOLD	ISSUE PRICE	FINISH	SP-68	SP-69
2011	Wayne Gretzky	114579	13,263	34.99	Specimen	25.	—

TWENTY FIVE CENTS, GEORGE V, STERLING SILVER, PROOF, 1911-2011.

This twenty-five-cent coin which carries the double date 1911-2011 is from the Special Edition Proof Set issued in 2011 to commemorate the 100th anniversary of the striking of Canada's 1911 silver dollar.

Designers and Engravers:

Obv.:	Sir E. B. MacKennal
Rev.:	Original design by L. C. Wyon,
	Modified by W. H. J. Blakemore
Composition:	92.5% Ag, 7.5% Cu
Silver content:	5.46 g, 0.17 tr oz
Weight:	5.9 g **Edge:** Reeded
Diameter:	23.9 mm **Die Axis:** ↑↑
Thickness:	1.7 mm **Finish:** Proof
Case of Issue:	See Special Issue Proof Sets, page 529

DATE	DESCRIPTION	RCM ITEM #	QUANTITY SOLD	ISSUE PRICE	FINISH	PR-69	PR-70
2011 (1911-)	George V, Sterling Silver	114121	5,952	N.I.I.	Proof	20.	—

OUR LEGENDARY NATURE SET

TWENTY-FIVE CENTS, OUR LEGENDARY NATURE: CANADIAN CONSERVATION SUCCESSES, 2011.

These coins were issued to commemorate three species brought back from near extinction by Canadian Conversation methods. The Wood Bison, Orca Whale and Peregrine Falcon twenty-five-cent coins were issued as a three-coin set.

Common Obverse	Wood Bison	Orca Whale	Peregrine Falcon

Designers:

Obv.:	Susanna Blunt
Rev.:	RCM Staff
Composition:	92.5% Ag, 7.5% Cu, Painted
Silver content:	5.46 g, 0.17 tr oz
Weight:	5.9 g
Diameter:	23.9 mm
Thickness:	1.5 mm
Case of Issue:	Three-hole maroon clam style case, black flocked insert, encapsulated coin, COA

Engravers:

Obv.:	Susan Taylor
Rev.:	Cecily Mok

Edge:	Reeded
Die Axis:	↑↑
Finish:	Proof

TWENTY-FIVE CENTS, OUR LEGENDARY NATURE: CANADIAN CONSERVATION SUCCESSES, 2011, PRICING TABLE.

DATE	DESCRIPTION	RCM ITEM #	QUANTITY SOLD	ISSUE PRICE	FINISH	PR-69	PR-70
2011	Wood Bison, Painted	N/A	—	N.I.I.	Proof	15.	—
2011	Orca Whale, Painted	N/A	—	N.I.I.	Proof	15.	—
2011	Peregrine Falcon, Painted	N/A	—	N.I.I.	Proof	15.	—
2011	Set of 3 coins	117008	5,290	49.95	Proof	40.	—

TWENTY-FIVE CENTS, *RMS TITANIC*, 1912-2012 (GIFTWARE).

On April 10th, 1912, *RMS Titanic* set sail from England on her maiden voyage to North America. Shortly before midnight on April 14th, 1912, *RMS Titanic* struck an iceberg and sank shortly before dawn on the following morning. This coin was issued to remember the event.

Designers and Engravers:
Obv.:   Susanna Blunt, Susan Taylor
Rev.:   Yves Bérubé, RCM Staff
Composition: Cupronickel, Decal
Weight: 13.8 g
Diameter: 35.0 mm
Thickness: 2.0 mm
Edge: Plain
Die Axis: ↑↑
Finish: Specimen
Case of Issue: Illustrated folder

DATE	DESCRIPTION	RCM ITEM #	QUANTITY SOLD	ISSUE PRICE	FINISH	SP-68	SP-69
2012 (1912-)	RMS Titanic	118244	34,309	25.95	Specimen	25.	—

TWENTY-FIVE CENTS, 100TH ANNIVERSARY OF THE CALGARY STAMPEDE, 2012 (GIFTWARE).

This twenty-five-cent coin is part of a coin and stamp set issued to commemorate the 100th anniversary of the Calgary Stampede. A domestic rate, and U.S. rate stamp are included in a colourful illustrated folder.

Designers and Engravers:
Obv.:   Susanna Blunt, Susan Taylor
Rev.:   Tony Bianco, Konrad Wachelko
Composition: Cupronickel, Decal
Weight: 13.9 g
Diameter: 35.0 mm
Thickness: 1.8 mm
Edge: Plain
Die Axis: ↑↑
Finish: Specimen
Case of Issue: See Derivatives, page 60-61

DATE	DESCRIPTION	RCM ITEM #	QUANTITY SOLD	ISSUE PRICE	FINISH	SP-68	SP-69
2012	100th Anniversary of the Calgary Stampede	118972	16,080	N.I.I.	Specimen	20.	—

PREHISTORIC CREATURES SERIES

TWENTY FIVE CENTS, PREHISTORIC CREATURES SERIES, 2012-2014 (GIFTWARE).

The coins in the Prehistoric Animal Series use a photo-luminescent technology (glow-in-the-dark) on the central image.

Common Obverse

Designers and Engravers:
Obv.: Susanna Blunt, Susan Taylor
Rev.: Julius T. Csotonyi, Cecily Mok
Composition: Cupronickel, Photo-luminescent
Weight: 13.8 g   **Edge:** Plain
Diameter: 35.0 mm   **Die Axis:** ↑↑
Thickness: 1.9 to 2.0 mm   **Finish:** Specimen
Case of Issue: Maroon leatherette clam style case, black flocked insert, encapsulated coin, COA, custom coloured sleeve

2012	2013	2013	2014
Pachyrhinosaurus Lakustai	Quetzalcoatlus	Tylosaurus Pembinensis	Tiktaalik

DATE	DESCRIPTION	RCM ITEM #	QUANTITY SOLD	ISSUE PRICE	FINISH	SP-68	SP-69
2012	Pachyrhinosaurus Lakustai	118274	24,422	29.95	Specimen	70.	—
2013	Quetzalcoatlus	118632	29,991	29.95	Specimen	20.	—
2013	Tylosaurus Pembinensis	118622	29,458	29.95	Specimen	20.	—
2014	Tiktaalik	127627	23,306	29.95	Specimen	20.	—

TWENTY-FIVE CENTS, 50TH ANNIVERSARY OF THE CANADIAN COAST GUARD, 2012 (GIFTWARE).

The CCGS Louis S. St. Laurent is depicted on this colourful twenty-five-cent coin. During a 1994 science expedition, the ship navigated through 3,700 kilometres of Arctic ice, visiting the North Pole as it made the first crossing of the Arctic Ocean from the Pacific to the Atlantic. It was a joint Canada-US expedition with the USCGC Polar Sea. On August 22nd, 1994, the Louis S. St. Laurent was the first Canadian ship to reach the North Pole.

Designers and Engravers:
Obv.: Susanna Blunt, Susan Taylor
Rev.: Yves Bérubé, RCM Staff
Composition: Cupronickel, Decal
Weight: 13.8 g
Diameter: 35.0 mm
Thickness: 1.9 mm
Edge: Plain
Die Axis: ↑↑
Finish: Specimen
Case of Issue: Illustrated folder

DATE	DESCRIPTION	RCM ITEM #	QUANTITY SOLD	ISSUE PRICE	FINISH	SP-68	SP-69
2012	50th Anniversary of the Canadian Coast Guard	117945	11,950	24.95	Specimen	20.	—

CANADIAN FOOTBALL LEAGUE SET

TWENTY-FIVE CENTS, CANADIAN FOOTBALL LEAGUE COIN AND STAMP SETS, 2012 (GIFTWARE).
These coin and stamp sets were issued by Canada Post to commemorate the 100th anniversary of the Canadian Football League. Each set honours a CFL team with a twenty-five-cent coin and two commemorative stamps.

Common Obverse

Designers and Engravers:

Obv.:	Susanna Blunt, Susan Taylor
Rev.:	Filip Mroz of Bensimon Byrne, Marcos Hallam
Composition:	Cupronickel, Decal
Weight:	13.8 g
Diameter:	35.0 mm
Thickness:	2.0 mm
Edge:	Plain
Die Axis:	↑↑
Finish:	Specimen
Case of Issue:	See Derivatives, page 61

British Columbia Lions

Calgary Stampeders

Edmonton Eskimos

Hamilton Tiger Cats

Montreal Alouettes

Saskatchewan Roughriders

Toronto Argonauts

Winnipeg Blue Bombers

DATE	DESCRIPTION	RCM ITEM #	QUANTITY SOLD	ISSUE PRICE	FINISH	SP-68	SP-69
2012	British Columbia Lions	119665	12,097	N.I.I.	Specimen	15.	—
2012	Calgary Stampeders	119663	12,104	N.I.I.	Specimen	15.	—
2012	Edmonton Eskimos	119664	12,120	N.I.I.	Specimen	15.	—
2012	Hamilton Tiger Cats	119659	11,906	N.I.I.	Specimen	15.	—
2012	Montreal Alouettes	119660	12,227	N.I.I.	Specimen	15.	—
2012	Saskatchewan Roughriders	119666	15,700	N.I.I.	Specimen	15.	—
2012	Toronto Argonauts	119661	12,434	N.I.I.	Specimen	15.	—
2012	Winnipeg Blue Bombers	119662	12,214	N.I.I.	Specimen	15.	—

DUCKS OF CANADA SERIES

TWENTY-FIVE CENTS, DUCKS OF CANADA SERIES, 2013-2015 (GIFTWARE).

Common Obverse

This series celebrates the 75th anniversary of Ducks Unlimited Canada, an organization committed to the preservation and conservation of Canadian wetlands and its inhabitants.

Mallard	Wood Duck	Northern Pintail	Harlequin Duck	Cinnamon Teal

Designers:
  Obv.:   Susanna Blunt
  Rev.:   2013-2014: Trevor Tennant
           2015: Denis Mayer Jr.
Composition: Cupronickel, Decal
Weight: 13.5 g
Diameter: 35.1 mm
Thickness: 1.8 mm
Case of Issue: Maroon leatherette clam style case, black flocked insert, encapsulated coin, COA

Engravers:
  Obv.:   Susan Taylor
  Rev.:   RCM Staff

Edge: Plain
Die Axis: ↑↑
Finish: Specimen

DATE	DESCRIPTION	RCM ITEM #	QUANTITY SOLD	ISSUE PRICE	FINISH	SP-68	SP-69
2013	Mallard	120710	17,521	29.95	Specimen	25.	—
2013	Wood Duck	123261	14,507	29.95	Specimen	25.	—
2014	Northern Pintail	127835	11,031	29.95	Specimen	25.	—
2014	Harlequin Duck	130588	6,592	29.95	Specimen	25.	—
2015	Cinnamon Teal	132478	5,535	29.95	Specimen	25.	—

TWENTY-FIVE CENTS, HER MAJESTY QUEEN ELIZABETH II CORONATION, 2013 (GIFTWARE).

This coin was issued to commemorate the Coronation of Queen Elizabeth II. The reverse image features a detail from Canadian artist Phil Richard's 2012 official portrait of Her Majesty Queen Elizabeth II in celebration of her Diamond Jubilee.

Designers and Engravers:
  Obv.:   Susanna Blunt, Susan Taylor
  Rev.:   Phil Richards, RCM Staff
Composition: Cupronickel, Decal
Weight: 13.9 g
Diameter: 35.0 mm
Thickness: 1.9 mm
Edge: Plain
Die Axis: ↑↑
Finish: Specimen
Case of Issue: Maroon leatherette clam style case, black flocked insert, encapsulated coin, COA

DATE	DESCRIPTION	RCM ITEM #	QUANTITY SOLD	ISSUE PRICE	FINISH	SP-68	SP-69
2013	HM Queen Elizabeth II Coronation	124543	15,000	24.95	Specimen	25.	—

TWENTY-FIVE CENTS, BIRTH OF THE ROYAL INFANT, 2013 (GIFTWARE).

This coin was issued to commemorate the birth of Prince George of Cambridge, third in the line to the British throne.

Designers and Engravers:

Obv.:	Susanna Blunt, Susan Taylor
Rev.:	Laurie McGaw, Susan Taylor

Composition: Cupronickel
Weight: 13.8 g
Diameter: 35.0 mm
Thickness: 1.9 mm
Edge: Plain
Die Axis: ↑↑
Finish: Specimen
Case of Issue: Coloured folder

DATE	DESCRIPTION	RCM ITEM #	QUANTITY SOLD	ISSUE PRICE	FINISH	SP-68	SP-69
2013	Birth of the Royal Infant	127143	15,003	24.95	Specimen	20.	—

TWENTY-FIVE CENTS, THE EASTERN PRICKLY PEAR CACTUS, 2013 (GIFTWARE).

This is the first coin in a new series featuring Canadian flowers.

 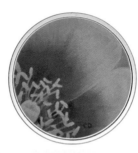

Designers and Engravers:

Obv.:	Susanna Blunt, Susan Taylor
Rev.:	Claudio D'Angelo, RCM Staff

Composition: Cupronickel, Decal
Weight: 13.7 g
Diameter: 35.0 mm
Thickness: 1.9 mm
Edge: Plain
Die Axis: ↑↑
Finish: Specimen
Case of Issue: Custom coloured cardboard box, encapsulated coin, COA

DATE	DESCRIPTION	RCM ITEM #	QUANTITY SOLD	ISSUE PRICE	FINISH	SP-68	SP-69
2013	The Eastern Prickly Pear Cactus	127291	7,189	24.95	Specimen	15.	—

TWENTY-FIVE CENTS, 2014 FIFA WORLD CUP™, 2014 (GIFTWARE).

In 2014 the FIFA World Cup™ was hosted by Brazil.

Designers and Engravers:

Obv.:	Susanna Blunt, Susan Taylor
Rev.:	Steve Hepburn, RCM Staff

Composition: Cupronickel, Decal
Weight: 13.7 g
Diameter: 35.0 mm
Thickness: 1.9 mm
Edge: Plain
Die Axis: ↑↑
Finish: Specimen
Case of Issue: Black and white clam style case, black flocked insert, encapsulated coin, COA, full colour sleeve

DATE	DESCRIPTION	RCM ITEM #	QUANTITY SOLD	ISSUE PRICE	FINISH	SP-68	SP-69
2014	2014 FIFA World Cup™	128587	8,825	29.95	Specimen	25.	—

HAUNTED CANADA SERIES

TWENTY-FIVE CENTS, HAUNTED CANADA, 2014-2016 (GIFTWARE).

There's a great tradition of storytelling across Canada, where many share a fascination with tales of unexplained apparitions, supernatural beings and haunted places – even if some might send shivers down one's spine! The *Haunted Canada* series bring some of Canada's most beloved spooky tales to life.

Common Obverse

Designers and Engravers:

Obv.:	Susanna Blunt, Susan Taylor
Rev.:	RCM Staff
Composition:	Cupronickel, Lenticular
Weight:	13.8 g
Diameter:	35.0 mm
Thickness:	1.9 mm
Edge:	Plain
Die Axis:	↑↑
Finish:	Specimen
Case of Issue:	Maroon leatherette clam style case, black flocked insert, encapsulated coin, COA,

Ghost Bride

Brakeman

Bell Island

DATE	DESCRIPTION	RCM ITEM #	QUANTITY SOLD	ISSUE PRICE	FINISH	SP-68	SP-69
2014	Ghost Bride	129430	15,007	29.95	Specimen	75.	—
2015	Brakeman	146941	15,175	29.95	Specimen	25.	—
2016	Bell Island	154468	12,678	31.95	Specimen	30.	—

NATIONAL HOCKEY LEAGUE SET

TWENTY-FIVE CENTS, NATIONAL HOCKEY LEAGUE COIN AND STAMP SETS, 2014 (GIFTWARE).
These coin and stamp sets were issued by Canada Post. Each set honours a Canadian NHL team with a twenty-five-cent coin and two commemorative stamps.

Common Obverse

Calgary Flames

Designers and Engravers:

Obv.:	Susanna Blunt, Susan Taylor
Rev.:	RCM Staff
Composition:	Cupronickel, Decal
Weight:	13.8 g
Diameter:	35.0 mm
Thickness:	2.0 mm
Edge:	Plain
Die Axis:	↑↑
Finish:	Specimen
Case of Issue:	See Derivatives, page 60-61

Edmonton Oilers

Montreal Canadiens

Ottawa Senators

Toronto Maple Leafs

Vancouver Canucks

Winnipeg Jets

DATE	DESCRIPTION	RCM ITEM #	QUANTITY SOLD	ISSUE PRICE	FINISH	SP-68	SP-69
2014	Calgary Flames	126173	5,721	29.95	Specimen	30.	—
2014	Edmonton Oilers	126199	5,772	29.95	Specimen	30.	—
2014	Montreal Canadiens	126165	5,973	29.95	Specimen	35.	—
2014	Ottawa Senators	126207	5,810	29.95	Specimen	30.	—
2014	Toronto Maple Leafs	126156	5,970	29.95	Specimen	30.	—
2014	Vancouver Canucks	126189	6,021	29.95	Specimen	30.	—
2014	Winnipeg Jets	126181	5,925	29.95	Specimen	30.	—

BIG COIN SERIES

TWENTY-FIVE CENTS, BIG COIN SET, 2015-2018.

The Big Coin Series started in 2015, features the classic Bluenose design for 2015, 2016, 2018 and 2019, which first appeared on the 1937 Canadian ten-cent coin designed by Emanuel Hahn, with Alex Colville's 1967 design for the 2017 coin. Other coins in the set include a 1¢ coin (page 7), 5¢ coin (page 12), 10¢ coin (page 17), 50¢ coin (page 57), $1 coin (page 131) and a $2 coin (page 145).

Designers and Engravers:
Obv.:	Susanna Blunt, Susan Taylor
Rev.:	Emanuel Hahn, Myron Cook
	Alex Colville
	Emanuel Hahn

Composition:
2015:	99.99% Ag, Selectively gold plated
2016:	99.99% Ag, Selectively coloured on reverse
2017:	99.99% Ag, Selectively gold plated
2018:	99.95% Ag, Selectively rose gold-plated
2019	99.99% Ag, Reverse gold plating

Silver content: 157.58 g, 5.06 tr oz
Weight: 157.6 g
Diameter: 65.25 mm
Thickness: N/A
Edge: Reeded
Die Axis: ↑↑
Finish: Proof
Case of Issue: Maroon clam style case, black flocked insert, encapsulated coin, COA, custom box

DATE	DESCRIPTION	RCM ITEM #	QUANTITY SOLD	ISSUE PRICE	FINISH	PR-69	PR-70
2015	25¢ Big Coin	133251	1,491	549.95	Proof	550.	—
2016	25¢ Big Coin	150841	1,484	519.95	Proof	500.	—
2017	25¢ Big Coin	156093	1,855	559.95	Proof	550.	—
2018	25¢ Big Coin	163720	1,500	559.95	Proof	560.	—
2019	25¢ Big Coin	170010	1,250	569.95	Proof	570.	—

Note: Coins illustrated smaller than actual size.

TWENTY-FIVE CENTS, LENTICULAR COIN, *BATMAN V SUPERMAN: DAWN OF JUSTICE*™, 2016.

Fearing the actions of a god-like super hero left unchecked, Gotham City's own formidable, forceful vigilante takes on Metropolis's most revered, modern-day saviour, while the world wrestles with what sort of hero it really needs. And with BATMAN™ and SUPERMAN™ at war with one another, a new threat quickly arises, putting mankind in greater danger than it's ever known before.

Designers and Engravers:

Obv.:	Susanna Blunt, Susan Taylor
Rev.:	DC Comics

Composition: Cupronickel, Lenticular

Weight:	13.7 g	**Edge:**	Plain
Diameter:	35 mm	**Die Axis:**	↑↑
Thickness:	N/A	**Finish:**	Specimen

Case of Issue: Custom presentation folder.

DATE	DESCRIPTION	RCM ITEM #	QUANTITY SOLD	ISSUE PRICE	FINISH	SP-68	SP-69
2016	Dawn of Justice	151185	27,120	29.95	Specimen	30.	—

TWENTY-FIVE CENTS, *STAR TREK*™: *ENTERPRISE*, 2016.

Beloved by millions, the originalf television series *Star Trek* has arguably helped shape the everyday lives of Canadians through its spirit of scientific innovation and discovery.

Designers and Engravers:

Obv.:	Susanna Blunt, Susan Taylor
Rev.:	RCM Staff

Composition: Three-ply nickel finished plated steel

Weight:	12.61 g	**Edge:**	Plain
Diameter:	35 mm	**Die Axis:**	↑↑
Thickness:	N/A	**Finish:**	Specimen

Case of Issue: Coin and stamp set, packaged in blister pack.

DATE	DESCRIPTION	RCM ITEM #	QUANTITY SOLD	ISSUE PRICE	FINISH	SP-68	SP-69
2016	Enterprise	153273	26,836	34.95	Specimen	35.	—

TWENTY-FIVE CENTS, LOVE MY CAT; LOVE MY DOG, 2017.

These special collectibles are a meaningful way to celebrate that special bond between Canadians and their beloved pets, who seem to ask little in return for their companionship.

Common Obverse   **Love My Cat**   **Love My Dog**

Designers and Engravers:

Obv.:	Susanna Blunt
Rev.:	RCM Staff

Composition: Three-ply nickel finished plated steel

Diameter:	35 mm	**Edge:**	Plain
Thickness:	N/A	**Die Axis:**	↑↑
Finish:	Specimen		

Case of Issue: Coin is set in blister in the card.

DATE	DESCRIPTION	RCM ITEM #	QUANTITY SOLD	ISSUE PRICE	FINISH	SP-68	SP-69
2017	Love My Cat	156823	16,529	31.95	Specimen	30.	—
2017	Love My Dog	156812	16,761	31.95	Specimen	30.	—

TWENTY-FIVE CENTS, LENTICULAR COIN, *THE JUSTICE LEAGUE*™, 2018.

Fueled by his restored faith in humanity and inspired by Superman's selfless act, Bruce Wayne enlists the help of his newfound ally, Diana Prince, to face an even greater enemy. Together, Batman and Wonder Woman work quickly to find and recruit a team of metahumans to stand against this newly awakened threat. But despite the formation of this unprecedented league of heroes—Batman, Wonder Woman, Aquaman, Cyborg and The Flash—it may already be too late to save the planet from an assault of catastrophic proportions. Each package contains two cards! Your coin comes two exclusive trading cards by Canadian artist Jason Fabok, with colours by Brad Anderson.

Designers and Engravers:

Obv.:	Susanna Blunt, Susan Taylor
Rev.:	Jason Fabak and Brad Anderson
Composition:	Cupronickel, Lenticular

Weight:	12.3 g	**Edge:**	Plain
Diameter:	35 mm	**Die Axis:**	↑↑
Thickness:	N/A	**Finish:**	Specimen
Case of Issue:	Custom presentation folder.		

DATE	DESCRIPTION	RCM ITEM #	QUANTITY SOLD	ISSUE PRICE	FINISH	SP-68	SP-69
2018	*The Justice League*™	162326	WSL	29.95	Specimen	30.	—

TWENTY-FIVE CENTS, DINOSAURS OF CANADA – 3-COIN SET, 2019.

Introducing three special-themed 25-cent coins that celebrate Canada's prehistoric past. These coins are only available in this set.

Common Obverse	*Albertosaurus sarcophagus*	*Pachyrhinosaurus Canadensis*	*Edmontonia longiceps*

Designers:

Obv.:	Susan Taylor
Rev.:	Julius Csotonyi
Composition:	Nickel plated steel
Weight:	4.4 g
Diameter:	23.88 mm
Finish:	Circulation

Engravers:

Obv.:	Susanna Blunt
Edge:	Plain
Die Axis:	↑↑
Case of Issue:	Display folder

DATE	DESCRIPTION	RCM ITEM #	QUANTITY SOLD	ISSUE PRICE	FINISH	PR-69	PR-70
2019	Dinosaurs of Canada – 3-Coin Set	172192	100,000	19.95	Circulation	20.	—

TWENTY-FIVE CENT DERIVATIVES

DATE	DESCRIPTION	QUANTITY SOLD	ISSUE PRICE	ISSUER	FINISH	MARKET PRICE
1999	**MILLENNIUM SET OF 12 CARDS** each containing a 1999 millennium twenty-five cent coin in a credit card format	N/A	N/A	RCM	MS-65	50.
1999	**JANUARY** "A Country Unfolds"	N/A	N/A	RCM	MS-65	6.
1999	**FEBRUARY** "Etched in Stone"	N/A	N/A	RCM	MS-65	6.
1999	**MARCH** "The Log Drive"	N/A	N/A	RCM	MS-65	6.
1999	**APRIL** "Our Northern Heritage"	N/A	N/A	RCM	MS-65	6.
1999	**MAY** "The Voyageurs"	N/A	N/A	RCM	MS-65	6.
1999	**JUNE** "From Coast to Coast"	N/A	N/A	RCM	MS-65	6.
1999	**JULY** "A Nation of People"	N/A	N/A	RCM	MS-65	6.
1999	**AUGUST** "The Pioneer Spirit"	N/A	N/A	RCM	MS-65	6.
1999	**SEPTEMBER** "Canada Through a Child's Eye"	N/A	N/A	RCM	MS-65	6.
1999	**OCTOBER** "A Tribute to the First Nation"	N/A	N/A	RCM	MS-65	6.
1999	**NOVEMBER** "The Airplane Opens the North"	N/A	N/A	RCM	MS-65	6.
1999	**DECEMBER** "This is Canada"	N/A	N/A	RCM	MS-65	6.
2000	**MILLENNIUM SET 24** silver 25-cent coins, medallion and case	N/A	N/A	RCM	PR-69	200.
2000	**MILLENNIUM SET OF 12 CARDS** each containing a 2000 millennium twenty-five cent coin in a credit card format	N/A	N/A	RCM	MS-65	50.
2000	**JANUARY** - Pride "Tomorrow Today"	N/A	N/A	RCM	MS-65	6.
2000	**FEBRUARY** - Ingenuity "Building for Tomorrow"	N/A	N/A	RCM	MS-65	6.
2000	**MARCH** - Achievement "The Power to Excel"	N/A	N/A	RCM	MS-65	6.
2000	**APRIL** - Health "Quest for a Cure"	N/A	N/A	RCM	MS-65	6.
2000	**MAY** - Natural Legacy "Our Natural Treasures"	N/A	N/A	RCM	MS-65	6.
2000	**JUNE** - Harmony "Hand in Hand"	N/A	N/A	RCM	MS-65	6.
2000	**JULY** - Celebration "Celebrating our Future"	N/A	N/A	RCM	MS-65	6.
2000	**AUGUST** - Family "The Ties That Bind"	N/A	N/A	RCM	MS-65	6.
2000	**SEPTEMBER** - Wisdom "The Legacy"	N/A	N/A	RCM	MS-65	6.
2000	**OCTOBER** - Creativity "Expression For All Time"	N/A	N/A	RCM	MS-65	6.
2000	**NOVEMBER** - Freedom "Strong and Free"	N/A	N/A	RCM	MS-65	6.
2000	**DECEMBER** - Community "Canada in the World"	N/A	N/A	RCM	MS-65	6.
2000	**APRIL**, CIBC "Run For The Cure" Credit Card	N/A	N/A	RCM, CIBC	MS-65	6.
2000	**THE ADVENTURES OF ZAC AND PENNY MONEY** Set of twelve 2000 Millennium twenty-five cent coins in a display card; six booklets of stories and games	6,888	N/A	RCM	MS-65	15.
2004P	**WALKING BUNDLE** Twenty-five cent 'Moose' coin, T-shirt, Water bottle, Pouch	11,413	19.95	RCM	MS-65	25.
2004	**2004 ROYAL CANADIAN MINT ANNUAL REPORT** Twenty-five cent "Poppy" coin, sterling silver, selectively gold plated	12,677	24.95	RCM	PR-69	40.
2005P	**BOOKMARK** Twenty-five cent "Poppy" coin; Victory pin	29,975	12.95	RCM	MS-65	20.
2005	**60TH ANNIV. 1945-2005** Liberation Set, Netherlands	3,500	49.95	RCM	SP-68	55.
2006P	**BOOKMARK** Twenty-five cent "Breast Cancer" coin; painted; Lapel pin	40,911	13.95	RCM	MS-65	35.
2006	**CANADA DAY 2006,** Twenty-five cents, colourised; Four crayons and a colouring sheet	N/A	9.95	RCM	MS-65	15.
2007	**CANADA DAY,** Twenty-five cents, colourised coin, activity kit	N/A	9.95	RCM	MS-65	20.
2008	**CANADA DAY,** Twenty-five cents, colourised coin, activity kit	N/A	9.95	RCM	MS-65	15.
2009	**CANADA DAY,** Twenty-five cents, colourised coin, activity kit	N/A	14.95	RCM	MS-65	20.

TWENTY-FIVE CENT DERIVATIVES (cont.).

DATE	DESCRIPTION	QUANTITY SOLD	ISSUE PRICE	ISSUER	FINISH	MARKET PRICE
2010	**REMEMBRANCE DAY COLLECTOR CARD,** includes 2010 twenty-five cent Remembrance Day coin; two die-cut holes for 2004 and 2008 twenty-five cent Poppy coins; postcard	21,738	9.95	RCM	MS-65	10.
2012	**TITANIC 100,** Twenty-five cent "Titanic" coin, White Star stock certificate, a re-created Titanic cancel, sheet of stamps, three Titanic postcards, leather-bound embossed album	10,000	140.95	RCM/CP	MS-65	110.
2012	**TITANIC PHILATELIC NUMISMATIC COVER,** Twenty-five cent coin, First Day Cover.	10,000	26.95	RCM/CP	MS-65	25.
2012	**CALGARY STAMPEDE COIN AND STAMP SET,** Twenty-five cents, colourised coin, a domestic rate and U.S. rate stamp	16,080	25.95	RCM/CP	SP-68	25.
2012	**CANADIAN FOOTBALL LEAGUE COIN AND STAMP SETS** Twenty-five cent coin, colourised, two commemorative stamps, coloured folder					
	British Columbia Lions	12,097	25.95	RCM/CP	SP-68	25.
	Calgary Stampeders	12,104	25.95	RCM/CP	SP-68	25.
	Edmonton Eskimos	12,120	25.95	RCM/CP	SP-68	25.
	Hamilton Tiger Cats	11,906	25.95	RCM/CP	SP-68	25.
	Montreal Alouettes	12,227	25.95	RCM/CP	SP-68	30.
	Saskatchewan Rough Riders	15,700	25.95	RCM/CP	SP-68	25.
	Toronto Argonauts	12,434	25.95	RCM/CP	SP-68	25.
	Winnipeg Blue Bombers	12,214	25.95	RCM/CP	SP-68	25.
2014	**NATIONAL HOCKEY LEAGUE COIN AND STAMP SETS** Twenty-five cent coin, colourised, two commemorative stamps, coloured folder					
	Calgary Flames	5,721	29.95	RCM/CP	SP-68	35.
	Edmonton Oilers	5,772	29.95	RCM/CP	SP-68	35.
	Montreal Canadiens	5,963	29.95	RCM/CP	SP-68	40.
	Ottawa Senators	5,810	29.95	RCM/CP	SP-68	35.
	Toronto Maple Leafs	5,969	29.95	RCM/CP	SP-68	35.
	Vancouver Canucks	5,986	29.95	RCM/CP	SP-68	35.
	Winnipeg Jets	5,925	29.95	RCM/CP	SP-68	35.
2016	***BATMAN V SPERMAN: DAWN OF JUSTICE*** Twenty-five cent coin, 2 collectable trading cards	27,120	29.95	RCM	SP-68	30.
2016	***STAR TREK: ENTERPRISE* COIN AND STAMP SET,** Twenty-five cent coin, 3 collectable stamps	26,836	34.95	RCM/CP	SP-68	35.

FIFTY CENTS

FIFTY CENTS, ELIZABETH II PROOF, 1996-2019.

Starting in 1996 the fifty-cent coin issued in the proof set, previously struck from cupronickel, was now struck on a sterling silver planchet. The use of sterling silver planchets was discontinued in 2011.

The year 2012 saw the introduction of the Premium Proof Set in which all coins were struck on fine silver planchets. Standard Proof Sets were issued for 2012, 2014-2019. The fifty-cent coin in these sets was struck on a nickel planchet. **Note:** Quantity sold figures are identical to those listed for Proof Sets sold.

| Obverse 1996-2003 | Obverse 2004-2006, 2015-2016 Without RCM Logo | Obverse 2007-2014, 2019 With RCM Logo | Reverse 1996-2019 | Reverse 2017 Canada 150 |

Designers:

Obv.: 1996-2003: Dora de Pédery-Hunt
2004-2019: Susanna Blunt

Rev.: 1996: Thomas Shingles
1997-2016: C. Bursey-Sabourin
2017: Heritage Canada contest

Engravers:

Obv.: 1996-2003: Dora de Pédery-Hunt
2004-2019: Susan Taylor

Rev.: 1996: Thomas Shingles
1997-2016: William Woodruff

	Sterling Silver	Nickel	Fine Silver
Composition:	92.5% Ag, 7.5% Cu	100.%	99.99% Ag
Silver content:	8.603 g, 0.277 tr oz	—	9.4 g, 0.302 tr oz
Weight:	9.3 g	6.9 g	9.4 g
Diameter:	27.1 mm	27.13 mm	27.0 mm
Thickness:	1.9 mm	1.9 mm	2.0 mm
Edge:	Reeded	Reeded	Reeded
Die Axis:	↑↑	↑↑	↑↑
Finish:	Proof	Proof	Proof
Case of Issue:	Included in Proof Sets, pages 524-526		

DATE	DESCRIPTION	COMP	QUANTITY SOLD	ISSUE PRICE	FINISH	PR-69	PR-70
1996	Diademed Portrait / Arms of Canada	Sterling	112,835	N.I.I.	Proof	10.	—
1997		Sterling	113,647	N.I.I.	Proof	10.	—
1998		Sterling	93,632	N.I.I.	Proof	10.	—
1999		Sterling	95,113	N.I.I.	Proof	15.	—
2000		Sterling	90,921	N.I.I.	Proof	15.	—
2001		Sterling	74,194	N.I.I.	Proof	15.	—
2002		Sterling	65,315	N.I.I.	Proof	15.	—
2003		Sterling	62,007	N.I.I.	Proof	20.	—
2004	Uncrowned Portrait / Arms of Canada	Sterling	57,614	N.I.I.	Proof	20.	—
2005		Sterling	63,562	N.I.I.	Proof	15.	—
2006		Sterling	53,822	N.I.I.	Proof	15.	—
2007	Uncrowned Portrait, Mint Logo / Arms of Canada	Sterling	37,413	N.I.I.	Proof	15.	—
2008		Sterling	38,630	N.I.I.	Proof	15.	—
2009		Sterling	27,549	N.I.I.	Proof	15.	—
2010		Sterling	32,342	N.I.I.	Proof	15.	—
2011		Sterling	32,910	N.I.I.	Proof	15.	—
2012		Nickel	27,254	N.I.I.	Proof	15.	—
2012	Premium Proof Set	Fine Silver	19,789	N.I.I.	Proof	15.	—
2013	Premium Proof Set	Fine Silver	20,182	N.I.I.	Proof	15.	—
2014		Nickel	11,251	N.I.I.	Proof	15.	—
2014	Premium Proof Set	Fine Silver	13,416	N.I.I.	Proof	15.	—
2015	Premium Proof Set	Fine Silver	20,000	N.I.I.	Proof	15.	—
2015		Nickel	20,000	N.I.I.	Proof	15.	—
2016	Premium Proof Set	Fine Silver	20,000	N.I.I.	Proof	25.	—
2016		Nickel	20,000	N.I.I.	Proof	25.	—
2017	Premium Proof Set, Arms of Canada	Fine Silver	20,000	N.I.I.	Proof	25.	—
2017	Premium Proof Set, Canada 150 Logo	Fine Silver	20,000	N.I.I.	Proof	30.	—
2017	Proof Set, Canada 150 Logo	Nickel	25,000	N.I.I.	Proof	15.	—
2017	Premium Proof Set 1967-2017	Fine Silver	20,000	N.I.I.	Proof	25.	—
2018	Premium Proof Set	Fine Silver	20,000	N.I.I.	Proof	25.	—
2018		Nickel	25,000	N.I.I.	Proof	15.	—
2019	Premium Proof Set	Fine Silver	15,000	N.I.I.	Proof	25.	—

DISCOVERING NATURE SERIES, 1995-2000

FIFTY CENTS, BIRDS OF CANADA SET, 1995.

The first set in the Discovering Nature Series commemorates birds that are native to Canada. This is the first of six sets totalling 24 coins. They are the first sterling silver fifty cents to be issued since 1919.

Common Obverse

Designers:		Engravers:	
Obv.:	Dora de Pédery-Hunt	Obv.:	Dora de Pédery-Hunt
Rev.:	Coins 1 - 4: Jean-Luc Grondin	Rev.:	See reverse illustrations
	Coins 5 - 8: Dwayne Harty		

Composition: 92.5% Ag, 7.5% Cu
Silver content: 8.603 g, 0.277 tr oz
Weight: 9.3 g   **Edge:** Reeded
Diameter: 27.1 mm   **Die Axis:** ↑↑
Thickness: 2.1 mm   **Finish:** Proof
Case of Issue: Coins 1 - 4   Encapsulated coin in presentation box with illustrated booklet.
Coins 5 - 6   (A) Two coin set; encapsulated coins
    (B) Four coin set; encapsulated coins

Coin No. 1	Coin No. 2	Coin No. 3	Coin No. 4
Atlantic Puffins	Whooping Crane	Gray Jays	White-tailed Ptarmigans
Sheldon Beveridge	Stan Witten	Sheldon Beveridge	Cosme Saffioti

FIFTY CENTS, LITTLE WILD ONES SET, 1996.

The second set commemorates the young wildlife of Canada in their natural habitat.

Coin No. 5	Coin No. 6	Coin No. 7	Coin No. 8
Moose Calf	Wood Ducklings	Cougar Kittens	Black Bear Cubs
Ago Aarand	Sheldon Beveridge	Stan Witten	Sheldon Beveridge

DATE	COIN No.	DESCRIPTION	QUANTITY SOLD	ISSUE PRICE	FINISH	PR-68	PR-69
1995	1	Atlantic Puffins	Total	—	Proof	15.	—
1995	2	Whooping Crane	mintage	29.95	Proof	15.	—
1995	3	Gray Jays	all coins	—	Proof	15.	—
1995	4	White-tailed Ptarmigans	172,377	29.95	Proof	15.	—
1995	—	Set of 4 coins	—	56.95	Proof	45.	*
1996	5	Moose Calf	Total	—	Proof	15.	—
1996	6	Wood Ducklings	mintage	29.95	Proof	15.	—
1996	7	Cougar Kittens	all coins	—	Proof	15.	—
1996	8	Black Bear Cubs	206,552	29.95	Proof	15.	—
1996	—	Set of 4 coins	—	56.95	Proof	45.	*

Note: Coins 1-2 and 3-4 were issued in two coin sets, issue price $29.95.

DISCOVERING NATURE SERIES, 1995-2000 (cont.).

FIFTY CENTS, CANADA'S BEST FRIENDS SET, 1997.

The 1997 set honours the friendship and loyalty of four of Canada's favourite canine companions.

Common Obverse

Designers:		Engravers:	
Obv.:	Dora de Pédery-Hunt	Obv.:	Dora de Pédery-Hunt
Rev.:	Coins 9 - 12: Arnold A. Nogy	Rev.:	See reverse illustrations
	Coins 13 - 16: Pierre Leduc		

Composition: 92.5% Ag, 7.5% Cu
Silver content: 8.603 g, 0.277 tr oz
Weight: 9.3 g
Diameter: 27.1 mm
Thickness: 2.1 mm
Case of Issue: Encapsulated coin in presentation box, plus illustrated booklet.

Edge: Reeded
Die Axis: ↑↑
Finish: Proof

Coin No. 9	Coin No. 10	Coin No. 11	Coin No. 12
Newfoundland	Nova Scotia Duck	Labrador Retriever	Canadian Eskimo Dog
William Woodruff	Tolling Retriever	Sheldon Beveridge	Cosme Saffioti
	Stan Witten		

FIFTY CENTS, CANADA'S OCEAN GIANTS SET, 1998.

The reverse designs of the 1998 set shows the grace and beauty of the whales that are seen off our coasts.

Coin No. 13	Coin No. 14	Coin No. 15	Coin No. 16
Killer Whale	Humpback Whale	Beluga Whale	Blue Whale
William Woodruff	Sheldon Beveridge	Cosme Saffioti	Stan Witten

DATE	COIN No.	DESCRIPTION	QUANTITY SOLD	ISSUE PRICE	FINISH	PR-68	PR-69
1997	9	Newfoundland	Total	19.95	Proof	15.	—
1997	10	Nova Scotia Duck Tolling Retriever	mintage	19.95	Proof	15.	—
1997	11	Labrador Retriever	all coins	19.95	Proof	15.	—
1997	12	Canadian Eskimo Dog	184,536	19.95	Proof	15.	—
1997	—	Set of 4 coins	—	59.95	Proof	45.	*
1998	13	Killer Whale	Total	19.95	Proof	15.	—
1998	14	Humpback Whale	mintage	19.95	Proof	15.	—
1998	15	Beluga Whale	all coins	19.95	Proof	15.	—
1998	16	Blue Whale	133,310	19.95	Proof	15.	—
1998	—	Set of 4 coins	—	59.95	Proof	45.	*

DISCOVERING NATURE SERIES, 1995-2000 (cont.).

FIFTY CENTS, CATS OF CANADA SET, 1999.
This set, issued in 1999, honours four species of domestic and wild felines found in Canada, a salute to our rich Canadian wildlife.

Common Obverse

Designers:		**Engravers:**	
Obv.:	Dora de Pédery-Hunt	Obv.:	Dora de Pédery-Hunt
Rev.:	Coins 17 - 20: John Crosby	Rev.:	See reverse illustrations
	Coins 21, 23: Jean-Luc Grondin		
	Coins 22, 24: Pierre Leduc		
Composition:	92.5% Ag, 7.5% Cu		
Silver content:	8.603 g, 0.277 tr oz		
Weight:	9.3 g	**Edge:**	Reeded
Diameter:	27.1 mm	**Die Axis:**	↑↑
Thickness:	2.1 mm	**Finish:**	Proof
Case of Issue:	Encapsulated coin in presentation box, plus illustrated booklet.		

Coin No. 17	Coin No. 18	Coin No. 19	Coin No. 20
Tonkinese	Lynx	Cymric	Cougar
Susan Taylor	Susan Taylor	Susan Taylor	Susan Taylor

FIFTY CENTS, CANADIAN BIRDS OF PREY, SET, 2000.
The sixth and last set of the series features the hunting birds indigenous to Canada.

Coin No. 21	Coin No. 22	Coin No. 23	Coin No. 24
Bald Eagle	Osprey	Great Horned Owl	Red-Tailed Hawk
William Woodruff	Susan Taylor	Susan Taylor	Stan Witten

DATE	COIN No.	DESCRIPTION	QUANTITY SOLD	ISSUE PRICE	FINISH	PR-68	PR-69
1999	17	Tonkinese	Total	19.95	Proof	20.	—
1999	18	Lynx	mintage	19.95	Proof	20.	—
1999	19	Cymric	all coins	19.95	Proof	20.	—
1999	20	Cougar	83,423	19.95	Proof	20.	—
1999	—	Set of 4 coins	—	59.95	Proof	65.	*
2000	21	Bald Eagle	Total	19.95	Proof	15.	—
2000	22	Osprey	mintage	19.95	Proof	15.	—
2000	23	Great Horned Owl	all coins	19.95	Proof	15.	—
2000	24	Red-Tailed Hawk	123,628	19.95	Proof	15.	—
2000	—	Set of 4 coins	—	59.95	Proof	45.	*

CANADIAN SPORTS FIRSTS SERIES, 1998-2000

FIFTY CENTS, CANADIAN SPORTS FIRSTS SET, 1998.

A new sport series of sterling silver fifty cent coins began in 1998 with the issue of four coins, which continued in 1999 and 2000, making a total of 12 coins.

Common Obverse

Designers:
Obv.:	Dora de Pédery-Hunt
Rev.:	Coins 1 - 4: F. G. Peter
	Coins 5 - 8: D. H. Curley

Composition: 92.5% Ag, 7.5% Cu
Silver content: 8.603 g, 0.277 tr oz
Weight: 9.3 g
Diameter: 27.1 mm
Case of Issue: Singles: Lithographed metal box, black flocked insert, encapsulated coin.
  Set: Twelve coin metal container.

Engravers:
Obv.:	Dora de Pédery-Hunt
Rev.:	See reverse illustrations

Thickness: 2.1 mm
Edge: Reeded
Die Axis: ↑↑
Finish: Proof

Coin No. 1
First Official Amateur
Figure Skating
Championships, 1888
Sheldon Beveridge

Coin No. 2
First Canadian Ski
Running/Ski Jumping
Championships, 1898
Ago Aarand

Coin No. 3
First Overseas Can.
Soccer Tour, 1888
Stan Witten, José Osio

Coin No. 4
Gilles Villeneuve
Victory, Grand Prix of
Canada for F1 Auto
Racing, 1978
C. Saffioti, J. Osio

FIFTY CENTS, CANADIAN SPORTS FIRSTS SET, 1999.

The 1999 fifty-cent sterling silver coin set commemorates important dates in the history of Canadian sports. The designs reflect both the history of the sport and the growth and development into national pastimes.

Coin No. 5
1904-1999 First
Canadian Open Golf
Championship, 1904
William Woodruff

Coin No. 6
1874-1999 First
Int'l Yacht Race
Canada vs U.S.A. 1874
Stan Witten

Coin No. 7
1909-1999 First Grey
Cup in Canadian
Football, 1909
Cosme Saffioti

Coin No. 8
1891-1999 Invention
of Basketball by
Canadian James Naismith
Sheldon Beveridge

DATE	COIN No.	DESCRIPTION	QUANTITY SOLD	ISSUE PRICE	FINISH	PR-68	PR-69
1998	1	First Official Amateur Figure Skating Chmpshp, 1888	Total	19.95	Proof	15.	—
1998	2	First Canadian Ski Running/Ski Jumping Chmpshp, 1898	mintage	19.95	Proof	15.	—
1998	3	First Overseas Canadian Soccer Tour, 1888	all coins	19.95	Proof	15.	—
1998	4	Gilles Villeneuve Victory, Grand Prix, F1 Auto Racing, 1978	56,428	19.95	Proof	15.	—
1998	—	Set of 4 coins	—	59.95	Proof	50.	*
1999	5	First Canadian Open Golf Chmpshp, 1904	Total	19.95	Proof	15.	—
1999	6	First Int'l Yacht Race between Canada and U.S.A., 1874	mintage	19.95	Proof	15.	—
1999	7	First Grey Cup in Canadian Football, 1909	all coins	19.95	Proof	15.	—
1999	8	Invention of Basketball by Canadian James Naismith, 1891	52,115	19.95	Proof	15.	—
1999	—	Set of 4 coins	—	59.95	Proof	50.	*

CANADIAN SPORTS FIRSTS SERIES, 1998-2000 (cont.).

FIFTY CENTS, CANADIAN SPORTS FIRSTS SET, 2000.

The 2000 fifty-cent sterling silver coin set celebrates the first competitions in Hockey, Curling, Steeplechase and Five Pin Bowling held in Canada. This is the last set in the twelve coin series.

Common Obverse

Designers:		**Engravers:**	
Obv.:	Dora de Pédery-Hunt	Obv.:	Dora de Pédery-Hunt
Rev.:	Brian Hughes	Rev.:	See reverse illustrations
Composition:	92.5% Ag, 7.5% Cu		
Silver content:	8.603 g, 0.277 tr oz		
Weight:	9.3 g	**Edge:**	Reeded
Diameter:	27.1 mm	**Die Axis:**	↑↑
Thickness:	2.1 mm	**Finish:**	Proof
Case of Issue:	Singles:	Lithographed metal box, black flocked insert, encapsulated coin.	
	Set:	Twelve coin metal case.	

Coin No. 9	Coin No. 10	Coin No. 11	Coin No. 12
1875-2000 First	1760-2000	1840-2000 First	1910-2000 Birth
Recorded Hockey Game	Introduction of Curling	Steeplechase Race in	of the First 5-Pin
Stan Witten	to North America	British North America	Bowling League
	Cosme Saffioti	Susan Taylor	William Woodruff

DATE	COIN No.	DESCRIPTION	QUANTITY SOLD	ISSUE PRICE	FINISH	PR-69	PR-70
2000	9	First Recorded Hockey Game, 1875	Total	19.95	Proof	15.	—
2000	10	Introduction of Curling to North America, 1760	mintage	19.95	Proof	15.	—
2000	11	First Steeplechase Race in British North America, 1840	all coins	19.95	Proof	15.	—
2000	12	Birth of the First 5-Pin Bowling League, 1910	50,091	19.95	Proof	15.	—
2000	—	Set of 4 coins	—	59.95	Proof	50.	*

FIFTY CENT HISTORICAL COMMEMORATIVE SERIES, 1998-2008

FIFTY CENTS, 90TH ANNIVERSARY OF THE ROYAL CANADIAN MINT, 1908-1998.

Issued to commemorate the opening of the Royal Canadian Mint, a five-coin set was struck featuring the same reverse designs as the original 1908 coins, except for the double date 1908-1998. The set was issued in two finishes, matte and mirror proof.

Designers and Engravers:			
Obv.:	Dora de Pédery-Hunt		
Rev.:	Ago Aarand, W. H. J. Blakemore		
Composition:	92.5% Ag, 7.5% Cu		
Silver content:	10.749 g, 0.346 tr oz		
Weight:	11.62 g	**Edge:**	Reeded
Diameter:	29.7 mm	**Die Axis:**	↑↑
Thickness:	2.0 mm	**Finish:**	See below
Case of Issue:	See Special Issue Proof Sets, page 527		

DATE	DESCRIPTION	QUANTITY SOLD	ISSUE PRICE	FINISH	PR-68	PR-69
1998 (1908-)	90th Anniv. R.C. Mint	18,376	N.I.I.	Matte Proof	20.	—
1998 (1908-)	90th Anniv. R.C. Mint	24,893	N.I.I.	Mirror Proof	20.	—

FIFTY CENTS, 50TH ANNIVERSARY OF THE CORONATION OF QUEEN ELIZABETH II, 1953-2003.

This fifty-cent coin is from the Special Edition Proof Set issued in 2003 to commemorate the 50th anniversary of the Coronation of Queen Elizabeth II.

Designers and Engravers:

Obv.:	Mary Gillick
Rev.:	Thomas Shingles

Composition: 92.5% Ag, 7.5% Cu
Silver content: 10.749 g, 0.346 tr oz

Weight:	11.62 g	Edge:	Reeded
Diameter:	29.7 mm	Die Axis:	↑↑
Thickness:	1.9 mm	Finish:	Proof

Case of Issue: See Special Issue Proof Sets, page 528

DATE	DESCRIPTION	QUANTITY SOLD	ISSUE PRICE	FINISH	PR-69	PR-70
2003 (1953-)	50th Anniv. Coronation Queen Elizabeth II	21,537	N.I.I.	Proof	25.	—

FIFTY CENTS, COAT OF ARMS OF CANADA, 2004.

The Coat of Arms of Canada, which graced the George VI fifty-cent coin in 1937, has evolved over the years. This four-coin set, besides tracing that evolution, records the portrait changes of Elizabeth II.

1953-1964	**1953-1958**	**1965-1989**	**1959-1996**

1990-2003	**1959-1996**	**2003-2004**	**1997-2004**

Obverse Designers: Portraits

1953-1964	Mary Gillick
1965-1989	Arnold Machin
1990-2003	Dora de Pédery-Hunt
2003-2004	Susanna Blunt

Reverse Designers: Arms of Canada

1953 Small date:	G. E. Kruger-Gray
Large date:	Thomas Shingles
1954-1958	Thomas Shingles after G. E. Kruger-Gray
1959-1996	Thomas Shingles
1997-2004	C. Bursey-Sabourin

Composition:	92.5% Ag, 7.5% Cu		
Silver content:	8.603 g, 0.277 tr oz		
Weight:	9.3 g	Edge:	Reeded
Diameter:	27.1 mm	Die Axis:	↑↑
Thickness:	2.1 mm	Finish:	Proof
Case of Issue:	Maroon leatherette case, black flocked interior, encapsulated coins, COA		

DATE	DESCRIPTION	QUANTITY SOLD	ISSUE PRICE	FINISH	PR-69	PR-70
2004	Laureate Portrait	—	—	Proof	15.	—
2004	Tiara Portrait	—	—	Proof	15.	—
2004	Royal Diademed Portrait	—	—	Proof	15.	—
2004	Uncrowned Portrait	—	—	Proof	15.	—
2004	Total coins	12,230	—	Proof	—	*
2004	Total Sets	3,057	79.95	Proof	50.	*

FIFTY CENT HISTORICAL COMMEMORATIVE SERIES, 1998-2008 (cont.).

FIFTY CENTS, ROYAL CANADIAN MINT ANNUAL REPORT, SELECTIVELY GOLD PLATED, 2006.

This sterling silver gold-plated fifty-cent coin dated 2006 was issued in 2007 with the 2006 Royal Canadian Mint Annual Report. This was the last year a coin was combined with the Royal Canadian Mint Report.

Designers and Engravers:
Obv.:	Susanna Blunt, Susan Taylor		
Rev.:	C. Bursey-Sabourin		
Composition:	92.5% Ag, 7.5% Cu,		
	Selectively gold plated		
Silver content:	8.603 g, 0.277 tr oz		
Weight:	9.3 g		
Diameter:	27.1 mm	**Edge:**	Reeded
Thickness:	1.9 mm	**Die Axis:**	↑↑
Finish:	Proof		
Case of Issue:	See Derivatives, page 89		

DATE	DESCRIPTION	QUANTITY SOLD	ISSUE PRICE	FINISH	PR-69	PR-70
2006	RCM Annual Report	4,162	25.95	Proof	30.	—

FIFTY CENTS, 100TH ANNIVERSARY OF THE ROYAL CANADIAN MINT, 1908-2008.

This fifty-cent coin is from the Coin and Stamp Set issued in 2008 to commemorate the 100th anniversary of the Royal Canadian Mint. It was also issued with the 2008 Royal Canadian Mint Centennial Book.

Designers and Engravers:
Obv.:	Susanna Blunt, Susan Taylor		
Rev.:	RCM Staff		
Composition:	92.5% Ag, 7.5% Cu		
Silver content:	10.915 g, 0.351 tr oz		
Weight:	11.8 g		
Diameter:	29.7 mm	**Edge:**	Reeded
Thickness:	2.0 mm	**Die Axis:**	↑↑
Finish:	Proof		
Case of Issue:	See Derivatives, page 89		

DATE	DESCRIPTION	QUANTITY SOLD	ISSUE PRICE	FINISH	PR-69	PR-70
2008 (1908-)	100th Anniversary, Royal Canadian Mint	3,248	44.95	Proof	40.	—

CANADIAN FESTIVALS SERIES, 2001-2002

FIFTY CENTS, CANADIAN FESTIVALS SERIES, 2001-2002.
The Royal Canadian Mint introduced a new series of sterling silver fifty-cent coins in 2001 commemorating Canadian Festivals. Each coin represents a Canadian Province, Territory or Community, celebrating its culture, history and traditions with colourful festivals. The 13-coin set was issued over three years, starting in 2001 and ending 2003. It was available by subscription in 2001 for $249.95 with coins being shipped as they became available.

ISSUES OF 2001

| Common Obverse | Coin No. 1
Quebec Winter Carnival
(Quebec)
S. Daigneault
S. Witten | Coin No. 2
Toonik Tyme
(Nunavut)
J. Mardon, J. Osio | Coin No. 3
Newfoundland and
Labrador Folk Festival
(Newfoundland)
D. Craig, C. Saffioti | Coin No. 4
Festival of Fathers
(Prince Edward Island)
B. Whiteway,
W. Woodruff |

ISSUES OF 2002

| Coin No. 5
Annapolis Valley
Blossom Festival
(Nova Scotia)
B. Ross, J. Osio | Coin No. 6
Stratford Festival
of Canada
(Ontario)
L. McGaw, S. Taylor | Coin No. 7
Folklorama
(Manitoba)
William Woodruff | Coin No. 8
Calgary Stampede
(Alberta)
M. Grant, S. Witten | Coin No. 9
Squamish Days
Logger Sports
(British Columbia)
José Osio |

Designers:
Obv.: Dora de Pédery-Hunt
Rev.: See reverse illustrations
Composition: 92.5% Ag, 7.5% Cu
Silver content: 8.603 g, 0.277 tr oz
Weight: 9.3 g
Diameter: 27.1 mm
Thickness: 2.1 mm
Case of Issue: (A) Singles: Multicoloured printed card folder with encapsulated coin.
(B) Thirteen coin set: Canadian Festivals subscription coffee table book.

Engravers:
Obv.: Dora de Pédery-Hunt
Rev.: See reverse illustrations

Edge: Reeded
Die Axis: ↑↑
Finish: Proof

DATE	COIN	DESCRIPTION	QUANTITY SOLD	ISSUE PRICE	FINISH	PR-69	PR-70
2001	1	Quebec	2001 total	21.95	Proof	15.	—
2001	2	Nunavut	mintage	21.95	Proof	15.	—
2001	3	Newfoundland	all coins	21.95	Proof	15.	—
2001	4	Prince Edward Island	58,123	21.95	Proof	15.	—
2002	5	Nova Scotia 2002	2002 total	21.95	Proof	15.	—
2002	6	Ontario	mintage	21.95	Proof	15.	—
2002	7	Manitoba	all	21.95	Proof	15.	—
2002	8	Alberta	coins	21.95	Proof	15.	—
2002	9	British Columbia	61,900	21.95	Proof	15.	—

FIFTY CENTS, CANADIAN FESTIVALS SERIES, 2003

This is the third issue in the 13-coin set which commemorates festivals across Canada.

ISSUES OF 2003

| Common Obverse | Coin No. 10
Yukon Festival
(Yukon)
Ken Anderson
José Osio | Coin No. 11
Back to Batoche
(Saskatchewan)
David Hannan
Stan Witten | Coin No. 12
Great Northern
Arts Festival
(Inuvik)
Dawn Oman
Susan Taylor | Coin No. 13
Festival Acadien de
Caraquet
(New Brunswick)
Hudson Design Group
Susan Taylor |

Designers:
Obv.: Dora de Pédery-Hunt
Rev.: See reverse illustrations
Composition: 92.5% Ag, 7.5% Cu
Silver content: 8.603 g, 0.277 tr oz
Weight: 9.3 g
Diameter: 27.1 mm
Thickness: 2.1 mm
Case of Issue:

Engravers:
Obv.: Dora de Pédery-Hunt
Rev.: See reverse illustrations

Edge: Reeded
Die Axis: ↑↑
Finish: Proof

(A) Singles: Multicoloured printed card folder with encapsulated coin.
(B) Thirteen coin set: Canadian Festivals subscription coffee table book.

DATE	COIN No.	DESCRIPTION	QUANTITY SOLD	ISSUE PRICE	FINISH	PR-69	PR-70
2003	10	Yukon	2003 total	21.95	Proof	15.	—
2003	11	Saskatchewan	mintage	21.95	Proof	15.	—
2003	12	Inuvik	all coins	21.95	Proof	15.	—
2003	13	New Brunswick	26,451	21.95	Proof	15.	—
2001-2003	—	Set of 13 coins	—	249.95	Proof	150.	*

CANADA'S FOLKLORE AND LEGENDS SERIES

FIFTY CENTS, CANADA'S FOLKLORE AND LEGENDS SERIES, 2001-2002.

A new series of fifty-cent sterling silver coins celebrates Canadian Folklore and Legends. The official release date was April 11, 2001.

ISSUES OF 2001

Common Obverse

Coin No. 1
The Sled
Valentina Hotz-Entin
Susan Taylor

Coin No. 2
The Maiden's Cave
Peter Kiss
Susan Taylor

Coin No. 3
Les Petits Sauteux
Miyuki Tanobe
José Osio

ISSUES OF 2002

Coin No. 4
**The Pig That Wouldn't
Get Over the Stile**
Laura Jolicoeur
José Osio

Coin No. 6
Le Vaisseau Fantome
Colette Boivin
William Woodruff

Coin No. 5
Shoemaker in Heaven
Francine Gravel
Cosme Saffioti

Designers:		Engravers:	
Obv.:	Dora de Pédery-Hunt	Obv.:	Dora de Pédery-Hunt
Rev.:	See reverse illustrations	Rev.:	See reverse illustrations
Composition:	92.5% Ag, 7.5% Cu		
Silver content:	8.603 g, 0.277 tr oz		
Weight:	9.3 g	**Edge:**	Reeded
Diameter:	27.1 mm	**Die Axis:**	↑↑
Thickness:	2.1 mm	**Finish:**	Proof
Case of Issue:	Multicoloured printed card folder with encapsulated coin.		

DATE	COIN No.	DESCRIPTION	QUANTITY SOLD	ISSUE PRICE	FINISH	PR-69	PR-70
2001	1	The Sled	Mintage 2001 coins 28,979	24.95	Proof	15.	—
2001	2	The Maiden's Cave		24.95	Proof	15.	—
2001	3	Les Petits Sauteux		24.95	Proof	15.	—
2002	4	The Pig That Wouldn't Get Over the Stile	Mintage 2002 coins 19,789	24.95	Proof	15.	—
2002	5	Shoemaker in Heaven		24.95	Proof	15.	—
2002	6	Le Vaisseau Fantome		24.95	Proof	15.	—

CANADA'S GOLDEN FLOWER SERIES

FIFTY CENTS, CANADA'S GOLDEN FLOWER SERIES, 2002-2007.

Beginning in 2002 the Royal Canadian Mint issued a series of sterling silver, selectively gold plated proof fifty-cent coins to commemorate different events which had a floral theme.

2002 and 2003
Common Obverse

2002
50th Anniversary of the
Canadian Tulip Festival
Anthony Testa
Stan Witten

2003
Golden Daffodil
Symbol of Hope
Christie Paquet
Stan Witten

Designers and Engravers:

2002-2003	
Obv.:	Dora de Pédery-Hunt
Rev.:	See reverse illustrations
2004-2007	
Obv.:	Susanna Blunt
	Susan Taylor
Rev.:	See reverse illustration
Composition:	92.5% Ag, 7.5% Cu,
	22-karat gold plate on design
Silver content:	8.603 g, 0.277 tr oz
Weight:	9.3 g
Diameter:	27.1 mm
Thickness:	2.2 mm
Edge:	Reeded
Die Axis:	↑↑
Finish:	Proof

2004 to 2007
Common Obverse

2004
Golden Easter Lily
Christie Paquet
Stan Witten

2005
Golden Rose
Christie Paquet

2006
Golden Daisy
Christie Paquet

2007
Golden Forget-Me-Not
Christie Paquet

Case of Issue:

2002-2004:	Folders dated 2002, 2003 and 2004, encapsulated coin
2005-2006:	Maroon plastic display case, black plastic insert, encapsulated coin, COA
2007:	Maroon clam style case, black flocked insert, encapsulated coin, COA

DATE	DESCRIPTION	RCM ITEM #	QUANTITY SOLD	ISSUE PRICE	FINISH	PR-69	PR-70
2002	Canadian Tulip Festival, 50th Anniversary	N/A	19,986	24.95	Proof	40.	—
2003	Golden Daffodil, Symbol of Hope	N/A	36,293	34.95	Proof	20.	—
2004	Golden Easter Lily	N/A	24,495	34.95	Proof	20.	—
2005	Golden Rose	N/A	17,418	34.95	Proof	30.	—
2006	Golden Daisy	N/A	18,190	36.95	Proof	40.	—
2007	Golden Forget-Me-Mot	624237	10,845	38.95	Proof	40.	—

CANADIAN BUTTERFLY SERIES

FIFTY CENTS, CANADIAN BUTTERFLY SERIES, 2004-2006.

This series on Canada's butterflies contains the first hologram fifty-cent coin.

Common Obverse

Designers:
Obv.:   Susanna Blunt
Rev.:   See reverse illustrations

Engravers:
Obv.:   Susan Taylor
Rev.:   See reverse illustrations

Composition: 92.5% Ag, 7.5% Cu, Selectively gold plated, Decal, Hologram
Silver content: 8.603 g, 0.277 tr oz
Weight: 9.3 g
Diameter: 27.1 mm
Thickness: 2.1 mm
Finish: Proof

Edge: Reeded
Die Axis: ↑↑

Case of Issue: 2004:   Red leatherette clam style case, black flocked insert, encapsulated coin, COA
2005-2006:   Maroon plastic display case, black plastic insert, encapsulated coin, COA

2004
Canadian Tiger
Swallowtail Butterfly
Des.: Jianping Yan
Engr.: RCM Staff

2004
Canadian Clouded
Sulphur Butterfly
Des.: Susan Taylor
Engr.: Susan Taylor

2005
Monarch Butterfly
Des.: Susan Taylor
Engr.: Susan Taylor

2005
Spangled Fritillary
Butterfly
Des.: Jianping Yan
Engr.: Jianping Yan

2006
Short-tailed Swallowtail
Butterfly
Des.: Susan Taylor
Engr.: Susan Taylor

2006
Silvery Blue Butterfly
Des.: Jianping Yan
Engr.: Jianping Yan

DATE	DESCRIPTION	QUANTITY SOLD	ISSUE PRICE	FINISH	PR-69	PR-70
2004	Canadian Tiger Swallowtail Butterfly, Hologram	20,462	39.95	Proof	35.	—
2004	Canadian Clouded Sulphur Butterfly, Selectively gold plated	15,281	39.95	Proof	35.	—
2005	Monarch Butterfly, Decal	35,950	39.95	Proof	35.	—
2005	Spangled Fritillary Butterfly, Hologram	Incl. above	39.95	Proof	35.	—
2006	Short-tailed Swallowtail Butterfly, Decal	24,568	39.95	Proof	35.	—
2006	Silvery Blue Butterfly, Hologram	Incl. above	39.95	Proof	35.	—

SECOND WORLD WAR SERIES

FIFTY CENTS, QUEST FOR PEACE AND FREEDOM DURING THE SECOND WORLD WAR, 2005.

The 60th anniversary of the end of World War II, 1945-2005, and the part Canada played, are commemorated in this six-coin sterling silver set. The coins were issued one per month from May 2005 to October 2005.

Common Obverse

Designers:		**Engravers:**	
Obv.:	Susanna Blunt	Obv.:	Susan Taylor
Rev.:	Peter Mossman	Rev.:	See reverse illustrations
Composition:	92.5% Ag, 7.5% Cu		
Silver content:	8.603 g, 0.277 tr oz		
Weight:	9.3 g	**Edge:**	Reeded
Diameter:	27.1 mm	**Die Axis:**	↑↑
Thickness:	2.1 mm	**Finish:**	Specimen
Case of Issue:	Red leatherette case, black flocked insert, encapsulated coin, COA		

**Battle of Britain
October 1940
Engr.: Stan Witten**

**Liberation of the
Netherlands
September 1944
Engr.: José Osio**

**Conquest of Sicily
August 1943
Engr.: RCM Staff**

**Battle of the Scheldt
November 1944
Engr.: RCM Staff**

**Raid on Dieppe
August 1942
Engr.: José Osio**

**Battle of the Atlantic
1939-1945
Engr.: Christie Paquet**

DATE	DESCRIPTION	ISSUE DATE	QUANTITY SOLD	ISSUE PRICE	FINISH	SP-68	SP-69
2005	Battle of Britain	May	20,000	—	Specimen	25.	—
2005	Liberation of the Netherlands	June	20,000	—	Specimen	25.	—
2005	Conquest of Sicily	July	20,000	—	Specimen	25.	—
2005	Battle of the Scheldt	August	20,000	—	Specimen	25.	—
2005	Raid on Dieppe	September	20,000	—	Specimen	25.	—
2005	Battle of the Atlantic	October	20,000	—	Specimen	25.	—
2005	Set of 6 coins and display case	—	20,000	149.95	Specimen	120.	*

CANADIAN NHL HOCKEY SERIES

During the years 2005 to 2010 the Royal Canadian Mint issued many coins, mostly giftware, commemorating the Canadian teams of the National Hockey League.

FIFTY CENTS, NHL HOCKEY LEGENDS, 2005.

Hockey greats are commemorated in this legends series, issued in sets of four coins each: Jean Beliveau, Guy Lafleur, Jacques Plante and Maurice Richard of the Montreal Canadiens, and Johnny Bower, Tim Horton, Darryl Sittler and Dave Keon of the Toronto Maple Leafs.

Common Obverse

Designers:		**Engravers:**	
Obv.:	Susanna Blunt	Obv.:	Susan Taylor
Rev.:	RCM Staff	Rev.:	RCM Staff
Composition:	92.5% Ag, 7.5% Cu, Painted		
Silver content:	8.603 g, 0.277 tr oz		
Weight:	9.3 g	**Edge:**	Reeded
Diameter:	27.1 mm	**Die Axis:**	↑↑
Thickness:	2.1 mm	**Finish:**	Specimen
Case of Issue:	Maroon plastic display case, black plastic insert, encapsulated coin, COA		

2005 MONTREAL CANADIENS

| Jean Beliveau | Guy Lafleur | Jacques Plante | Maurice Richard |

DATE	DESCRIPTION	QUANTITY SOLD	ISSUE PRICE	FINISH	SP-68	SP-69
2005	Jean Beliveau	N/A	N.I.I.	Specimen	35.	—
2005	Guy Lafleur	N/A	N.I.I.	Specimen	35.	—
2005	Jacques Plante	N/A	N.I.I.	Specimen	35.	—
2005	Maurice Richard	N/A	N.I.I.	Specimen	35.	—
2005	Set of 4 coins (Montreal)	N/A	99.95	Specimen	120.	*

2005 TORONTO MAPLE LEAFS

| Johnny Bower | Tim Horton | Darryl Sittler | Dave Keon |

DATE	DESCRIPTION	QUANTITY SOLD	ISSUE PRICE	FINISH	SP-68	SP-69
2005	Johnny Bower	N/A	N.I.I.	Specimen	25.	—
2005	Tim Horton	N/A	N.I.I.	Specimen	25.	—
2005	Darryl Sittler	N/A	N.I.I.	Specimen	25.	—
2005	Dave Keon	N/A	N.I.I.	Specimen	25.	—
2005	Set of 4 coins (Toronto)	N/A	99.95	Specimen	90.	*

Note: The Royal Canadian Mint Report of 2005 lists the quantity sold as 11,765 total sets.

CANADIAN NHL HOCKEY SERIES (cont.).

FIFTY CENTS, 2008-2009 NHL SEASON, 2009 (GIFTWARE).

The fifty-cent issues for the 2008-2009 Hockey Season were embedded in an official NHL puck and then blister packed. Each coin has a lenticular (dual images) reverse which by rotating the coin transfers from the old to the new team logo.

2009   HOCKEY PUCKS

Common Obverse

Designers and Engravers:

Obv.:	Susanna Blunt, Susan Taylor
Rev.:	Logos of the NHL
Composition:	Nickel plated steel, Lenticular
Weight:	6.9 g
Diameter:	35.0 mm
Thickness:	2.0 mm
Edge:	Plain
Die Axis:	↑↑
Finish:	Specimen
Case of Issue:	Blister packaged

Calgary Flames

Edmonton Oilers

Montreal Canadiens

Ottawa Senators

Toronto Maple Leafs

Vancouver Canucks

DATE	DESCRIPTION	RCM ITEM #	QUANTITY SOLD	ISSUE PRICE	FINISH	SP-68	SP-69
2009	Calgary Flames	102648	270	24.95	Specimen	35.	—
2009	Edmonton Oilers	102650	248	24.95	Specimen	35.	—
2009	Montreal Canadiens	102646	1,266	24.95	Specimen	60.	—
2009	Ottawa Senators	102647	310	24.95	Specimen	35.	—
2009	Toronto Maple Leafs	102648	606	24.95	Specimen	35.	—
2009	Vancouver Canucks	102651	318	24.95	Specimen	35.	—

CANADIAN NHL HOCKEY SERIES (cont.).

FIFTY CENTS, MONTREAL CANADIENS CENTENNIAL COIN SERIES, 1909-2009 (GIFTWARE).

The 100th anniversary of the Montreal Canadiens hockey club was commemorated in 2009 with six giftware fifty-cent coins displaying the hockey jerseys worn by the Montreal players over the last 100 years. Each coin is sealed within a plastic sport card.

2009   MONTREAL CANADIENS CENTENNIAL

Common Obverse

Designers and Engravers:

Obv.:	Susanna Blunt, Susan Taylor
Rev.:	Logos of the NHL
Composition:	Nickel plated steel, Decal
Weight:	N/A
Diameter:	30.0 mm
Thickness:	N/A
Edge:	Plain
Die Axis:	↑↑
Finish:	Specimen
Case of Issue:	Collector Card

Coin No. 1
Montreal Canadiens
Home Jersey

Coin No. 2
1945-1946
Montreal Canadiens
Road Jersey

Coin No. 3
1915-1916
Le Club de
Hockey Canadiens

Coin No. 4
1912-1913
"CAC"

Coin No 5
1910-1911
Club Athletique
Canadien

Coin No 6
1909-1910
Club de Hockey
le Canadien

DATE	DESCRIPTION	RCM ITEM #	QUANTITY SOLD	ISSUE PRICE	FINISH	SP-68	SP-69
2009 (1909-)	Montreal Canadiens Home Jersey	N/A	N/A	9.99	Specimen	15.	—.
2009 (1909-)	Montreal Canadiens Road Jersey	N/A	N/A	9.99	Specimen	15.	—.
2009 (1909-)	Le Club de Hockey Canadiens	N/A	N/A	9.99	Specimen	15.	—
2009 (1909-)	"CAC"	N/A	25,016	9.99	Specimen	15.	—
2009 (1909-)	Club Athletique Canadien	N/A	25,004	9.99	Specimen	15.	—
2009 (1909-)	Club de Hockey le Canadien	N/A	25,004	9.99	Specimen	15.	—.
2009 (1909-)	Complete Set, 6 coins and an album	106797	496	59.95	Specimen	75.	*

Note: 1. Single Collector Cards were issued by Jean Coutu, while the Royal Canadian Mint issued only complete sets.
2. Quantity sold figures are incomplete due to year-end overruns.

CANADIAN NHL HOCKEY SERIES (cont.).

FIFTY CENTS, 2009-2010 NHL SEASON, 2009-2010 (GIFTWARE).

Common Obverse

Designers and Engravers:

Obv.:	Susanna Blunt, Susan Taylor
Rev.:	RCM Staff
Composition:	Nickel plated steel, Decal
Weight:	12.9 g
Diameter:	35.0 mm
Thickness:	2.0 mm
Edge:	Plain
Die Axis:	↑↑
Finish:	Specimen
Case of Issue:	Tent Card

Calgary Flames

Edmonton Oilers

Montreal Canadiens

Ottawa Senators

Toronto Maple Leafs

Vancouver Canucks

DATE	DESCRIPTION	RCM ITEM #	QUANTITY SOLD	ISSUE PRICE	FINISH	SP-68	SP-69
2009-2010	Calgary Flames	106836	3,518	14.95	Specimen	20.	—
2009-2010	Edmonton Oilers	106837	3,562	14.95	Specimen	20.	—
2009-2010	Montreal Canadiens	106833	9,865	14.95	Specimen	20.	—
2009-2010	Ottawa Senators	106834	3,293	14.95	Specimen	20.	—
2009-2010	Toronto Maple Leafs	106835	5,981	14.95	Specimen	20.	—
2009-2010	Vancouver Canucks	106838	3,563	14.95	Specimen	20.	—

HOLIDAY LENTICULAR SERIES

FIFTY CENTS, HOLIDAY LENTICULAR SERIES, 2007-2018 (GIFTWARE).

Obverse with RCM Logo
2007-2008

Obverse without
RCM Logo
2009-2011

Obverse without
RCM Logo
2012-2018

2007
Holiday Ornaments
Des.: C. Bursey-Sabourin

2008
Holiday Snowman
Des.: C. Bursey-Sabourin

2009
Holiday Toy Train
Des.: C. Bursey-Sabourin

2010 - Santa Claus and
the Red-nosed Reindeer
Des.: C. Bursey-Sabourin

2011
Gifts From Santa
Des.: C. Bursey-Sabourin

2012
Santa's Magical Visit
Des.: Tony Bianco

2013
Snowman
Des.: Tony Bianco

2014
Christmas Tree
Des.: Steve Hepburn

2015
Holiday Toy Box
Des.: Joel Kimmel

2016
Snow Angels
Des.: Joel Kimmel

2018
Snowball Fight
Des.: Tony Bianco

Designers:			Engravers:		
Obv.:	Susanna Blunt		Obv.:	Susan Taylor	
Rev.:	See reverse illustrations				
Composition:	2007-2009:	Brass plated steel	2010-2011:	Copper plated steel	
	2012-2015:	Cupronickel	2016, 2018:	Nickel-plated steel	
Weight:	12.61 to 13.8 g				
Diameter:	35.0 mm		**Edge:**	Plain	
Thickness:	2.0 mm		**Die Axis:**	↑↑	
Finish:	Specimen, Lenticular				
Case of Issue:	2007-2008, 2010-2018: Maroon leatherette clam style case, black flocked insert, encapsulated coin, COA				
	2009: Black leatherette clam style case, black flocked insert, encapsulated coin, COA				

Note: There was no 2017 50-cent Holiday Lenticular Coin issued.

FIFTY CENTS, HOLIDAY LENTICULAR SERIES, 2007-2015 (GIFTWARE) PRICING TABLE:

DATE	DESCRIPTION	RCM ITEM #	QUANTITY SOLD	ISSUE PRICE	FINISH	SP-68	SP-69
2007	Holiday Ornaments	N/A	16,989	25.95	Specimen	40.	—
2008	Holiday Snowman	102745	21,679	25.95	Specimen	40.	—
2009	Holiday Toy Train	105343	19,103	25.95	Specimen	40.	—
2010	Santa Claus and the Red-Nosed Reindeer	111426	21,394	26.95	Specimen	30.	—
2011	Gifts from Santa	116709	21,837	26.95	Specimen	30.	—
2012	Santa's Magical Visit	120220	22,304	29.95	Specimen	30.	—
2013	Snowman	126279	19,939	29.95	Specimen	30.	—
2014	Christmas Tree	130619	19,945	29.95	Specimen	30.	—
2015	Holiday Tox Box	146460	19,736	29.95	Specimen	30.	—
2016	Snow Angels	153943	12,853	31.95	Specimen	30.	—
2018	Snowball Fight	164695	20,000	29.95	Specimen	30.	

TRIANGULAR COIN SERIES

FIFTY CENTS (triangular), MILK DELIVERY, 2008.

From the late 19th century to the middle of the 20th century milk and other dairy products were delivered to the home by a milkman who was paid by a token previously purchased.

Designers and Engravers:
Obv.: Susanna Blunt, Susan Taylor
Rev.: RCM Staff, Christie Paquet
Composition: 92.5% Ag, 7.5% Cu,
Enamel effect on reverse
Silver content: 18.50 g, 0.595 tr oz
Weight: 20.0 g **Edge:** Interrupted serrations
Size: 36.0 x 34.1 mm **Die Axis:** ↑↑
Thickness: 2.7 mm **Finish:** Proof
Case of Issue: Maroon leatherette clam style case, black flocked insert, encapsulated coin, COA

FIFTY CENTS (triangular), SIX STRING NATION GUITAR, 2009.

Jowi Taylor brought together the rich Canadian Heritage of materials to produce the Six String Nation Guitar. The guitar made its debut on Parliament Hill during the 2006 Canada Day celebrations.

Designers and Engravers:
Obv.: Susanna Blunt, Susan Taylor
Rev.: RCM Staff, Christie Paquet
Composition: 75% Cu, 25% Ni,
Selective hologram on reverse
Weight: 19.1 g **Edge:** Interrupted serrations
Size: 36.0 x 34.1 mm **Die Axis:** ↑↑
Thickness: 2.70 mm **Finish:** Specimen
Case of Issue: Folder

DATE	DESCRIPTION	RCM ITEM #	QUANTITY SOLD	ISSUE PRICE	FINISH	SP-68	SP-69	PR-69	PR-70
2008	Milk Delivery	100306	24,448	49.95	Proof	—	—	30.	—
2009	Six String Nation Guitar	104732	13,602	34.95	Specimen	30.	—	30.	—

SPECIAL NOTE ON FINISHES

It is very important to understand the different finishes the Royal Canadian Mint uses on their various issues. These finishes are altered from time-to-time as the Mint develops new products.

For example, the brilliant relief against a parallel lined background finish first used on bullion coins was carried forward in 1996 to be used on the coins contained in the specimen set.

In 2006 this finish was used on giftware coins such as the twenty-five cent coin issued to celebrate the 80th birthday of Queen Elizabeth II.

In 2010 a new specimen finish, brilliant relief against a laser-lined background, was used for the coins contained in the specimen set. There are now two different specimen finishes being utilised on Canadian coinage.

Circulation and Brilliant Uncirculated (proof-like) finishes are another very confusing mixture of finishes, see pages xvi-xvii for a further explanation.

VANCOUVER 2010 OLYMPIC AND PARALYMPIC WINTER GAMES

FIFTY CENTS, MASCOT COLLECTOR CARDS, 2010 (GIFTWARE).

Three mascots were adopted for the Vancouver 2010 Winter Games, Miga and Quatchi for the Olympic Games and Sumi for the Paralympic Games.

These crown-size fifty-cent coins are embedded in plastic within a collector card format. As with all embedded Royal Canadian Mint giftware, the coins are very difficult to remove from their packaging without damaging the image on the coin.

Designers:		**Engravers:**	
Obv.:	Susanna Blunt	Obv.:	Susan Taylor
Rev.:	RCM Staff	Rev.:	RCM Staff
Composition:	Nickel plated steel, Decal	**Thickness:**	2.0 mm
Weight:	12.61 g	**Edge:**	Plain
Diameter:	35.0 mm	**Die Axis:**	↑↑
Finish:	Specimen		

Case of Issue: Twelve collector cards were issued with the mascots in different sport poses. These coins are embedded in plastic.

Common Obverse

Coin No. 1
Miga Ice Hockey

Coin No. 2
Quatchi Ice Hockey

Coin No. 3
Sumi Paralympic
Ice Sledge Hockey

Coin No. 4
Quatchi and Miga
Figure Skating

Coin No. 5
Quatchi and Miga
Bobsleigh

Coin No. 6
Miga Ariels

Coin No. 7
Miga Skeleton

Coin No. 8
Quatchi Snowboard Cross

Coin No. 9
Miga Alpine Skiing

Coin No. 10
Sumi Paralympic
Alpine Skiing

Coin No.11
Quatchi Parallel
Giant Slalom

Coin No. 12
Miga Speed Skating

VANCOUVER 2010 OLYMPIC AND PARALYMPIC WINTER GAMES (cont.).

FIFTY CENTS, MASCOT COLLECTOR CARDS, 2010 (GIFTWARE) PRICING TABLE.

DATE	CARD No.	DESCRIPTION	QUANTITY SOLD	ISSUE PRICE	FINISH	SP-68	SP-69
2010	1	Miga Ice Hockey	3,096	9.95	Specimen	15.	—
2010	2	Quatchi Ice Hockey	3,010	9.95	Specimen	15.	—
2010	3	Sumi Paralympic Ice Sledge Hockey	2,137	9.95	Specimen	15.	—
2010	4	Quatchi and Miga Figure Skating	2,981	9.95	Specimen	15.	—
2010	5	Quatchi and Miga Bobsleigh	2,119	9.95	Specimen	15.	—
2010	6	Miga Ariels	2,114	9.95	Specimen	15.	—
2010	7	Miga Skeleton	1,672	9.95	Specimen	15.	—
2010	8	Quatchi Snowboard Cross	2,090	9.95	Specimen	15.	—
2010	9	Miga Alpine Skiing	2,309	9.95	Specimen	15.	—
2010	10	Sumi Paralympic Alpine Skiing	1,902	9.95	Specimen	15.	—
2010	11	Quatchi Parallel Giant Slalom	1,730	9.95	Specimen	15.	—
2010	12	Miga Speed Skating	1,825	9.95	Specimen	15.	—
—	—	Collector Card Album	—	12.95	—	15.	*

FIFTY CENTS, MASCOT HOCKEY PUCKS, 2010.
The Miga, Quatchi, and Sumi ice hockey coins were also issued embedded in NHL official hockey pucks.

| Miga Ice Hockey | Quatchi Ice Hockey | Sumi Ice Hockey |

Designers:	Engravers:	
Obv.: Susanna Blunt	Obv.: Susan Taylor	
Rev.: RCM Staff	Rev.: RCM Staff	
Composition: Nickel plated steel, Decal	Thickness: 2.0 mm	
Weight: 12.61 g	Edge: Plain	
Diameter: 35.0 mm	Die Axis: ↑↑	
Finish: Specimen	Case of Issue: Blister packaged	

DATE	CARD No.	DESCRIPTION	QUANTITY SOLD	ISSUE PRICE	FINISH	SP-68	SP-69
2010	1	Miga Ice Hockey	2,179	25.95	Specimen	25.	—
2010	2	Quatchi Ice Hockey	2,524	25.95	Specimen	25.	—
2010	3	Sumi Paralympic Ice Sledge Hockey	1,570	25.95	Specimen	25.	—

FIFTY CENTS, VANCOUVER 2010 OLYMPIC AND PARALYMPIC WINTER GAMES, 2010 (GIFTWARE).

This fifty-cent lenticular coin with images of the Vancouver skyline, and Inukshuk is found in the Vancouver 2010 Gold Collector's Set. It was issued in conjunction with Canada Post (see page 516).

Designers and Engravers:
Obv.:	Susanna Blunt, Susan Taylor
Rev.:	RCM Staff

Composition: Nickel plated steel, Lenticular

Weight:	13.0 g	**Edge:**	Plain
Diameter:	35.0 mm	**Die Axis:**	↑↑
Thickness:	2.0 mm	**Finish:**	Specimen

Case of Issue: See Collector Sets, page 516

DATE	DESCRIPTION	QUANTITY SOLD	ISSUE PRICE	FINISH	SP-68	SP-69
2010	Lenticular Images of Vancouver and Inukshuk	11,384	N.I.I.	Specimen	40.	—

DINOSAUR EXHIBIT SET

FIFTY CENTS, DINOSAUR EXHIBIT LENTICULAR SET, 2010 (GIFTWARE).

The Royal Canadian Mint in conjunction with various Canadian Museums created this new set of lenticular coins featuring prehistoric dinosaurs found in Canada.

Designers and Engravers:
Obv.:	Susanna Blunt, Susan Taylor
Rev.:	RCM Staff

Composition: Brass-plated steel, Lenticular
Weight: 12.9 g
Diameter: 35.0 mm
Thickness: 2.0 mm
Edge: Plain
Die Axis: ↑↑
Finish: Specimen
Case of Issue: Folded panel containing six collector trading cards

Common Obverse   Daspletosaurus Torosus

Albertosaurus   Sinosauropteryx

DATE	DESCRIPTION	RCM ITEM #	QUANTITY SOLD	ISSUE PRICE	FINISH	SP-68	SP-69
2010	Daspletosaurus Torosus	110200	11,652	24.95	Specimen	25.	—
2010	Albertosaurus	110392	14,325	24.95	Specimen	25.	—
2010	Sinosauropteryx	111398	19,865	24.95	Specimen	25.	—

FIFTY CENTS, 100TH ANNIVERSARY OF THE STRIKING OF CANADA'S 1911 SILVER DOLLAR, 1911-2011.

This fifty-cent coin which carries the double date 1911-2011 is from the Special Edition Proof Set issued in 2011 to commemorate the 100th anniversary of the striking of Canada's 1911 silver dollar.

Designers and Engravers:
Obv.:	Sir E. B. MacKennal
Rev.:	Original design by L. C. Wyon, Modified by W. H. J. Blakemore

Composition: 92.5% Ag, 7.5% Cu
Silver content: 10.76 g, 0.345 tr oz

Weight:	11.629 g	**Edge:**	Reeded
Diameter:	29.7 mm	**Die Axis:**	↑↑
Thickness:	2.0 mm	**Finish:**	Proof

Case of Issue: See Special Issue Proof Sets, page 529

DATE	DESCRIPTION	RCM ITEM #	QUANTITY SOLD	ISSUE PRICE	FINISH	PR-69	PR-70
2011 (1911-)	George V, Sterling Silver	114121	5,952	N.I.I.	Proof	35.	—

FIFTY CENTS, WINNIPEG JETS, 2011-2012.

Designers and Engravers:
Obv.:	Susanna Blunt, Susan Taylor
Rev.:	William Woodruff, RCM Staff

Composition: Nickel plated steel

Weight:	7.0 g	**Edge:**	Reeded
Diameter:	27.1 mm	**Die Axis:**	↑↑
Thickness:	1.9 mm	**Finish:**	Uncirculated

Case of Issue: Colourised folder

DATE	DESCRIPTION	RCM ITEM #	QUANTITY SOLD	ISSUE PRICE	FINISH	MS-65 NC
2011-2012	Winnipeg Jets	117316	23,712	14.95	Circulation	15.

FIFTY CENTS, ROYAL CYPHER, THE QUEEN'S DIAMOND JUBILEE, 1952-2012 (GIFTWARE).

This coin which carries the double date 1952 2012 celebrates the Queen's Diamond Jubilee. The design is a reproduction of the Diamond Jubilee Emblem for Canada by the Royal Canadian Mint. The reverse design is a garland of maple leaves with the Queen's monogram and St. Edward's crown at the centre.

Designers and Engravers:
Obv.:	Susanna Blunt, Susan Taylor
Rev.:	Christie Paquet

Composition: Silver-plated copper, Decal

Weight:	32.82 g	**Edge:**	Reeded
Diameter:	42.0 mm	**Die Axis:**	↑↑
Thickness:	3.0 mm	**Finish:**	Specimen

Case of Issue: Colourised folder

DATE	DESCRIPTION	RCM ITEM #	QUANTITY SOLD	ISSUE PRICE	FINISH	SP-68	SP-69
2012 (1952-)	Royal Cypher Queen's Diamond Jubilee	116030	30,900	29.95	Specimen	20.	—

FIFTY CENTS, *RMS TITANIC*, 2012 (GIFTWARE).

This fifty-cent coin was issued to remember those who perished when *RMS Titanic* sank on April 15th, 1912.

Designers and Engravers:
Obv.:	Susanna Blunt, Susan Taylor
Rev.:	Yves Bérubé, Konrad Wachelko

Composition: Silver-plated copper, Coloured

Weight:	32.82 g	**Edge:**	Reeded
Diameter:	42.0 mm	**Die Axis:**	↑↑
Thickness:	3.0 mm	**Finish:**	Proof

Case of Issue: Maroon leatherette clam style case, black flocked insert, encapsulated coin,COA

DATE	DESCRIPTION	RCM ITEM #	QUANTITY SOLD	ISSUE PRICE	FINISH	PR-69	PR-70
2012	*RMS Titanic*	118359	14,997	34.95	Proof	65.	—

FIFTY CENTS, 75TH ANNIVERSARY OF SUPERMAN™: THEN AND NOW, COIN AND STAMP SET, 2013 (GIFTWARE).

This fifty-cent coin was issued to commemorate the 75th anniversary of Superman™.

Designers and Engravers:
Obv.:	Susanna Blunt, Susan Taylor
Rev.:	DC Comic/Warner Brothers, Nick Martin

Composition: Cupronickel, Lenticular

Weight:	13.7 g	**Edge:**	Plain
Diameter:	35.0 mm	**Die Axis:**	↑↑
Thickness:	2.0 mm	**Finish:**	Specimen

Case of Issue: See Derivatives page 89

DATE	DESCRIPTION	RCM ITEM #	QUANTITY SOLD	ISSUE PRICE	FINISH	SP-68	SP-69
2013	Superman™: Then and Now	125870	24,967	29.75	Specimen	45.	—

FIFTY CENTS, BUTTERFLIES OF CANADA SERIES, CANADIAN TIGER SWALLOWTAIL, 2013 (GIFTWARE).

Featuring the Swallowtail as it rests on a dandelion, this fifty-cent coin is the first in the new Butterflies of Canada Series.

Designers and Engravers:
Obv.:	Susanna Blunt, Susan Taylor
Rev.:	Celia Godkin, Samantha Strath

Composition: Silver-plated copper, Painted

Weight:	33.2 g	**Edge:**	Reeded
Diameter:	42.0 mm	**Die Axis:**	↑↑
Thickness:	3.2 mm	**Finish:**	Proof

Case of Issue: Maroon leatherette clam style case, black flocked insert, encapsulated coin, COA

DATE	DESCRIPTION	RCM ITEM #	QUANTITY SOLD	ISSUE PRICE	FINISH	PR-69	PR-70
2013	Canadian Tiger Swallowtail	121878	11,851	34.95	Proof	30.	—

FIFTY CENTS, LOST SHIPS IN CANADIAN WATERS: *RMS EMPRESS OF IRELAND*, 1914-2014 (GIFTWARE).

This coin commemorates the worst diaster in Canada's maritime history, the loss of the ill-fated *RMS Empress of Ireland*.

Designers and Engravers:
Obv.:	Susanna Blunt, Susan Taylor
Rev.:	Yves Bérubé, RCM Staff

Composition: Silver plated copper, Decal

Weight:	32.82 g	**Edge:**	Reeded
Diameter:	42.0 mm	**Die Axis:**	↑↑
Thickness:	N/A	**Finish:**	Matte Proof

Case of Issue: Maroon leatherette clam style case, black flocked insert, encapsulated coin, COA,

DATE	DESCRIPTION	RCM ITEM #	QUANTITY SOLD	ISSUE PRICE	FINISH	PR-69	PR-70
2014 (1914-)	*RMS Empress of Ireland*	130544	15,000	34.95	Matte Proof	35.	—

FIFTY CENTS, 100 BLESSINGS OF GOOD FORTUNE, 2014 (GIFTWARE).

Designers and Engravers:
Obv.:	Susanna Blunt, Susan Taylor
Rev.:	Three Degrees Creative Group, RCM Staff

Composition: Silver-plated copper

Weight:	32.5 g	**Edge:**	Reeded
Diameter:	42.0 mm	**Die Axis:**	↑↑
Thickness:	3.0 mm	**Finish:**	Proof, Coloured

Case of Issue: Silver satin-like clam style case, black flocked insert, encapsulated coin, COA, red sleeve

DATE	DESCRIPTION	RCM ITEM #	QUANTITY SOLD	ISSUE PRICE	FINISH	PR-69	PR-70
2014	100 Blessings of Good Fortune	128210	5,900	34.95	Proof	30.	—

FIFTY CENTS, TORONTO 2015™ PAN AM/PARAPAN AM GAMES: CELEBRATING EXCELLENCE, 2015.

Detailed engraving provides a showcase for the breathtaking combination of artistry and storytelling, resulting in a truly stunning numismatic version of the gold medals awarded at the TORONTO 2015 Pan Am/Parapan Am Games.

Designers and Engravers:
Obv.:	Susanna Blunt, Susan Taylor
Rev.:	Christi Belcourt

Composition: Gold plated copper

Weight:	32.5 g	**Edge:**	Reeded
Diameter:	42.0 mm	**Die Axis:**	↑↑
Thickness:	N/A	**Finish:**	Proof

Case of Issue: Maroon clamshell with custom beauty box.

DATE	DESCRIPTION	RCM ITEM #	QUANTITY SOLD	ISSUE PRICE	FINISH	PR-69	PR-70
2015	Celebrating Excellence	144779	4,556	44.95.	Proof	40.	—

BIG COIN SERIES

FIFTY CENTS, BIG COIN SET, 2015-2019.

The Big Coin Series started in 2015 features Thomas Shingles' Coat of Arms design first used in 1959 on the 2015, 2016, 2018 and 2019 issues, with the Howling Wolf design from the Centennial issue of 1967, designed by Alex Colville. For other coins in this set, see (pages 7, 12, 17, 57, 87, 131, 145).

2015	**2016**	**2017**

2018	**2019**

Designers and Engravers:

Obv.:   Susanna Blunt, Susan Taylor
Rev.:   Thomas Shingles (2015, 2016, 2018)
      Alex Colville (2017)
      Cathy Bursey Sabourin (2019)

Silver content: 157.58 g, 5.06 tr oz
Weight: 157.6 g
Diameter: 65.25 mm
Thickness: N/A
Case of Issue: Maroon clam style case, black flocked insert, encapsulated coin, COA, custom box

Composition:

2015:   99.99% Ag, Selectively gold plated
2016:   99.99% Ag, Selectively coloured on reverse
2017   99.99% Ag, Selectively gold plated
2018   99.99% Ag, Selevely rose gold-plated
2019   99.99% Ag, Reverse gold plating

Edge: Reeded
Die Axis: ↑↑
Finish: Proof

DATE	DESCRIPTION	RCM ITEM #	QUANTITY SOLD	ISSUE PRICE	FINISH	PR-69	PR-70
2015	50¢ Big Coin	134873	1,499	549.95	Proof	550.	—
2016	50¢ Big Coin	151549	1,497	519.95	Proof	550.	—
2017	50¢ Big Coin	156102	2,150	559.95	Proof	560.	—
2018	50¢ Big Coin	163842	1,500	559.95	Proof	560.	—
2019	50¢ Big Coin	170837	1,250	569.95	Proof	570.	—

FIFTY CENTS, 100TH ANNIVERSARY OF THE 1917 HALF-DOLLAR, 2017.

A collectible retrospective: This meticulously engraved coin revisits the reverse design that graced Canada's 50-cent coin until 1936.

Designers and Engravers:
Obv.:	Susanna Blunt, Susan Taylor
Rev.:	RCM Staff

Composition: 99.99% Ag, Selectively gold plated
Weight: 62.29 g
Diameter: 50.0 mm
Thickness: N/A
Edge: Reeded
Die Axis: ↑↑
Finish: Proof
Case of Issue: Wood case with graphic beauty box.

DATE	DESCRIPTION	RCM ITEM #	MINTAGE	ISSUE PRICE	FINISH	PR-69	PR-70
2017	100th Anniversary of the 1917 Half Dollar	157091	4,000	194.95	Proof	250.	—

FIFTY CENTS, 75TH ANNIVERSARY OF THE 1943 HALF-DOLLAR, 2018.

This exclusive coin looks back at the half-dollar issued in 1943, which is re-created here in pure silver with a celebratory touch of gold plating.

Designers and Engravers:
Obv.:	Susanna Blunt, Susan Taylor
Rev.:	RCM Staff

Composition: 99.99% Ag, Selectively gold plated
Weight: 62.29 g
Diameter: 50.0 mm
Thickness: N/A
Edge: Reeded
Die Axis: ↑↑
Finish: Proof
Case of Issue: Wood case with graphic beauty box. COA.

DATE	DESCRIPTION	RCM ITEM #	MINTAGE	ISSUE PRICE	FINISH	PR-69	PR-70
2018	75th Anniversary of the 1943 Half-Dollar	164747	4,000	194.95	Proof	195.	—

FIFTY CENTS, 60TH ANNIVERSARY OF THE 1959 HALF-DOLLAR, 2019.

This exclusive coin looks back at the half-dollar issued in 1959, reflects the revised Canadian coat-of-arms from 1957.

Designers and Engravers:
Obv.:	Mary Gillick
Rev.:	Thomas Shingles

Composition: 99.99% Ag, Selectively gold plated
Weight: 62.29 g
Diameter: 50.0 mm
Thickness: N/A
Edge: Reeded
Die Axis: ↑↑
Finish: Proof
Case of Issue: Wood case with graphic beauty box. COA.

DATE	DESCRIPTION	RCM ITEM #	MINTAGE	ISSUE PRICE	FINISH	PR-69	PR-70
2019	60th Anniversary of the 1959 Half-Dollar	170142	2,500	194.95	Proof	220.	—

Note: Coin on this page are illustrated smaller than actual size. These exclusive coins were only available to members of the Masters Club.

FIFTY CENTS, QUEEN VICTORIA JUBILEE, 2019.

This stamp-inspired collectible commemorates Her Majesty Queen Victoria's Diamond Jubilee. It is a tribute to a long-reigning sovereign, born in 1819, who played a key role in Canadian history.

Designers and Engravers:

Obv.:	Susanna Blunt, Susan Taylor
Rev.:	RCM Staff

Composition:	99.99% Ag		
Silver content:	51.86 g, 1.67 tr oz		
Weight:	51.86 g	**Edge:**	Perforated
Diameter:	51 mm x 30 mm	**Die Axis:**	↑↑
Thickness:	N/A	**Finish:**	Proof
Case of Issue:	Maroon clamshell with custom beauty box.		

DATE	DESCRIPTION	RCM ITEM #	MINTAGE	ISSUE PRICE	FINISH	PR-69	PR-70
2019	Queen Victoria Jubilee	172482	5,000	139.95	Proof	149.	—

FIFTY CENT DERIVATIVES

DATE	DESCRIPTION	QUANTITY SOLD	ISSUE PRICE	ISSUER	FINISH	MARKET PRICE
1999	**MILLENNIUM SET OF 12 CARDS** each containing a 1999	N/A	N/A	RCM	MS-65	40.
2001	**CANADA PROVINCIAL CREST** Credit Card Type	N/A	N/A	RCM	MS-65	8.
2003	**CORONATION COIN AND STAMP SET** Two one cent coins, 1953 and 2003; Two fifty cent coins, 2002 Jubilee, 2003 Uncrowned Portrait; Two mint and two cancelled stamps of Her Majesty's Jubilee and Coronation; Presentation case	14,743	N/A	RCM	MS-65	30.
2006	**ROYAL CANADIAN MINT ANNUAL REPORT** Fifty cent coin, Selectively gold plated	4,162	25.95	RCM	PR-69	35.
2008	**100TH ANNIVERSARY COIN AND STAMP SET** Fifty cent coin, double-dated 1908-2008, fifty-two cent postage stamp, wooden presentation case, booklet	16,000	44.95	RCM/CP	PR-69	45.
2008	**ROYAL CANADIAN MINT CENTENNIAL BOOK** Fifty cent coin, double-dated 1908-2008, postage stamp, 200-page book					
	English	136	99.95	RCM	PR-69	75.
	French	46	99.95	RCM	PR-69	75.
2010	**DASPLETOSAURUS TOROSUS** Fifty cent coin, six trading cards, folder	N/A	24.95	RCM	MS-65	35.
2010	**ALBERTOSAURUS** Fifty cent coin, six trading cards, folder	N/A	24.95	RCM	MS-65	35.
2010	**SINOSAUROPTERYX** Fifty cent coin, six trading cards, folder	N/A	24.95	RCM	MS-65	35.
2012	**TITANIC 100,** Fifty cent coin, twenty-five cent coin, White Star stock certificate, a re-created Titanic cancel, sheet of stamps, three Titanic postcards, leather-bound embossed album	10,000	140.95	RCM/CP	MS-65	130.
2012	**PHILATELIC NUMISMATIC COVER** Royal Cypher fifty cent coin, two dollar Diamond Jubilee stamp	10,000	25.95	RCM/CP	MS-65	25.
2013	**75TH ANNIVERSARY OF SUPERMAN™: THEN AND NOW COIN AND STAMP SET,** Fifty cent coin, collectable stamp	25,038	29.75	RCM/CP	SP-68	50.
2014	**BLESSING COIN AND STAMP COLLECTABLES** Fifty cent coin 100 Blessings of Good Fortune; Chinese stamp 120 fen, "Blossom of Fortune" (issue date Oct. 9, 2008).	N/A	38.88	RCM/CP	PR-69	30.
2014	**RMS EMPRESS OF IRELAND COLLECTOR SET** Fifty-cent coin, two reproduction Empress postcards, domestic stamp, souvenir sheet international stamps, two first day covers, booklet.	15,000	99.95	RCM/CP	PR-69	100.

ONE DOLLAR ISSUES

SILVER DOLLAR ISSUES, 1971-1989

Designers:		**Engravers:**	
Obv.:	See obverse illustrations	Obv.:	See obverse illustrations
Rev.:	See reverse illustrations	Rev.:	See reverse illustrations
Composition:	50% Ag, 50% Cu		
Silver content:	11.65 g, 0.375 tr oz		
Weight:	23.3 g	**Edge:**	Reeded
Diameter:	36.07 mm	**Die Axis:**	↑↑
Thickness:	2.95 mm	**Finish:**	Specimen

Case of Issue:
    (A) Black leatherette clam style case, Coat of Arms, maroon and black insert
    (B) Black leatherette clam case, Coat of Arms, white and black insert
    (C) Blue leatherette clam style case, gilt RCMP crest, maroon and black insert
    (D) Black leatherette clam style case, Coat of Arms, maroon and black plastic insert, encapsulated coin
    (E) Blue leatherette clam style case, Coat of Arms, light blue insert with purple satin cloth printed "Library of Parliament - Bibliothèque Du Parlément 1876-1976
    (F) Maroon leatherette case, Coat of Arms, maroon and black plastic insert, encapsulated coin
    (G) Maroon velveteen case, Coat of Arms, maroon velveteen insert, encapsulated coin
    (H) Black leatherette square case, Coat of Arms, maroon and black plastic insert, encapsulated coin, COA
    (I) Black leatherette square case, maroon insert, encapsulated coin, COA
    (J) Clear plastic outer case, black plastic insert, silver sleeve, encapsulated coin

OBVERSES 1971-1989

1971-1976, 1979-1984, 1986-1989	1977	1978	1985
Designer: A. Machin	Designer: A. Machin	Designer: A. Machin	Designer: A. Machin
Engraver: P. Brindley	Engraver: RCM Staff	Engraver: RCM Staff	Engraver: P. Brindley

REVERSES 1971-1989

1971	1972	1973
British Columbia Centennial	Voyageur Design	R.C.M.P.
Designer and Engraver:	Designer: E. Hahn	Designer: P. Cedarberg
P. Brindley	Engraver: T. Smith	Engraver: P. Brindley

1974 Winnipeg Centennial Designer: P. Pederson Engraver: P. Brindley	**1975** Calgary Centennial Designer: D. D. Paterson Engraver: P. Brindley	**1976** Library of Parliament Designer and Engraver: Walter Ott	**1977** Silver Jubilee Elizabeth II Designer: R. Lee Engraver: A. Aarand

1978 11th Commonwealth Games Designer: R. Taylor Engraver: V. Coté	**1979** Griffon Tricentennial Designer: W. Schluep Engraver: T. Smith	**1980** Arctic Territories Centennial Designer: D. D. Paterson Engraver: W. Ott	**1981** Trans-Canada Railway Designer: C. Gorey Engraver: W. Ott

1982 Regina Centennial Designer: H. Brown Engraver: W. Ott	**1983** World University Games Designer: C. Tietz Engraver: W. Ott	**1984** Toronto Sesquicentennial Designer: D. J. Craig Engraver: W. Ott	**1985** National Parks Centennial Designer: K. Rohlicek Engraver: W. Ott

1986 Vancouver Centennial Designer: E. J. Morrison Engraver: V. Coté, W. Ott	**1987** John Davis Designer: C. Gorey Engraver: V. Coté	**1988** Saint-Maurice Ironworks Designer: R. R. Carmichael Engraver: S. Beveridge	**1989** Mackenzie River Bicentennial Designer: J. Mardon Engraver: S. Beveridge

SILVER DOLLAR SPECIMEN ISSUES, 1971-1980 PRICING TABLE.

Case of Issue:

(A)   Black leatherette clam style case, Coat of Arms, maroon and black insert
(B)   Black leatherette clam case, Coat of Arms, white and black insert
(C)   Blue leatherette clam style case, gilt RCMP crest, maroon and black insert
(D)   Black leatherette clam style case, Coat of Arms, maroon and black plastic insert, encapsulated coin
(E)   Blue leatherette clam style case, Coat of Arms, light blue insert with purple satin cloth printed "Library of Parliament - Bibliothèque Du Parlément 1876-1976
(F)   Maroon leatherette case, Coat of Arms, maroon and black plastic insert, encapsulated coin
(G)   Maroon velveteen case, Coat of Arms, maroon velveteen insert, encapsulated coin
(H)   Black leatherette square case, Coat of Arms, maroon and black plastic insert, encapsulated coin, COA
(I)   Black leatherette square case, maroon insert, encapsulated coin, COA
(J)   Clear plastic outer case, black plastic insert, silver sleeve, encapsulated coin

DATE	DESCRIPTION	CASE	QUANTITY SOLD	ISSUE PRICE	FINISH	SP-68	SP-69
1971 (1871-)	British Columbia Centennial	A	585,217	3.00	Specimen	15.	—
1971 (1871-)	British Columbia Centennial	B	Included	3.00	Specimen	20.	—
1972	Voyageur Design	A	341,581	3.00	Specimen	15.	—
1973 (1873-)	R.C.M.P.	A	904,723	3.00	Specimen	15.	—
1973 (1873-)	R.C.M.P.	C	Included	3.00	Specimen	25.	—
1974 (1874-)	Winnipeg Centennial	D	628,183	3.50	Specimen	15.	—
1975 (1875-)	Calgary Centennial, ↑↑ Medal Axis	D	833,095	3.50	Specimen	15.	—
1975 (1875-)	Calgary Centennial, ↑↓ Coinage Axis	D	Included	3.50	Specimen	Only one known	—
1976 (1876-)	Library of Parliament	D	433,722	4.00	Specimen	15.	—
1976 (1876-)	Library of Parliament	E	Included	4.00	Specimen	25.	—
1977 (1952-)	Silver Jubilee Queen Elizabeth II	D	744,848	4.25	Specimen	15.	—
1977 (1952-)	Silver Jubilee Queen Elizabeth II	F	Included	—	Specimen	30.	—
1977 (1952-)	Silver Jubilee Queen Elizabeth II	G	Included	—	Specimen	30.	—
1978	Commonwealth Games, Edmonton	H	640,000	4.50	Specimen	15.	—
1979 (1679-)	Griffon Tricentennial	H	688,671	5.50	Specimen	15.	—
1980	Arctic Territories Centennial	H	389,564	22.00	Specimen	15.	—

SILVER DOLLAR PROOF AND BRILLIANT UNCIRCULATED ISSUES, 1981-1989 PRICING TABLE.

Case of Issue: **Proof:**   Black leatherette square case, maroon insert, encapsulated coin, COA
BU: Clear plastic outer case, black plastic insert, silver sleeve, encapsulated coin

DATE	DESCRIPTION	QUANTITY SOLD	ISSUE PRICE	FINISH	SP-68	SP-69	PR-68	PR-69
1981	Trans-Canada Railway Centennial	353,742	18.00	Proof	—	—	15.	—
1981	Trans-Canada Railway Centennial	148,647	14.00	BU	14.	—	—	—
1982 (1882-)	Regina Centennial	577,959	15.25	Proof	—	—	15.	—
1982 (1882-)	Regina Centennial	144,989	10.95	BU	14.	—	—	—
1983	World University Games	340,068	16.15	Proof	—	—	15.	—
1983	World University Games	159,450	10.95	BU	14.	—	—	—
1984 (1834-)	Toronto Sesquicentennial	571,563	17.50	Proof	—	—	15.	—
1984 (1834-)	Toronto Sesquicentennial	133,563	11.40	BU	14.	—	—	—
1985 (1885-)	National Parks Centennial	537,297	17.50	Proof	—	—	15.	—
1985 (1885-)	National Parks Centennial	162,873	12.00	BU	14.	—.	—	—
1986 (1886-)	Vancouver Centennial	496,418	18.00	Proof	—	—	15.	—
1986 (1886-)	Vancouver Centennial	124,574	12.25	BU	14.	—	—	—
1987 (1587-)	John Davis	405,688	19.00	Proof	—	—	15.	—
1987 (1587-)	John Davis	118,722	14.00	BU	14.	—	—	—
1988	Saint-Maurice Ironworks	259,230	20.00	Proof	—	—	16.	—
1988	Saint-Maurice Ironworks	106,702	15.00	BU	14.	—	—	—
1989	Mackenzie River Bicentennial	272,319	21.75	Proof	—	—	20.	—
1989	Mackenzie River Bicentennial	110,650	16.25	BU	14.	—	—	—

SILVER DOLLAR ISSUES, 1990-1991

1990-1991
Common Obverse

1990
Henry Kelsey Tricentennial
Engraver: Ago Aarand

1991
175th Anniv. of the Frontenac
Engraver: Sheldon Beveridge

Designers:		**Engravers:**	
Obv.:	Dora de Pédery-Hunt	Obv.:	Dora de Pédery-Hunt
Rev.:	D. J. Craig	Rev.:	See reverse illustrations
Composition:	50% Ag, 50% Cu		
Silver content:	11.65 g, 0.375 tr oz		
Weight:	23.3 g	**Thickness:**	2.95 mm
Diameter:	36.07 mm	**Die Axis:**	↑↑
Edge:	Reeded	**Finish:**	Proof or Brilliant Uncirculated
Case of Issue:	**Proof:** Black leatherette square case, maroon insert, encapsulated coin, COA		
	BU: Clear plastic outer case, black plastic insert, silver sleeve, encapsulated coin		

DATE	DESCRIPTION SOLD	QUANTITY PRICE	ISSUE	FINISH	SP-68	SP-69	PR-68	PR-69
1990 (1690-)	Henry Kelsey Tricentennial	222,983	22.95	Proof	—	—	18.	—
1990 (1690-)	Henry Kelsey Tricentennial	85,763	16.75	BU	14.	—	—	—
1991 (1816-)	175th Anniversary of the Frontenac	222,892	22.95	Proof	—	—	18.	—
1991 (1816-)	175th Anniversary of the Frontenac	82,642	16.75	BU	14.	—	—	—

SILVER DOLLAR ISSUES, 1992-2002

Designers:		Engravers:	
Obv.:	Dora de Pédery-Hunt	Obv.:	Dora de Pédery-Hunt
Rev.:	See reverse illustrations	Rev.:	See reverse illustrations
Composition:	92.5% Ag, 7.5% Cu	Thickness:	2.95 mm
Silver content:	23.29 g, 0.75 tr oz	Edge:	Reeded
Weight:	25.175 g	Die Axis:	↑↑
Diameter:	36.07 mm	Finish:	Proof or Brilliant Uncirculated

Case of Issue: 1992-1997: **Proof**: Black leatherette square case, maroon insert, encapsulated coin, COA
BU: Clear plastic outer case, black plastic insert, silver sleeve, encapsulated coin
1998-2002: **Proof**: Dark green clam display case, green insert, encapsulated coin, COA
BU: Multicoloured plastic slide case, encapsulated coin
1999: **Proof**: Multicoloured case, black insert, encapsulated coin, COA

1992-2002
Common Obverse

1992
Kingston to York Stagecoach
Designer: K. Smith
Engraver: S. Taylor

1993
100th Anniv. Stanley Cup
Designer: S. Sherwood
Engraver: S. Beveridge

1994
R.C.M.P. Northern Dog
Team Patrol
Designer: I. Sparkes
Engraver: A. Aarand

1995
325th Anniv. of the
Hudson's Bay Company
Designer: V. McIndoe
Engraver: S. Taylor

1996
200th Anniv. John McIntosh
Designer: R. Hill
Engraver: S. Beveridge

1997
25th Anniversary 1972
Canada/Russia Hockey Series
Designer: W. Burden
Engraver: S. Witten

1997
10th Anniv. of the
One Dollar Loon
Designer: J. Grondin
Engraver: S. Beveridge

1998
125th Anniv. R.C.M.P.
Designer: A. Halvorson
Engraver: S. Beveridge

1999
225th Anniversary of the
Voyage of Juan Perez
Designer: D. Craig
Engraver: S. Witten

1999
Int'l Year of Older Persons
Des.: S. Armstrong-Hodgson
Engr.: W. Woodruff

2000
Voyage of Discovery
Designer: D. F. Warkentin
Engraver: C. Saffioti

2001	2001	2002	2002
50th Anniv. of the National Ballet of Canada Designer: S. McKowen Engraver: S. Taylor	90th Anniv. of the Striking of Canada's 1911 Silver Dollar Designer: RCM Staff Engraver: C. Saffioti	50th Anniversary Queen Elizabeth II's Accession to the Throne Designer: RCM Staff Engraver: S. Taylor	Queen Elizabeth the Queen Mother Designer: RCM Staff Engraver: S. Taylor

DATE	DESCRIPTION	QUANTITY SOLD	ISSUE PRICE	FINISH	SP-68	SP-69	PR-68	PR-69
1992	Kingston to York Stagecoach	187,612	23.95	Proof	—	—	25.	—
1992	Kingston to York Stagecoach	78,160	17.50	BU	22.	—	—	—
1993 (1893-)	100th Anniv. of the Stanley Cup	294,314	23.95	Proof	—	—	28.	—
1993 (1893-)	100th Anniv. of the Stanley Cup	88,150	17.50	BU	22.	—	—	—
1994 (1969-)	R.C.M.P. Northern Dog Team Patrol	178,485	24.50	Proof	—	—	28.	—
1994 (1969-)	R.C.M.P. Northern Dog Team Patrol	65,295	17.95	BU	22.	—	—	—
1995	325th Anniv. Hudson's Bay Co.	166,259	24.50	Proof	—	—	28.	—
1995	325th Anniv. Hudson's Bay Co.	61,819	17.95	BU	22.	—	—	—
1996 (1796-)	200th Anniv. John McIntosh	133,779	29.95	Proof	—	—	28.	—
1996 (1796-)	200th Anniv. John McIntosh	58,834	19.95	BU	22.	—	—	—
1997 (1972-)	25th Anniv. Canada/Russia Hockey Series	184,965	29.95	Proof	—	—	28.	—
1997 (1972-)	25th Anniv. Canada/Russia Hockey Series	155,252	19.95	BU	22.	—	—	—
1997 (1987-)	10th Anniv. of the One Dollar Loon	24,995	49.95	Proof	—	—	75.	—
1998 (1873-)	125th Anniv. R.C.M.P.	130,795	29.95	Proof	—	—	28.	—
1998 (1873-)	125th Anniv. R.C.M.P.	81,376	19.95	BU	22.	—	—	—
1999 (1774-)	225th Anniv. Voyage Juan Perez	126,435	29.95	Proof	—	—	28.	—
1999 (1774-)	225th Anniv. Voyage Juan Perez	67,655	19.95	BU	22.	—	—	—
1999	International Year of Older Persons	24,976	49.95	Proof	—	—	45.	—
2000	Voyage of Discovery	121,575	29.95	Proof	—	—	28.	—
2000	Voyage of Discovery	62,975	19.95	BU	22.	—	—	—
2001 (1951-)	50th Anniv. National Ballet of Canada	89,390	30.95	Proof	—	—	28.	—
2001 (1951-)	50th Anniv. National Ballet of Canada	53,668	20.95	BU	22.	—	—	—
2001 (1911-)	90th Anniv. Canada's 1911 Silver Dollar	24,996	49.95	Proof	—	—	50.	—
2002 (1952-)	50th Anniv. Elizabeth II's Accession, Silver	29,688	33.95	Proof	—	—	28.	—
2002 (1952-)	50th Anniv. Elizabeth II's Accession, GP*	65,315	N.I.I.	Proof	—	—	55.	—
2002 (1952-)	50th Anniv. Elizabeth II's Accession, Silver	65,410	24.95	BU	22.	—	—	—
2002 (1900-)	Queen Elizabeth, the Queen Mother	9,994	49.95	Proof	—	—	225.	—

Note: GP* refers to Gold Plated

ONE DOLLAR, 100TH ANNIVERSARY OF THE COBALT DISCOVERY, 1903-2003.

This coin marks 100 years since Fred LaRose, a blacksmith, threw his hammer at a fox, of course missing the fox, but striking a rock revealing a gleaming vein of silver. This is the first issue of a pure silver (.9999 fine) dollar by the Royal Canadian Mint.

Designers and Engravers:
Obv.: Dora de Pédery-Hunt
Rev.: John Mardon, William Woodruff
Composition: 99.99% Ag
Silver content: 25.172 g, 0.809 tr oz
Weight: 25.175 g
Diameter: 36.07 mm   **Edge:** Reeded
Thickness: 3.02 mm   **Die Axis:** ↑↑
Finish: Proof or Brilliant Uncirculated
Proof: Dark green clam case, green insert, encapsulated coin, COA
BU: Multicoloured plastic slide case, encapsulated coin

DATE	DESCRIPTION	QUANTITY SOLD	ISSUE PRICE	FINISH	SP-68	SP-69	PR-69	PR-70
2003 (1903-)	100th Anniv. Cobalt Silver Discovery	88,536	36.95	Proof	—	—	30.	—
2003 (1903-)	100th Anniv. Cobalt Silver Discovery	51,130	28.95	BU	22.	—	—	—

GOLD ONE DOLLAR, 50TH ANNIVERSARY QUEEN ELIZABETH II'S ACCESSION TO THE THRONE, 2003.

This undated gold issue is based on the 2002 reverse Accession design, and the new uncrowned obverse design for 2003. This gold dollar was sold on eBay, September 25th, 2003, with 100% of the proceeds being donated to charities.

Designers and Engravers:
Obv.: Susanna Blunt, Susan Taylor
Rev.: RCM Staff, Susan Taylor
Composition: 99.99% Au
Gold content: 25.172 g, 0.809 tr oz
Weight: 25.175 g   **Edge:** Reeded
Diameter: 36.07 mm   **Die Axis:** ↑↑
Thickness: 2.66 mm   **Finish:** Proof
Case of Issue: Not known

DATE	DESCRIPTION	QUANTITY SOLD	ISSUE PRICE	FINISH	SP-68	SP-69	PR-69	PR-70
2003	50th Anniv. Accession/Coronation of Elizabeth II, Gold	One	—	Proof		UNIQUE		

ONE DOLLAR, 50TH ANNIVERSARY OF THE CORONATION OF QUEEN ELIZABETH II, 1953-2003.

This silver dollar is a reissue of the dollar first struck during the coronation year 1953. The design is differentiated by the double dates 1953-2003 on the obverse, as opposed to the single date on the reverse of the 1953 dollar.

Designers and Engravers:
Obv.: Mary Gillick, Thomas Shingles
Rev.: Emanuel Hahn
Composition: 99.99% Ag
Silver content: 25.172 g, 0.809 tr oz
Weight: 25.175 g   **Edge:** Reeded
Diameter: 36.07 mm   **Die Axis:** ↑↑
Thickness: 3.02 mm   **Finish:** Proof
Case of Issue: See Special Issue Proof Sets, page 528

DATE	DESCRIPTION	QUANTITY SOLD	ISSUE PRICE	FINISH	PR-69	PR-70
2003 (1953-)	50th Anniv. Coronation Elizabeth II	21,537	N.I.I.	Proof	70.	—

ONE DOLLAR, UNCROWNED PORTRAIT OF QUEEN ELIZABETH II, 2003.

This was a special edition dollar with the new obverse design for 2003, and the reverse honouring the "Voyageurs" design of Canada's first circulating silver dollar. A fine gold (.9999) example of this design was struck by the Royal Canadian Mint and sold on eBay with the proceeds going to charities.

Designers and Engravers:

Obv.:	Susanna Blunt, Susan Taylor
Rev.:	Emanuel Hahn, RCM Staff
Composition:	Gold: 99.99% Au
Silver:	99.99% Ag
Bullion content:	Gold: 25.172 g, 0.809 tr oz
	Silver: 25.172 g, 0.809 tr oz
Weight:	Gold: 25.175 g, Silver: 25.175 g
Diameter:	36.07 mm
Thickness:	Gold: 2.66 mm
Silver:	3.02 mm
Edge:	Reeded
Die Axis:	↑↑
Finish:	Proof

Case of Issue: Gold: Unknown
Silver: Black leatherette clam case, maroon insert, encapsulated coin, COA

DATE	DESCRIPTION	QUANTITY SOLD	ISSUE PRICE	FINISH	PR-69	PR-70
2003	Uncrowned Portrait Queen Elizabeth II, Silver	29,586	51.95	Proof	35.	—
2003	Uncrowned Portrait Queen Elizabeth II, Gold	One	—	Proof	UNIQUE	

ONE DOLLAR, 400TH ANNIVERSARY OF THE FIRST FRENCH SETTLEMENT IN NORTH AMERICA, 1604-2004.

In 1604 a tiny island, in what was to be called the St. Croix River, became the first French settlement in North America.
A 2004 Ile Sainte-Croix stamp and coin set was issued containing this silver dollar counterstamped with a fleur-de-lis privy mark.

Common Obverse	Proof	BU, with Privy Mark

Designers:

		Engravers:	
Obv.:	Susanna Blunt	Obv.:	Susan Taylor
Rev.:	R. R. Carmichael	Rev.:	Stan Witten

Composition:	99.99% Ag
Silver content:	25.172 g, 0.809 tr oz
Weight:	25.175 g
Diameter:	36.07 mm
Thickness:	3.02 mm
Finish:	Proof or Brilliant Uncirculated

Edge:	Reeded
Die Axis:	↑↑

Case of Issue:
(A) Dark green leatherette clam case, green insert, encapsulated coin, COA
(B) Multicoloured plastic slide case, encapsulated coin
(C) Privy Mark Dollar, see Derivatives, page 130

DATE	DESCRIPTION	QUANTITY SOLD	ISSUE PRICE	FINISH	SP-68	SP-69	PR-69	PR-70
2004 (1604-)	First French Settlement	106,974	36.95	Proof	—	—	32.	—
2004 (1604-)	First French Settlement	42,582	28.95	BU	24.	—	—	—
2004 (1604-)	First French Settlement, with Privy Mark	8,315	N.I.I.	BU	60.	—	—	—

ONE DOLLAR, "THE POPPY" ARMISTICE DAY COMMEMORATIVE, 2004.

Throughout the world the poppy has become one of the most powerful symbols that honours the men and women who gave their lives for freedom. For the circulation "Poppy" twenty-five-cent coin, see Canadian Coins, Volume One, Numismatic Issues.

Designers and Engravers:

Obv.:	Susanna Blunt, Susan Taylor
Rev.:	Cosme Saffioti, Stan Witten
Composition:	99.99% Ag
Silver content:	25.172 g, 0.809 tr oz
Weight:	25.175 g
Diameter:	36.07 mm **Edge:** Reeded
Thickness:	2.95 mm **Die Axis:** ↑↑
Finish:	Proof
Case of Issue:	Maroon leatherette clam style case, black flock insert, encapsulated coin, COA

DATE	DESCRIPTION	QUANTITY SOLD	ISSUE PRICE	FINISH	PR-69	PR-70
2004	"The Poppy" Armistice Day	24,527	49.95	Proof	50.	—

ONE DOLLAR, 40TH ANNIVERSARY OF CANADA'S NATIONAL FLAG, 1965-2005.

The Canadian flag, which is composed of the symbolic maple leaf and the national colours first proclaimed in 1921, was raised for the first time February 15th, 1965, on Parliament Hill

The 2005 brilliant uncirculated silver dollar was also issued in a gift set which included an interactive CD Rom (see Derivatives, page 135).

Proof	Proof, Selectively gold plated	Proof, Red enamel

Designers:			**Engravers:**	
Obv.:	Susanna Blunt		Obv.:	Susan Taylor
Rev.:	William Woodruff		Rev.:	William Woodruff

Composition:	99.99% Ag		
Silver content:	25.172 g, 0.809 tr oz	**Thickness:**	3.02 mm
Weight:	25.175 g	**Die Axis:**	↑↑
Diameter:	36.07 mm	**Edge:**	Reeded

Finish:
1. Proof
2. Proof, Selectively gold plated
3. Proof, Red enamel
4. Brilliant Uncirculated

Case of Issue: Maroon plastic slide case, black plastic insert, encapsulated coin, COA

DATE	DESCRIPTION	SOURCE	QUANTITY SOLD	ISSUE PRICE	FINISH	SP-68	SP-69	PR-69	PR-70
2005 (1965-)	Proof	Pr. Single	95,431	34.95	Proof	—	—	35.	—
2005 (1965-)	Proof, Selectively Gold plated	Pr. Set	63,562	N.I.I.	Proof	—	—	65.	—
2005 (1965-)	Proof, Red enamel	Pr. Single	4,898	99.95	Proof	—	—	240.	—
2005 (1965-)	Brilliant Uncirculated	BU Single	50,948	24.95	BU	22.	—	*	*

ONE DOLLAR, 150TH ANNIVERSARY OF THE VICTORIA CROSS, 2006.

In 1856 Queen Victoria Instituted the Victoria Cross medal. A total of 1,351 Victoria Cross medals have been awarded with 94 being awarded to Canadians.

<table>
<tr><td></td><td>Proof</td><td>Proof, Selectively gold plated</td></tr>
</table>

Designers:
Obv.:	Susanna Blunt
Rev.:	RCM Staff

Composition: 99.99% Ag
Silver content: 25.172 g, 0.809 tr oz
Weight: 25.175 g
Diameter: 36.07 mm
Finish: 1. Proof 2. Proof, Selectively gold plated 3. Brilliant Uncirculated
Case of Issue: Maroon plastic slide case, black plastic insert, encapsulated coin, COA

Engravers:
Obv.:	Susan Taylor
Rev.:	RCM Staff

Thickness: 3.02 mm
Edge: Reeded
Die Axis: ↑↑

DATE	DESCRIPTION	SOURCE	QUANTITY SOLD	ISSUE PRICE	FINISH	SP-68	SP-69	PR-69	PR-70
2006	Victoria Cross, Proof	Pr. Single	55,599	34.95	Proof	—	—	35.	—
2006	Victoria Cross, Proof, Selectively gold plated	Pr. Set	53,822	N.I.I.	Proof	—	—	70.	—
2006	Victoria Cross, Brilliant Uncirculated	BU Single	27,254	24.95	BU	22.	—	*	*

ONE DOLLAR, MEDAL OF BRAVERY, 2006.

The Canadian Medal of Bravery was established in 1972 and is awarded by the Governor General of Canada in recognition of "Acts of Bravery in hazardous circumstances".

<table>
<tr><td></td><td>Proof</td><td>Proof, Red Enamel</td></tr>
</table>

Designers:
Obv.:	Susanna Blunt
Rev.:	Konrad Wachelko

Composition: 99.99% Ag
Silver content: 25.172 g, 0.809 tr oz
Weight: 25.175 g
Diameter: 36.07 mm
Finish: 1. Proof 2. Proof, Red enamel
Case of Issue: Maroon plastic slide case, black plastic insert, encapsulated coin, COA

Engravers:
Obv.:	Susan Taylor
Rev.:	Konrad Wachelko

Thickness: 3.02 mm
Edge: Reeded
Die Axis: ↑↑

DATE	DESCRIPTION	SOURCE	QUANTITY SOLD	ISSUE PRICE	FINISH	PR-69	PR-70
2006	Medal of Bravery	Pr. Single	8,343	54.95	Proof	60.	—
2006	Medal of Bravery, Red enamel	Pr. Single	4,999	99.95	Proof	140.	—

ONE DOLLAR (HALF OUNCE), SILVER WOLF, 2006.

Designers and Engravers:

Obv.:	Susanna Blunt, Susan Taylor
Rev.:	William Woodruff
Composition:	99.99% Ag
Weight:	15.552 g, 0.50 tr oz
Diameter:	34.0 mm	**Edge:**	Reeded
Thickness:	2.1 mm	**Die Axis:**	↑↑
Finish:	Bullion
Case of Issue:	Mylar Pouch

DATE	DESCRIPTION	QUANTITY SOLD	ISSUE PRICE	FINISH	MS-65	MS-66	MS-67
2006	$1 (½ oz), Silver Wolf	106,800	BV	Bullion	22.	32.	—

ONE DOLLAR, THAYENDANEGEA, 2007.

Born in 1743, Thayendanegea (Joseph Brant) was a Mohawk Chief who fought along side the British during the American Revolution. Brant died in Canada, November 24th, 1807.

	Proof	Proof, Selectively gold plated	Proof, Enamelled

Designers:

			Engravers:	
Obv.:	Susanna Blunt		Obv.:	Susan Taylor
Rev.:	Laurie McGaw		Rev.:	William Woodruff

Composition: 92.5% Ag, 7.5% Cu

Silver content: 23.29 g, 0.749 tr oz   Thickness: 3.02 mm

Weight: 25.175 g   Edge: Reeded

Diameter: 36.07 mm   Die Axis: ↑↑

Finish: 1. Proof
                2. Proof, Selectively gold plated
                3. Proof, Enamelled
                4. Brilliant Uncirculated

Case of Issue: (A) Proof, Enamelled: Maroon plastic slide case, black plastic insert, encapsulated coin, COA
                (B) Proof / BU: Maroon leatherette clam style case, black flocked insert, encapsulated coin, COA

DATE	DESCRIPTION	SOURCE	RCM ITEM #	QUANTITY SOLD	ISSUE PRICE	FINISH	SP-68	SP-69	PR-69	PR-70
2007	Thayendanegea, Proof	Pr. Single	6240007	32,837	42.95	Proof	*	*	35.	—
2007	Thayendanegea, Proof, Selectively gold plated	Pr. Set	6260007	37,413	89.95	Proof	*	*	70.	—
2007	Thayendanegea, Proof, Enamelled	Pr. Single	N/A	5,181	129.95	Proof	*	*	90.	—
2007	Thayendanegea, Brilliant Uncirculated	BU Single	6240407	16,378	34.95	BU	22.	—	*	*

ONE DOLLAR, CELEBRATION OF THE ARTS, 2007.

This coin was issued to commemorate the 50th anniversary of the founding of the Canada Council of the Arts.

Designers and Engravers:

Obv.:	Susanna Blunt, Susan Taylor		
Rev.:	Friedrich Peter, RCM Staff		
Composition:	92.5% Ag, 7.5% Cu		
Silver content:	23.29 g, 0.749 tr oz		
Weight:	25.175 g		
Diameter:	36.07 mm	**Edge:**	Reeded
Thickness:	2.95 mm	**Die Axis:**	↑↑
Finish:	Proof		
Case of Issue:	Maroon plastic slide case, black plastic insert, encapsulated coin, COA		

DATE	DESCRIPTION	RCM ITEM #	QUANTITY SOLD	ISSUE PRICE	FINISH	PR-69	PR-70
2007	Celebration of the Arts	624037	6,704	54.95	Proof	160.	—

ONE DOLLAR, 400TH ANNIVERSARY OF QUEBEC CITY, 1608-2008.

Founded in 1608 by Samuel de Champlain, Quebec City is one of the oldest cities in North America, and the only one north of Mexico with its ramparts surrounding the Old City still intact.

Proof   Proof, Selectively gold plated

Designers:			**Engravers:**	
Obv.:	Susanna Blunt		Obv.:	Susan Taylor
Rev.:	Suzanne Duranceau		Rev.:	Susan Taylor, Cecily Mok, Konrad Wachelko
Composition:	92.5% Ag, 7.5% Cu			
Silver Content:	23.29 g, 0.749 tr oz			
Weight:	25.175 g			
Diameter:	36.07 mm		**Edge:**	Reeded
Thickness:	3.02 mm		**Die Axis:**	↑↑
Finish:	1. Proof			
	2. Proof, Selectively gold plated			
	3. Brilliant Uncirculated			
Case of Issue:	Maroon leatherette clam style case, black flocked insert, encapsulated coin, COA			

DATE	DESCRIPTION	SOURCE	RCM ITEM #	QUANTITY SOLD	ISSUE PRICE	FINISH	SP-68	SP-69	PR-69	PR-70
2008 (1608-)	Quebec City, Proof	Pr. Single	6240008	65,000	42.95	Proof	*	*	40.	—
2008 (1608-)	Quebec City, Proof, Selectively gold plated	Pr. Set	6260008	38,630	89.95	Proof	*	*	75.	—
2008 (1608-)	Quebec City, Brilliant Uncirculated	BU Single	6240108	35,000	34.95	BU	25.	—	*	*

ONE DOLLAR, CELEBRATING THE ROYAL CANADIAN MINT CENTENNIAL, 1908-2008.

The Ottawa Branch of the Royal Mint, London, struck their first coins on January 2nd, 1908. Control of the Ottawa Mint passed to Canada in 1931 and was renamed the Royal Canadian Mint.

Designers and Engravers:

Obv.:	Susanna Blunt, Susan Taylor
Rev.:	Jason Bouwman, José Osio
Composition:	92.5% Ag, 7.5% Cu, Selectively gold plated
Silver content:	23.29 g, 0.749 tr oz
Weight:	25.175 g	Edge:	Reeded
Diameter:	36.07 mm	Die Axis:	↑↑
Thickness:	3.1 mm	Finish:	Proof
Case of Issue:	Maroon leatherette clam style case, black flocked insert, encapsulated coin, COA

DATE	DESCRIPTION	RCM ITEM #	QUANTITY SOLD	ISSUE PRICE	FINISH	PR-69	PR-70
2008 (1908-)	Royal Canadian Mint Centennial	100682	15,000	59.95	Proof	140.	—

ONE DOLLAR, "THE POPPY" ARMISTICE, 1918-2008.

A red poppy is worn every November 11th, in memory of our war veterans.

Designers and Engravers:

Obv.:	Susanna Blunt, Susan Taylor
Rev.:	Cosme Saffioti, Stan Witten
Composition:	92.5% Ag, 7.5% Cu
Silver content:	27.75 g, 0.892 tr oz
Weight:	30.0 g	Edge:	Reeded
Diameter:	36.2 mm	Die Axis:	↑↑
Thickness:	3.3 mm	Finish:	Proof
Case of Issue:	Maroon leatherette clam style case, black flocked insert, encapsulated coin, COA

DATE	DESCRIPTION	RCM ITEM #	QUANTITY SOLD	ISSUE PRICE	FINISH	PR-69	PR-70
2008 (1918-)	"The Poppy" Armistice	103526	4,994	139.95	Proof	150.	—

Note: There is slight confusion in the Royal Canadian Mint's press release in which the finish on this coin is stated as "proof" in one section and "proof-like" in another. It is listed in this table as proof as that is the finish carried on the certificate of authenticity which accompanies the coins.

ONE DOLLAR, 100TH ANNIVERSARY MONTREAL CANADIENS, 1909-2009.

The Montreal Canadiens, Montreal's hockey team, celebrated their 100th anniversary in 2009.

Designers and Engravers:

Obv.:	Susanna Blunt, Susan Taylor
Rev.:	Jason Bouwman, Konrad Wachelko
Composition:	92.5% Ag, 7.5% Cu, Selectively gold plated
Silver content:	23.29 g, 0.749 tr oz
Weight:	25.175 g	Edge:	Reeded
Diameter:	36.07 mm	Die Axis:	↑↑
Thickness:	3.1 mm	Finish:	Proof
Case of Issue:	(A) Black leatherette clam style case, black flocked insert, encapsulated coin, COA (B) Acrylic stand

DATE	DESCRIPTION	SOURCE	RCM ITEM #	QUANTITY SOLD	ISSUE PRICE	FINISH	PR-69	PR-70
2009 (1909-)	Montreal Canadiens	Pr. Single	105660	10,093	69.95	Proof	160.	—
2009 (1909-)	Montreal Canadiens	With stand	105094	4,907	74.95	Proof	160.	—

ONE DOLLAR, 100TH ANNIVERSARY OF FLIGHT IN CANADA, 1909-2009.

J. A. Douglas McCurdy, a native of Baddeck, flew the Aerial Experiment Association's Silver Dart on February 23rd, 1909 over the frozen Bras d'Or Lakes, in Nova Scotia. This was the first controlled flight in Canada and the British Empire.

| | Proof | Proof, Selectively gold plated | Brilliant Uncirculated |

Designers:
| Obv.: | Susanna Blunt |
| Rev.: | Jason Bouwman |

Composition: 92.5% Ag, 7.5% Cu
Silver content: 23.29 g, 0.749 tr oz
Weight: 25.175 g
Diameter: 36.07 mm
Thickness: 3.1 mm
Finish:
1. Proof
2. Proof, Selectively gold plated
3. Brilliant Uncirculated

Engravers:
| Obv.: | Susan Taylor |
| Rev.: | William Woodruff |

Edge: Reeded
Die Axis: ↑↑

Case of Issue: Maroon leatherette clam style case, black flocked insert, encapsulated coin, COA

DATE	DESCRIPTION	SOURCE	RCM ITEM #	QUANTITY SOLD	ISSUE PRICE	FINISH	SP-68	SP-69	PR-69	PR-70
2009 (1909-)	Flight, Proof	Pr. Single	103716	25,000	47.95	Proof	*	*	45.	—
2009 (1909-)	Flight, Proof, Selectively gold plated	Pr. Set	103749	27,549	99.95	Proof	*	*	75.	—
2009 (1909-)	Flight, Brilliant Uncirculated	BU Single	103709	13,074	39.95	BU	28.	—	*	*

ONE DOLLAR, VANCOUVER 2010, THE SUN, 2010.

The Sun, representing life, abundance, healing and peace, has been the cornerstone in the cultures of Canada's many First Nation communities.

Designers and Engravers:
| Obv.: | Susanna Blunt, Susan Taylor |
| Rev.: | Xwa lack tun (Ricky Harry), Cecily Mok |

Composition: 92.5% Ag, 7.5% Cu
Silver content: 27.75 g, 0.892 tr oz
Weight: 30.0 g   **Edge:** Plain
Diameter: 36.2 mm   **Die Axis:** ↑↑
Thickness: 3.3 mm   **Finish:** Proof
Case of Issue: Black leatherette clam style case, black flocked insert, encapsulated coin, COA, Vancouver 2010 Olympic Winter Games theme sleeve

DATE	DESCRIPTION	RCM ITEM #	QUANTITY SOLD	ISSUE PRICE	FINISH	PR-69	PR-70
2010	The Sun	106938	5,000	139.95	Proof	230.	—

ONE DOLLAR, 100TH ANNIVERSARY OF THE ROYAL CANADIAN NAVY, 1910-2010.

Founded in 1910 by the passage of the Naval Service Act, the Royal Canadian Navy served in three wars and many conflicts during the last 100 years. *HMCS Sackville*, one of the original Flower Class Corvettes is portrayed on this commemorative silver dollar.

| Proof | Proof, Selectively gold plated | Brilliant Uncirculated |

Designers
   Obv.:   Susanna Blunt
   Rev.:   Yves Bérubé
Composition: 92.5% Ag, 7.5% Cu, Selectively gold plated
Silver content: 23.29 g, 0.749 tr oz
Weight: 25.175 g
Diameter: 36.07 mm
Thickness: 3.0 mm
Case of Issue: Maroon leatherette clam style case, black flocked insert, encapsulated coin

Engravers:
   Obv.:   Susan Taylor
   Rev.:   Stan Witten

Edge: Reeded
Die Axis: ↑↑
Finish: Proof

DATE	DESCRIPTION	SOURCE	RCM ITEM #	QUANTITY SOLD	ISSUE PRICE	FINISH	SP-68	SP-69	PR-69	PR-70
2010 (1910-)	Proof	Pr. Single	105795	29,141	52.95	Proof	*	*	45.	—
2010 (1910-)	Proof, Selectively gold plated	Pr. Set	105793	32,342	109.95	Proof	*	*	75.	—
2010 (1910-)	Brilliant Uncirculated	BU	105797	12,946	46.95	BU	28.	—	*	*

ONE DOLLAR, 75TH ANNIVERSARY OF CANADA'S VOYAGEUR SILVER DOLLAR, 1935-2010.

The first circulating silver dollar was released in 1935. Emanuel Hahn's Voyageur design has become the classic symbol of Canada's silver dollars. This coin was also included in the 75th Anniversary of Canada's First Silver Dollar set, see page 529.

Designers and Engravers:
   Obv.:   Emanuel Hahn
   Rev.:   Percy Metcalfe
Composition: 92.5% Ag, 7.5% Cu
Silver content: 23.29 g, 0.749 tr oz
Weight: 25.175 g   **Edge:**   Reeded
Diameter: 36.07 mm   **Die Axis:**   ↑↑
Thickness: 3.0 mm   **Finish:**   Proof
Case of Issue: Maroon leatherette clam style case, black flocked insert, encapsulated coin

DATE	DESCRIPTION	RCM ITEM #	QUANTITY SOLD	ISSUE PRICE	FINISH	PR-69	PR-70
2010 (1935-)	75th Anniv. First Canadian Silver Dollar	111134	7,494	69.95	Proof	75.	—

ONE DOLLAR, ENAMELLED POPPY, 2010.

The poppy commemorated in the poem "In Flander's Fields" has become the flower of remembrance for Allied Service Personnel lost in battle.

Designers and Engravers:

Obv.:	Susanna Blunt, Susan Taylor
Rev.:	Christie Paquet, Christie Paquet
Composition:	92.5% Ag, 7.5% Cu, Red enamel
Silver content:	23.29 g, 0.749 tr oz

Weight:	25.175 g	**Edge:**	Reeded
Diameter:	36.07 mm	**Die Axis:**	↑↑
Thickness:	3.1 mm	**Finish:**	Proof

Case of Issue: Maroon leatherette clam style case, black flocked insert, encapsulated coin, COA

DATE	DESCRIPTION	RCM ITEM #	QUANTITY SOLD	ISSUE PRICE	FINISH	PR-69	PR-70
2010	Poppy, Enamelled	111624	4,907	139.95	Proof	180.	—

ONE DOLLAR, 100TH ANNIVERSARY OF THE STRIKING OF CANADA'S 1911 SILVER DOLLAR, 1911-2011.

This one dollar coin which carries the double date 1911-2011 is from the Special Edition Proof Set issued in 2011 to commemorate the 100th anniversary of the striking of Canada's 1911 silver dollar.

Designers and Engravers:

Obv.:	Sir E. B. MacKennal
Rev.:	W. H. J. Blakemore
Composition:	92.5% Ag, 7.5% Cu
Silver content:	23.29 g, 0.749 tr oz

Weight:	25.175 g	**Edge:**	Reeded
Diameter:	36.07 mm	**Die Axis:**	↑↑
Thickness:	3.0 mm	**Finish:**	Proof

Case of Issue: See Special Issue Proof Sets, page 553

DATE	DESCRIPTION	RCM ITEM #	QUANTITY SOLD	ISSUE PRICE	FINISH	PR-69	PR-70
2011 (1911-)	100th Anniv. Canada's 1911 Silver Dollar	114097	14,569	65.95	Proof	60.	—

ONE DOLLAR, 100TH ANNIVERSARY OF PARKS CANADA, 1911-2011.

The Dominion Parks Branch, known today as Parks Canada was founded in 1911. Parks Canada is the world's first system of national parks.

       Proof   **Proof, Selectively gold plated**   **Brilliant Uncirculated**

Designers:			**Engravers:**	
Obv.:	Susanna Blunt		Obv.:	Susan Taylor
Rev.:	Luc Normandson		Rev.:	Marcos Hallam
Composition:	92.5% Ag, 7.5% Cu		**Silver Content:**	23.29 g, 0.749 tr oz
Weight:	25.175 g		**Edge:**	Reeded
Diameter:	36.07 mm		**Die Axis:**	↑↑
Thickness:	3.02 mm			

Finish: **1.** Proof   **2.** Proof, Selectively gold plated   **3.** Brilliant Uncirculated

Case of Issue: Maroon leatherette clam style case, black flocked insert, encapsulated coin, COA

DATE	DESCRIPTION	SOURCE	RCM ITEM #	QUANTITY SOLD	ISSUE PRICE	FINISH	SP-68	SP-69	PR-69	PR-70
2011 (1911-)	Parks Canada, Proof	Pr. Single	111711	30,692	55.95	Proof	*	*	50.	—
2011 (1911-)	Parks Canada, Proof, Selectively gold plated	Pr. Set	111244	32,910	114.95	Proof	*	*	75.	—
2011 (1911-)	Parks Canada, Brilliant Uncirculated	BU Single	111718	16,394	49.95	BU	30.	—	*	*

ONE DOLLAR, 200TH ANNIVERSARY OF THE WAR OF 1812, 1812-2012.

The issue of these coins marks the two-hundredth anniversary of the first conflict between the American forces, and the English of Upper Canada, the French of Lower Canada, and the First Nations People who successfully defended against an American invasion. The conflict ran for three years, 1812-1814.

| | Proof | Proof, Selectively gold plated | Brilliant Uncirculated |

Designers:		Engravers:	
Obv.:	Susanna Blunt	Obv.:	Susan Taylor
Rev.:	Ardell Bourgeois	Rev.:	Konrad Wachelko
Composition:	99.99% Ag	Silver Content:	23.17 g, 0.75 tr oz
Weight:	23.17 g	Edge:	Reeded
Diameter:	35.9 mm	Die Axis:	↑↑
Thickness:	2.8 mm		

Finish: **1.** Proof   **2.** Proof, Selectively gold plated   **3.** Brilliant Uncirculated
Case of Issue: Maroon leatherette clam style case, black flocked insert, encapsulated coin, COA

DATE	DESCRIPTION	SOURCE	RCM ITEM #	QUANTITY SOLD	ISSUE PRICE	FINISH	SP-68	SP-69	PR-69	PR-70
2012 (1812-)	War of 1812, Proof	Pr. Single	116864	39,569	59.95	Proof	*	*	35.	—
2012 (1812-)	War of 1812, Proof, Selectively gold plated Set	Prem. Pr.	116689	19,789	224.95	Proof	*	*	80.	—
2012 (1812-)	War of 1812, Brilliant Uncirculated	BU Single	116870	19,623	54.95	BU	25.	—	*	*

ONE DOLLAR (¾ OUNCE), THE WAR OF 1812, 1812-2012.

Designers and Engravers:	
Obv.:	Susanna Blunt, Susan Taylor
Rev.:	Cathy Bursey-Sabourin, K. Wachelko
Composition:	99.99% Ag
Weight:	23.33 g, 0.50 tr oz
Diameter:	38.0 mm
Thickness:	2.4 mm
Edge:	Reeded
Die Axis:	↑↑
Finish:	Bullion
Case of Issue:	Tubes of 30

DATE	DESCRIPTION	RCM ITEM #	QUANTITY SOLD	ISSUE PRICE	FINISH	MS-65	MS-66	MS-67
2012	$1 (¾ oz), The War of 1812	N/A	N/A	BV	Bullion	28.	35.	—

ONE DOLLAR, TWO LOONS, 2012.

This coin was issued to celebrate the 25th anniversary of the loon coin which replaced the one dollar bill in 1987.

Designers and Engravers:

Obv.:	Susanna Blunt, Susan Taylor
Rev.:	Richard Hunt, Cecily Mok

Composition: 99.99% Ag, Coloured
Silver content: 31.39 g, 1.00 tr oz

Weight:	31.39 g	**Edge:**	Reeded
Diameter:	38.0 mm	**Die Axis:**	↑↑
Thickness:	3.10 mm	**Finish:**	Proof

Case of Issue: Maroon leatherette clam style case, black flocked insert, encapsulated coin, COA, custom coloured sleeve

DATE	DESCRIPTION	RCM ITEM #	QUANTITY SOLD	ISSUE PRICE	FINISH	PR-69	PR-70
2012	Two Loons	118919	9,965	109.95	Proof	100.	—

ONE DOLLAR, 100 YEARS OF THE CALGARY STAMPEDE, 2012.

First held in 1912, the Calgary Stampede is billed as the greatest outdoor show on earth.

Designers and Engravers:

Obv.:	Susanna Blunt, Susan Taylor
Rev.:	Steve Hepburn, Konrad Wachelko

Composition: 99.99% Ag
Silver content: 23.17 g, 0.75 tr oz

Weight:	23.17 g	**Edge:**	Reeded
Diameter:	36.07 mm	**Die Axis:**	↑↑
Thickness:	2.80 mm	**Finish:**	Proof

Case of Issue: Maroon leatherette clam style case, black flocked insert, encapsulated coin, COA, custom coloured sleeve

DATE	DESCRIPTION	RCM ITEM #	QUANTITY SOLD	ISSUE PRICE	FINISH	PR-69	PR-70
2012	100 Years of the Calgary Stampede	119102	9,996	69.95	Proof	65.	—

ONE DOLLAR, THE 100TH GREY CUP, 2012.

The first Grey Cup game took place in 1909, with the University of Toronto defeating the Parkdale Canoe Club. There were 3,807 fans in attendance at the game which generated revenues of $2,616.40 for the Canadian Rugby Union.

Designers and Engravers:

Obv.:	Susanna Blunt, Susan Taylor
Rev.:	Filip Mroz of Bensimon Byrne, Konrad Wachelko

Composition: 99.99% Ag
Silver content: 23.17 g, 0.75 tr oz

Weight:	23.17 g	**Edge:**	Reeded
Diameter:	36.0 mm	**Die Axis:**	↑↑
Thickness:	2.75 mm	**Finish:**	Proof

Case of Issue: Maroon leatherette clam style case, black flocked insert, encapsulated coin, COA, custom box

DATE	DESCRIPTION	RCM ITEM #	QUANTITY SOLD	ISSUE PRICE	FINISH	PR-69	PR-70
2012	The 100th Grey Cup	119651	9,985	69.95	Proof	65.	—

ONE DOLLAR, 100TH ANNIVERSARY OF THE CANADIAN ARCTIC EXPEDITION, 1913-2013.

In 1913, Canadian Prime Minister Sir Robert Borden commissioned an expedition, led by Manitoba-born ethnologist Vilhjalmur Stefansson, to explore and map the western Canadian Arctic. Stefansson and zoologist Rudolph Anderson had travelled through the Far North the previous decade. Stefansson planned to continue his earlier journey, but the government of Canada, recognizing the importance of the new sovereign territory, hosted the Expedition and broadened its mission significantly. A Northern Party led by Stefansson would undertake the mapping exercise while the Southern Party led by Anderson would explore the geology, resources, and native inhabitants of the northern mainland.

The year 2013 saw the first fine silver dollar to be included in a Specimen Set.

| Brilliant Uncirculated | Proof | Proof, Selectively gold plated | Specimen |

Designers:
Obv.: Susanna Blunt
Rev.: Bonnie Ross
Composition: 99.99% Ag
Silver Content: 23.17g, 0.74 tr oz
Weight: 23.17 g
Diameter: 36.07 mm
Finish:
1. Proof
2. Proof, Selectively gold plated

Engravers:
Obv.: Susan Taylor
Rev.: RCM Staff, Konrad Wachelko

Thickness: 2.8 mm
Edge: Reeded
Die Axis: ↑↑
3. Specimen
4. Brilliant Uncirculated

Case of Issue: Maroon leatherette clam style case, black flocked insert, encapsulated coin, COA

DATE	DESCRIPTION	SOURCE	RCM ITEM #	QUANTITY SOLD	ISSUE PRICE	FINISH	SP-68	SP-69	PR-69	PR-70
2013 (1913-)	Canadian Arctic Expedition, Proof	Pr. Single	121842	26,006	59.95	Proof	*	*	45.	—
2013 (1913-)	Canadian Arctic Expedition, Proof, Selectively gold plated	Pr. Set	121827	20,494	229.95	Proof	*	*	80.	—
2013 (1913-)	Canadian Arctic Expedition, Specimen	Sp. Set	127214	9,787	99.95	Specimen	35.	—	*	*
2013 (1913-)	Canadian Arctic Expedition, Brilliant Uncirculated	BU Single	121849	13,325	54.95	BU	35.	—	*	*

ONE DOLLAR, 250TH ANNIVERSARY OF THE END OF THE SEVEN YEARS WAR, 2013.

The Seven Years War (1756-1763) was the world's first global conflict extending far beyond North America to Europe, India and Africa. In North America the war was fought between the English, French, and the First Nations People.

Designers and Engravers:
Obv.: Susanna Blunt, Susan Taylor
Rev.: Tony Bianco, RCM Staff
Composition: 99.99% Ag
Silver content: 23.17 g, 0.74 tr oz
Weight: 23.17 g   **Edge:** Reeded
Diameter: 36.0 mm   **Die Axis:** ↑↑
Thickness: 2.75 mm   **Finish:** Proof
Case of Issue: Maroon leatherette clam style case, black flocked insert, encapsulated coin, COA, custom design box

DATE	DESCRIPTION	RCM ITEM #	QUANTITY SOLD	ISSUE PRICE	FINISH	PR-69	PR-70
2013	250th Anniv. End of the Seven Years War	124755	10,004	69.95	Proof	50.	—

ONE DOLLAR, 60TH ANNIVERSARY OF THE KOREAN ARMISTICE AGREEMENT, 2013.

The reverse design on this coin is a reproduction of the Korean General Service Medal awarded to all troops who participated in the Korean War during 1950-1958.

Designers and Engravers:

Obv.:	Susanna Blunt, Susan Taylor
Rev.:	Edward Carter Preston, Steven Stewart

Composition: 99.99% Ag
Silver content: 23.0 g, 0.74 tr oz

Weight:	23.0 g	**Edge:**	Reeded
Diameter:	36.0 mm	**Die Axis:**	↑↑
Thickness:	2.75 mm	**Finish:**	Proof

Case of Issue: Maroon leatherette clam style case, black flocked insert, encapsulated coin, COA, custom design box

DATE	DESCRIPTION	RCM ITEM #	QUANTITY SOLD	ISSUE PRICE	FINISH	PR-69	PR-70
2013	60th Anniv. Korean Armistice Agreement	124118	6,858	69.95	Proof	65.	—

ONE DOLLAR, 100TH ANNIVERSARY OF THE DECLARATION OF THE FIRST WORLD WAR, 2014.

The First World War began in August 1914 and ended November 1918. Thousands of Canadian men and women took part on the battlefields of Europe.

| | Proof | Proof, Selectively gold plated | Brilliant Uncirculated |

Designers:

Obv.:	Susanna Blunt
Rev.:	Bonnie Ross

Composition: 99.99% Ag
Silver Content: 22.8 g, .73 tr oz
Weight: 22.8 g
Diameter: 36.0 mm
Finish:
1. Proof
2. Proof, Selectively gold plated
3. Brilliant Uncirculated

Engravers:

Obv.:	Susan Taylor
Rev.:	Christie Paquet

Thickness: 2.8 mm
Edge: Reeded
Die Axis: ↑↑

Case of Issue: Maroon leatherette clam style case, black flocked insert, encapsulated coin, COA

DATE	DESCRIPTION	SOURCE	RCM ITEM #	QUANTITY SOLD	ISSUE PRICE	FINISH	SP-68	SP-69	PR-69	PR-70
2014	100th Anniv. Declaration WWI, Proof	Pr. Single	128296	22,721	59.95	Proof	*	*	50.	—
2014	100th Anniv. Declaration WWI, Proof, Selectively gold plated	Prem. Pr. Set	128624	13,416	229.95	Proof	*	*	100.	—
2014	100th Anniv. Declaration WWI, Brilliant Uncirculated	BU Single	128305	9,405	54.95	BU	40.	—	*	*

Note: Coins illustrated smaller than actual size.

ONE DOLLAR, 75TH ANNIVERSARY OF THE DECLARATION OF THE SECOND WORLD WAR, 1939-2014.

This limited edition silver dollar commemorating the declaration of World War Two, depicts the pivotal role women played in the Allied war effort as they build an Avro 683 Lancaster.

Designers and Engravers:

Obv.:	Susanna Blunt, Susan Taylor
Rev.:	Silvia Pecota, RCM Staff
Composition:	99.99% Ag
Silver content:	23.17 g, 0.74 tr oz

Weight:	23.17 g	**Edge:**	Reeded
Diameter:	36.07 mm	**Die Axis:**	↑↑
Thickness:	N/A	**Finish:**	Proof
Case of Issue:	Maroon leatherette clam style case, black flocked insert, encapsulated coin, COA		

DATE	DESCRIPTION	RCM ITEM #	QUANTITY SOLD	ISSUE PRICE	FINISH	PR-69	PR-70
2014 (1939-)	75th Anniv. Declaration Second World War	130549	7,017	69.95	Proof	70.	—

ONE DOLLAR, 50TH ANNIVERSARY OF THE CANADIAN FLAG, 1965-2015.

Celebrating the 50th anniversary of the Canadian flag, the proof, proof coloured, and brilliant uncirculated coins depict the symbolic power that the Canadian flag has come to assume abroad and at home.

Proof	Proof, Coloured Brilliant	Uncirculated

Designers:

Obv.:	Susanna Blunt
Rev.:	John Mantha
Composition:	99.99% Ag
Silver Content:	23.17 g, 0.74 tr oz
Weight:	23.17 g
Diameter:	36.07 mm
Finish:	1. Proof
	2. Proof, Coloured
	3. Brilliant Uncirculated

Engravers:

Obv.:	Susan Taylor
Rev.:	RCM Staff
Thickness:	2.8 mm
Edge:	Reeded
Die Axis:	↑↑

Case of Issue: Maroon leatherette clam style case, black flocked insert, encapsulated coin, COA

DATE	DESCRIPTION	SOURCE	RCM ITEM #	QUANTITY SOLD	ISSUE PRICE	FINISH	SP-68	SP-69	PR-69	PR-70
2015 (1965-)	50th Anniv. of the Canadian Flag, Proof	Pr. Single	133232	19,982	59.95	Proof	*	*	60.	—
2015 (1965-)	50th Anniv. of the Canadian Flag, Proof, Coloured	Prem. Pr.	133233	14,006	229.95	Proof	*	*	110.	—
2015 (1965-)	50th Anniv. of the Canadian Flag, Brilliant Uncirculated	BU Single	133231	10,014	54.95	BU	45.	—	*	*

Note: Coins illustrated smaller than actual size.

ONE DOLLAR, 100TH ANNIVERSARY OF *IN FLANDERS FIELDS*, 2015.

The year 2015 marked the 100th anniversary of the poem *In Flanders Fields*, which was written by Canadian physician Lieutenant Colonel John McCrae amid the horrors of the Second Battle of Ypres in May 1915.

Designers and Engravers:

Obv.:	Susanna Blunt, Susan Taylor
Rev.:	Tony Bianco

Composition: 99.99% Ag, with enamel
Silver content: 23.17 g, 0.74 tr oz

Weight:	23.17 g	**Edge:**	Reeded
Diameter:	36.07 mm	**Thickness:**	N/A
Die Axis:	↑↑	**Finish:**	Proof

Case of Issue: Maroon clamshell with custom beauty box, encapsulated coin, COA

DATE	DESCRIPTION	RCM ITEM #	QUANTITY SOLD	ISSUE PRICE	FINISH	PR-69	PR-70
2015	*In Flanders Fields*	145850	9,998	79.95	Proof	75.	—

RENEWED SILVER DOLLAR SERIES, 2015-2018

ONE DOLLAR, RENEWED SILVER DOLLAR SERIES, 2015-2018.

The Renewed Silver Dollar Series celebrates historic proof dollar designs. **Note:** This series was exclusively sold to the Mint Master's Club Members only.

   (top row)

    (bottom row)

2015 The Voyager	**2016 Library of Parliament**	**2017 Parliament Building**	**2018 The National War Memorial**
Obv.: Percy Metcalf	Obv.: Arnold Machin	Obv.: Humphrey Paget	Obv.:
Rev.: Emanuel Hahn	Rev.: Walter Ott	Rev.: Emanuel Hahn	

Designers:

Obv.:	See illustrations
Rev.	See illustrations

Composition: 99.99% Ag, selective gold plating
Silver content: 62.67 g, 2.0 tr oz
Diameter: 54 mm (2015), 50 mm (2016-2017)
Thickness: N/A
Finish: Proof

Engravers:

Obv.:	See illustrations
Rev.:	See illustrations

Weight: 62.67 g - 62.69 g
Edge: Reeded
Die Axis: ↑↑
Case of Issue: Maroon clamshell with custom beauty box, encapsulated coin, COA

DATE	DESCRIPTION	RCM ITEM #	QUANTITY SOLD	ISSUE PRICE	FINISH	PR-69	PR-70
2015	The Voyageur	147240	2,200	189.95	Proof	800.	—
2016	Library of Parliament	153701	2,037	189.95	Proof	240.	—
2017	Commemorative Royal Visit, Parliament Building	162442	4,000	194.95	Proof	200.	—
2018	The National War Memorial	169458	4,000	194.95	Proof	195.	—

ONE DOLLAR, CELEBRATING CANADIAN ATHLETES, 2016.

Designers and Engravers:

Obv.:	Susanna Blunt, Susan Taylor
Rev.:	Three Degrees Creative Group
Composition:	99.99% Ag
Silver content:	23.17 g, 0.74 tr oz
Weight:	23.17 g
Diameter:	36.07 mm
Thickness:	N/A
Case of Issue:	Maroon clamshell with black beauty box, encapsulated coin, COA

Edge: Reeded
Die Axis: ↑↑
Finish: Proof

DATE	DESCRIPTION	RCM ITEM #	QUANTITY SOLD	ISSUE PRICE	FINISH	PR-69	PR-70
2016	Celebrating Canadian Athletes	154221	5,328	79.95	Proof	70.	—

ONE DOLLAR, 150TH ANNIVERSARY OF THE TRANSLATLANTIC CABLE, 2016.

On July 27, 1866, a new era of global communication began as S.S. *Great Eastern* steamed into Heart's Content, Newfoundland, to complete a link that could relay messages quickly between the Old world and the New.

Proof	Proof, Selectively gold plated	Proof, Coloured

Designers:

Obv.:	Susanna Blunt
Rev.:	Yves Bérubé

Composition: 99.99% Ag
Silver content: 23.17 g, 0.74 tr oz
Weight: 23.17 g
Diameter: 36.07 mm
Thickness: N/A

Engravers:

Obv.:	Susan Taylor
Obv.:	RCM Staff

Edge: Reeded
Die Axis: ↑↑

Finish: **1.** Proof   **2.** Proof, Selectively gold plated   **3.** Brilliant Uncirculated
Case of Issue: Maroon clamshell with black beauty box, encapsulated coin, COA   Note: Coins illustrated smaller than actual size.

DATE	DESCRIPTION	SOURCE	RCM ITEM #	QUANTITY SOLD	ISSUE PRICE	FINISH	SP-68	SP-69	PR-69	PR-70
2016	150th Anniversary, Proof	Pr. Single	149997	9,913	59.95	Proof	60.	—	60.	—
2016	150th Anniversary, Proof, Selectively gold plated	Pr. Set	150180	9,211	—	Proof	110.	—	110.	—
2016	150th Anniversary, Proof, Coloured	Pr. Set	151850	12,312	99.95	Proof	60.	—	*	*

150TH ANNIVERSARY OF CANADIAN CONFEDERATION

ONE DOLLAR, 150TH ANNIVERSARY OF CANADIAN CONFEDERATION, 2017.

Proof   **Proof, Selectively gold plated**

Designers:
    Obv.:   Susanna Blunt
    Rev.:   Rebecca Yanovskaya

Engravers:
    Obv.:   Susan Taylor

Composition: 99.99% Ag
Silver content: 23.17 g, 0.74 tr oz
Weight: 23.17 g
Diameter: 36.07 mm   **Edge:**   Reeded
Thickness: N/A   **Die Axis:**   ↑↑
Finish: 1. Proof   2. Proof, Selectively gold plated
Case of Issue: Maroon clamshell with a standard black beauty box, encapsulated coin, COA

DATE	DESCRIPTION	SOURCE	RCM ITEM #	QUANTITY SOLD	ISSUE PRICE	FINISH	SP-68	SP-69	PR-69	PR-70
2017	150th Anniversary of Canadian Confederation	PR Single	157486	30,000	59.95	Proof	70.	—	60.	—
2017	150th Anniversary of Canadian Confederation, Selectively gold plated	PR Set	157076	8,017	234.95	Proof	130.	—	110.	—

ONE DOLLAR, OUR HOME AND NATIVE LAND, 2017.

Common Obverse

Designers and Engravers:
    Obv.:   Susanna Blunt, Susan Taylor
    Rev.:   Jamie Desrochers
Composition: 99.99% Ag
Silver content: 23.17 g, 0.74 tr oz
Weight: 23.17 g
Diameter: 36.07 mm   **Edge:**   Reeded
Thickness: N/A   **Die Axis:**   ↑↑
Finish: 1. Proof   2. Proof, Selectively gold plated
        3. Proof, Coloured   4. SE Proof, Coloured
Case of Issue: Maroon clamshell with a standard black beauty box, with Canada 150 logo, COA

Proof   **Proof, Selectively gold plated**   **Proof, Coloured**   **Special Editon Proof, Coloured**

DATE	DESCRIPTION	SOURCE	RCM ITEM #	MINTAGE	ISSUE PRICE	FINISH	PR-69	PR-70
2017	Our Home and Native Land	Pr. Single	158838	20,000	59.95	Proof	65.	—
2017	Our Home and Native Land, Selectively gold plated	Pr. Set	158348	20,000	229.95	Proof	130.	—
2017	Our Home and Native Land, Coloured	Pr. Set	159428	25,000	99.95	Proof	65.	—
2017	Our Homeand Native Land, Coloured	SE Pr. Single	162283	10,000	69.95	Proof	65.	—

240TH ANNIVERSARY OF CAPTAIN COOK AT NOOTKA SOUND

ONE DOLLAR, 240TH ANNIVERSARY OF CAPTAIN COOK AT NOOTKA SOUND, 2018.

Commemorating the arrival of Captain James Cook at the summer village of the Nuu-chah-nulth people, at Nootka Sound, which drew more explorers and traders to Canada's western shores.

| Common Obverse | Proof | Proof, Selectively gold plated | Special Edition Proof, Colour |

Designers:
  Obv.:   Susanna Blunt
  Rev.:   John Horton
Composition: 99.99% Ag
Silver content: 23.17 g, 0.74 tr oz
Weight: 23.17 g
Diameter: 36.07 mm
Thickness: N/A
Finish: 1. Proof   2. Proof, Selectively gold plated   3. Brilliant Uncirculated
Case of Issue: Maroon clamshell with a standard black beauty box, encapsulated coin, COA

Engravers:
  Obv.:   Susan Taylor

Edge: Reeded
Die Axis: ↑↑

DATE	DESCRIPTION	SOURCE	RCM ITEM #	MINTAGE	ISSUE PRICE	FINISH	SP-68	SP-69	PR-69	PR-70
2018	240th Anniversary of Captain Cook at Nootka Sound	PR Single	164257	20,000	59.95	Proof	60.	—	60.	—
2018	240th Anniversary of Captain Cook at Nootka Sound, Selectively gold plated	PR Set	164786	15,000	234.95	Proof	120.	—	110.	—
2018	240th Anniversary of Caption Cook at Nootka Sound, colour	SP Proof Set	165601	15,000	104.95	Proof	75.	—	*	*

ONE DOLLAR, 100TH ANNIVERSARY OF THE ARMISTICE OF THE FIRST WORLD WAR, 2018.

November 11, 1918: A date synonymous with peace and remembrance. The 2018 Special Edition Proof Dollar commemorates the centennial of the Armistice of 1918.

Designers and Engravers:
  Obv.:   Susanna Blunt, Susan Taylor
  Rev.:   Jamie Desrochers
Composition: 99.99% Ag, Selective gold plating
Silver content: 23.17 g, 0.74 tr oz
Weight: 23.17 g   **Edge:**   Reeded
Diameter: 36.07 mm   **Die Axis:**   ↑↑
Thickness: N/A   **Finish:**   Proof
Case of Issue: Standard maroon clamshell with black beauty box, COA

DATE	DESCRIPTION	RCM ITEM #	MINTAGE	ISSUE PRICE	FINISH	PR-69	PR-70
2018	100th Anniversary of the Armistice of the First World War	166534	15,000	69.95	Proof	70.	—

ONE DOLLAR, THE VOYAGEUR, 2018.

This history-inspired image was a fixture on Canada's dollar coins between 1935 and 1986, and it has since appeared on several commemorative issues. But the Voyageur has never made its way onto a kilo coin—until now.

Designers and Engravers:

Obv.:	Susanna Blunt, Susan Taylor
Rev.:	Emanuel Hahn

Composition: 99.99% Ag, Selective gold plating
Silver content: 1006 g, 32.35 tr oz

Weight:	1006 g	**Edge:**	Plain
Diameter:	102.1 mm	**Die Axis:**	↑↑
Thickness:	N/A	**Finish:**	Proof

Case of Issue: Premium wooden case with black beauty box, COA

DATE	DESCRIPTION	RCM ITEM #	MINTAGE	ISSUE PRICE	FINISH	PR-69	PR-70
2018	The Voyageur	169996	350	2,329.95	Proof	2,330.	—

ONE DOLLAR, 70TH ANNIVERSARY OF NEWFOUNDLAND JOINING CANADA, 2019.

Just like the 1949 silver dollar, this $1 con's obverse features the effigy of King George VI by T. H. Paget.

Designers and Engravers:

Obv.:	Susanna Blunt, Susan Taylor
Rev.:	Thomas Shingles

Composition: 99.99% Ag
Silver content: 157.6 g, 5.068 tr oz

Weight:	157.6 g	**Edge:**	Reeded
Diameter:	65.25 mm	**Die Axis:**	↑↑
Thickness:	N/A	**Finish:**	Proof

Case of Issue: Black clamshell with black beauty box, COA

DATE	DESCRIPTION	RCM ITEM #	MINTAGE	ISSUE PRICE	FINISH	PR-69	PR-70
2019	70th Anniv. of Newfoundland Joining Canada	170673	1,000	529.95	Proof	530.	—

75TH ANNIVERSARY OF D-DAY

ONE DOLLAR, 75TH ANNIVERSARY OF D-DAY, 2019.

Proof	Proof, Selectively gold plated

Designers:
   Obv.:   Susanna Blunt
   Rev.:   Tony Bianco
Composition: 99.99% Ag
Silver content: 23.17 g, 0.74 tr oz
Weight: 23.17 g
Diameter: 36.07 mm
Thickness: N/A
Finish: **1.** Proof   **2.** Proof, Selectively gold plated

Engravers:
   Obv.:   Susan Taylor

Edge: Reeded
Die Axis: ↑↑

Case of Issue: Proof Set: Genuine leather book-style packaging; Proof Single: Maroon clamshell with a standard black beauty box, encapsulated coin, COA

DATE	DESCRIPTION	RCM ITEM #	SOURCE	MINTAGE	ISSUE PRICE	FINISH	PR-69	PR-70
2019	75th Anniversary of D-Day	170515	PR Single	20,000	59.95	Proof	60.	—
2019	75th Anniversary of D-Day, Selectively gold plated	170630	PR Set	15,000	234.95	Proof	235.	—

CASED NICKEL DOLLAR ISSUES, 1968-1984

At the start of 1968 the Royal Canadian Mint began the conversion from silver to nickel coinage. The first to participate was the Numismatic Department, which was based in Hull, Quebec. The Hull Mint was opened circa 1965 to carry the increased demand for numismatic products which was overwhelming the Ottawa facilities.

The first full set of nickel coinage, the five, ten and fifty cents, and the one dollar coin are found in the Royal Canadian Mint's uncirculated set of 1968.

Nickel coinage is more difficult to strike than silver coinage, and the Mint needed to adjust their process. One of these adjustments was to reduce the size of the fifty-cent and one dollar coins.

The finish on the coin was also a problem. The proof-like finish of silver was not as easily duplicated on nickel. Thus, the quality of finish varied from 1968 to 1976 when new presses for the Olympic Coin Program were put into use. The Mint did produce proof-like nickel coinage for their uncirculated sets, but not consistently, for at times the standard of finish dropped to circulation. It is best to treat the finish for this period as "brilliant uncirculated" not proof-like, for even the experts have difficulty determining the quality of the finish during this time period.

ONE DOLLAR, VOYAGEUR DESIGN, 1968 AND 1969.

A cased 1968 and 1969 nickel dollar was available from the Numismatic Department of the Mint during 1968-69, but the department did not aggressively market this product until 1970. Thus the years 1968 and 1969 saw the development of the "cased dollar" line with the evolution of a "clam" style case.

Designers and Engravers:

Obv.:	Arnold Machin, Patrick Brindley		
Rev.:	Raymond Taylor, Walter Ott		
Composition:	Nickel		
Weight:	15.62 g		
Diameter:	32.13 mm	**Edge:**	Reeded
Thickness:	2.3 mm	**Die Axis:**	↑↑
Finish:	Brilliant Uncirculated		
Case of Issue:	Black leatherette, gold side trim, gilt Royal Canadian Mint Building crest, blue interior, black insert, gilt Coat of Arms of Canada		

DATE	DESCRIPTION	QUANTITY SOLD	ISSUE PRICE	FINISH	MS-65 NC	MS-66 NC	MS-67 NC
1968	Voyageur	N/A	N/A	BU	4.	8.	—
1968	Voyageur, Small Island	N/A	N/A	BU	20.	30.	—
1968	Voyageur, No Island	N/A	N/A	BU	10.	25.	—
1969	Voyageur	N/A	N/A	BU	4.	8.	—

ONE DOLLAR, MANITOBA CENTENNIAL, 1870-1970.

Canada's first commemorative nickel dollar has a special reverse featuring a prairie crocus in recognition of the centenary of Manitoba's entry into Confederation. The finish on the cased dollar is brilliant uncirculated.

Designers and Engravers:

Obv.:	Arnold Machin, Patrick Brindley		
Rev.:	Raymond Taylor, Walter Ott		
Composition:	Nickel		
Weight:	15.62 g		
Diameter:	32.13 mm	**Edge:**	Reeded
Thickness:	2.3 mm	**Die Axis:**	↑↑
Finish:	Brilliant Uncirculated		

Case of Issue: (A) Black leatherette square case, gilt RCM crest, blue insert
(B) Maroon leatherette rectangular case, gold stamped crest of Canada, red interior, black insert
(C) Black leatherette rectangular case, gold stamped Japanese characters, Maple Leaf, Canada, red interior, black insert. Card insert. (Sold at the Canada pavilion in Japan, during 1970.)

DATE	DESCRIPTION	QUANTITY SOLD	ISSUE PRICE	FINISH	MS-65 NC	MS-66 NC	MS-67 NC
1970 (1870-)	Manitoba, Case A	349,120	2.00	BU	4.	8.	—
1970 (1870-)	Manitoba, Case B	Included	N/A	BU	10.	—	—
1970 (1870-)	Manitoba, Case C	Included	N/A	BU	10.	—	—

ONE DOLLAR, BRITISH COLUMBIA CENTENNIAL, 1871-1971.

The nickel dollar for 1971 commemorates the entry in 1871 of British Columbia into Confederation. Its design is based on the arms of the province, with a shield at the bottom and dogwood blossoms at the top. The design of the brilliant uncirculated nickel dollar is identical to that of the circulating issue.

Designers and Engravers:

Obv.:	Arnold Machin, Patrick Brindley
Rev.:	Thomas Shingles
Composition:	Nickel
Weight:	15.62 g
Diameter:	32.13 mm
Thickness:	2.3 mm
Finish:	Brilliant Uncirculated
Case of Issue:	Blue leatherette clam case, Coat of Arms of Canada, blue and black insert

Edge: Reeded
Die Axis: ↑↑

DATE	DESCRIPTION	QUANTITY SOLD	ISSUE PRICE	FINISH	MS-65 NC	MS-66 NC	MS-67 NC
1971 (1871-)	British Columbia Centennial	181,091	2.00	BU	4.	8.	—

ONE DOLLAR, VOYAGEUR DESIGN, 1972.

The cased brilliant uncirculated nickel dollar issued by the numismatic department of the Royal Canadian Mint has the same design as the circulating dollar with the exception of beads instead of denticles.

Designers and Engravers:

Obv.:	Arnold Machin, Patrick Brindley
Rev.:	Emanuel Hahn, Terry Smith
Composition:	Nickel
Weight:	15.62 g
Diameter:	32.13 mm
Thickness:	2.3 mm
Finish:	Brilliant Uncirculated
Case of Issue:	Blue leatherette clam case, Coat of Arms of Canada, blue and black insert

Edge: Reeded
Die Axis: ↑↑

DATE	DESCRIPTION	QUANTITY SOLD	ISSUE PRICE	FINISH	MS-65 NC	MS-66 NC	MS-67 NC
1972	Voyageur	143,392	2.00	BU	4.	8.	—

ONE DOLLAR, PRINCE EDWARD ISLAND CENTENNIAL, 1873-1973.

The 100th anniversary of the entry of Prince Edward Island into Confederation is commemorated with the reverse design depicting the provincial legislature building in Charlottetown.

Designers and Engravers:

Obv.:	Arnold Machin, Patrick Brindley
Rev.:	Terry Manning, Walter Ott
Composition:	Nickel
Weight:	15.62 g
Diameter:	32.13 mm
Thickness:	2.3 mm
Finish:	Brilliant Uncirculated
Case of Issue:	Blue leatherette clam case, Coat of Arms of Canada, blue and black insert

Edge: Reeded
Die Axis: ↑↑

DATE	DESCRIPTION	QUANTITY SOLD	ISSUE PRICE	FINISH	MS-65 NC	MS-66 NC	MS-67 NC
1973 (1873-)	Prince Edward Island Centennial	466,881	2.00	BU	4.	8.	—

ONE DOLLAR, WINNIPEG CENTENNIAL, 1874-1974.

The 100th anniversary of the establishment of Winnipeg, Manitoba, as a city is marked by the reverse of the 1974 dollar. The 1974 cased specimen silver dollar carries the same design, see page 91.

Designers and Engravers:

Obv.:	Arnold Machin, Patrick Brindley
Rev.:	Paul Pederson, Patrick Brindley
Composition:	Nickel
Weight:	15.62 g
Diameter:	32.13 mm **Edge:** Reeded
Thickness:	2.3 mm **Die Axis:** ↑↑
Finish:	Brilliant Uncirculated
Case of Issue:	Blue leatherette clam case, Coat of Arms of Canada, blue and black insert

DATE	DESCRIPTION	QUANTITY SOLD	ISSUE PRICE	FINISH	MS-65 NC	MS-66 NC	MS-67 NC
1974 (1874-)	Winnipeg Centennial, Single Yoke	363,786	2.00	BU	4.	10.	—
1974 (1874-)	Winnipeg Centennial, Double Yoke #1	Included	2.00	BU	750.	—	—
1974 (1874-)	Winnipeg Centennial, Double Yoke #3	Included	2.00	BU	100.	—	—

ONE DOLLAR, VOYAGEUR DESIGN, 1975-1976.

With falling popularity, the cased nickel dollars were discontinued in 1976.

Designers and Engravers:

Obv.:	Arnold Machin, Patrick Brindley
Rev.:	Emanuel Hahn, Terry Smith
Composition:	Nickel
Weight:	15.62 g
Diameter:	32.13 mm **Edge:** Reeded
Thickness:	2.3 mm **Die Axis:** ↑↑
Finish:	Specimen
Case of Issue:	Blue leatherette clam case, Coat of Arms of Canada, blue and black insert

DATE	DESCRIPTION	QUANTITY SOLD	ISSUE PRICE	FINISH	MS-65 NC	MS-66 NC	MS-67 NC
1975	Voyageur, Attached Jewel	88,102	2.50	BU	4.	10.	—
1976	Voyageur	74,209	2.50	BU	4.	10.	—

ONE DOLLAR, CONSTITUTION, 1867-1982

The reverse design of the 1982 nickel dollar commemorates Canada's Constitution. It features a faithful reproduction of the celebrated painting Fathers of Confederation, with the inscription 1867 CONFEDERATION above the painting and CONSTITUTION 1982 beneath.

Designers and Engravers:

Obv.:	Arnold Machin, RCM Staff
Rev.:	Ago Aarand, RCM Staff
Composition:	Nickel
Weight:	15.62 g
Diameter:	32.13 mm **Edge:** Reeded
Thickness:	2.3 mm **Die Axis:** ↑↑
Finish:	Specimen
Case of Issue:	Maroon square case with maple leaf logo, maroon insert, encapsulated coin

DATE	DESCRIPTION	QUANTITY SOLD	ISSUE PRICE	FINISH	SP-68	SP-69
1982 (1867-)	Constitution	107,353	9.75	Specimen	8.	—

ONE DOLLAR, 450TH ANNIVERSARY OF JACQUES CARTIER LANDING, 1534-1984.

The 450th year of Jacques Cartier's landing at Gaspé, Quebec, was honoured on July 24, 1984, by the issuing of a commemorative nickel dollar.

Designers and Engravers:

Obv.:	Arnold Machin, RCM Staff
Rev.:	Hector Greville, Victor Coté
Composition:	Nickel
Weight:	15.62 g
Diameter:	32.13 mm
Thickness:	2.3 mm
Finish:	Proof
Case of Issue:	Green velvet square case, green insert, encapsulated coin

Edge:	Reeded
Die Axis:	↑↑

DATE	DESCRIPTION	QUANTITY SOLD	ISSUE PRICE	FINISH	PR-69	PR-70
1984 (1534-)	450th Anniv. of Jacques Cartier Landing	87,776	9.75	Proof	8.	—

NOTES ON NICKEL AND BRONZE DOLLARS

It is important to remember the nickel dollar series 1968 to 1987 was issued, in most instances, for circulation (business strikes), however, they were also issued as collector items either singly or in sets. This section, pages 116 to 119, lists only the single pliofilm pouched or cased nickel dollars for the period 1968 to 1984.

The term "proof-like" which applied to the silver dollars and sets of the period 1953-1967, was not carried forward to the nickel dollar coinage of 1968-1987. Coins of the period 1968 to 1984 have a brilliant uncirculated finish.

Pricing is based on third party, professionally graded coins. It is difficult for the average collector to determine the niceties between MS-65 (NC), MS-66 (NC) and MS-67 (NC). NC is non-circulating.

MS-65 (NC) pricing is based on the coin still being in its original packaging from the Mint. While MS-66 (NC) and MS-67 (NC) pricing is based on the coin being graded by a reputable third-party grading service.

NICKEL-BRONZE DOLLAR PROOF ISSUES, 1987-1995

ONE DOLLAR, LOON, 1987.

A proof striking of the loon dollar was issued by the numismatic department of the Royal Canadian Mint in 1987 commemorating the introduction of the nickel-bronze dollar.

Designers and Engravers:

Obv.:	Arnold Machin, Patrick Brindley,
Rev.:	R. R. Carmichael, Terry Smith
Composition:	91.5% Ni, 8.5 Bronze
Weight:	7.0 g
11-sided:	26.5 mm
Thickness:	1.9 mm
Case of Issue:	Royal blue velvet square case, blue insert, encapsulated coin

Edge: Plain
Die Axis: ↑↑
Finish: Proof

ONE DOLLAR, 125TH ANNIVERSARY OF CANADA, 1867-1992.

This coin was part of the "125" coin program by the numismatic department of the Royal Canadian Mint. This proof coin is the companion piece to the circulating issue of the same design.

Designers and Engravers:

Obv.:	Dora de Pédery-Hunt
Rev.:	Rita Swanson, Ago Aarand
Composition:	91.5% Ni, 8.5% Bronze
Weight:	7.0 g
11-sided:	26.5 mm
Thickness:	1.9 mm
Case of Issue:	Royal blue velvet square case, blue insert, encapsulated coin

Edge: Plain
Die Axis: ↑↑
Finish: Proof

ONE DOLLAR, REMEMBRANCE, 1994.

The 1994 nickel Loon dollar depicts the War Memorial, built to commemorate the participation of all Canadians in the First World War. The memorial was rededicated in 1982 to include veterans of the Second World War and the Korean War.

Designers and Engravers:

Obv.:	Dora de Pédery-Hunt
Rev.:	Terry Smith, Ago Aarand
Composition:	91.5% Ni, 8.5% Bronze
Weight:	7.0 g
11-sided:	26.5 mm
Thickness:	1.9 mm
Case of Issue:	Royal blue velvet square case, blue insert, encapsulated coin, COA

Edge: Plain
Die Axis: ↑↑
Finish: Proof

ONE DOLLAR, PEACEKEEPING, 1995.

This coin commemorates Canada's role in the United Nations peacekeeping forces. For the circulating issues see Canadian Coins, Volume One.

Designers and Engravers:

Obv.:	Dora de Pédery-Hunt
Rev.:	J.K. Harman, R.G. Henriguez
	C. H. Oberlander, S. Taylor, A. Aarand
Composition:	91.5% Ni, 8.5% Bronze
Weight:	7.0 g
11-sided:	26.5 mm
Thickness:	1.9 mm
Case of Issue:	Royal blue velvet square case, blue insert, encapsulated coin, COA

Edge: Plain
Die Axis: ↑↑
Finish: Proof

DATE	DESCRIPTION	QUANTITY SOLD	ISSUE PRICE	FINISH	PR-68	PR-69
1987	Loon, Nickel-Bronze	178,120	13.50	Proof	8.	—
1992 (1867)	125th Anniversary of Canada	24,227	19.95	Proof	10.	—
1994	Remembrance	54,524	19.95	Proof	10.	—
1995	Peacekeeping	43,293	17.95	Proof	10.	—

NICKEL-BRONZE DOLLAR SPECIMEN ISSUES, THE BIRD SERIES, 1997-2019

ONE DOLLAR, BIRD SERIES, 1997-2019.

First released in 1997 as The Flying Loon to commemorate the 10th anniversary of the one dollar coin, the Bird Series of nickle-bronze dollar specimen issues celebrates the diverse winged wildlife of Canada. Of note are the 2002 15th anniversary of the "Loonie" release, as well as the 2004 Canada Goose dollar paying tribute to Jack Miner, an influential conservationist.

OBVERSES 1997, 2002, 2004-2019

Obverse	Obverse	Obverse	Obverse	Obverse
1997	2002	2004	2004-2006,	2007-2009
Diademed Portrait	Diademed Portrait	Uncrowned Portrait	2010-2019	Uncrowned Portrait
	Double Date	With Date	Uncrowned Portrait	With RCM Logo

REVERSES 1997, 2002, 2004-2019

1997	2002	2004	2004
10th Ann. Loon Dollar	15th Ann. Loon Dollar	Canada Goose	Elusive Loon
Des.: J. Grondin	Des.: Dora de Pédery-Hunt	Des. and Engr.:	Des. and Engr.:
Engr.: S. Beveridge	Engr.: C. Saffioti	Susan Taylor	Christie Paquet

2005	2006	2007	2008	2009
Tufted Puffin	Snowy Owl	Trumpeter Swan	Common Eider	Great Blue Heron
Des. and Engr.:	Des.: G. Loates	Des.: K. Burnett	Des.: M. Dobson	Des.: C. Jordison
Christie Paquet	Engr.: RCM Staff	Engr.: C. Paquet	Engr.: S. Witten	Engr.: J. Osio

2010	2011	2012	2013	2014
Northern Harrier	Great Gray Owl	25th Ann. Loon Dollar	Blue-Winged Teal	Ferruginous Hawk
Des.: A. Nogy	Des.: A. Nogy	Des.: A. Nogy	Des.: G. Loates	Des.: T. Tennant
Engr.: S. Taylor	Engr.: C. Paquet	Engr.: S. Taylor	Engr.: M. Bowen	Engr.: RCM Staff

ONE DOLLAR, BIRD SERIES, 1997-2019 (cont.).

2015	2016	2017	2018	2019
Blue Jay	Tundra Swan	Snow Goose	Burrowing Owl	Pileated Woodpecker
Des.: E. Spera	Des.: G. Scrimshaw	Des.: Derek C. Wicks	Des.: Pierre Girard	Des.: Jean-Charles Daumas
Engr.: RCM Staff	Engr.: RCM Staff	Engr.: RCM Staff	Engr.: RCM Staff	Engr.: RCM Staff

Designers:
- Obv.: 1997, 2002: Dora de Pédery-Hunt
  2004-2019: Susanna Blunt
- Rev.: See reverse illustrations

Composition: 91.5% Ni, 8.5% Bronze
Weight: 7.0 g
11-sided: 26.5 mm
Thickness: 1.9 mm
Case of Issue: See Sets, pages 521

Engravers:
- Obv.: 1997, 2002: Dora de Pédery-Hunt
  2004-2019: Susan Taylor
- Rev.: See reverse illustrations

Edge: Plain
Die Axis: ↑↑
Finish: Specimen

DATE	DESCRIPTION	RCM ITEM #	QUANTITY SOLD	ISSUE PRICE	FINISH	SP-68	SP-69
1997 (1987-)	10th Anniversary of the Loon Dollar	N/A	181,719	N.I.I.	Specimen	25.	—
2002 (1987-)	15th Anniversary of the Loon Dollar	N/A	67,672	N.I.I.	Specimen	25.	—
2004	Canada Goose	N/A	46,493	N.I.I.	Specimen	30.	—
2004	Elusive Loon	N/A	12,550	N.I.I.	Specimen	50.	—
2005	Tufted Puffin	N/A	39,818	N.I.I.	Specimen	45.	—
2006	Snowy Owl	N/A	39,935	N.I.I.	Specimen	45.	—
2007	Trumpeter Swan	6260107	27,056	N.I.I.	Specimen	45.	—
2008	Common Eider	6260108	21,227	N.I.I.	Specimen	40.	—
2009	Great Blue Heron	103608	21,677	N.I.I.	Specimen	45.	—
2010	Northern Harrier	105794	21,111	N.I.I.	Specimen	45.	—
2011	Great Gray Owl	111265	25,665	N.I.I.	Specimen	50.	—
2012	25th Anniversary of the Loon Dollar	116582	34,975	N.I.I.	Specimen	40.	—
2013	Blue-Winged Teal	121282	28,884	N.I.I.	Specimen	45.	—
2014	Ferruginous Hawk	127671	24,381	N.I.I.	Specimen	45.	—
2015	Blue Jay	133241	22,739	N.I.I.	Specimen	45.	—
2016	Tundra Swan	149524	21,565	N.I.I.	Specimen	45.	—
2017	Snow Goose	156169	4,515	N.I.I.	Specimen	45.	—
2018	Burrowing Owl	164602	30,000	N.I.I.	Specimen	40.	—
2019	Pileated Woodpecker	170696	30,000	N.I.I.	Specimen	35.	—

NOTE TO COLLECTORS

When the initials N.I.I. appear in the pricing table it indicates the coin was part of a set issued by the Royal Canadian Mint, and not issued individually. Coin designs that are found only in sets offered by the Royal Canadian Mint are listed individually by denomination, and date in Volume Two.

SP-68 / PR-69   This price is based on the item still being in the original package as sold by the Mint.

SP-69 / PR-70   This price is based on them item being graded by a reputable third-party grading company.

NICKEL-BRONZE DOLLAR PROOF ISSUES, 2002-2012

ONE DOLLAR, CENTRE ICE LOON, 1987-2002.

A "Centre Ice" 22-karat gold-plated loon dollar coin was issued as part of a souvenir album entitled "Going For Gold." It was jointly offered by the Royal Canadian Mint, Canada Post, and Maclean's Magazine to commemorate the Olympic gold medals for hockey won by the Canadian Men's and Women's teams in the Salt Lake City Winter Olympic Games in 2002.

Designers and Engravers:

Obv.:	Dora de Pédery-Hunt		
Rev.:	R. R. Carmichael, Cosme Saffioti		
Composition:	91.5% Ni, 8.5% Bronze, Gold plated		
Weight:	7.0 g	**Edge:**	Plain
11-sided:	26.5 mm	**Die Axis:**	↑↑
Thickness:	1.9 mm	**Finish:**	Proof
Case of Issue:	See Derivatives, page 135		

DATE	DESCRIPTION	QUANTITY SOLD	ISSUE PRICE	FINISH	PR-69	PR-70
2002 (1987-)	Centre Ice Loon, Gold-plated bronze	25,000	N.I.I.	Proof	50.	—

ONE DOLLAR, 100TH ANNIVERSARY OF THE MONTREAL CANADIENS, 1909-2009.

Canada Post and the Royal Canadian Mint offered two different sets in 2009 for the 100th anniversary of the Montreal Canadiens:

1. Montreal Canadiens 100th Anniversary Pack which included a lacquered anniversary dollar and a lenticular souvenir sheet
2. Montreal Canadiens 100th Anniversary Set which included three different dollar coins (lacquered, painted Canadiens crest, and gold plated) plus a lenticular souvenir sheet.

Common Obverse	Lacquered	Painted Crest	Gold plated

Designers:

Obv.:	Susanna Blunt
Rev.:	RCM Staff
Composition:	91.5% Ni, 8.5% Bronze
Weight:	7.0 g
11-sided:	26.5 mm
Finish:	1. Circulation, Lacquered
	2. Circulation, Painted crest
	3. Circulation, Gold plated
Case of Issue:	See Derivatives, page 134

Engravers:

Obv.:	Susan Taylor
Rev.:	Konrad Wachelko
Thickness:	2.0 mm
Die Axis:	↑↑
Edge:	Plain

DATE	DESCRIPTION	SOURCE	QUANTITY SOLD	ISSUE PRICE	FINISH	MS-65 NC	MS-66 NC
2009 (1909-)	Montreal Canadiens, Lacquered	Collector Set / Pack	N/A	N.I.I.	Lacquered	10.	—
2009 (1909-)	Montreal Canadiens, Painted crest	Collector Set	526	N.I.I.	Painted	50.	—
2009 (1909-)	Montreal Canadiens, Gold plated	Collector Set	9,500	N.I.I.	Gold plated	50.	—

ONE DOLLAR, 100TH ANNIVERSARY OF THE CANADIAN NAVY, 1910-2010.

An enlisted seaman of 1910, and a female officer of 2010, in front of *HMCS Halifax* the lead ship in the Navy's current fleet are depicted on this commemorative coin.

Designers and Engravers:

Obv.:	Susanna Blunt, Susan Taylor		
Rev.:	Bonnie Ross, Stan Witten		
Composition:	1. Nickel bronze		
	2. Nickel bronze, Gold plated		
Weight:	7.0 g	**Edge:**	Plain
11-sided:	26.5 mm	**Die Axis:**	↑↑
Thickness:	1.9 mm	**Finish:**	Circulation
Case of Issue:	See Derivatives, page 135, and		
	Special Edition Uncirculated Sets, page 502		

DATE	DESCRIPTION	RCM ITEM #	QUANTITY SOLD	ISSUE PRICE	FINISH	MS-65 NC	MS-66 NC
2010 (1910-)	Canadian Navy Centennial, Gold plated		10,085	19.95	Circulation	15.	—
2010 (1910-)	Canadian Navy Centennial	112237	N/A	N.I.I.	Circulation	5.	—

ONE DOLLAR, 100TH ANNIVERSARY OF THE SASKATCHEWAN ROUGHRIDERS, 1910-2010.

Designers and Engravers:

Obv.:	Susanna Blunt, Susan Taylor		
Rev.:	Saskatchewan Roughriders Football		
	Club, RCM Staff		
Composition:	1. Nickel bronze		
	2. Nickel bronze, Gold plated		
Weight:	7.0 g	**Edge:**	Reeded
11-sided:	26.5 mm	**Die Axis:**	↑↑
Thickness:	1.9 mm	**Finish:**	Circulation
Case of Issue:	See Derivatives, page 135, and		
	Special Edition Uncirculated Sets, page 502		

DATE	DESCRIPTION	RCM ITEM #	QUANTITY SOLD	ISSUE PRICE	FINISH	MS-65 NC	MS-66 NC
2010 (1910-)	Saskatchewan Roughriders, Gold plated	111818	32,676	19.95	Circulation	12.	—
2010 (1910-)	Saskatchewan Roughriders	113179	N/A	N.I.I.	Circulation	5.	—

ONE DOLLAR, 25TH ANNIVERSARY OF THE LOON DOLLAR, 1987-2012.

This coin was issued to celebrate the 25th anniversary of the loon dollar which was first introduced in 1987.

Designers and Engravers:

Obv.:	Susanna Blunt, Susan Taylor		
Rev.:	R. R. Carmichael, RCM Staff		
Composition:	Silver plated bronze plated steel		
Weight:	7.0 g	**Edge:**	Plain
11-sided:	26.5 mm	**Die Axis:**	↑↑
Thickness:	1.9 mm	**Finish:**	Circulation
Case of Issue:	See Derivatives, page 135		

DATE	DESCRIPTION	RCM ITEM #	QUANTITY SOLD	ISSUE PRICE	FINISH	MS-65 NC	MS-66 NC
2012 (1987-)	25th Anniversary of the Loon Dollar (Set)	116542	8,890	24.95	Circulation	25.	—

NOTE TO COLLECTORS

The Canadian Navy and Saskatchewan Roughriders uncirculated nickel-bronze dollars are also found in the 2010 Special Edition Uncirculated Set, see page 502.

LOON STYLE NICKEL DOLLAR ISSUES, 2008-2010

ONE DOLLAR, 2007-2008 CANADIAN NHL HOCKEY SEASON, 2008 (GIFTWARE).

ROAD JERSEY CRESTS

This series of dollars is found in the NHL Teams Sets (see page 508).

| Common obverse | Calgary Flames | Edmonton Oilers | Montreal Canadiens |

| Ottawa Senators | Toronto Maple Leafs | Vancouver Canucks |

HOME JERSEY CRESTS

This series of dollars is found embedded in official NHL hockey pucks which are blister packaged.

| Common obverse | Calgary Flames | Edmonton Oilers | Montreal Canadiens |

Designers and Engravers:

Obv.:	Susanna Blunt, Susan Taylor
Rev.:	RCM Staff
Composition:	Nickel, Decal
Weight:	7.0 g
11-sided:	26.5 mm
Thickness:	1.9 mm
Edge:	Plain
Die Axis:	↑↑
Finish:	Uncirculated

| Ottawa Senators | Toronto Maple Leafs | Vancouver Canucks |

Case of Issue: Road Jersey Crests: Coloured folder
Home Jersey Crests: Embedded in an official NHL puck, blister packaged

DATE	DESCRIPTION	SOURCE	RCM ITEM #	QUANTITY SOLD	ISSUE PRICE	FINISH	MS-65 NC	MS-66 NC
2008	Calgary Flames, Road Jersey	NHL Set	N/A	N/A	N.I.I.	Uncirculated	20.	—
2008	Edmonton Oilers, Road Jersey	NHL Set	N/A	1,584	N.I.I.	Uncirculated	20.	—
2008	Montreal Canadiens, Road Jersey	NHL Set	N/A	2,659	N.I.I.	Uncirculated	35.	—
2008	Ottawa Senators, Road Jersey	NHL Set	N/A	1,633	N.I.I.	Uncirculated	20.	—
2008	Toronto Maple Leafs, Road Jersey	NHL Set	N/A	N/A	N.I.I.	Uncirculated	20.	—
2008	Vancouver Canucks, Road Jersey	NHL Set	N/A	1,302	N.I.I.	Uncirculated	20.	—
2008	Calgary Flames, Home Jersey	NHL Puck	102649	1,304	15.95	Uncirculated	20.	
2008	Edmonton Oilers, Home Jersey	NHL Puck	102650	484	15.95	Uncirculated	20.	
2008	Montreal Canadiens, Home Jersey	NHL Puck	102646	62	15.95	Uncirculated	30.	
2008	Ottawa Senators, Home Jersey	NHL Puck	102647	775	15.95	Uncirculated	20.	
2008	Toronto Maple Leafs, Home Jersey	NHL Puck	102648	2,605	15.95	Uncirculated	20.	
2008	Vancouver Canucks, Home Jersey	NHL Puck	102651	1,160	15.95	Uncirculated	20.	

ONE DOLLAR, 2008-2009 CANADIAN NHL HOCKEY SEASON, 2009 (GIFTWARE).

These nickel coloured dollar coins which feature the team logos are each embedded in a mini puck attached to a key chain. The key chain along with a mini hockey stick and an informative insert card are enclosed in a blister pack.

Common Obverse

Calgary Flames

Edmonton Oilers

Montreal Canadiens

Ottawa Senators

Toronto Maple Leafs

Vancouver Canucks

Designers:		Engravers:	
Obv.:	Susanna Blunt	Obv.:	Susan Taylor
Rev.:	RCM Staff	Rev.:	RCM Staff
Composition:	Nickel, Decal		
Weight:	6.50 g	**Edge:**	Plain
11-sided:	26.5 mm	**Die Axis:**	↑↑
Thickness:	1.7 mm	**Finish:**	Uncirculated
Case of Issue:	Blister packaged, See Derivatives page 135		

DATE	DESCRIPTION	SOURCE	RCM ITEM #	QUANTITY SOLD	ISSUE PRICE	FINISH	MS-65 NC	MS-66 NC
2009	Calgary Flames, Home Jersey	Mini Puck	102661	73	24.95	Uncirculated	25.	—
2009	Edmonton Oilers, Home Jersey	Mini Puck	102662	49	24.95	Uncirculated	25.	—
2009	Montreal Canadiens, Home Jersey	Mini Puck	102658	326	24.95	Uncirculated	30.	—
2009	Ottawa Senators, Home Jersey	Mini Puck	102659	95	24.95	Uncirculated	25.	—
2009	Toronto Maple Leafs, Home Jersey	Mini Puck	120660	199	24.95	Uncirculated	25.	—
2009	Vancouver Canucks, Home Jersey	Mini Puck	102663	101	24.95	Uncirculated	25.	—

Note: Mintage numbers are from the 2009 Royal Canadian Mint Annual Report. The 2008 and 2010 Annual Reports do not carry mintage numbers for these coins.

ONE DOLLAR, 2008-2009 CANADIAN NHL HOCKEY SEASON, 2009 (GIFTWARE) [cont.].

Road hockey jerseys folded in the shape of a heart are the central device on these nickel dollars. The coloured dollars are included in NHL Team Uncirculated Sets for the 2008-2009 season, see page 508.

Common Obverse

Calgary Flames

Edmonton Oilers

Montreal Canadiens

Ottawa Senators

Toronto Maple Leafs

Vancouver Canucks

Designers:
- Obv.:   Susanna Blunt
- Rev.:   RCM Staff

Composition: Nickel, Decal
Weight: 7.0 g
11-sided: 26.5 mm
Thickness: 1.9 mm
Case of Issue: Blister packaged

Engravers:
- Obv.:   Susan Taylor
- Rev.:   RCM Staff

Edge: Plain
Die Axis: ↑↑
Finish: Uncirculated

DATE	DESCRIPTION	SOURCE	RCM ITEM #	QUANTITY SOLD	ISSUE PRICE	FINISH	MS-65 NC	MS-66 NC
2009	Calgary Flames, Road Jersey	NHL Sets	102534	382	24.95	Uncirculated	25.	—
2009	Edmonton Oilers, Road Jersey	NHL Sets	102535	472	24.95	Uncirculated	25.	—
2009	Montreal Canadiens, Road Jersey	NHL Sets	102531	4,857	24.95	Uncirculated	35.	—
2009	Ottawa Senators, Road Jersey	NHL Sets	102532	387	24.95	Uncirculated	25.	—
2009	Toronto Maple Leafs, Road Jersey	NHL Sets	102533	1,328	24.95	Uncirculated	25.	—
2009	Vancouver Canucks, Road Jersey	NHL Sets	102536	794	24.95	Uncirculated	25.	—

ONE DOLLAR, VANCOUVER 2010 LUCKY LOONIE, 2010.

This painted nickel dollar bearing the official emblem of the Vancouver 2010 Olympic Winter Games was used extensively in many giftware products (see Derivatives, page 135). An identical variety in sterling silver, and with a proof finish, was issued as a Lucky Loonie, see page 129-130.

Designers and Engravers:
- Obv.:   Susanna Blunt, Susan Taylor
- Rev.:   José Osio

Composition: Nickel, Painted
Weight: 6.4 g
11-sided: 26.5 mm   **Edge:**   Plain
Thickness: 1.9 mm   **Die Axis:**   ↑↑
Finish: Circulation
Case of Issue: See Derivatives, page 135

DATE	DESCRIPTION	RCM ITEM #	QUANTITY SOLD	ISSUE PRICE	FINISH	MS-65 NC	MS-66 NC
2010	Inukshuk, Vancouver 2010 Lucky Loonie, Painted	6261710	N/A	21.95	Uncirculated	25.	—

LOON STYLE STERLING and FINE SILVER DOLLAR PROOF ISSUES, 2004-2019

ONE DOLLAR, STERLING SILVER AND FINE SILVER ISSUES, 2004-2019.

Issued in a proof finish, these uncirculated one-dollar coins commemorate the Olympics, occasions, and various historical and numismatic anniversaries.

Obverse P
2013-2016
"Plated"

OBVERSES 2004-2019

Obverse 2004 and 2006	Obverse 2006-2008	Obverse 2010	Obverse 2013-2016	Obverse 2017-2019

REVERSES 2004-2018

2004 Lucky Loonie Des.: R. R. Carmichael Engr.: RCM Staff	2006 Snowflake Des. and Engr.: Marcos Hallam	2006 Loon Settling Lucky Loonie Des.: RCM Staff Engr.: Cecily Mok	2006 Lullaby Loonie Des. and Engr.: Susan Taylor	2007 Baby Rattle Des.: RCM Staff Engr.: Cecily Mok

2007 "ABC" Building Blocks Des. and Engr.: Susan Taylor	2007-2008 Sterling Silver Loon Des.: R. R. Carmichael Engr.: Terry Smith	2008 Olympic Loon Dance Des. and Engr.: RCM Staff	2010 Anticipating The Game Des. and Engr.: José Osio	2012 (1987-) Silver, Gold Plated Loon Des.: R. R. Carmichael Engr.: RCM Staff

2012 25th Anniv. of Loonie Des.: R. R. Carmichael Engr.: RCM Staff	2012 25th Anniversary Lucky Loonie Des.: Emily Damstra Engr.: RCM Staff	2013-2019 Silver, Gold Plated Loon Des.: R. R. Carmichael Engr.: RCM Staff	2014 Lucky Loonie Des.: Emily Damstra Engr.: RCM Staff	2016 Lucky Loonie Des.: Derek Wicks Engr.: RCM Staff	2017 Connecting a Nation Des.: Wesley Klassen Engr.: RCM Staff

ONE DOLLAR, STERLING SILVER AND FINE SILVER ISSUES, 2004-2019 (continued).

Desigers		Engravers:	
Obv.:	Susanna Blunt	Obv.:	Susan Taylor
Rev.:	See reverse illustrations	Rev.:	See reverse illustrations
Composition:	**2004-2010**		**2012-2019**
	92.5% Ag, 7.5% Cu, Painted		99.99% Ag
Silver content:	6.475 g, 0.208 tr oz		7.0, 0.225 tr oz to 8.1 g, .26 tr oz
Weight:	7.0 g		7.0 to 8.1 g
11-sided:	26.5 mm		26.5 mm
Thickness:	1.7 to 1.9 mm		1.8 to 1.9
Edge:	Plain		Plain
Die Axis:	↑↑		↑↑
Finish:	Proof		Proof

Case of Issue: Proof singles: Maroon leatherette clam style case, black flocked insert, encapsulated coin, COA
　　　　　　　 Proof single:　 2010 Black leatherette clam style case, black flocked insert, encapsulated coin, COA Olympic themed sleeve

DATE	DESCRIPTION	SOURCE	RCM ITEM #	QUANTITY SOLD	ISSUE PRICE	FINISH	MS-65 NC	MS-66 NC
2004	"Lucky Loonie", Painted	Proof. Single	N/A	19,994	39.95	Proof	40.	—
2006	Snowflake, Painted	Holiday Set, Blue folder	N/A	34,014	34.95	Proof	50.	—
2006	Loon Settling, Lucky Loonie, Painted	Pr. Single	N/A	19.973	39.95	Proof	35.	—
2006	Lullaby Loonie, Sterling silver	Folder and CD 1	N/A	8,225	29.95	Proof	125.	—
2006	Lullaby Loonie, Sterling silver	Keepsake Box Included	N/A		34.95	Proof	180.	—
2006	Lullaby Loonie, Sterling silver	CD and Picture Frame	N/A	Included	34.95	Proof	140.	—
2006	Lullaby Loonie, Sterling silver	Premium Baby Gift Set	N/A	Included	N.I.I.	Proof	180.	—
2007	Baby Rattle, Silver	Folder and CD	624447	3,207	34.95	Proof	70.	—
2007	Baby Rattle, Gold plated	Premium Baby Gift Set	6260017	1,911	N.I.I	Proof	200.	—
2007	"ABC" Building Blocks	Keepsake Box	624477	3,229	34.95	Proof	400.	—
2007	Sterling Silver Loon	Premium Wedding Gift Set	6260027	849	N.I.I.	Proof	200.	—
2008	Sterling Silver Loon	Premium Wedding Gift Set	6260808	N/A	N.I.I.	Proof	50.	—
2008	Sterling Silver Loon	Premium Baby Gift Set	100614	N/A	N.I.I.	Proof	50.	—
2008	Sterling Silver Loon	Keepsake Box	N/A	N/A	N.I.I.	Proof	75.	—
2008	Sterling Silver Loon	CD & Picture Frame Holder	N/A	N/A	N.I.I.	Proof	50.	—
2008	Olympic Loon Dance, Painted	Proof. Single	6249608	52,987	49.95	Proof	40.	—
2010	Anticipating the Games, Painted	Proof. Single	6249610	13,285	54.95	Proof	50.	—
2012	Fine Silver, Gold Plated Premium	Proof Set	N/A	19,789	N.I.I.	Proof	60.	—
2012	25th Anniv. Loonie	Proof. Single	119085	15,004	34.95	Proof	35.	—
2012	25th Anniv. Lucky Loonie, Painted	Proof. Single	119096	19,982	39.95	Proof	40.	—
2013	Fine Silver, Gold Plated Premium	Proof Set	N/A	20,182	N.I.I.	Proof	35.	—
2014	Fine Silver, Gold Plated Premium	Proof Set	N/A	13,416	N.I.I.	Proof	35.	—
2014	Olympic Lucky Loonie, Painted	Proof. Single	132740	14,449	39.95	Proof	40.	—
2015	Fine Silver, Gold Plated Premium	Proof Set	N/A	20,000	N.I.I.	Proof	35.	—
2016	Olympic Lucky Loonie	Proof Single	152093	13,690	39.95	Proof	40.	—
2016	Fine Silver, Gold Plated Premium	Proof Set	N/A	20,000	N.I.I.	Proof	35.	—
2017	Fine Silver, Gold Plated Premium	Premium Proof Set	N/A	20,000	N.I.I.	Proof	40.	—
2017	Connecting a Nation, Gold Plated	Premium Proof Set	157731	20,000	N.I.I.	Proof	50.	—
2017	Connecting a Nation	Proof Set	159428	25,000	N.I.I.	Proof	15.	—
2018	Fine Silver, Gold Plated Premium	Proof Set	N/A	20,000	N.I.I.	Proof	35.	—
2019	Fine Silver, Gold Plated Premium	Proof Set	N/A	15,000	N.I.I.	Proof	35.	—
2019		Proof Set	N/A	15,000	N.I.I.	Proof	20.	—

BIG COIN SERIES

ONE DOLLAR, BIG COIN SET, 2015-2019.

The Big Coin Series started in 2015, features Robert Carmichael's iconic loon design on the 2015, 2016, 2018 and 2019 coins, first used in 1987, with Alex Colville's 1967 design for the 2017 coin. The coins illustrated are smaller than actual size. For other coins in the set, see pages 7, 12, 17, 57, 87, 131 and 145.

| 2015 | 2016 | 2017 |

| 2018 | 2019 |

Designers and Engravers:
Obv.: Susanna Blunt, Susan Taylor
Rev.: Robert-Ralph Carmichael, RCM Staff
Alex Colville
Emanuel Hahn

Composition:
2015: 99.99% Ag, Selectively gold plated
2016: 99.99% Ag, Selectively coloured on reverse
2017: 99.99% Ag, Selectively gold plated
2018: 99.95% Ag, Selectively rose gold-plated
2019: 99.99% Ag, Reverse gold plating

Silver content: 157.58 g, 5.07 tr oz
Weight: 157.6 g
Diameter: 65.25 mm
Thickness: N/A
Case of Issue: Maroon clam style case, black flocked insert, encapsulated coin, COA, custom box

Edge: Reeded
Die Axis: ↑↑
Finish: Proof

DATE	DESCRIPTION	SOURCE	RCM ITEM #	QUANTITY SOLD	ISSUE PRICE	FINISH	PR-69	PR-70
2015	$1 Big Coin	Pr. Single	132891	1,500	549.95	Proof	700.	—
2016	$1 Big Coin	Pr. Single	150828	1,500	519.95	Proof	600.	—
2017	$1 Big Coin	Pr. Single	156111	2,111	549.95	Proof	600.	—
2018	$1 Big Coin	Pr. Single	163694	1,500	559.95	Proof	600.	—
2019	$1 Big Coin	Pr. Single	169626	1,250	569.95	Proof	570.	—

THREE-PLY BRASS-PLATED STEEL DOLLAR ISSUES, 2014-2019

ONE DOLLAR, LOON, OCCASIONS SETS, 2014-2019.

These one dollar coins are from the Occasions and Holiday Gift Sets. See pages 509-515.

Designers:		Engravers:	
Obv.:	Susanna Blunt	Obv.:	Susan Taylor
Rev.:	See reverse illustrations	Rev.:	RCM Staff
Composition:	3-ply brass plated steel	Thickness:	1.9 mm
Weight:	6.27 g	Edge:	Plain
11-sided:	26.5 mm	Die Axis:	↑↑
Finish:	Uncirculated	Case of Issue:	Coloured folder

Common Obverse
2014-2018

Born in 2014
Stork
Des.: Steven Stewart

Happy Birthday 2014
Gifts and Balloons
Des.: Matt Bowen

O Canada 2014
Maple Leaf
Des.: RCM Staff

Married in 2014
Two Turtle Doves
Des.: RCM Staff

2014 Holiday Gift Set
Reindeer
Des.: RCM Staff

Born in 2015
Teddy Bear
Des.: RCM Staff

Happy Birthday 2015
Three Balloons
Des.: RCM Staff

O Canada 2015
Large Maple Leaf
Des.: Ali Giroux

Married in 2015
Two Swans
Des.: RCM Staff

2015 Holiday Gift Set
Snowflake
Des.: RCM Staff

Married in 2016
Wedding Bells
Des.: Joel Kimmel

O Canada 2016
Large Maple Leaf
Des.: Joel Kimmel

Born in 2016
Building Blocks
Des.: Joel Kimmel

Happy Birthday 2016
Cupcake, Party Hat, Present
Des.: Joel Kimmel

2016 Holiday Gift Set
Holly and Pine Cone
Des.: Joel Kimmel

Married in 2017
Hearts, Wedding Rings
Des.: RCM Staff

O Canada 2017
Large Maple Leaf
Des.: RCM Staff

Born in 2017
Rocking Horse
Des.: RCM Staff

Happy Birthday 2017
Birthday Presents
Des.: RCM Staff

ONE DOLLAR, LOON, OCCASIONS SETS, 2014-2019 (cont.).

2017 Holiday Gift Set
Ornaments and Holly
Des.: Joel Kimmel

Married in 2018
Doves, Wedding Rings
Des.: RCM Staff

O Canada 2018
Two Large Maple Leaves
& Keys
Des.: RCM Staff

Born in 2018
Crib & Teddy Bears
Des.: RCM Staff

Happy Birthday 2018
Birthday Cake
Des.: RCM Staff

2018 Holiday Gift Set
Holly and Candy Canes
Des.: RCM Staff

Married in 2019
Wedding Cake
Des.: RCM Staff

O Canada 2019
Three Large Maple Leaves
Des.: RCM Staff

Born in 2019
Baby Shoes
Des.: RCM Staff

Happy Birthday 2019
Party Hat & Balloons
Des.: RCM Staff

DATE	DESCRIPTION	RCM ITEM #	QUANTITY SOLD	ISSUE PRICE	FINISH	MS-65
2014	Born in 2014, Stork	128286	54,122	19.95	Uncirculated	20.
2014	Happy Birthday 2014, Gifts and Balloon	128280	44,539	19.95	Uncirculated	15.
2014	O Canada 2014, Maple Leaf	128260	32,289	19.95	Uncirculated	15.
2014	Married in 2014, Two Turtle Doves	128267	35,742	19.95	Uncirculated	15.
2014	Holiday Gift 2014 Set, Reindeer	128274	31,951	19.95	Uncirculated	15.
2015	Born in 2015, Teddy Bear	133223	42,074	19.95	Uncirculated	20.
2015	Happy Birthday 2015,Three Balloons	133220	19,280	19.95	Uncirculated	15.
2015	O Canada 2015, Large Maple Leaf	133222	23,705	19.95	Uncirculated	15.
2015	Married in 2015, Two Swans	133221	18,427	19.95	Uncirculated	15.
2015	Holiday Gift Set 2015, Snowflake	141476	32,994	19.95	Uncirculated	15.
2016	Married in 2016, Wedding Bells	148987	23,788	19.95	Uncirculated	15.
2016	O Canada 2016, Large Maple Leaf	148977	40,169	19.95	Uncirculated	15.
2016	Born in 2016, Building Blocks	148982	47,733	19.95	Uncirculated	15.
2016	Happy Birthday 2016, Cupcake, Party Hat, Present	148972	25,648	19.95	Uncirculated	15.
2016	Holiday Gift Set 2016, Holly and Pine Cone	149270	23,696	19.95	Uncirculated	15.
2017	Married in 2017, Rose, Hearts, Wedding Rings	153968	14,145	21.95	Uncirculated	15.
2017	O Canada 2017, Large Maple Leaf	153969	20,652	21.95	Uncirculated	15.
2017	Born in 2017, Rocking Horse	153970	20,189	21.95	Uncirculated	15.
2017	Happy Birthday 2017, Birthday Presents	153967	14,149	21.95	Uncirculated	15.
2017	Holiday Gift Set 2017, Ornaments and Holly	153971	WSL	21.95	Uncirculated	17.
2018	Married in 2018, Doves, Wedding Rings	164004	WSL	21.95	Uncirculated	17.
2018	O Canada 2018, Two Large Maple Leaves, Maple Key	164007	WSL	21.95	Uncirculated	17.
2018	Born in 2018, Crib & Teddy Bears	164003	WSL	21.95	Uncirculated	17.
2018	Happy Birthday 2018, Birthday Cake	164006	WSL	21.95	Uncirculated	17.
2018	Holiday Gift Set 2018, Holly & Candy Canes	164005	WSL	21.95	Uncirculated	17.
2019	Married in 2019, Wedding Cake	170928	WSL	21.95	Uncirculated	17.
2019	O Canada 2019, Three Large Maple Leaves	171469	WSL	21.95	Uncirculated	17.
2019	Born in 2019, Baby Shoes	170583	WSL	21.95	Uncirculated	17.
2019	Happy Birthday 2019, Party Hat & Balloons	170906	WSL	21.95	Uncirculated	17.

ONE DOLLAR, ELIZABETH II PROOF, 2014.

This coin is from the 2014 Standard Proof Set.

Designers and Engravers:

Obv.:	Susanna Blunt, Susan Taylor
Rev.:	RCM Staff
Composition:	3-ply brass plated steel
Weight:	6.27
11-sided:	26.5 mm
Thickness:	1.9 mm
Finish:	Proof
Case of Issue:	See Proof Sets, page 526

Edge: Plain
Die Axis: ↑↑

DATE	DESCRIPTION	RCM ITEM #	QUANTITY SOLD	ISSUE PRICE	FINISH	PR-69	PR-70
2014	Elizabeth II Proof Coin	N/A	11,251	N.I.I.	Proof	15.	—

ONE DOLLAR, 30TH ANNIVERSARY OF THE LOONIE, 1987-2017.

A special edition of the looinie is paired with the Voyageur design that was intended to appear on the one-dollar coin. It's a unique opportunity to view what is, next to what could have been – the coin that never was!

Common Obverse

Loon
Designer: Robert-Ralph Carmichael

Voyageur
Designer: Emanuel Hahn

Designers:

Obv.:	Susanna Blunt
Rev.:	See reverse illustrations
Composition:	99.99% Ag
Weight:	7.89 g
Diameter	26.5 mm
Finish:	Proof

Engravers:

Obv.:	Susan Taylor
Thickness:	N/A
Die Axis:	↑↑
Edge:	Plain
Case of Issue:	Maroon clamshell with a black beauty box, COA

DATE	DESCRIPTION	RCM ITEM #	MINTAGE	ISSUE PRICE	FINISH	PR-69	PR-70
2017 (1987-)	30th Anniversary of the Loonie 2-coin set	160374	10,000	79.95	Proof	100.	—

ONE DOLLAR DERIVATIVES

DATE	DESCRIPTION	QUANTITY SOLD	ISSUE PRICE	ISSUER	FINISH	MARKET PRICE
1993	**Silver Dollar, 100th Anniversary of the Stanley Cup**, 43¢ Stanley Cup Commemorative Stamp	N/A	28.95	RCM, CP	MS-65	35.
1997	**Silver Dollar, Canada/Russia Hockey**; Two 45¢ mint stamps; $5 phone card; Multicoloured folder	N/A	29.95	RCM, CP	MS-65	45.
1997	**Silver Dollar, Canada/Russia Hockey**; Sterling silver pin	N/A	29.95	RCM	MS-65	30.
1997	**Silver Dollar, Canada/Russia Hockey**; Print	N/A	24.95	RCM	MS-65	35.
1997	**Silver Dollar, Canada/Russia Hockey**; Phone card/stamp set	N/A	N/A	RCM	MS-65	35.
1998	**Loon Dollar**; Mint and cancelled one dollar stamps; Blue presentation case	N/A	17.99	RCM, CP	MS-65	10.
1998	**Silver Dollar, 125th Anniv. R.C.M.P.**; Pin	N/A	29.95	RCM	MS-65	30.
1999	**Silver Dollar, 225th Anniv. Juan Perez**; Journal Gift Set; Multicoloured folder	N/A	N/A	RCM, CP	MS-65	40.
2000	**Loon Dollar**, Mint and cancelled one dollar stamps; Blue presentation case	N/A	17.99	RCM, CP	MS-65	10.
2000	**Loon Dollar**, Encapsulated in a credit card	N/A	N/A	RCM	MS-65	6.
2001	**Loon Dollar**, Encapsulated in a credit card	N/A	N/A	RCM	MS-65	6.
2001	**Loon /Sacagawea Dollars**, Folder	N/A	N/A	RCM, USM	MS-65	10.
2002	**Centre Ice Loon**, 22kt gold-plated bronze; block of four 48¢ stamps, Two Olympic Edition Macleans' magazines (one English, one French); "Going For Gold" Souvenir album, COA	25,000	54.95	RCM, CP, MM	PR-67	50.
2004	**Silver Dollar, 2004 French Settlement with privy mark**; 2004 silver ¼ Euro; Canada 49¢ stamps, mint/cancelled; France .90 Euro stamps, mint/cancelled; Wooden presentation case, blue insert, encapsulated coins, COA	8,315	99.95	RCM, CP	MS-65	90.
2004	**Elusive Loon with Privy Mark**, Mint and cancelled one dollar stamps; Wooden presentation case	12,550	25.22	RCM, CP	PR-67	50.
2005	**Silver Dollar, 40th Anniversary of Canada's National Flag**, CD-Rom; Presentation folder	N/A	34.95	RCM	MS-65	35.
2006	**Lucky Loonie Bookmark** "Celebrate the Legend"	10,095	N/A	RCM	MS-65	15.
2008	**Nickel Bronze Lucky Loonie** embedded in Lucite	N/A	N/A	RCM	MS-65	15.
2009	**Montreal Canadiens 100th Anniversary Pack**, 100th anniv. dollar coin and a lenticular souvenir sheet	15,473	19.95	RCM	MS-65	30.
2009	**Montreal Canadiens 100th Anniversary Collector Set**, three one dollar coins (lacquered, coloured crest, gold plated),a sheet of three stamps, a lenticular souvenir sheet, 15 named retired jersey plaquettes, souvenir booklet	526	149.95	RCM	MS-65	150.
2009	**NHL Canadian Team Crest Mini-Puck Mini-Stick Key Rings**, Colourised NHL team coin embedded in a mini puck key chain, 5" mini hockey stick	N/A	24.95	RCM	MS-65	40.
2010	**Vancouver 2010 Colourised Nickel Bronze Lucky Loonie**, encapsulated and embedded in NHL puck; Blister packaged	30,396	19.95	RCM	MS-65	30.
2010	**Sport Bag Tag**, colourised Vancouver 2010 Lucky Loonie dollar and lapel pin, green "See In Tin" container.	N/A	14.95	RCM	MS-65	30.
2010	**Lanyard**, colourised Vancouver 2010 Lucky Loonie dollar	N/A	14.95	RCM	MS-65	35.
2010	Hockey Player Lapel Pin Set, colourised 2010 Lucky Loonie dollar and six "hockey player" lapel pins.	N/A	N/A	RCM	MS-65	75.
2010	**100th Anniversary Canadian Navy Coin and Stamp Set**, Gold plated nickel-bronze dollar; souvenir stamp sheet; 40-page booklet; square aluminum tin	20,000	39.95	RCM, CP	MS-65	20.
2010	**100th Anniversary Saskatchewan Roughriders**, Gold plated nickel-bronze dollar; pop-up helmet packaging	N/A	19.95	RCM	MS-65	25.
2012	**25th Anniversary of the Loonie Coin Card**, "Build Your Own" paper toy, Mini-book, Coin card	N/A	24.95	RCM	MS-65	25.
2012	**CFL Ultimate Collector Set**, Grey Cup circulation loon style dollar, a special pane of nine commemorative stamps, a souvenir sheet featuring the eight CFL team logos, 100th Grey Cup 1 oz pure silver wafer, a replica Grey Cup, ten silver-edged collectable pins, souvenir booklet	8,000	199.95	RCM, CP	MS-65	125.

Note: CP = Canada Post; MM = Maclean's Magazine; RCM = Royal Canadian Mint; USM = United States Mint

TWO DOLLARS

The first Canadian two dollar coin was issued in 1996 to replace the two dollar bank note which was then withdrawn from circulation. To mark this event the Numismatic Department of the Royal Canadian Mint issued four different planchet varieties, in two different finishes.

TWO DOLLARS, POLAR BEAR, 1996.

The 1996 two dollar Piedfort was not issued singly, but as part of a set. See the Two Dollar Derivatives, page 145.

Obverse: Nickel / Bronze	Reverse: Nickel / Bronze	Obverse: Gold / Gold	Reverse: Gold / Gold

Designers:

		Engravers:	
Obv.:	Dora de Pédery-Hunt	Obv.:	Dora de Pédery-Hunt
Rev.:	Brent Townsend	Rev.:	Ago Aarand

Composition:	**Nickel Ring**	**Silver Ring**	**White Gold Ring**
	99.0% Ni	92.5% Ag	17.2% Au
	07.5% Cu	77.6% Ag,	5.2% Cu
	Bronze Core	**Silver Gilt Core**	**Yellow Gold Core**
	92.0 % Cu	92.5% Ag	91.7% Au
	6.0% Al, 2.0% Ni	07.5% Cu	04.1% Ag, 4.2% Cu

		Standard	Standard	Piedford	Standard
Weight (g):		Ring 4.84	Ring 5.86	Ring 11.72	Ring 6.31
		Core 2.46	Core 2.97	Core 5.94	Core 5.09
		Total 7.3	Total 8.83	Total 17.66	Total 11.4
Content:	Gold	—	—	—	0.185 tr oz
	Silver	—	0.263 tr oz	0.525 tr oz	0.164 tr oz
Diameter (mm):		Ring 28.0	Ring 28.1	Ring 28.1	Ring 28.0
		Core 16.8	Core 16.8	Core 16.8	Core 16.8
Thickness (mm):		1.8	1.9	3.6	1.8
Edge:		Interrupted	Interrupted	Interrupted	Interrupted
		serrations	serrations	serrations	serrations
Die Axis:		↑↑	↑↑	↑↑	↑↑
Finish:		Specimen, Proof	Proof	Proof	Proof

Case of Issue: Nickel / Bronze, Specimen: Blue presentation folder
Nickel / Bronze, Proof: Black leatherette case, blue insert, encapsulated coin, COA
Silver / Gilt, Proof: Black suede case, blue insert, encapsulated coin, COA
Gold / Gold, Proof: Blue suede case, blue insert, encapsulated coin, COA

DATE	DESCRIPTION	QUANTITY SOLD	ISSUE PRICE	FINISH	SP-67	SP-68	PR-69	PR-70
1996	Nickel / Bronze, Blue folder	74,669	10.95	Specimen	6.	—	10.	*
1996	Nickel / Bronze, Black leatherette case	66,843	24.95	Proof	—	—	12.	—
1996	Silver / Gilt, Black suede case	N/A	N/A	Proof	—	—	20.	—
1996	Silver / Gilt, Piedfort, See Derivatives	11,526	N.I.I.	Proof	—	—	90.	—
1996	Gold / Gold, Blue case	5,000	299.95	Proof	—	—	375.	—

NOTE ON TWO DOLLAR ISSUES

1.   The blue presentation folder was printed "uncirculated" but the $2 coin has a specimen finish.
2.   Piedfort is a term used to describe a double thickness or essaie coin, usually struck for approval, see Derivatives page 145.

TWO DOLLARS, STERLING SILVER PROOF COINS, 1997-2011.

In 1997 the two-dollar coin was added to the proof set. The standard nickel/bronze composition was not used, instead planchets were made from sterling silver with a gold-plated core.

| Obverse 1997-2003 | Obverse 2004-2006 Without Mint Logo | Obverse 2007-2011 With Mint Logo | Reverse 1997-2011 |

Designers:
Obv.:   1997-2003: Dora de Pédery-Hunt
        2004-2011: Susanna Blunt
Rev.:   1997-2011: Brent Townsend
Composition: 92.5% Ag, 7.5% Cu
Silver content: 8.17 g, 0.263 tr oz
Weight: 8.83 g
Diameter: 28.1 mm
Thickness: 1.9 mm

Engravers:
Obv.:   1997-2003: Dora de Pédery-Hunt
        2004-2011: Susan Taylor
Rev.:   1997-2011: Ago Aarand

Edge: Interrupted serrations
Die Axis: ↑↑
Finish: Proof
Case of Issue: See Proof Sets, page 524-525

DATE	DESCRIPTION	QUANTITY SOLD	ISSUE PRICE	FINISH	PR-69	PR-70
1997	Diademed Portrait / Polar Bear; Sterling Silver	113,647	N.I.I.	Proof	20.	—
1998		93,632	N.I.I.	Proof	20.	—
1999		95,113	N.I.I.	Proof	20.	—
2000		90,921	N.I.I.	Proof	20.	—
2001		74,194	N.I.I.	Proof	20.	—
2002		65,315	N.I.I.	Proof	20.	—
2003		62,007	N.I.I.	Proof	20.	—
2004	Uncrowned Portrait / Polar Bear; Sterling Silver	57,614	N.I.I.	Proof	20.	—
2005		63,562	N.I.I.	Proof	20.	—
2006		53,822	N.I.I.	Proof	20.	—
2007	Uncrowned Portrait, Mint Logo / Polar Bear; Sterling Silver	37,413	N.I.I.	Proof	20.	—
2008		38,630	N.I.I.	Proof	20.	—
2009		27,549	N.I.I.	Proof	20.	—
2010		32,342	N.I.I.	Proof	20.	—
2011		32,910	N.I.I.	Proof	20.	—

Note: 1.   Quantity sold figures are identical to those listed for Proof Sets sold.
2.   Continuation from 2012 forward of the two-dollar Proof coins is listed on page 143. The break in the listing is due to a change in composition.

TWO DOLLARS, NUNAVUT, PROOF COMMEMORATIVE, 1999.

This coin commemorates the formation of Nunavut, Canada's third territory, in 1999. The design honours the native drum dance.

| Obverse: Nickel / Bronze | Reverse: Nickel / Bronze | Obverse: Gold / Gold | Reverse: Gold / Gold |

Designers:

		Engravers:	
Obv.:	Dora de Pédery-Hunt	Obv.:	Dora de Pédery-Hunt
Rev.:	G. Arnaktauyok	Rev.:	Ago Aarand, José Osio

Composition:	**Nickel Ring**	**Silver Ring**	**White Gold Ring**
	99.0% Ni	92.5% Ag	17.2% Au
		07.5% Cu	77.6% Ag, 5.2% Cu
	Bronze Core	**Silver Gilt Core**	**Yellow Gold Core**
	92.0 % Cu	92.5% Ag	91.7% Au
	6.0% Al, 2.0% Ni	07.5% Cu	04.1% Ag, 4.2% Cu
	Standard	**Standard**	**Standard**
Weight (g):	Ring 4.84	Ring 5.86	Ring 6.31
	Core 2.46	Core 2.97	Core 5.09
	Total 7.3	Total 8.83	Total 11.4
Content: Gold	—	—	0.185 tr oz
** Silver**	—	0.263 tr oz	0.164 tr oz
Diameter (mm):	Ring 28.0	Ring 28.1	Ring 28.0
	Core 16.8	Core 16.8	Core 16.8
Thickness (mm):	1.8	1.9	1.8
Edge:	Interrupted	Interrupted	Interrupted
	serrations	serrations	serrations
Die Axis:	↑↑	↑↑	↑↑
Finish:	Brilliant Uncirculated,	Proof	Proof
	Specimen		

Case of Issue:	Nickel / Bronze, Brilliant Uncirculated: Blue presentation folder
	Nickel / Bronze, Specimen: Maple wood case, encapsulated coin, window box
	Silver / Gilt, Proof: Green leatherette case, black insert, encapsulated coin, COA
	Gold / Gold, Proof: Antique case, black insert, encapsulated coin, COA

DATE	DESCRIPTION	SOURCE	QUANTITY SOLD	ISSUE PRICE	FINISH	AS ISSUED
1999	Nickel / Bronze	BU Set	N/A	N/A	BU	10.
1999	Nickel / Bronze	Specimen Set, Maple wood case	20,000	N/A	Specimen	20.
1999	Silver / Gilt	Proof Set, Single	39,873	24.95	Proof	25.
1999	Gold / Gold	Single Case	4,298	299.95	Proof	375.

VARIETIES OF 1999.

Three different reverse dies were used to produce the three different finishes on the 1999 Nunavut commemorative two dollar coins.

1. Reverse Circulation Die: Raised narrow ring encircling the join between the ring and the core.
2. Reverse Specimen Die: Raised wide ring encircling the join between the ring and the core.
3. Reverse Proof Die: No encircling ring between the ring and the core.

Reverse
Narrow Ring
Brilliant Uncirculated
Dies

Reverse
Wide Ring
Specimen Dies

Reverse
No Ring
Proof Dies

Two varieties of brilliant uncirculated sets were produced in 1999. The standard set, where the $2 coin was produced with a pair of brilliant uncirculated dies, and the Mule variety where the $2 coin was produced with an obverse brilliant uncirculated die and a reverse proof die. See page 516 for the listings of the 1999 brilliant uncirculated sets.

Nickel/bronze, no ring reverse mule

DATE	DESCRIPTION	QUANTITY SOLD	ISSUE PRICE	FINISH	SP-67	SP-68	PR-68	PR-69
1999	Mule from Brilliant Uncirculated Sets	Unknown	N.I.I.	BU	275.	—	—	—

TWO DOLLARS, PATH OF KNOWLEDGE COMMEMORATIVE, 2000.

The mother polar bear passes to her cubs the lesson of survival on the Arctic ice floes.

Obverse	Reverse	Obverse	Reverse
Nickel / Bronze	Nickel / Bronze	Gold / Gold	Gold / Gold

Designers:
Obv.:   Dora de Pédery-Hunt
Rev.:   Tony Bianco

Engravers:
Obv.:   Dora de Pédery-Hunt
Rev.:   Cosme Saffioti

Composition:	**Nickel Ring**	**Silver Ring**	**White Gold Ring**
	99.0% Ni	92.5% Ag	17.2% Au
		07.5% Cu	77.6% Ag, 5.2% Cu
	Bronze Core	**Silver Gilt Core**	**Yellow Gold Core**
	92.0 % Cu	92.5% Ag	91.7% Au
	6.0% Al, 2.0% Ni	07.5% Cu	04.1% Ag, 4.2% Cu
	Standard	**Standard**	**Standard**
Weight (g):	Ring 4.84	Ring 5.86	Ring 6.31
	Core 2.46	Core 2.97	Core 5.09
	Total 7.3	Total 8.83	Total 11.4
Content: Gold	—	—	0.185 tr oz
Silver	—	0.263 tr oz	0.164 tr oz
Diameter (mm):	Ring 28.0	Ring 28.1	Ring 28.0
	Core 16.8	Core 16.8	Core 16.8
Thickness (mm):	1.8	1.9	1.8
Edge:	Interrupted	Interrupted	Interrupted
	serrations	serrations	serrations
Die Axis:	↑↑	↑↑	↑↑
Finish:	Brilliant Uncirculated,	Proof	Proof
	Specimen		

Case of Issue: Nickel / Bronze, Specimen: Maple wood case, encapsulated coin, sleeve
Silver / Gilt, Proof: Green leatherette case, black insert, encapsulated coin, COA
Gold / Gold, Proof: Antique case, black insert, encapsulated coin, COA

DATE	DESCRIPTION	SOURCE	QUANTITY SOLD	ISSUE PRICE	FINISH	AS ISSUED
2000	Nickel / Bronze, wood case	BU Set	186,985	15.95	BU	10.
2000	Nickel / Bronze	Specimen Single	1,500	N/A	Specimen	20.
2000	Nickel / Bronze	Specimen Set	N/A	34.95	Specimen	20.
2000	Silver / Gilt Silver	Proof Single	39,768	24.95	Proof	25.
2000	Gold / Gold	Proof Single	5,881	299.95	Proof	375.

TWO DOLLARS, POLAR BEAR, 2000-2001.

Designers and Engravers:

Obv.:	Dora de Pédery-Hunt
Rev.:	Brent Townsend, Ago Aarand

Composition: Bronze
Ring: 99.0% Nickel
Core: 92.0% Cu, 6.0% Al, 2.0% Ni
Weight: Ring: 4.84 g, Core: 2.46 g
Total weight: 7.3 g
Diameter: Ring: 28.5 mm, Core: 16.8 mm
Thickness: 1.8 mm
Edge: Interrupted serrations
Die Axis: ↑↑   **Finish:** Specimen
Case of Issue: Maple wood case, encapsulated coin, sleeve

DATE	DESCRIPTION	QUANTITY SOLD	ISSUE PRICE	FINISH	SP-68	SP-69
2000	Nickel / Bronze, wood case	20,000	N/A	Specimen	20.	—
2001	Nickel / Bronze, wood case	20,000	N/A	Specimen	20.	—

TWO DOLLARS, PROUD POLAR BEAR, STERLING SILVER, 2004.

Issued jointly by the Royal Canadian Mint and Canada Post, the $2 Proud Polar Bear Stamp and Coin Set contains the first single metal two dollar Canadian coin. The set comprises mint and cancelled $2.00 stamps, along with the $2.00 sterling silver coin. The two dollar coin is unusual in that it carries two maple leaf privy marks.

Designer and Engravers:

Obv.:	Susanna Blunt, Susan Taylor
Rev.:	Stan Witten

Composition: 92.5% Ag, 7.5% Cu
Silver content: 8.14 g, 0.262 tr oz
Weight: 8.8 g   **Edge:** Reeded
Diameter: 28.0 mm   **Die Axis:** ↑↑
Thickness: 1.7 mm   **Finish:** Proof
Case of Issue: See Derivatives, page 139

DATE	DESCRIPTION	QUANTITY SOLD	ISSUE PRICE	FINISH	PR-69	PR-70
2004	Proud Polar Bear, Sterling silver	12,607	N.I.I.	Proof	40.	—

TWO DOLLARS, 10TH ANNIVERSARY, GOLD, 1996-2006.

This gold two dollar coin does not carry the karat marks similar to the previous gold issues of 1996, 1999 and 2000.

Designers and Engravers:

Obv.:	Susanna Blunt, Susan Taylor
Rev.:	Brent Townsend, Ago Aarand

Composition:
Yellow Gold Ring: 91.7% Au, 4.1% Ag, 4.2% Cu
White Gold Core: 17.5% Au, 77.6 Ag, 5.2% Cu
Gold content: Gold: 10.352 g, 0.333 tr oz
Silver: 3.151 g, 0.101 tr oz
Weight: Ring: 10.62 g, Core: 3.6 g
Total: 14.22 g
Diameter: Ring: 28.0 mm, Core: 16.8 mm
Thickness: 1.8 mm
Edge: Interrupted serrations
Die Axis: ↑↑   **Finish:** Proof
Case of Issue: Maroon clam style case, black insert,
encapsulated coin, COA

DATE	DESCRIPTION	QUANTITY SOLD	ISSUE PRICE	FINISH	PR-69	PR-70
2006 (1996-)	Yellow gold ring / White gold core	2,068	399.95	Proof	600.	—

TWO DOLLARS, CHURCHILL REVERSE, RCM LOGO, 1996-2006.

In 2006 a contest was held to name a new polar bear design to appear on the 10th anniversary two dollar coin. The name "Churchill" was the winner. The 10th anniversary coin has the double dates above the Queen's portrait and the Royal Mint logo below.

Designers and Engravers:
- Obv.: Susanna Blunt, Susan Taylor
- Rev.: Tony Bianco, Stan Witten

Composition:
- Ring: 99.9% Ni
- Core: 92.0% Cu, 6.0% Al, 2.0% Ni

Weight: 7.3 g
Diameter: Ring: 28.0 mm, Core: 16.8 mm
Thickness: 1.8 mm
Edge: Interrupted serrations   **Die Axis:** ↑↑
Finish: Brilliant Uncirculated
Case of Issue: See Special Uncirculated Sets, page 499

DATE	DESCRIPTION	QUANTITY SOLD	ISSUE PRICE	FINISH	MS-65 NC	MS-66 NC
2006 (1996-)	"Churchill" Polar Bear	31,636	N.I.I.	BU	10.	—

YOUNG WILDLIFE SERIES

TWO DOLLARS, YOUNG WILDLIFE SERIES, 2010-2015.

These two dollar coins are from the Special Edition Specimen Sets.

Common Obverse   2010 Lynx Kittens   2011 Elk Calf

2012 Wolf Cubs   2013 Black Bear Cubs   2014 Baby Rabbits   2015 Baby Racoons

Designers:
- Obv.: Susanna Blunt
- Rev.: 2010-2012: Christie Paquet
  2013: Glen Loates; 2014: Pierre Leduc

Composition:
- Ring: 99.9% Ni
- Core: 92.0% Cu, 6.0% Al, 2.0% Cu

Weight: 7.5 g
Edge: Interrupted serrations
Finish: Specimen; Brilliant portrait, frosted relief lined background

Engravers:
- Obv.: Susan Taylor
- Rev.: 2010-2012: Christie Paquet
  2013: Eric Boyer; 2014: RCM Staff

Diameter:
- Ring: 28.0 mm
- Core: 16.8 mm

Thickness: 1.9 mm
Die Axis: ↑↑
Case of Issue: See Special Edition Specimen Sets, page 522

DATE	DESCRIPTION	RCM ITEM #	QUANTITY SOLD	ISSUE PRICE	FINISH	SP-68	SP-69
2010	Lynx Kittens	107118	14,790	N.I.I.	Specimen	45.	—
2011	Elk Calf	112456	13,899	N.I.I.	Specimen	60.	—
2012	Wolf Cubs	116619	14,968	N.I.I.	Specimen	40.	—
2013	Black Bear Cubs	123462	17,218	N.I.I.	Specimen	40.	—
2014	Baby Rabbits	130292	11,886	N.I.I.	Specimen	40.	—
2015	Baby Racoons	143341	8,504	N.I.I.	Specimen	40.	—

TWO DOLLARS, ELIZABETH II, FINE SILVER, GOLD PLATED INNER CORE, PROOF, 2012-2019

During 2012 and 2019 the Mint produced two varieties of proof sets, a Premium Set in which the planchets used are of fine silver, and a Standard Set, of which the planchets used are of the standard alloys. In 2017, a glow-in-the-dark version was created to celebrate Canada 150.

| Obverse: 2012 With Mint Logo | Obverse: 2013-2016 With No Mint Logo | Obverse: 2017 With Canada 150 Logo | Common Reverse 2012-2018 | Reverse: 2017 Dance of the Spirits Des.: Timothy Hsia |

Designers:
Obv.: Susanna Blunt
Rev.: Tony Bianco

Premium - Fine Silver

Composition: Outer ring: Fine silver
Inner Core: Gold plated, 99.99% Ag,

Silver content: 9.0 g, 0.289 tr oz
Weight: 9.0 g
Diameter: Ring: 28.0 mm
Core: 16.8 mm
Thickness: 1.80 mm
Edge: Interrupted serrations
Die Axis: ↑↑
Finish: Proof
Case of Issue: See Proof and Premium Proof Sets, page 524-526

Engravers:
Obv.: Susan Taylor
Rev.: Stan Witten

Standard - Nickel Brass

Outer ring: Three-ply nickel finish plated steel
Inner Core: Brass-plated aluminum bronze

6.99 g
Ring: 28.0 mm
Core: 16.8 mm
1.80 mm
Interrupted serrations
↑↑
Proof

Reverse: 2017
Colourised
Dance of the Spirits
Des.: Timothy Hsia

DATE	DESCRIPTION	COMPOSITION	QUANTITY SOLD	ISSUE PRICE	FINISH	PR-69	PR-70
2012	Elizabeth II	Nickel brass	27,254	N.I.I.	Proof	15.	—
2012	Elizabeth II	Fine silver	19,789	N.I.I.	Proof	35.	—
2013	Elizabeth II	Fine silver	20,338	N.I.I.	Proof	35.	—
2014	Elizabeth II	Nickel brass	11,251	N.I.I.	Proof	15.	—
2014	Elizabeth II	Fine silver	13,416	N.I.I.	Proof	35.	—
2015	Elizabeth II	Fine silver	20,000	N.I.I.	Proof	35.	—
2015	Polar Bear, Proof Set	Nickel brass	20,000	N.I.I.	Proof	15.	—
2016	Elizabeth II	Fine silver	20,000	N.I.I.	Proof	35.	—
2016	Polar Bear, Proof Set	Nickel brass	20,000	N.I.I.	Proof	15.	—
2017	Polar Bear, Premium Proof Set	Fine silver	20,000	N.I.I.	Proof	45.	—
2017	Dance of the Spirits, Proof Set	Fine silver	20,000	N.I.I.	Proof	45.	—
2017	Dance of the Spirits (colourised), Proof Set	Nickel brass	25,000	N.I.I.	Proof	25.	—
2018	Polar Bear, Proof Set	Nickel brass	25,000	N.I.I.	Proof	15.	—
2018	Polar Bear, Premium Proof Set	Fine silver	20,000	N.I.I.	Proof	35.	—
2019	Polar Bear, Premium Proof Set	Fine silver	15,000	N.I.I.	Proof	15.	—
2019	Polar Bear, Proof Set	Nickel brass	15,000	N.I.I.	Proof	15.	—

TWO DOLLAR SILVER COINS

TWO DOLLARS (¾ OUNCE), DEVIL'S BRIGADE, 2013.

Designers and Engravers:

Obv.:	Susanna Blunt, Susan Taylor
Rev.:	Ardell Bourgeois, Cecily Mok
Composition:	99.99% Ag
Weight:	23.33 g, 0.50 tr oz
Diameter:	38.07 mm
Thickness:	2.4 mm
Edge:	Reeded
Die Axis:	↑↑
Finish:	Bullion
Case of Issue:	Tubes of 30

DATE	DESCRIPTION	QUANTITY SOLD	ISSUE PRICE	FINISH	MS-65	MS-66	MS-67
2013	$2 (¾ oz), Devil's Brigade	N/A	BV	Bullion	30.	40.	60.

TWO DOLLAR BULLION ISSUES, 2015-2017.

Designers and Engravers:

Obv.:	Susanna Blunt, Susan Taylor
Rev.:	Pierre Leduc, Stan Witten
Composition:	99.99% Ag
Weight:	23.33 g, 0.75 tr oz
Diameter:	38.1 mm
Thickness:	2.4 mm
Edge:	Reeded
Die Axis:	↑↑
Finish:	Bullion, Radial lines
Case of Issue:	Tubes of 30

DATE	DESCRIPTION	MINTAGE	ISSUE PRICE	FINISH	MS-65	MS-66	MS-67
2015	$2 (¾ oz), Grey Wolf	300,000	BV	Bullion	25.	30.	—
2015	$2 (1/2 oz), Calgary Stampede	N/A	BV	Bullion	18.	25.	—
2015	$2 (1/2 oz), Eagle	N/A	BV	Bullion	22.	30.	—
2016	$2 (1/2 oz), Eagle	N/A	BV	Bullion	22.	30.	—
2016	$2 (3/4 oz), Howling Wolves	1,000,000	BV	Bullion	24.	30.	—
2017	$2 (3/4 oz), Howling Wolves	N/A	BV	Bullion	22.	26.	—

BIG COIN SERIES

TWO DOLLARS, BIG COIN SERIES, 2015-2018.

These two-dollar coins, which are part of the Big Coin started started in 2015, features Brent Townsend's iconic polar bear design first introduced in 1996. Other coins in the set include a 1¢ coin (page 7), 5¢ coin (page 12), 10¢ coin (page 17), 25¢ coin (page 57), 50¢ coin (page 87), $1 coin (page 131), and a $2 coin (page 145).

Designers and Engravers:
Obv.:	Susanna Blunt, Susan Taylor
Rev.:	Robert-Ralph Carmichael, RCM Staff
	Brent Townsend

Silver content: 157.58 g, 5.07 tr oz
Weight: 157.6 g
Diameter: 65.25 mm
Thickness: N/A
Case of Issue: Maroon clam style case, black flocked insert, encapsulated coin, COA, custom box

Composition:
2015:	99.99% Ag, Selectively gold plated
2016:	99.99% Ag, Selectively coloured on reverse
2018:	99.99% Ag, Selectively rose-gold plated

Edge: Reeded
Die Axis: ↑↑
Finish: Proof

DATE	DESCRIPTION	RCM ITEM #	QUANTITY SOLD	ISSUE PRICE	FINISH	PR-69	PR-70
2015	$2 Big Coin	134871	1,488	549.95	Proof	550.	—
2016	$2 Big Coin	151551	1,469	519.95	Proof	550.	—
2018	$2 Big Coin	163887	1,500	559.95	Proof	560.	—

Note: Coins illustrated smaller than actual size.

TWO DOLLAR DERIVATIVES

The following single coins, coin and note sets, or coin and stamp sets, are based on the numismatic two dollar coins.

DATE	DESCRIPTION	QUANTITY SOLD	ISSUE PRICE	ISSUER	FINISH	MARKET PRICE
1996	Two Dollar Coin, Specimen; $2 Regular bank note; Blue folder	91,427	29.95	RCM	SP-66	15.
1996	Encapsulated Two Dollar Coin, Proof; Encapsulated $2 BRX Replacement note; Blue presentation case	27,103	79.95	RCM	PR-69	25.
1996	Encapsulated Two Dollar Coin, Piedfort; Encapsulated pair of uncut $2 BRX replacement notes; Blue/green presentation case	11,526	179.95	RCM	PR-69	100.
1996	Two Dollar Coin, Brilliant Uncirculated; $2 regular issue note; 45¢ mint stamp; Blue/green presentation case	N/A	N/A	RCM, CP	MS-65	15.
1998W	Two Dollar Coin; Mint and cancelled $2 stamps; Blue presentation case	N/A	N/A	RCM, CP	MS-65	15.
1999	Two Dollar Nunavut Coin; Mint and cancelled 46¢ stamps; Blue presentation case	N/A	17.95	RCM, CP	MS-65	15.
2000W	Two Dollar Coin; Mint and cancelled $2 stamps; Blue presentation case	20,000	19.99	RCM, CP	MS-65	15.
2000	Two Dollar Coin, "Path of Knowledge" (Three Bears); Credit card-like holder	N/A	N/A	RCM	MS-65	8.
2001	Two Dollar Coin; Credit card-like holder	N/A	N/A	RCM	MS-65	8.
2004	Two Dollar Proud Polar Bear Coin; Mint and cancelled $2 stamps; Wooden presentation case	12,607	29.95	RCM, CP	PR-69	45.
2016	Two Dollar 4-Coin Set, 20 Years in the Minting Includes one uncut 2-dollar banknote sheet from 1986 series.	150	11,499.95	RCM	PR-69	10,000.

THREE DOLLARS

THREE DOLLARS, THE BEAVER, SQUARE, 2006.

Designers and Engravers:

Obv.:	Susanna Blunt, Cosme Saffioti
Rev.:	Cosme Saffioti, Cosme Saffioti
Composition:	92.50% Ag, 7.50% Cu
	plated in 24kt gold
Silver content:	10.84 g, 0.349 tr oz
Weight:	11.72 g
Size:	27.0 x 27.0 mm	**Edge:**	Plain
Thickness:	1.80 mm	**Die Axis:**	↑↑
Finish:	Specimen
Case of Issue:	Maroon plastic slide case, black plastic insert, encapsulated coin, COA

DATE	DESCRIPTION	QUANTITY SOLD	ISSUE PRICE	FINISH	SP-68	SP-69
2006	The Beaver	20,000	45.95	Specimen	60.	—

THREE DOLLARS, RETURN OF THE TYEE, 2010.

Salmon has long been the essential food source of the Northwest Coast people. The largest species of Pacific salmon is the Chinook, or black salmon, called the Tyee (King) by the First Nation People. Two tyee are arranged in a circle, representing the "Circle of Life."

Designers and Engravers:

Obv.:	Susanna Blunt, Susan Taylor
Rev.:	Jody Broomfield, Christie Paquet
Composition:	99.99% Ag, Selectively plated in pink and yellow gold
Silver content:	7.96 g, 0.256 tr oz
Weight:	7.96 g
Diameter:	27.0 mm	**Edge:**	Reeded
Thickness:	1.9 mm	**Die Axis:**	↑↑
Finish:	Proof
Case of Issue:	Maroon leatherette clam style case, black flocked insert, encapsulated coin, COA

DATE	DESCRIPTION	RCM ITEM #	QUANTITY SOLD	ISSUE PRICE	FINISH	PR-69	PR-70
2010	Return of the Tyee	105362	8,301	54.95	Proof	50.	—

ROYAL CANADIAN MINT MARKS ON COINS

"P" is a composition mark for coins struck on multi-ply plated (nickel or copper on steel) planchets

"W" is the mint mark for coins struck at the Winnipeg Mint.

The "Circle M" is the Royal Canadian Mint logo

CANADA'S WILDLIFE CONSERVATION SERIES

THREE DOLLARS, CANADA'S WILDLIFE CONSERVATION SERIES, SQUARE, 2010-2011.

Common Obverse	Barn Owl Engr.: Christie Paquet	Polar Bear Engr.: Stan Witten	Orca Whale Engr.: José Osio	Black-Footed Ferret Engr.: K. Wachelko

Designers:
Obv.: Susanna Blunt
Rev.: Jason Bouwman
Composition: 92.50% Ag; 7.50% Cu, Gold plated
Silver content: 11.1 g, 0.357 tr oz
Weight: 12.0 g
Size: 27.1 x 27.1 mm
Thickness: 2.0 mm

Engravers:
Obv.: Susan Taylor
Rev.: See reverse illustrations

Edge: Plain
Die Axis: ↑↑
Finish: Specimen

Case of Issue: Maroon leatherette clam style case, black flocked insert, encapsulated coin, COA

DATE	DESCRIPTION	RCM ITEM #	QUANTITY SOLD	ISSUE PRICE	FINISH	SP-68	SP-69
2010	Barn Owl	109971	10,578	59.95	Specimen	40.	—
2010	Polar Bear	109976	8,544	59.95	Specimen	40.	—
2011	Orca Whale	112442	10,698	62.95	Specimen	40.	—
2011	Black-Footed Ferret	112448	8,237	62.95	Specimen	40.	—

THREE DOLLARS, FAMILY SCENE, 2011.

Designers and Engravers:
Obv.: Susanna Blunt, Susan Taylor
Rev.: Andrew Qappik, RCM Staff
Composition: 99.99% Ag, Selectively plated in pink and yellow gold
Silver content: 7.96 g, 0.256 tr oz
Weight: 7.96 g
Diameter: 27.0 mm
Thickness: 2.0 mm
Edge: Reeded
Die Axis: ↑↑
Finish: Proof
Case of Issue: Maroon leatherette clam style case, black flocked insert, encapsulated coin, COA

DATE	DESCRIPTION	RCM ITEM #	QUANTITY SOLD	ISSUE PRICE	FINISH	PR-69	PR-70
2011	Family Scene	111446	6,687	64.95	Proof	40.	—

BIRTH STONE COLLECTION

THREE DOLLARS, BIRTH STONE COLLECTION, 2011 (GIFTWARE).

Common Obverse

Designers and Engravers:

Obv.:	Susanna Blunt, Susan Taylor
Rev.:	Christie Paquet

Composition: 99.99% Ag, Swarovski element
Silver content: 7.96 g, 0.25 tr oz

Weight:	7.96 g	**Edge:**	Reeded
Diameter:	27.0 mm	**Die Axis:**	↑↑
Thickness:	1.8 mm	**Finish:**	Proof

Case of Issue: Maroon leatherette clam style case, black flocked insert, encapsulated coin, COA

January - Garnet

February - Amethyst

March - Aquamarine

April - Diamond

May - Emerald

June - Alexandrite

July - Ruby

August - Peridot

September - Sapphire

October - Tourmaline

November - Topaz

December - Zircon

DATE	DESCRIPTION	RCM ITEM #	QUANTITY SOLD	ISSUE PRICE	FINISH	PR-69	PR-70
2011	January - Garnet	112355	2,534	64.95	Proof	50.	—
2011	February - Amethyst	112356	2,571	64.95	Proof	50.	—
2011	March - Aquamarine	112357	2,560	64.95	Proof	50.	—
2011	April - Diamond	112358	2,528	64.95	Proof	50.	—
2011	May - Emerald	112359	2,915	64.95	Proof	50.	—
2011	June - Alexandrite	112360	2,724	64.95	Proof	50.	—
2011	July - Ruby	112361	3,073	64.95	Proof	50.	—
2011	August - Peridot	112362	2,673	64.95	Proof	50.	—
2011	September - Sapphire	112363	2,717	64.95	Proof	50.	—
2011	October - Tourmaline	112364	2,593	64.95	Proof	50.	—
2011	November - Topaz	112365	2,870	64.95	Proof	50.	—
2011	December - Zircon	112366	2,879	64.95	Proof	50.	—
2011	Set of 12 coins	—	—	—	Proof	550.	*

BIRTH STONE COLLECTION (cont.).

THREE DOLLARS, BIRTH STONE COLLECTION, 2012 (GIFTWARE).

Common Obverse

Designers and Engravers:

Obv.:	Susanna Blunt, Susan Taylor
Rev.:	Maurice Gervais, Konrad Wachelko

Composition: 99.99% Ag, Swarovski element
Silver content: 7.96 g, 0.25 tr oz

Weight:	7.96 g	**Edge:**	Reeded
Diameter:	27.0 mm	**Die Axis:**	↑↑
Thickness:	1.8 mm	**Finish:**	Proof

Case of Issue: 12-holed black clam style case, black flocked insert, encapsulated coin, COA, grey sleeve

January - Garnet

February - Amethyst

March - Aquamarine

April - Diamond

May - Emerald

June - Alexandrite

July - Ruby

August - Peridot

September - Sapphire

October - Tourmaline

November - Topaz

December - Zircon

DATE	DESCRIPTION	RCM ITEM #	QUANTITY SOLD	ISSUE PRICE	FINISH	PR-69	PR-70
2012	January - Garnet	112367	1,926	64.95	Proof	50.	—
2012	February - Amethyst	112368	2,017	64.95	Proof	50.	—
2012	March - Aquamarine	112369	2,229	64.95	Proof	50.	—
2012	April - Diamond	112370	2,181	64.95	Proof	50.	—
2012	May - Emerald	112371	2,613	64.95	Proof	50.	—
2012	June - Alexandrite	112372	2,135	64.95	Proof	50.	—
2012	July - Ruby	112373	2,464	64.95	Proof	50.	—
2012	August - Peridot	112374	2,193	64.95	Proof	50.	—
2012	September - Sapphire	112375	2,334	64.95	Proof	50.	—
2012	October - Tourmaline	112376	2,094	64.95	Proof	50.	—
2012	November - Topaz	112377	2,060	64.95	Proof	50.	—
2012	December - Zircon	112378	2,230	64.95	Proof	50.	—
2012	Set of 12 coins	117466	200	779.40	Proof	550.	*

THREE DOLLARS, HUMMINGBIRD WITH MORNING GLORY, 2013 (GIFTWARE).

The ruby-throated hummingbird depicted on this coin is one of Canada's most common hummingbird species. Measuring 2.75 to 3.5 inches and weighing three to four grams, it is about the size of a large moth.

Designers and Engravers:

Obv.:	Susanna Blunt, Susan Taylor		
Rev.:	Yves Bérubé, José Osio		
Composition:	99.99% Ag, Siam red Swarovski crystal element		
Silver content:	8.06 g, 0.257 tr oz		
Weight:	8.0 g	Edge:	Reeded
Diameter:	27.0 mm	Die Axis:	↑↑
Thickness:	2.0 mm	Finish:	Reverse Proof
Case of Issue:	Maroon leatherette clam style case, black flocked insert, encapsulated coin, COA, custom sleeve		

DATE	DESCRIPTION	RCM ITEM #	QUANTITY SOLD	ISSUE PRICE	FINISH	PR-69	PR-70
2013	Hummingbird with Morning Glory	122576	7,392	69.95	Proof	50.	—

CANADA'S ANIMAL ARCHITECTS SERIES

THREE DOLLARS, CANADA'S ANIMAL ARCHITECTS SERIES, 2013-2014 (GIFTWARE).

Common Obverse	Bee and Hive Des.: Yves Bérubé	Spider and Web Des.: Yves Bérubé	(Monarch) Caterpillar and Chrysalis Des.: Trevor Tennant

Designers:

Obv.:	Susanna Blunt	
Rev.:	See reverse illustrations	
Composition:	99.99%, Ag, Painted	
Silver content:	7.96 g, 0.256 tr oz	
Weight:	7.96 g	
Diameter:	26.9 mm	
Thickness:	1.9 - 2.0 mm	
Case of Issue:	Maroon leatherette clam style case, black flocked insert, encapsulated coin, COA	

Engravers:

Rev.:	Susan Taylor
Rev.:	Susan Taylor
Edge:	Reeded
Die Axis:	↑↑
Finish:	Proof

DATE	DESCRIPTION	RCM ITEM #	QUANTITY SOLD	ISSUE PRICE	FINISH	PR-69	PR-70
2013	Bee and Hive	123312	9,993	69.95	Proof	40.	—
2014	Spider and Web	124312	5,431	69.95	Proof	40.	—
2014	Caterpillar and Chrysalis	130534	5,827	69.95	Proof	40.	—

THREE DOLLARS, FISHING, 2013.

Designers and Engravers:

Obv.:	Susanna Blunt, Susan Taylor		
Rev.:	John Mantha, Steven Stewart		
Composition:	99.99% Ag		
Silver content:	7.96 g, 0.256 tr oz		
Weight:	7.96 g	Edge:	Reeded
Diameter:	26.9 mm	Die Axis:	↑↑
Thickness:	1.8 mm	Finish:	Proof
Case of Issue:	Maroon leatherette clam style case, black flocked insert, encapsulated coin, COA		

DATE	DESCRIPTION	RCM ITEM #	QUANTITY SOLD	ISSUE PRICE	FINISH	PR-69	PR-70
2013	Fishing	126017	14,985	34.95	Proof	35.	—

THREE DOLLARS, MISS CANADA: AN ALLEGORY, 2013.

Miss Canada, a visual representation of national value and identity, who first appeared after confederation in 1867.

Designers and Engravers:
- Obv.: Susanna Blunt, Susan Taylor
- Rev.: Laurie McGaw, José Osio

Composition:	Bronze		
Weight:	19.2 g	**Edge:**	Plain
Diameter:	35.75 mm	**Die Axis:**	↑↑
Thickness:	2.7 mm	**Finish:**	Proof

Case of Issue: Maroon leatherette clam style case, black flocked insert, encapsulated coin, COA

DATE	DESCRIPTION	RCM ITEM #	QUANTITY SOLD	ISSUE PRICE	FINISH	PR-69	PR-70
2013	Miss Canada: An Allegory	125761	11,232	34.95	Proof	25.	—

THREE DOLLARS, MARTIN SHORT PRESENTS CANADA, 2013.

Designers and Engravers:
- Obv.: Susanna Blunt, Susan Taylor
- Rev.: Tony Bianco, RCM Staff

Composition:	99.99% Ag		
Silver content:	7.96 g, 0.256 tr oz		
Weight:	7.96 g	**Edge:**	Reeded
Diameter:	26.9 mm	**Die Axis:**	↑↑
Thickness:	1.8 mm	**Finish:**	Proof

Case of Issue: Maroon leatherette clam style case, black flocked insert, encapsulated coin, COA, custom case

DATE	DESCRIPTION	RCM ITEM #	QUANTITY SOLD	ISSUE PRICE	FINISH	PR-69	PR-70
2013	Martin Short Presents Canada	125687	5,923	49.95	Proof	25.	—

THREE DOLLARS, MAPLE LEAF IMPRESSION, 2013.

The impression of a large maple leaf is framed by 100 smaller maple leaves, creating a three dimensional illusion. The design was also issued on the red and green coloured twenty dollar coins (see page 261).

Designers and Engravers:
- Obv.: Susanna Blunt, Susan Taylor
- Rev.: José Osio, RCM Staff

Composition:	99.99% Ag		
Silver content:	7.96 g, 0.256 tr oz		
Weight:	7.96 g	**Edge:**	Reeded
Diameter:	27.0 mm	**Die Axis:**	↑↑
Thickness:	1.8 mm	**Finish:**	Proof

Case of Issue: Maroon leatherette clam style case, black flocked insert, encapsulated coin, COA

DATE	DESCRIPTION	RCM ITEM #	QUANTITY SOLD	ISSUE PRICE	FINISH	PR-69	PR-70
2013	Maple Leaf Impression	126334	9,820	59.95	Proof	40.	—

THREE DOLLARS, 100TH ANNIVERSARY OF CANADIAN ARCTIC EXPEDITION: LIFE IN THE NORTH, 2013.

Celebrating the 100th anniversary of the historic arctic expedition led by Vilhjalmur Stefansson and Rudolph Anderson, this three dollar coin's reverse was designed by Kinngait Nunavut artist Tim Pitsiulak to celebrate life in the north. This coin's design was also released on the twenty-five cent coin in the Special Edition Uncirculated Set 2013-2014 (see page 504).

Designers and Engravers:
- Obv.: Susanna Blunt, Susan Taylor
- Rev.: Tim Pitsiulak, RCM Staff

Composition:	99.99% Ag		
Silver content:	7.96 g, 0.256 tr oz		
Weight:	7.96 g	**Edge:**	Reeded
Diameter:	26.85 mm	**Die Axis:**	↑↑
Thickness:	1.8 mm	**Finish:**	Proof

Case of Issue: Maroon leatherette clam style case, black flocked insert, encapsulated coin, COA

DATE	DESCRIPTION	RCM ITEM #	QUANTITY SOLD	ISSUE PRICE	FINISH	PR-69	PR-70
2013	Life in the North	128560	4,492	34.95	Proof	35.	—

THREE DOLLARS, JEWEL OF LIFE, 2014.

Featuring the artistry of Quebec actor, singer and jewellery designer Caroline Néron, this three dollar coin combines Swarovski crystals to depict the silhouette of a tree in winter.

Designers and Engravers:
Obv.: Susanna Blunt, Susan Taylor
Rev.: Caroline Néron, Konrad Wachelko
Composition: 99.99% Ag, Selectively gold plated, Swarovski elements
Silver content: 7.96 g, 0.256 tr oz
Weight: 7.96 g   **Edge:** Reeded
Diameter: 27.0 mm   **Die Axis:** ↑↑
Thickness: 1.8 mm   **Finish:** Proof
Case of Issue: Maroon leatherette clam style case, black flocked insert, encapsulated coin, COA, custom beauty box

DATE	DESCRIPTION	RCM ITEM #	QUANTITY SOLD	ISSUE PRICE	FINISH	PR-69	PR-70
2014	Jewel of Life	128684	15,000	59.95	Proof	50.	—

THREE DOLLARS, "WAIT FOR ME, DADDY", 2014.

Based on the iconic 1940 photograph taken in British Columbia by photographer Claude Dettloff, this three dollar coin commemorates the 75th anniversary of the declaration of the Second World War.

Designers and Engravers:
Obv.: Susanna Blunt, Susan Taylor
Rev.: Claude Dettloff, RCM Staff
Composition: 99.99% Ag
Silver content: 7.96 g, 0.256 tr oz
Weight: 7.96 g   **Edge:** Reeded
Diameter: 27.0 mm **Die Axis:** ↑↑
Thickness: N/A   **Finish:** Matte Proof
Case of Issue: Maroon leatherette clam style case, black flocked insert, encapsulated coin, COA

DATE	DESCRIPTION	RCM ITEM #	QUANTITY SOLD	ISSUE PRICE	FINISH	PR-69	PR-70
2014	"Wait For Me, Daddy"	132619	6,374	44.95	Matte Proof	45.	—

THREE DOLLARS, 50TH ANNIVERSARY OF THE CANADIAN FLAG, 1965-2015.

Designers and Engravers:
Obv.: Susanna Blunt, Susan Taylor
Rev.: RCM Staff
Composition: 99.99% Ag, Coloured
Silver content: 7.96 g, 0.256 tr oz
Weight: 7.96 g   **Edge:** Reeded
Diameter: 27.0 mm **Die Axis:** ↑↑
Thickness: N/A   **Finish:** Proof
Case of Issue: Maroon leatherette clam style case, black flocked insert, encapsulated coin, COA, custom box

DATE	DESCRIPTION	RCM ITEM #	QUANTITY SOLD	ISSUE PRICE	FINISH	PR-69	PR-70
2015 (1965-)	50th Anniv. of the Canadian Flag	144430	14,998	29.95	Proof	40.	—

THREE DOLLARS, 400TH ANNIVERSARY OF SAMUEL DE CHAMPLAIN IN HURONIA, 2015.

The year 2015 marks the 400th anniversary of Samuel de Champlain's voyage of discovery through Huronia.

Designers and Engravers:
Obv.: Susanna Blunt
Rev.: Laurie McGaw
Composition: 99.99% Ag
Silver content: 7.96 g, 0.256 tr oz
Weight: 7.96 g   **Edge:** Reeded
Diameter: 27 mm   **Die Axis:** ↑↑
Thickness: N/A   **Finish:** Proof
Case of Issue: Maroon leatherette clam style case, black flocked insert, encapsulated coin, COA, custom box

DATE	DESCRIPTION	RCM ITEM #	QUANTITY SOLD	ISSUE PRICE	FINISH	PR-69	PR-70
2015	400th Anniv. of Samuel de Champlain in Huronia	130553	4,292	29.95	Proof	40.	—

THREE DOLLARS, 100TH ANNIVERSARY OF *IN FLANDERS FIELDS*, 2015.

The year 2015 marks the 100th anniversary of the poem *In Flanders Fields*.

Designers and Engravers:
Obv.:	Susanna Blunt		
Rev.:	Laurie McGaw		
Composition:	99.99% Ag		
Silver content:	7.96 g, 0.256 tr oz		
Weight:	7.96 g	**Edge:**	Reeded
Diameter:	27.0 mm	**Die Axis:**	↑↑
Thickness:	N/A	**Finish:**	Matte Proof
Case of Issue:	Maroon leatherette clam style case, black flocked insert, encapsulated coin, COA, custom box		

DATE	DESCRIPTION	RCM ITEM #	QUANTITY SOLD	ISSUE PRICE	FINISH	PR-69	PR-70
2015	100th Anniversary of *In Flanders Fields*	145687	14,810	29.95	Matte Proof	35.	—

THREE DOLLARS, QUEEN ELIZABETH ROSE, 2016.

Designers and Engravers:
Obv.:	Susanna Blunt		
Rev.:	Claudio D'Angelo		
Composition:	99.99% Ag		
Silver content:	7.96 g, 0.256 tr oz		
Weight:	7.96 g	**Edge:**	Reeded
Diameter:	27 mm	**Die Axis:**	↑↑
Thickness:	N/A	**Finish:**	Proof
Case of Issue:	Maroon leatherette clam style case, black flocked insert, encapsulated coin, COA, custom box		

DATE	DESCRIPTION	RCM ITEM #	QUANTITY SOLD	ISSUE PRICE	FINISH	PR-69	PR-70
2016	Queen Elizabeth Rose	170828	9,999	44.95	Proof	50.	—

THREE DOLLARS, MAPLE LEAF QUARTET, 2017.

Like pieces of a puzzle, Canada and its history have been shaped by the many who have come together to define this nation through its people. In this spirit, the RCM has introduced a quartet of coins whose individual images come together to form a single, complete image of a proud Canadian icon.

Common obverse

Designers and Engravers:
Obv.:	Susanna Blunt		
Rev.:	Celia Godkin		
Composition:	99.99% Ag		
Silver content:	11.85 g, 0.381 tr oz		
Weight:	11.85 g (each)	**Edge:**	Plain
Diameter:	27 x 27 mm (each)	**Die Axis:**	↑↑
Thickness:	N/A	**Finish:**	Reverse Proof
Case of Issue:	Presented in a clamshell case with a graphic beauty box.		

DATE	DESCRIPTION	RCM ITEM #	QUANTITY SOLD	ISSUE PRICE	FINISH	PR-69	PR-70
2017	Silver Maple Leaf Quartet	151530	4,527 (each)	204.95	Reverse Proof	200.	—

THREE DOLLARS, HEART OF OUR NATION, 2017.

This coin is filled with inspiring symbols, and even if you haven't seen or experienced them all, you'll likely notice they all feel like "home" – Canada, a rich and ever-changing combination of people, histories and aspirations that come together with the maple leaf at their heart.

Designers and Engravers:
Obv.:	Susanna Blunt
Rev.:	Laurie McGaw

Composition: 99.99% Ag
Silver content: 7.96 g, 0.256 tr oz
Weight: 7.96 g
Diameter: 27 mm
Thickness: N/A
Case of Issue: Folder with easel back.

Edge: Reeded
Die Axis: ↑↑
Finish: Specimen

DATE	DESCRIPTION	RCM ITEM #	MINTAGE	ISSUE PRICE	FINISH	SP-68	SP-69
2017	Heart Of Our Nation	160069	W.S.L.	19.95	Specimen	20.	—

THREE DOLLARS, CELEBRATION OF LOVE, 2017-2019.

Swarovski® crystal elements add elegance and a timeless beauty to the revese of these coins.

2016-2017	**2017**	**2018**	**2019**	**2019**
Common Obverse	Celebraiton of Love	Celebration of Love	Obverse	Celebration of Love
	Des.: Joel Kimmel	Des.: Anna Bucciarelli		Des: Anna Bucciarelli

Designers:
Obv.:	Susanna Blunt
Rev.:	See reverse illustrations

Composition: 99.99% Ag
Silver content: 7.96 g, 0.256 tr oz
Weight: 7.96 g
Diameter: 27 mm
Thickness: N/A
Case of Issue: Premium graphic box.

Engravers:
Rev.:	Susan Taylor

Edge: Reeded
Die Axis: ↑↑
Finish: Proof

DATE	DESCRIPTION	RCM ITEM #	MINTAGE	ISSUE PRICE	FINISH	PR-69	PR-70
2017	Celebration of Love	158025	17,500	54.95	Proof	55.	—
2018	Celebration of Love	163630	15,000	54.95	Proof	55.	—
2019	Celebration of Love	170526	15,000	54.95	Proof	55.	—

THREE DOLLARS, THE SPIRIT OF CANADA, 2017.

Designers and Engravers:
Obv.:	Susanna Blunt
Rev.:	Steve Hepburn

Composition: 99.99% Ag
Silver content: 7.96 g, 0.256 tr oz
Weight: 7.96 g
Diameter: 27 mm
Thickness: N/A
Case of Issue: Folder-style packaging with pop-out easel back.

Edge: Reeded
Die Axis: ↑↑
Finish: Specimen

DATE	DESCRIPTION	RCM ITEM #	MINTAGE	ISSUE PRICE	FINISH	SP-68	SP-69
2017	The Spirit of Canada	157882	33,983	19.95	Specimen	20.	—

2017 ZODIAC SERIES

THREE DOLLARS, *ZODIAC* SERIES, 2017.

The zodiac has a long, rich history that dates back to Hellenic and Babylonian civilizaitons, which astrology and astronomy were viturally inseparable. Today, its 12 signs entertain, intrigue or inspire millions of people worldwide, who find hope or guidance in the cyclical alignment of the stars and planets! The stars align in the *2017 Zodiac* series, which features sparkling Swarovski® crystal embellshiments within a coloured rendition of the zodiac.

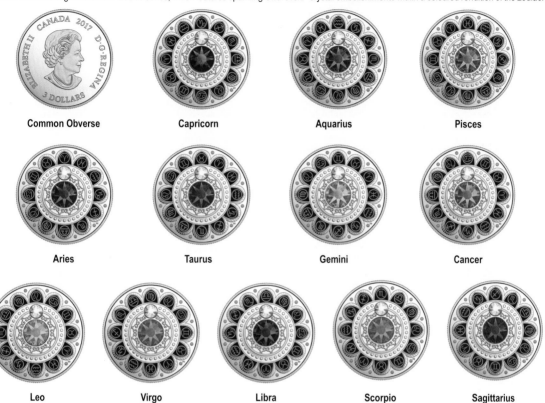

| Common Obverse | Capricorn | Aquarius | Pisces |

| Aries | Taurus | Gemini | Cancer |

| Leo | Virgo | Libra | Scorpio | Sagittarius |

Designers:		Engravers:	
Obv.:	Susanna Blunt	Rev.:	Susan Taylor
Rev.:	Pandora Young	Rev.:	Susan Taylor
Composition:	99.99%, Ag,		
Silver content:	7.96 g, 0.256 tr oz		
Weight:	7.96 g	**Edge:**	Reeded
Diameter:	27 mm	**Die Axis:**	↑↑
Thickness:	N/A	**Finish:**	Proof
Case of Issue:	Maroon clamshell with black beauty box.		

DATE	DESCRIPTION	RCM ITEM #	QUANTITY SOLD	ISSUE PRICE	FINISH	PR-69	PR-70
2017	Capricorn	157234	2,286	54.95	Proof	55.	—
2017	Aquarius	158338	1,000	54.95	Proof	55.	—
2017	Pisces	158406	5,500	54.95	Proof	55.	—
2017	Aries	158412	5,500	54.95	Proof	55.	—
2017	Taurus	159290	5,500	54.95	Proof	55.	—
2017	Gemini	159159	5,500	54.95	Proof	55.	—
2017	Cancer	159012	5,500	54.95	Proof	55.	—
2017	Leo	159544	5,500	54.95	Proof	55.	—
2017	Virgo	159545	5,500	54.95	Proof	55.	—
2017	Libra	159546	5,500	54.95	Proof	55.	—
2017	Scorpio	159547	5,500	54.95	Proof	55.	—
2017	Sagittarius	159548	5,500	54.95	Proof	55.	—

THREE DOLLARS, 100TH ANNIVERSARY OF THE BATTLE OF VIMY RIDGE, 2017.

The Battle of Vimy Ridge (April 9, 1917) marks the beginning of its rise to independent greatness — born of valour and sacrifice on the battlefield, where the Canadian National Vimy Memorial now stands, this coin commemorates the 100th anniversaray of Canada's historic battle.

Designers and Engravers:

Obv.:	Susanna Blunt
Rev.:	Laurie McGaw

Composition: 99.99% Ag
Silver content: 7.96 g, 0.256 tr oz
Weight: 7.96 g   **Edge:** Reeded
Diameter: 27 mm   **Die Axis:** ↑↑
Thickness: N/A   **Finish:** Specimen
Case of Issue: Folder-style packaging with pop-out easel back.

DATE	DESCRIPTION	RCM ITEM #	MINTAGE	ISSUE PRICE	FINISH	SP-68	SP-69
2017	100th Anniv. of the Battle of Vimy Ridge	161068	W.S.L.	19.95	Specimen	20.	—

THREE DOLLARS, 100TH ANNIVERSARY OF THE TORONTO MAPLE LEAFS™, 2017.

In 1917, the Toronto Maple Leafs™ were born. This coin embodies the enduring spirit of Leafs™ Nation — a passion that united people on and off the ice, and inspired young and old alike to carve fond memories on winter ice.

Designers and Engravers:

Obv.:	Susanna Blunt
Rev.:	Steven Rosati

Composition: 99.99% Ag
Silver content: 7.96 g, 0.256 tr oz
Weight: 7.96 g   **Edge:** Reeded
Diameter: 27 mm   **Die Axis:** ↑↑
Thickness: N/A   **Finish:** Matte Proof
Case of Issue: Folder-style packaging with pop-out easel back.

DATE	DESCRIPTION	RCM ITEM #	MINTAGE	ISSUE PRICE	FINISH	PR-69	PR-70
2017	100th Anniv. of the Toronto Maple Leafs	162066	W.S.L.	34.95	Matte Proof	35.	—

THREE DOLLARS, CARIBOU, 2018.

Designers and Engravers:

Obv.:	Susanna Blunt
Rev.:	Steve McPhee

Composition: 99.99% Ag
Silver content: 7.96 g, 0.256 tr oz
Weight: 7.96 g   **Edge:** Reeded
Diameter: 27 mm   **Die Axis:** ↑↑
Thickness: N/A   **Finish:** Specimen
Case of Issue: Folder-style packaging with pop-out easel back.

DATE	DESCRIPTION	RCM ITEM #	MINTAGE	ISSUE PRICE	FINISH	SP-68	SP-69
2018	Caribou	167504	W.S.L.	19.95	Specimen	20.	—

Note: W.S.L. = While Supplies Last.

MAPLE LEAF QUARTET

THREE DOLLARS, MAPLE LEAF QUARTET, THIRTY YEARS, (1988-2018).

Introduced in 1988, the Royal Canadian Mint's Silver Maple Leaf (SML) coin remains one of the most recognized and sought-after investment pieces in the world. This selectively rose gold-plated quartet is a tribute to the SML's solitary maple leaf as a true mark of excellence.

Common obverse

Designers and Engravers:
Obv.: Susanna Blunt
Rev.: Pierre Leduc
Composition: 99.99% Ag, Selective rose gold-plated
Silver content: 11.85 g, 0.381 tr oz
Weight: 11.85 g (each)   **Edge:** Plain
Diameter: 27 x 27 mm (each) **Die Axis:** ↑↑
Thickness: N/A   **Finish:** Reverse Proof
Case of Issue: Maroon clamshell case with a black beauty box.

DATE	DESCRIPTION	RCM ITEM #	MINTAGE	ISSUE PRICE	FINISH	PR-69	PR-70
2018	Silver Maple Leaf Quartet, Thirty Years (1988-2018)	161561	6,500 (each)	204.95	Reverse Proof	205.	—

CANADIAN COASTS

THREE DOLLARS, CANADIAN COASTS SERIES, 2018.

Canadian Coasts is a limited series of three square-shaped coins that are a combined tribute to the longest coastline in the world!

Common obverse

Pacific Sunset

True North

Atlantic Coves

Designers:
Obv.: Susanna Blunt
Rev.: Maurade Baynton
Composition: 99.99% Ag, Selective gold plating
Silver content: 11.72 g, 0.377 tr oz
Weight: 11.72 g (each)
Diameter: 27 x 27 mm
Thickness: N/A
Case of Issue: Maroon clamshell case with a black beauty box.

Engravers:
Rev.: Susan Taylor

Edge: Plain
Die Axis: ↑↑
Finish: Proof

DATE	DESCRIPTION	RCM ITEM #	MINTAGE	ISSUE PRICE	FINISH	PR-69	PR-70
2018	Canadian Coasts – Pacific Sunset	166782	5,000	74.95	Proof	75.	—
2018	Canadian Coasts –True North	166783	5,000	74.95	Proof	75.	—
2018	Canadian Coasts – Atlantic Coves	166784	5,000	74.95	Proof	75.	—

TEACHINGS FROM GRANDMOTHER MOON SERIES

THREE DOLLARS, TEACHINGS FROM GRANDMOTHER MOON, 2018.

Canada's Indigenous people view every aspect of nature as a living relation that plays an active role in their lives, and Grandmother Moon is ever-present, making 13 appearances throughout the year as she watches over Mother Earth's children and lights up their paths.

| Common obverse | Spirit Moon | Bear Moon | Sugar Moon |

| Sucker Moon | Flower Moon | Strawberry Moon | Raspberry Moon | Thimbleberry Moon |

| Corn Moon | Falling Leaves Moon | Freezing Moon | Little Spirit Moon | Big Spirit Moon |

Designers:
Obv.: Susanna Blunt
Rev.: Frank Polson
Composition: 99.99%, Ag, Painted
Silver content: 7.96 g, 0.256 tr oz
Weight: 7.96 g
Diameter: 27 mm
Thickness: N/A

Engravers:
Rev.: Susan Taylor

Edge: Reeded
Die Axis: ↑↑
Finish: Proof

Case of Issue: Maroon leatherette clam style case, black flocked insert, encapsulated coin, COA

DATE	DESCRIPTION	RCM ITEM #	MINTAGE	ISSUE PRICE	FINISH	PR-69	PR-70
2018	Spirit Moon	164977	4,000	49.95	Proof	50.	—
2018	Bear Moon	164988	4,000	49.95	Proof	50.	—
2018	Sugar Moon	165183	4,000	49.95	Proof	50.	—
2018	Sucker Moon	165161	4,000	49.95	Proof	50.	—
2018	Flower Moon	165195	4,000	49.95	Proof	50.	—
2018	Strawberry Moon	165950	4,000	49.95	Proof	50.	—,
2018	Raspberry Moon	165943	4,000	49.95	Proof	50.	—
2018	Thimbleberry Moon	166272	4,000	49.95	Proof	50.	—
2018	Corn Moon	166273	4,000	49.95	Proof	50.	—
2018	Falling Leaves Moon	166274	4,000	49.95	Proof	50.	—
2018	Freezing Moon	166276	4,000	49.95	Proof	50.	—
2018	Little Spirit Moon	166275	4,000	49.95	Proof	50.	—
2018	Big Spirit Moon	166277	4,000	49.95	Proof	50.	—
2018	13-Coin Subscription	166278	4,000	N.A.	Proof	—	—

THE ELEMENTS

THREE DOLLARS, THE ELEMENTS, 2019.

Fire. Air. Earth. Water. Each square coin is a quadrant; when all four coins are tiled, they complete a circular illustration of the four elements of nature in Canada.

Common obverse

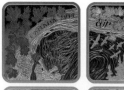

Designers and Engravers:
Obv.:   Susanna Blunt
Rev.:   Rebecca Yanovskaya
Composition: 99.99% Ag, Selective colour on each coin
Silver content: 11.72 g, 0.377 tr oz

Weight: 11.72 g (each)	**Edge:**	Plain
Diameter: 27 x 27 mm (each)	**Die Axis:**	↑↑
Thickness: N/A	**Finish:**	Proof

Case of Issue: Maroon clamshell
case with a black beauty box.

DATE	DESCRIPTION	RCM ITEM #	MINTAGE	ISSUE PRICE	FINISH	PR-69	PR-70
2019	The Elements	172239	2,000	199.95	Proof	200.	—

CELEBRATING CANADIAN FUN AND FESTIVITIES SERIES

THREE DOLLARS, CELEBRATING CANADIAN FUN AND FESTIVITIES, 2019.

The 12-coin Celebrating Canadian Fun and Festivities series is a month-by-month exploration of Canada, where life is a four-season adventure.

Designers:	
Obv.:	Susanna Blunt
Rev.:	Steve Hepburn
Composition:	99.99%, Ag, Painted
Silver content:	7.96 g, 0.256 tr oz
Weight:	7.96 g
Diameter:	27 mm
Thickness:	N/A
Case of Issue:	Black clamshell with black beauty box, COA

Engravers:	
Rev.:	Susan Taylor
Edge:	Reeded
Die Axis:	↑↑
Finish:	Proof

Niagara Falls Winter Lights   Dogsledding   Maple Syrup Tasting   Cherry Blossom   Tulips

DATE	DESCRIPTION	RCM ITEM #	MINTAGE	ISSUE PRICE	FINISH	PR-69	PR-70
2019	Niagara Falls Winter Lights	171019	4,000	49.95	Reverse Proof	50.	—
2019	Dogsledding	171169	4,000	49.95	Reverse Proof	50.	—
2019	Maple Syrup Tasting	171180	4,000	49.95	Reverse Proof	50.	—
2019	Cherry Blossom	171690	4,000	49.95	Reverse Proof	50.	—
2019	Tulips	171866	4,000	49.95	Reverse Proof	50.	—

THREE DOLLARS, QUEEN ELIZABETH ROSE BLOSSOMS, 2019.

Designers and Engravers:
Obv.:	Susanna Blunt
Rev.:	Claudio D'Angelo

Composition: 99.99% Ag
Silver content: 7.96 g, 0.256 tr oz
Weight: 7.96 g   **Edge:** Reeded
Diameter: 27 mm   **Die Axis:** ↑↑
Thickness: N/A   **Finish:** Proof
Case of Issue: Maroon clamshell with black beauty box, COA.

DATE	DESCRIPTION	RCM ITEM #	MINTAGE	ISSUE PRICE	FINISH	PR-69	PR-70
2019	Queen Elizabeth Rose Blossoms	170828	10,000	54.95	Proof	55.	—

THREE DOLLARS, 75TH ANNIVERSARY OF THE NORMANDY CAMPAIGN D-DAY AT JUNO BEACH, 2019.

Designers and Engravers:
Obv.:	Susanna Blunt
Rev.:	Glenn Loates

Composition: 99.99% Ag
Silver content: 7.96 g, 0.256 tr oz
Weight: 7.96 g   **Edge:** Reeded
Diameter: 27 mm   **Die Axis:** ↑↑
Thickness: N/A   **Finish:** Reverse Proof
Case of Issue: Presentation folder.

DATE	DESCRIPTION	RCM ITEM #	MINTAGE	ISSUE PRICE	FINISH	PR-69	PR-70
2019	75th Anniv. D-Day at Juno Beach	171817	10,000	24.95	Reverse Proof	25.	—

FOUR DOLLARS
DINOSAUR COLLECTION

FOUR DOLLARS, DINOSAUR COLLECTION, 2007-2010.

Over 65 million years ago Alberta and Saskatchewan were covered by a great subtropical inland sea, home to more than thirty-five dinosaur species. There are five coins in this series.

| Obverse 2007-2010 With RCM Logo | 2007 Parasaurolophus Eng.: Christie Paquet | 2008 Triceratops Eng.: Konrad Wachelko | 2009 Tyrannosaurus Rex Eng.: Marcos Hallam | 2010 Dromaeosaurus Eng.: Cecily Mok |

Designers:
   Obv.: Susanna Blunt
   Rev.: Kerri Burnett
Engravers:
   Obv.: Susan Taylor
   Rev.: See reverse illustrations
Composition: 99.99% Ag, Selective aging effect
Silver content: 15.87 g, 0.510 tr oz
Weight: 15.87 g
Diameter: 34.0 mm
Thickness: 2.1 mm
Edge: Reeded
Die Axis: ↑↑
Finish: Proof
Case of Issue: Maroon leatherette clam style case, black flocked insert, encapsulated coin, COA

| Obverse 2010 Without RCM Logo | 2010 Euoplocephalus Tutus Engraver: Christie Paquet |

DATE	DESCRIPTION	RCM ITEM #	QUANTITY SOLD	ISSUE PRICE	FINISH	PR-69	PR-70
2007	Parasaurolophus	N/A	14,946	39.95	Proof	70.	—
2008	Triceratops	623428	13,046	39.95	Proof	70.	—
2009	Tyrannosaurus Rex	623429	13,572	39.95	Proof	45.	—
2010	Dromaeosaurus	623420	8,982	42.95	Proof	45.	—
2010	Euoplocephalus Tutus	110991	6,256	49.95	Proof	45.	—

FOUR DOLLARS, HANGING THE STOCKINGS, 2009.

The link between stockings and Christmas began to emerge with the legend of Saint Nicholas, when he dropped three small bags of gold down the chimney and into the stockings of the three daughters of a poor man, to help with their dowries.

Designers and Engravers:
   Obv.: Susanna Blunt, Susan Taylor
   Rev.: Tony Bianco, RCM Staff
Composition: 99.99% Ag
Silver content: 15.87 oz, 0.510 tr oz
Weight: 15.87 g
Diameter: 34.0 mm
Thickness: 2.0 mm
Edge: Reeded
Die Axis: ↑↑
Finish: Proof
Case of Issue: Maroon leatherette clam style case, black flocked insert, encapsulated coin, COA

DATE	DESCRIPTION	RCM ITEM #	QUANTITY SOLD	ISSUE PRICE	FINISH	PR-69	PR-70
2009	Hanging The Stockings	105336	6,011	42.95	Proof	40.	—

FOUR DOLLARS, WELCOME TO THE WORLD, 2011.

This design is also featured on the twenty-five-cent coins contained in the Baby Gift Sets for 2011 and 2013 (see pages 33-34). It is also featured on the $10 silver issue of 2012-2015 (see page 199).

Designers and Engravers:
Obv.:	Susanna Blunt, Susan Taylor
Rev.:	José Osio, Matt Bowan

Composition: 99.99% Ag
Silver content: 15.87 oz, 0.510 tr oz
Weight: 15.87 g
Diameter: 34.0 mm
Thickness: 2.2 mm
Edge: Reeded
Die Axis: ↑↑
Finish: Proof
Case of Issue: Black leatherette clam style case, black flocked insert, encapsulated coin, COA

DATE	DESCRIPTION	RCM ITEM #	QUANTITY SOLD	ISSUE PRICE	FINISH	PR-69	PR-70
2011	Welcome to the World	114073	7,059	59.95	Proof	150.	—

THE HEROES OF 1812 SERIES

FOUR DOLLARS, THE HEROES OF 1812 SERIES, 2012-2013.

The War of 1812 was one of the fundamental turning points in Canada's history. It profoundly influenced British North America's (Canada's) sense of identity uniting French and English-speaking inhabitants and Aboriginal communities against an American invasion.

| Obverse | Tecumseh
Engr.: Nick Martin | Sir Isaac Brock
Engr.: Matt Bowen | Charles-Michel
de Salaberry
Engr.: Steven Stewart | Laura Secord
Engr.: Samantha Strath |

Designers:
Obv.:	Susanna Blunt
Rev.:	Bonnie Ross

Composition: 99.99% Ag, Coloured
Silver content: 7.96 g, 0.255 tr oz
Weight: 7.96 g
Diameter: 27.0 mm
Thickness: 1.8 mm

Engravers:
Obv.:	Susan Taylor
Rev.:	See reverse illustrations

Edge: Reeded
Die Axis: ↑↑
Finish: Proof

Case of Issue: Maroon leatherette clam style case, black flocked insert, encapsulated coin, COA, custom coloured box

DATE	DESCRIPTION	RCM ITEM #	QUANTITY SOLD	ISSUE PRICE	FINISH	PR-69	PR-70
2012	Tecumseh	119726	7,521	49.95	Proof	40.	—
2012	Sir Isaac Brock	119763	6,980	49.95	Proof	40.	—
2013	Charles-Michel de Salaberry	119772	5,383	49.95	Proof	40.	—
2013	Laura Secord	119749	5,104	49.95	Proof	40.	—

Note: These Heroes of 1812 four dollar coins, plus the Battle of Chateuguay kilo silver coin, were issued as a five-coin set. They were issued in a custom wooden maple wood box, limited to an issue of 80 sets.

FIVE DOLLARS

FIVE DOLLARS, NORMAN BETHUNE COMMEMORATIVE, 1998.

In 1998 the Royal Canadian Mint produced a $5 silver coin to commemorate the 60th anniversary of Dr. Norman Bethune's arrival in China. The coin was issued as part of a two-coin set in conjunction with China Gold Coin Incorporation (CGCI).

Designers:		Engravers:	
Obv.:	Dora de Pédery-Hunt	Obv.:	Dora de Pédery-Hunt
Rev.:	Harry Chan	Rev.:	Ago Aarand, Stan Witten

Case of Issue: Brown plastic two-hole red insert, encapsulated coin, COA, box cover in Chinese brocade

MINT	COMPOSITION	WEIGHT (G)	SILVER CONTENT	DIAMETER	THICKNESS	EDGE	DIE AXIS
CGCI	99.99% silver	31.10	31.10 g, 1.00 tr oz	40.0	3.2 mm	Reeded	↑↑
RCM	99.99% silver	31.39	31.39 g, 1.01 tr oz	38.0	3.3 mm	Reeded	↑↑

DATE	DESCRIPTION	QUANTITY SOLD	ISSUE PRICE	FINISH	PR-68	PR-69
1998	Bethune - CGCI	N.I.I.	—	Proof	40.	—
1998	Bethune - RCM	N.I.I.	—	Proof	40.	—
1998	Set of 2 coins	65,831	98.00	Proof	75.	*

FIVE DOLLARS, THE VIKING SETTLEMENT, 1999.

This coin commemorates the Viking landing at L'Anse-aux-Meadows, Newfoundland, circa 1000 A.D. Norway issued a 20-Kroner coin in 1999 also commemorating the same Viking Landing. These two coins were offered as a set.

1999 Obverse Designer and Engraver: Dora de Pédery-Hunt	Canada $5 Designer: D. Curley Engraver: S. Witten	1999 Obverse Designer and Engraver: Unknown	Norway 20 Kroner Designer and Engraver: Unknown

Composition:	81.0% Cu, 9.0% Ni, 10.0 Zi		
Weight:	9.9 g	**Edge:**	Plain
Diameter:	27.0 mm	**Die Axis:**	↑↑
Thickness:	2.5 mm	**Finish:**	Proof
Case of Issue:	Oval imitation resin stone case, two-holes, brown insert, encapsulated coins, printed cardboard outer sleeve.		

DATE	DESCRIPTION	QUANTITY SOLD	ISSUE PRICE	FINISH	PR-68	PR-69
1999	Canada $5	—	—	Proof	30.	—
1999	Norway 20 Kroner	—	—	Proof	30.	—
1999	Set of 2 coins	28,450	N/A	Proof	50.	*

FIVE DOLLARS, 100TH ANNIVERSARY OF THE FIRST WIRELESS TRANSMISSION, 2001.

On December 12th, 1901, Gugliemo Marconi (1874-1937) successfully transmitted the first wireless message across the Atlantic from Poldhu in Cornwall, England, to Signal Hill in St. John's, Newfoundland. To commemorate this anniversary, the Royal Canadian Mint in conjunction with the Royal Mint issued this two-coin set.

2001 Obverse	Canada $5	2001 Obverse	British £2
Designer and Engraver:	Designer and Engraver:	Des.: I. Rank-Bradley	Des.: Royal Mint Staff
Dora de Pédery-Hunt	Cosme Saffioti	Engraver: Robert Evans	Engraver: Robert Evans

Composition: Coin: 92.5% Ag, 7.5% Cu
Cameo: 24-karat gold plated
                                                Coin: 92.5% Ag, 7.5% Cu
                                                Outer circle: Plated 22kt gold
                                                Inner disc: 92.5% Ag, 7.5% Cu

Silver Content:	15.69 g, 0.504 tr oz	22.2 g, 0.714 tr oz
Weight:	16.96 g	24.0 g
Diameter:	28.4 mm	28.4 mm
Thickness:	N/A	N/A
Edge:	Reeded	Lettering
Die Axis:	↑↑	↑↑
Finish:	Proof	

Case of Issue: Brown resin oval case with a Marconi stamp on upper lid, brown flocked insert, encapsulated coin, COA, brown printed cardboard box.

DATE	DESCRIPTION	QUANTITY SOLD	ISSUE PRICE	FINISH	PR-68	PR-69
2001	Canada $5	—	—	Proof	30.	—
2001	U.K. £2	—	—	Proof	30.	—
2001	Set of 2 coins	15,011	99.95	Proof	50.	*

FIVE DOLLARS, 2006 F.I.F.A.™ WORLD CUP, 2003.

The Canadian Soccer Association, founded in 1912, has been affiliated with the Federation International de Football Association since 1913. The 2006 World Cup championship was held in Germany.

Designers and Engravers:
    Obv.:   Susanna Blunt, Susan Taylor
    Rev.:   Urszula Walerzak, José Osio
Composition: 99.99% Ag
Silver content: 31.30 g, 1.01 tr oz

Weight:	31.3 g	**Edge:**	Reeded
Diameter:	38.0 mm	**Die Axis:**	↑↑
Thickness:	3.1 mm	**Finish:**	Proof

Case of Issue: Black case, black flocked insert, encapsulated coin, COA, multicoloured sleeve

DATE	DESCRIPTION	QUANTITY SOLD	ISSUE PRICE	FINISH	PR-68	PR-69
2003	2006 F.I.F.A.™ World Cup	21,542	39.95	Proof	35.	—

FIVE DOLLARS, 100TH ANNIVERSARY OF THE CANADIAN OPEN CHAMPIONSHIP, 2004

Issued jointly by the Royal Canadian Mint and Canada Post to celebrate the 100th Anniversary of the tournament, this limited edition framed set contains both a five-dollar note and a ten-cent coin. These coins were issued in various combinations.

Designers and Engravers:

Obv.:	Susanna Blunt, Susan Taylor
Rev.:	Cosme Saffioti

Composition: 99.99% Ag
Silver content: 27.90 g, 0.90 tr oz

Weight:	27.9 g	**Edge:**	Reeded
Diameter:	38.0 mm	**Die Axis:**	↑↑
Thickness:	3.0 mm	**Finish:**	Proof

Case of Issue: See Derivatives, page 179

DATE	DESCRIPTION	QUANTITY SOLD	ISSUE PRICE	FINISH	PR-68	PR-69
2004	100th Anniv. Canadian Open Championship	18,750	N.I.I.	Proof	45.	—

Note: N.I.I. denotes Not Issued Individually.

CANADIAN WILDLIFE SERIES

FIVE DOLLARS, CANADIAN WILDLIFE SERIES, 2004-2006.

These five dollar coins were part of a coin and stamp set series which was issued jointly by the Royal Canadian Mint and Canada Post to pay homage to Canada's diverse wildlife. See Derivatives, page 179.

2004
The Majestic Moose
Obv. Designer: Susanna Blunt
Obv. Engraver: Susan Taylor
Rev. Designer: D. Preston-Smith
Rev. Engraver: Stan Witten

2005 & 2006 Common Obverse	White-tailed Deer & Fawn	The Atlantic Walrus & Calf	Peregrine Falcon & Nestlings	Sable Island Horse & Foal
Designer: Susanna Blunt	Designer: Xerxes Irani	Designer: Pierre Leduc	Designer: Dwayne Harty	Designer: N/A
Engraver: Susan Taylor	Engraver: José Osio	Engraver: José Osio	Engraver: José Osio	Engraver: Christie Paquet

Composition:	99.99% Ag		**Thickness:**	3.0 mm
Silver content:	28.0 g, 0.9 tr oz		**Edge:**	Reeded
Weight:	28.0 g		**Die Axis:**	↑↑
Diameter:	38.0 mm		**Finish:**	Proof
Case of Issue:	See Derivatives, page 179			

DATE	DESCRIPTION	QUANTITY SOLD	ISSUE PRICE	FINISH	PR-69	PR-70
2004	The Majestic Moose	12,822	N.I.I.	Proof	80.	—
2005	White-tailed Deer and Fawn	6,439	N.I.I.	Proof	40.	—
2005	The Atlantic Walrus and Calf	5,519	N.I.I.	Proof	40.	—
2006	Peregrine Falcon and Nestlings	7,226	N.I.I.	Proof	40.	—
2006	Sable Island Horse and Foal	10,108	N.I.I.	Proof	40.	—

FIVE DOLLARS, 60TH ANNIVERSARY OF THE END OF THE SECOND WORLD WAR, 2005.

In the six years of conflict Canada had enlisted more than one million men and women in His Majesty's Armed Forces. Of these, more than 45,000 gave their lives in the cause of peace. A $50 gold version was also issued (see page 424).

Designers and Engravers:

Obv.:	Susanna Blunt, Susan Taylor
Rev.:	Peter Mossman, Christie Paquet

Composition: 99.99% Ag
Silver content: 31.50 g, 1.01 tr oz

Weight:	31.5 g	**Edge:**	Reeded
Diameter:	38.0 mm	**Die Axis:**	↑↑
Thickness:	3.2 mm	**Finish:**	See below
Case of Issue:	Maroon plastic display case, black plastic insert, encapsulated coin, COA		

Obverse	Reverse	Reverse with Maple Leaf Privy Mark

DATE	DESCRIPTION	QUANTITY SOLD	ISSUE PRICE	FINISH	68	69	70
2005	60th Anniv. WWII	25,000	39.95	Specimen	45.	60.	—
2005	60th Anniv. WWII with Maple Leaf Privy Mark	10,000	N.I.I.	Proof	—	70.	—

FIVE DOLLARS, COMMEMORATING THE CENTENNIAL OF THE PROVINCES OF ALBERTA AND SASKATCHEWAN, 2005.

Composition: 99.99% Ag
Silver content: 25.20 g, 0.81 tr oz
Weight: 25.2 g
Diameter: 36.0 mm
Edge: Reeded
Die Axis: ↑↑
Thickness: 3.1 mm
Finish: Proof
Case of Issue: Maroon plastic display case, black plastic insert, encapsulated coin, COA

Common Obverse	Alberta Centennial	Saskatchewan Centennial
Des.: Susanna Blunt	Des.: Michelle Grant	Des.: Paulett Sapergia
Eng.: Susan Taylor	Eng.: Stan Witten	Eng.: José Osio

DATE	DESCRIPTION	QUANTITY SOLD	ISSUE PRICE	FINISH	PR-68	PR-69
2005	Alberta Centennial	20,000	49.95	Proof	40.	—
2005	Saskatchewan Centennial	20,000	49.95	Proof	40.	—

FIVE DOLLARS, BREAST CANCER AWARENESS, 2006.

Designers and Engravers:

Obv.:	Susanna Blunt, Susan Taylor
Rev.:	Christie Paquet, Christie Paquet

Composition: 99.99% Ag, Painted
Silver content: 25.17 g, 0.81 tr oz

Weight:	25.175 g	**Edge:**	Reeded
Diameter:	36.1 mm	**Die Axis:**	↑↑
Thickness:	3.1 mm	**Finish:**	Proof
Case of Issue:	Maroon plastic display case, black plastic insert, encapsulated coin, COA		

DATE	DESCRIPTION	QUANTITY SOLD	ISSUE PRICE	FINISH	PR-68	PR-69
2006	Breast Cancer Awareness, Painted	11,048	59.95	Proof	45.	—

FIVE DOLLARS, CANADIAN FORCES SNOWBIRDS, 2006.

Designers and Engravers:
Obv.: Susanna Blunt, Susan Taylor
Rev.: Jianping Yan, RCM Staff
Composition: 99.99% Ag, Double hologram
Silver content: 25.17 g, 0.81 tr oz
Weight: 25.175 g **Edge:** Reeded
Diameter: 36.1 mm **Die Axis:** ↑↑
Thickness: 3.1 mm **Finish:** Proof
Case of Issue: See Derivatives, page 179

DATE	DESCRIPTION	QUANTITY SOLD	ISSUE PRICE	FINISH	PR-68	PR-69
2006	Canadian Forces Snowbirds, Double hologram	10,034	N.I.I.	Proof	40.	—

FIVE DOLLARS, 80TH ANNIVERSARY OF CANADA IN JAPAN, 2009.

The legation of Japan opened in Ottawa in 1928, and in 1929 Canada established its mission in Tokyo. With a mintage of 27,872 worldwide, only 5,000 coins were for sale in Canada.

Designers and Engravers:
Obv.: Susanna Blunt, Susan Taylor
Rev.: José Osio
Composition: 92.5% Ag, 7.5% Cu
Silver content: 23.29 g, 0.75 tr oz
Weight: 25.175 g **Edge:** Reeded
Diameter: 36.1 mm **Die Axis:** ↑↑
Thickness: 3.1 mm **Finish:** Proof
Case of Issue: Maroon leatherette clam style case, black flocked insert, encapsulated coin, COA

DATE	DESCRIPTION	RCM ITEM #	QUANTITY SOLD	ISSUE PRICE	FINISH	PR-68	PR-69
2009 (1929-)	80th Anniversary of Canada in Japan	106093	27,872	47.95	Proof	50.	—

CANADIAN WILDLIFE SERIES (BULLION ISSUES)

FIVE DOLLARS (1 ounce), CANADIAN WILDLIFE SERIES (BULLION ISSUES), 2011-2017.

2011-2017 Common Obverse (except for date)	2011 Timber Wolf Des. and Eng.: William Woodruff	2011 Grizzly Des. and Eng.: William Woodruff	2012 Moose Des. and Eng.: William Woodruff

2012 Cougar Des. and Eng.: José Osio	2013 Pronghorn Antelope Designer and Engraver: Emily Damstra	2013 Wood Bison Designer: Emily Damstra Engraver: Christie Paquet	2014 Peregrine Falcon Designer: Emily Damstra Engraver: RCM Staff	2014 Bald Eagle Designer: Emily Damstra Engraver: RCM Staff

2015 Red Tailed Hawk Designer: Emily Damstra Engraver: RCM Staff	2015 Great Horned Owl Designer and Engraver: RCM Staff	2016 Peregrine Falcon Designer and Engraver: RCM Staff	2017 Bald Eagle Designer and Engraver: RCM Staff

Designers:
Obv.: Susanna Blunt
Rev.: See reverse illustrations
Composition: 99.99% Ag
Weight: 31.11 g, 1.00 tr oz
Diameter: 38.0 mm
Thickness: 3.0 mm
Case of Issue: Mylar pouch

Engravers:
Obv.: Susan Taylor

Edge: Reeded
Die Axis: ↑↑
Finish: Bullion

DATE	DESCRIPTION	RCM ITEM #	QUANTITY SOLD	ISSUE PRICE	FINISH	MS-65	MS-66
2011	Timber Wolf		1,000,000	BV	Bullion	35.	—
2011	Grizzly		1,000,000	BV	Bullion	30.	—
2012	Moose		1,000,000	BV	Bullion	30.	—
2012	Cougar		1,000,000	BV	Bullion	30.	—
2013	Pronghorn Antelope		1,000,000	BV	Bullion	30.	—
2013	Wood Bison		1,000,000	BV	Bullion	30.	—
2014	Peregrine Falcon		1,000,000	BV	Bullion	30.	—
2014	Bald Eagle		1,000,000	BV	Bullion	30.	—
2015	Red Tailed Hawk		1,000,000	BV	Bullion	30.	—
2015	Great Horned Owl		1,000,000	BV	Bullion	30.	—
2016	Peregrine Falcon		1,000,000	BV	Bullion	30.	—
2017	Bald Eagle		1,000,000	BV	Bullion	30.	—

CALENDAR IN THE SKY SERIES

FIVE DOLLARS, CALENDAR IN THE SKY SERIES, 2011-2012.

This series depicts the Full Moons of the Algonquin people. The first coin in the series, Full Buck Moon, is also known as Thunder Moon or Summer Moon. The second coin, Full Hunter's Moon, is also known as Travel Moon or Dying Moon. The third coin, Full Wolf's Moon, is also known as Snow Moon or Old Moon. The April full moon known as the Pink Moon, is a tribute to the pink flowers such as the wild ground phlox depicted on the coin that appears in the springtime.

Common Obverse

Designers and Engravers:

Obv.:	Susanna Blunt, Susan Taylor
Rev.:	John Mantha, Cecily Mok

Composition: Outer ring: 92.50% Ag, 0.75% Cu
Inner core obverse: 92.50% Ag, 0.75% Cu
Inner core reverse: Niobium
Silver content: 6.56 g, 0.21 tr oz
Weight: 8.5 g (including 1.4 g Niobium)   **Edge:** Interrupted serrations
Diameter: 28.0 mm   **Die Axis:** ↑↑
Thickness: 1.8 mm   **Finish:** Proof
Case of Issue: Maple wood display case, black flocked insert, encapsulated coin, COA

Full Buck Moon

Full Hunter's Moon

Full Wolf Moon

Full Pink Moon

DATE	DESCRIPTION	RCM ITEM #	QUANTITY SOLD	ISSUE PRICE	FINISH	PR-69	PR-70
2011	Full Buck Moon	113355	6,412	119.95	Proof	75.	—
2011	Full Hunter's Moon	113364	5,446	119.95	Proof	75.	—
2012	Full Wolf Moon	113371	7,496	121.95	Proof	110.	—
2012	Full Pink Moon	113378	7,238	121.95	Proof	75.	—
—	Set of 4 coins	116529	—	487.80	Proof	300.	*

FIVE DOLLARS, 25TH ANNIVERSARY OF THE RICK HANSEN MAN-IN-MOTION TOUR, 1987-2012.

This coin was issued to commemorate the 25th anniversary of Rick Hansen's Man-in-Motion world tour between March 1985 and May 1987. Hansen covered more than 40,000 km through thirty-four countries on four continents during the 26-month trek. He raised $26,000,000 for spinal cord research.

Designers and Engravers:

Obv.:	Susanna Blunt, Susan Taylor
Rev.:	Chris Reid, Rosina Li, Christie Paquet

Composition: 99.99% Ag
Silver content: 23.17 g, 0.74 tr oz
Weight: 23.17 g   **Edge:** Reeded
Diameter: 36.0 mm   **Die Axis:** ↑↑
Thickness: 2.8 mm   **Finish:** Proof
Case of Issue: Maroon leatherette clam style case, black
flocked insert, encapsulated coin, COA,
custom sleeve

DATE	DESCRIPTION	RCM ITEM #	QUANTITY SOLD	ISSUE PRICE	FINISH	PR-69	PR-70
2012 (1987-)	Rick Hansen	118573	3,409	69.95	Proof	30.	—

FIVE DOLLARS, GEORGINA POPE, 2012.

In 1899 Georgina Pope was one of four volunteer nurses who travelled to South Africa to assist British troops during the South African War. Each nurse was given the rank of lieutenant in the military.

Designers and Engravers:

Obv.:	Susanna Blunt, Susan Taylor
Rev.:	Laurie McGaw, Susan Taylor, Matt Bowen

Composition: 99.99% Ag
Silver content: 23.17 g, 0.74 tr oz

Weight:	23.17 g	Edge:	Reeded
Diameter:	36.0 mm	Die Axis:	↑↑
Thickness:	2.7 mm	Finish:	Proof

Case of Issue: Maroon leatherette clam style case, black flocked insert, encapsulated coin, COA

DATE	DESCRIPTION	RCM ITEM #	QUANTITY SOLD	ISSUE PRICE	FINISH	PR-69	PR-70
2012	Georgina Pope	120805	3,154	69.95	Proof	40.	—

FIVE DOLLARS, DEVIL'S BRIGADE, 2013.

During World War II Canada joined forces with the United States to create the First Special Service Force.

Designers and Engravers:

Obv.:	Susanna Blunt, Susan Taylor
Rev.:	Ardell Bourgeois, Cecily Mok

Composition: 99.99% Ag
Silver content: 23.0 g, 0.74 tr oz

Weight:	23.0 g	Edge:	Reeded
Diameter:	36.00 mm	Die Axis:	↑↑
Thickness:	2.8 mm	Finish:	Proof

Case of Issue: Maroon leatherette clam style case, black flocked insert, encapsulated coin, COA

DATE	DESCRIPTION	RCM ITEM #	QUANTITY SOLD	ISSUE PRICE	FINISH	PR-69	PR-70
2013	Devil's Brigade	126711	7,255	59.95	Proof	55.	—

CONTEMPORARY ABORIGINAL ART SET

FIVE DOLLARS, CONTEMPORARY ABORIGINAL ART SET, 2013.

This set honours contemporary Aboriginal art.

Designers and Engravers:

Obv.:	Susanna Blunt, Susan Taylor
Rev.:	Ulaayu Pilurtuut, Alex Tirabasso

Composition: 99.99% Ag, Niobium
Silver content: 8.5 g, 0.273 tr oz
Weight: 8.5 g (including 1.4 g Niobium)
Diameter: 28.0 mm
Thickness: 1.8 mm
Edge: Interrupted serrations
Die Axis: ↑↑
Finish: Proof
Case of Issue: Black leatherette clam style case, black flocked insert, encapsulated coin, COA

Common Obverse   Mother and Baby Ice Fishing   Father Ice Fishing

DATE	DESCRIPTION	RCM ITEM #	QUANTITY SOLD	ISSUE PRICE	FINISH	PR-69	PR-70
2013	Mother and Baby Ice Fishing	125430	4,791	139.95	Proof	80.	—
2013	Ice Fishing Father	125421	2,968	139.95	Proof	80.	—

ABORIGINAL TRADITION OF HUNTING SERIES

FIVE DOLLARS, ABORIGINAL TRADITION OF HUNTING SERIES, 2013-2014.

This series honours the rich heritage of Aboriginal hunting from a boy's inaugural hunt (coin one) to the Cree geese hunting in spring (coin four).

Common Obverse	Deer	Bison	Hunting in Harmony	Canada Goose
	Designer: Darlene Gait	Designer: Darlene Gait	(The Seal)	Designer: Tim Whiskeychan
	Engraver: Christie Paquet	Engraver: Eric Boer	Designer: Darlene Gait	Engraver: RCM Staff
			Engraver: RCM Staff	

Designers:
Obv.: Susanna Blunt
Rev.: See Reverse illustrations
Composition: 99.99% Ag
Silver content: 22.9 g, 0.736 tr oz
Weight: 22.9 g
Diameter: 36.0 mm
Thickness: 2.8 mm
Case of Issue: Maroon leatherette clam style case, black flocked insert, encapsulated coin, COA

Engravers:
Obv.: Susan Taylor
Edge: Reeded
Die Axis: ↑↑
Finish: Proof

DATE	DESCRIPTION	RCM ITEM #	QUANTITY SOLD	ISSUE PRICE	FINISH	PR-69	PR-70
2013	Deer	123676	4,758	69.95	Proof	50.	—
2013	Bison	123669	1,726	69.95	Proof	50.	—
2014	Hunting in Harmony (The Seal)	129478	2,751	69.95	Proof	50.	—
2014	Canada Goose	130595	2,554	69.95	Proof	50.	—

FIVE DOLLARS, ROYAL INFANT TOYS, 2013.

Designers and Engravers:
Obv.: Susanna Blunt, Susan Taylor
Rev.: Laurie McGaw, Samantha Strath
Composition: 99.99% Ag, Selectively gold plated
Silver content: 23.17 g, 0.75 tr oz
Weight: 23.17 g   **Edge:** Reeded
Diameter: 36.0 mm   **Die Axis:** ↑↑
Thickness: 2.7 mm   **Finish:** Proof
Case of Issue: Maroon leatherette clam style case, black flocked insert, encapsulated coin, COA custom box

DATE	DESCRIPTION	RCM ITEM #	QUANTITY SOLD	ISSUE PRICE	FINISH	PR-69	PR-70
2013	Royal Infant Toys	127107	9,739	74.95	Proof	50.	—

HISTORICAL DESIGNS ON CANADIAN BANK NOTE SERIES

FIVE DOLLARS, CANADIAN BANK NOTES SERIES, 2013-2015.

This series depicts the colourful vignettes used on early Canadian bank notes.

| Common Obverse | Seascape Themed Vignette Engr.: Matt Bowen | Saint George Slaying the Dragon Vignette Engr.: José Osio | Lion on the Mountain Vignette Engr.: RCM Staff | Canadian Banknote Vignette Engr.: RCM Staff |

Designers:
Obv.: Susanna Blunt
Rev.: RCM Staff, See reverse illustrations
Composition: 99.99% Ag
Silver content: 23.0 g, 0.74 tr oz
Weight: 23.0 g
Diameter: 36.0 mm
Thickness: 2.8 mm
Case of Issue: Maroon clam style case, black flocked insert, encapsulated coin, COA, custom box

Engravers:
Obv.: Susan Taylor

Edge: Reeded
Die Axis: ↑↑
Finish: Proof

DATE	DESCRIPTION	RCM ITEM #	QUANTITY SOLD	ISSUE PRICE	FINISH	PR-69	PR-70
2013	Seascape Theme Vignette (Canadian Bank of Commerce 1888 $20)	124052	7,155	69.95	Proof	60.	—
2014	Saint George Slaying the Dragon Vignette (1859 Bank of Western Canada $5)	126312	8,497	69.95	Proof	60.	—
2014	Lion on the Mountain Vignette (Northern Crown Bank)	130281	7,560	69.95	Proof	60.	—
2015	Canadian Banknote Vignette (1929 Barclay's Bank $5)	N/A	3,695	69.95	Proof	60.	—

FIVE DOLLARS, ALICE MUNRO, 2014.

Canadian author Alice Munro, whose short stories are revered the world over, was the recipient of the 2013 Nobel Prize in Literature.

Designers and Engravers:
Obv.: Susanna Blunt, Susan Taylor
Rev.: Laurie McGaw, RCM Staff
Composition: 99.99% Ag
Silver content: 23.17 g, 0.74 tr oz
Weight: 23.17 g
Diameter: 36.0 mm
Thickness: 2.7 mm
Case of Issue: Maroon leatherette clam style case, black flocked insert, encapsulated coin, COA

Edge: Reeded
Die Axis: ↑↑
Finish: Proof

DATE	DESCRIPTION	RCM ITEM #	QUANTITY SOLD	ISSUE PRICE	FINISH	PR-69	PR-70
2014	Alice Munro	132669	4,587	69.95	Proof	45.	—

FIVE DOLLARS, 100TH ANNIVERSARY OF THE CANADIAN EXPEDITIONARY FORCE, 2014.

This coin was issued to pay tribute to those who served in the regiments, battalions and ancilliary units of the Canadian Expeditionary Force (CEF) during the First World War.

Designers and Engravers:

Obv.:	Susanna Blunt, Susan Taylor
Rev.:	Scott Waters, RCM Staff
Composition:	99.99% Ag
Silver content:	23.17 g, 0.74 tr oz
Weight:	23.17 g
Diameter:	36.0 mm
Thickness:	2.7 mm
Case of Issue:	Maroon leatherette clam style case, black flocked insert, encapsulated coin, COA

Edge:	Reeded
Die Axis:	↑↑
Finish:	Proof

DATE	DESCRIPTION	RCM ITEM #	QUANTITY SOLD	ISSUE PRICE	FINISH	PR-69	PR-70
2014	100th Anniversary of the Canadian Expeditionary Force	130545	6,384	64.95	Proof	55.	—

FIVE DOLLARS, PRINCESS TO MONARCH, 2014.

In celebration of the United Kingdom's longest-reigning monarch Queen Elizabeth II, this coin's reverse features an interpretation of a 1951 photograph in which Princess Elizabeth is seen inspecting the troops in Fredericton, New Brunswick.

Designers and Engravers:

Obv.:	Susanna Blunt, Susan Taylor
Rev.:	Trevor Tennant, RCM Staff
Composition:	99.99% Ag
Silver content:	23.17 g, 0.74 tr oz
Weight:	23.17 g
Diameter:	36.0 mm
Thickness:	2.7 mm
Case of Issue:	Maroon leatherette clam style case, black flocked insert, encapsulated coin, COA

Edge:	Reeded
Die Axis:	↑↑
Finish:	Proof

DATE	DESCRIPTION	RCM ITEM #	QUANTITY SOLD	ISSUE PRICE	FINISH	PR-69	PR-70
2014	Princess to Monarch	132679	2,821	64.95	Proof	55.	—

Note: This is one coin of a twenty-four coin set issued by twelve different Commonwealth countries.

FLOWERS IN CANADA SET

FIVE DOLLARS, FLOWERS IN CANADA SET, 2014.

Featuring the art of Bert Liverance on the coins' reverses, this set of three coins uses a niobium insert to capture some of the beauty seen in Canada's flowers.

Common Obverse | **Tulip**

Rose | **Poinsettia**

Designers:		**Engravers:**	
Obv.:	Susanna Blunt	Obv.:	Susan Taylor
Rev.:	Bert Liverance	Rev.:	RCM Staff
Composition:	99.99% Ag, Niobium	Silver content:	9.0 g, 0.289 tr oz
Weight:	9.0 g (including 1.4 g Niobium)	Edge:	Interrupted serrations
Diameter:	28.0 mm	Die Axis:	↑↑
Thickness:	N/A	Finish:	Proof
Case of Issue:	Maroon clam style case, black flocked insert, encapsulated coin, COA		

DATE	DESCRIPTION	RCM ITEM #	QUANTITY SOLD	ISSUE PRICE	FINISH	PR-69	PR-70
2014	Tulip	130933	4,046	139.95	Proof	90.	—
2014	Rose	130934	2,977	139.95	Proof	90.	—
2014	Poinsettia	130936	2,565	139.95	Proof	90.	—

FIVE DOLLARS (1 ounce), FIVE BLESSINGS, 2014.

| Common Obverse | 2014 Proof Finish, Coloured | 2014 Bullion Finish |

Designers:
- Obv.: Susanna Blunt
- Rev.: RCM Staff

Composition: 99.99% Ag
Weight: 31.39 g, 1.01 tr oz
Diameter: 38.0 mm
Thickness: 3.2 mm
Case of Issue: Proof: Maroon leatherette clam style case, black flock insert, encapsulated coin, COA
Bullion: Unknown

Engravers:
- Obv.: Susan Taylor
- Rev.: RCM Staff

Edge: Reeded
Die Axis: ↑↑
Finish: Proof, coloured; Bullion

DATE	DESCRIPTION	RCM ITEM #	QUANTITY SOLD	ISSUE PRICE	FINISH	SP-68	SP-69	PR-69	PR-70
2014	Five Blessings, Proof, Colourised	133938	4,559	99.95	Proof	*	*	100.	—
2014	Five Blessings, Bullion Finish	N/A	N/A	BV	Bullion	35.	45.	*	*

FIVE DOLLARS, YEAR OF THE SHEEP, 2015.

This coin celebrates the Chinese New Year and the wealth, warmth and prosperity that the Year of the Sheep ushers in.

Designers and Engravers:
- Obv.: Susanna Blunt, Susan Taylor
- Rev.: Simon Ng, RCM Staff

Composition: 99.99% Ag
Silver content: 23.17 g, 0.74 tr oz
Weight: 23.17 g
Diameter: 36.0 mm
Thickness: N/A
Case of Issue: Maroon leatherette clam style case, black flocked insert, encapsulated coin, COA

Edge: Reeded
Die Axis: ↑↑
Finish: Proof

DATE	DESCRIPTION	RCM ITEM #	QUANTITY SOLD	ISSUE PRICE	FINISH	PR-69	PR-70
2015	Year of the Sheep	130569	7,975	74.95	Proof	65.	—

FIVE DOLLARS, POLAR BEAR AND CUB, 2015.

Designers and Engravers:
- Obv.: Susanna Blunt, Susan Taylor
- Rev.: Germaine Arnaktauyok

Composition: 99.99% Ag
Silver content: 31.39 g, 1.01 tr oz
Weight: 31.39 g
Diameter: 36.0 mm
Thickness: N/A
Case of Issue: Maroon leatherette clam style case, black beauty, COA

Edge: Reeded
Die Axis: ↑↑
Finish: Proof

DATE	DESCRIPTION	RCM ITEM #	QUANTITY SOLD	ISSUE PRICE	FINISH	PR-69	PR-70
2015	Polar Bear and Cub	141550	3,585	89.95	Proof	80.	—

CORNELIUS KRIEGHOFF 200TH ANNIVERSARY SET

**FIVE DOLLARS, CORNELIUS KRIEGHOFF
200TH ANNIVERSARY SET, 2015.**

This set of three coins celebrates the 200th anniversary of the birth of Cornelius Krieghoff, one of Canada's most well-known artists depicting 19th century life among French-Canadian settlers and First Nations peoples.

Common Obverse   **Hunter in Winter**

Designers and Engravers:

Obv.:	Susanna Blunt, Susan Taylor
Rev.:	Cornelius Krieghoff, RCM Staff

Composition: 99.99% Ag
Silver content: 23.17 g, 0.74 tr oz
Weight: 23.17 g
Diameter: 36.07 mm
Edge: Reeded
Die Axis: ↑↑
Finish: Proof
Thickness: N/A
Case of Issue: Three-hole red wooden lacquered box, black flocked insert, encapsulated coin, COA

**Moccasin Seller Crossing the
St. Lawrence at Quebec City**   **Indian Wigwam in
Lower Canada**

DATE	DESCRIPTION	RCM ITEM #	QUANTITY SOLD	ISSUE PRICE	FINISH	PR-69	PR-70
2015	Hunter in Winter	N/A	123	N.I.I.	Proof	60.	—
2015	Moccasin Seller Crossing the St. Lawrence at Quebec City	N/A	131	N.I.I.	Proof	60.	—
2015	Indian Wigwam in Lower Canada	N/A	131	N.I.I.	Proof	60.	—
2015	Set of 3 coins	148043	1,803	199.95	Proof	150.	*

FIVE DOLLARS, TODAY'S MONARCH, YESTERYEAR'S PRINCESS, 2015.

As the UK's longest-reigning monarch, Elizabeth II's unexpected role as queen was undoubtedly shaped by her experiences as a princess during the Second World War.

Designers and Engravers:

Obv.:	Susanna Blunt, Susan Taylor
Rev.:	Trevor Tennant

Composition: 99.99% Ag
Silver content: 23.17 g, 0.74 tr oz

Weight:	23.17 g	**Edge:**	Reeded
Diameter:	36.07 mm	**Die Axis:**	↑↑
Thickness:	N/A	**Finish:**	Proof

Case of Issue: Maroon leatherette clam style case, black flocked insert, encapsulated coin, COA

DATE	DESCRIPTION	RCM ITEM #	QUANTITY SOLD	ISSUE PRICE	FINISH	PR-69	PR-70
2015	Today's Monarch, Yesteryear's Princess	133249	1,865	64.95	Proof	60.	—

FIVE DOLLARS (1 ounce), BULLION SUPERMAN SHIELD, 2016.

Designers and Engravers:

Obv.:	Susanna Blunt, Susan Taylor
Rev.:	DC Comics

Composition: 99.99% Ag

Weight:	31.1 g, 1.0 tr oz	**Edge:**	Reeded
Diameter:	38.0 mm	**Die Axis:**	↑↑
Thickness:	3.3 mm	**Finish:**	Bullion

Case of Issue: Plastic tubes of 25 coin

DATE	DESCRIPTION	RCM ITEM #	QUANTITY SOLD	ISSUE PRICE	FINISH	MS-65	MS-66
2016	$5 (1 oz), Superman Shield	N/A	N/A	BV	Bullion	30.	—

BIRTH STONE COLLECTION

FIVE DOLLARS, BIRTH STONE COLLECTION, 2016 (GIFTWARE).

Designers and Engravers:

Obv.: Susanna Blunt, Susan Taylor
Rev.: Three Degrees Creative Group
Composition: 99.99% Ag, Swarovski element
Silver content: 7.96 g, 0.25 tr oz
Weight: 7.96 g
Diameter: 27.0 mm
Thickness: 1.8 mm
Edge: Reeded
Die Axis: ↑↑
Finish: Proof
Case of Issue: Maroon leatherette clam style case, black flocked insert, encapsulated coin, COA

Common Obverse | January | February

March | April | May | June | July

August | September | October | November | December

DATE	DESCRIPTION	RCM ITEM #	QUANTITY SOLD	ISSUE PRICE	FINISH	PR-69	PR-70
2016	January	149966	3,000	49.95	Proof	70.	—
2016	February	149973	3,001	49.95	Proof	70.	—
2016	March	149981	3,000	49.95	Proof	45.	—
2016	April	149988	2,900	49.95	Proof	45.	—
2016	May	150722	3,000	49.95	Proof	45.	—
2016	June	150729	2,993	49.95	Proof	45.	—
2016	July	150736	2,999	49.95	Proof	45.	—
2016	August	151132	2,974	49.95	Proof	45.	—
2016	September	151286	2,990	49.95	Proof	45.	—
2016	October	151293	2,994	49.95	Proof	45.	—
2016	November	151301	2,983	49.95	Proof	45.	—
2016	December	151308	2,973	49.95	Proof	45.	—

BULLION PREDATOR SERIES

FIVE DOLLARS (1 ounce), PREDATOR SERIES, 2016-2017.

Common Obverse   2016 Cougar  2017 Lynx

Designers:
Obv.: Susanna Blunt
Rev.: Emily Damstra
Composition: 99.99% Ag
Weight: 31.1 g, 1.0 tr oz
Diameter: 38.0 mm
Thickness: 3.3 mm
Case of Issue: Plastic tubes of 25 coin

Engravers:
Obv.: Susan Taylor

Edge: Reeded
Die Axis: ↑↑
Finish: Bullion

DATE	DESCRIPTION	RCM ITEM #	QUANTITY SOLD	ISSUE PRICE	FINISH	MS-65	MS-66
2016	$5 (1 oz), Cougar	N/A	50,000	BV	Bullion	30.	—
2017	$5 (1 oz), Lynx	N/A	50,000	BV	Bullion	30.	—

FIVE DOLLARS, PROUDLY CANADIAN, 2017

This unique coin features a dynamic Canadian flag surrounded by brightly coloured fireworks. The flag and fireworks glow in the dark!

Designers and Engravers:
Obv.: Susanna Blunt
Rev.: Tony Bianco
Composition: 99.99% Ag
Silver content: 7.96 g, 0.256 tr oz
Weight: 7.96 g   **Edge:** Reeded
Diameter: 27.0 mm   **Die Axis:** ↑↑
Thickness: N/A   **Finish:** Specimen
Case of Issue: Folder with easel back.

DATE	DESCRIPTION	RCM ITEM #	MINTAGE	ISSUE PRICE	FINISH	SP-68	SP-69
2017	Proudly Canadian	160837	N/D	29.95	Specimen	30.	—

FIVE DOLLARS, HEARTS AGLOW, 2018

Designers and Engravers:
Obv.: Susanna Blunt
Rev.: Jose Osio
Composition: 99.99% Ag
Silver content: 7.96 g, 0.256 tr oz
Weight: 7.96 g   **Edge:** Reeded
Diameter: 27.0 mm   **Die Axis:** ↑↑
Thickness: N/A   **Finish:** Specimen
Case of Issue: Folder with easel back.

DATE	DESCRIPTION	RCM ITEM #	MINTAGE	ISSUE PRICE	FINISH	SP-68	SP-69
2018	Hearts Aglow	167191	W.S.L.	29.95	Specimen	30.	—

BIRTHSTONE SERIES

FIVE DOLLARS, BIRTHSTONES, 2018.

Like a kaleidoscope of ornate shapes and patterns, the mandala is a spellbinding representation of symmetry, harmony and unity! Art, astronomy and geometry intersect in this monthly Birthstone Series, which features a colourful henn-inspired motif and a Swarovoski® crystal that adds vibrant symbolism.

Common Obverse

Designers:			**Engravers:**	
Obv.:	Susanna Blunt		Obv.:	Susan Taylor
Rev.:	Pandora Young		Rev.:	Susan Taylor
Composition:	99.99% Ag		**Silver content:**	7.96 g, 0.256 tr oz
Weight:	7.96 g		**Edge:**	Reeded
Diameter:	27 mm		**Die Axis:**	↑↑
Thickness:	N/A		**Finish:**	Proof
Case of Issue:	Maroon clamshell with black beauty box, COA			

January	February	March	April	May	June

July	August	September	October	November	December

DATE	DESCRIPTION	RCM ITEM #	MINTAGE	ISSUE PRICE	FINISH	PR-69	PR-70
2018	January	164206	4,000	54.95	Proof	55.	—
2018	February	164214	4,000	54.95	Proof	55.	—
2018	March	164222	4,000	54.95	Proof	55.	—
2018	April	164230	4,000	54.95	Proof	55.	—
2018	May	164341	4,000	54.95	Proof	55.	—
2018	June	164351	4,000	54.95	Proof	55.	—
2018	July	164928	4,000	54.95	Proof	55.	—
2018	August	165445	4,000	54.95	Proof	55.	—
2018	September	165496	4,000	54.95	Proof	55.	—
2018	October	165505	4,000	54.95	Proof	55.	—
2018	November	165513	4,000	54.95	Proof	55.	—
2018	December	165521	4,000	54.95	Proof	55.	—,

ZODIAC SERIES

FIVE DOLLARS, ZODIAC SERIES, 2019.

One by one, the 12 zodiac constellations rise and march across the night sky in the Royal Canadian Mint's 2019 Zodiac series, with each coin featuring a ring of 20 Swarovoski® crystals.

Designers:		**Engravers:**	
Obv.:	Susanna Blunt	Obv.:	Susan Taylor
Rev.:	Jori van de Linde	Rev.:	Susan Taylor
Composition:	99.99% Ag	**Silver content:**	7.96 g, 0.256 tr oz
Weight:	7.96 g	**Edge:**	Reeded
Diameter:	27 mm	**Die Axis:**	↑↑
Thickness:	N/A	**Finish:**	Proof
Case of Issue:	Standard maroon clamshell with black beauty box, COA		

Common Obverse

Capricorn	Aquarius	Pisces	Aries	Taurus	Gemini

DATE	DESCRIPTION	RCM ITEM #	MINTAGE	ISSUE PRICE	FINISH	PR-69	PR-70
2019	Capricorn	170819	4,000	54.95	Proof	55.	—
2019	Aquarius	171006	4,000	54.95	Proof	55.	—
2019	Pisces	171040	4,000	54.95	Proof	55.	—
2019	Aries	171048	4,000	54.95	Proof	55.	—
2019	Taurus	171032	4,000	54.95	Proof	55.	—
2019	Gemini	171056	4,000	54.95	Proof	55.	—

FIVE DOLLAR DERIVATIVES

DATE	DESCRIPTION	QUANTITY SOLD	ISSUE PRICE	ISSUER	FINISH	MARKET PRICE
2004	**Five Dollar Coin** Majestic Moose. Two $5 stamps (one mint, one cancelled), COA, Wooden presentation case	12,822	39.95	RCM, CP	PR-69	80.
2004	**Five Dollar and Ten Cent Coins** Canadian Open Championship. Two commemorative stamps (one mint, one cancelled), two golf tees, RCM medallion, Framed, COA	18,750	49.99	RCM, CP	PR-69	60.
2005	**Allied Forces Silver Proof Set**, six coins: Australia, Canada, Russia, U.S.A. and U.K.	10,000	£245.	RCM, BRM	PR-69	400.
2005	**Five Dollar Coin** White-tailed Deer and Fawn. Two $1 stamps (one mint, one cancelled), COA, Wooden presentation case.	6,439	49.55	RCM, CP	PR-69	40.
2005	**Five Dollar Coin** Atlantic Walrus and Calf. Two $1 stamps (one mint, one cancelled), COA, Wooden presentation case.	5,519	49.55	RCM, CP	PR-69	40.
2006	**Five Dollar Coin** Peregrine Falcon and Nestlings.. Two $2 stamps (one mint, one cancelled), COA, Wooded presentation case.	7,226	49.55	RCM, CP	PR-69	40.
2006	**Five Dollar Coin** Sable Island Horse and Foal. Two $2 stamps (one mint, one cancelled), COA, Wooded presentation case.	10,108	49.55	RCM, CP	PR-69	40.
2006	**Five Dollar Coin Snowbirds**. Four 51¢ stamps (two mint, two on a "uniquely cancelled" souvenir sheet); Booklet; Numbered plaque; Metallic box	10,034	59.95	RCM, CP	PR-69	40.

FIVE AND TEN DOLLARS

MONTREAL SUMMER OLYMPIC GAMES, SILVER ISSUES, 1973-1976.

In 1976, Montreal, Quebec, hosted the XXI Olympiad. To commemorate and help finance Canada's first Olympics, the federal government agreed to produce a series of twenty-eight silver and two gold coins (see page 440 for the $100 gold coins). There are seven series of silver coins. Each series has two $5 and two $10 coins, making a total of fourteen coins of each denomination. Each series depicts different Olympic themes on the reverse and has a common design (except for the date) on the obverse. The date on the coins is usually the year of minting. Orders for the Olympic coins were accepted up to the end of December 1976, so a small unit continued to function into 1977 on the Olympic Coin Program. Mintage by series was never recorded, but the annual reports of the Royal Canadian Mint give the following figures by year: 1973 - 537,898 $10, 543,098 $5; 1974 - 3,949,878 $10, 3,981,140 $5; 1975 - 4,952,433 $10, 3,970,000 $5; 1976 - 3,970,514 $10, 3,775,259 $5. These figures do not necessarily coincide with the actual post office sales figures for the coins.

The Olympic coins were offered to the collector in two finishes, brilliant uncirculated and proof. The uncirculated issues were packaged and offered for sale in four different formats: (1) encapsulated (single coins only in styrene crystal capsules); (2) encapsulated one-coin "standard" case (single coins in black case with red interior); (3) encapsulated four-coin "custom" set (two $5 and two $10 coins by series in black case with gold trim and red insert); and (4) encapsulated four-coin "prestige" set (two $5 and two $10 coins by series in matte black leatherette case with blue insert).

The proof coins were only offered in sets, and the "deluxe" case of issue was made of Canadian white birch with a specially tanned steer hide cover with a black insert. All coins in the set are encapsulated.

Because of the fluctuating price of silver during the years of the program (1973 to 1976), the original issue prices varied somewhat from series to series.

SERIES I TO VII

The following information is common to all twenty-eight $5.00 and $10.00 silver coins. Naturally, the date changes with the year of issue.

SPECIFICATIONS

FIVE DOLLARS		**TEN DOLLARS**	
Composition:	92.5% Ag, 7.5% Cu	Composition:	92.5% Ag, 7.5% Cu
Silver content:	22.48 g, 0.72 tr oz	Silver content:	44.95 g, 1.44 tr oz
Weight:	24.30 g	Weight:	48.60 g
Diameter:	38.0 mm	Diameter:	45.0 mm
Thickness:	2.4 mm	Thickness:	3.2 mm
Edge:	Reeded	Edge:	Reeded
Die Axis:	↑↑	Die Axis:	↑↑
Finish:	Proof and Circulation	Finish:	Proof and Circulation
Case of Issue:	See above	Case of Issue:	See above

Original Issue Prices

PACKAGE TYPE	SERIES I	SERIES II	SERIES III-VII
$5 Encapsulated	6.00	7.50	8.00
$10 Encapsulated	12.00	15.00	15.75
Set of 4 Encapsulated	36.00	45.00	47.50
$5 in Standard Case	7.50	9.00	9.00
$10 in Standard Case	14.00	17.00	17.00
Set of 4 in Standard Case	43.00	52.00	52.00
Custom Set	45.00	55.00	55.00
Prestige Set	50.00	60.00	60.00
Deluxe Proof Set	72.50	82.50	82.50

MONTREAL SUMMER OLYMPIC GAMES — SERIES I

1973 $10 Obverse
Designer: Arnold Machin
Engraver: Patrick Brindley

Coin No. 1
Map of the World
Reverse design was
photochemically etched

Coin No. 3
Montreal Skyline
Ago Aarand

1973 $5 Obverse
Designer: Arnold Machin
Engraver: Patrick Brindley

Coin No. 2
Map of North America
Reverse design was
photochemically etched

Coin No. 4
Kingston and Sailboats
Terrence Smith

Theme: Geographic
Official Release Date: December 13, 1973. The Series I issuing period began in late 1973 and was carried over into 1974.
Designer of Reverse: Georges Huel, worked by invitation.
Reverse Engravers: See above
Issue Price: See page 180
Finish: Proof and circulation

DATE	DESCRIPTION	QUANTITY SOLD	FINISH	MS-65	MS-66	MS-67/PR-68	PR-69
1973	$5 Map of North America	537,898	Circulation	20.	25.	—	*
1973	$5 Map of North America	Included	Proof	—	—	25.	—
1973	$5 Kingston and Sailboats	Included	Circulation	20.	25.	—	*
1973	$5 Kingston and Sailboats	Included	Proof	—	—	25.	—
1973	$10 Map of the World	543,098	Circulation	40.	50.	—	*
1973	$10 Map of the World	Included	Proof	—	—	50.	—
1973	$10 Montreal Skyline	Included	Circulation	40.	50.	—	—
1973	$10 Montreal Skyline	Included	Proof	—	—	50.	—

Note: Mintage numbers are simply estimates based on the 1974-1976 Royal Canadian Mint reports.

MONTREAL SUMMER OLYMPIC GAMES — 1973-1974 Mule

During the latter half of 1974, a dated obverse die - possibly made in advance for the Series II coins - was paired inadvertently with a Series I reverse die of the Map of the World resulting in the production and release of a Series I-Series II mule dated 1974. The 1973-1974 Mule was found in the 1973 four-coin custom sets, and mostly those with a European release location.

DATE	DESCRIPTION	QUANTITY SOLD	FINISH	MS-65	MS-66	MS-67
1973-74	$10 1974 Obverse - 1973 Map Reverse	Unknown	Circulation	350.	450.	—

NOTE TO COLLECTORS

1. The 1976 Montreal Summer Olympic Games were financed by the sale of five and ten dollar sterling silver coins issued over a four-year period (1973-1976). The volume of coins soon overcame any collector demand. Their value is based on face, or intrinsic value, whichever is greater. Currently, the intrinsic value is the driving force, and this will vary day-to-day with the silver market.

2. A quantity of Series One coins was issued in Styrofoam rolls to the banks for circulation. For these coins see *Canadian Coins, Volume One*. The remainders of Series One coins, and coins from Series Two through Seven were encapsulated. They are assigned a grade of MS-65 or PR-69. To obtain a higher grade the coin must be removed from the capsule and graded by a reputable grading company.

INTRINSIC VALUE OF MONTREAL OLYMPIC COINS AT VARIOUS SILVER VALUES

PRICE OF SILVER	$5	$10	FOUR COIN SET
$20.00	$14.40	$28.80	$84.40
$25.00	$18.00	$36.00	$108.00
$30.00	$21.60	$43.20	$129.60
$35.00	$25.20	$50.40	$151.10
$40.00	$28.80	$57.60	$172.80
$45.00	$32.40	$64.80	$194.40
$50.00	$36.00	$72.00	$216.00
$55.00	$39.60	$79.20	$237.60
$60.00	$43.20	$86.40	$259.20
$65.00	$46.80	$93.60	$280.80
$70.00	$50.40	$100.80	$302.40
$75.00	$54.00	$108.00	$324.00
$80.00	$57.60	$115.20	$345.60
$85.00	$61.20	$122.40	$367.20
$90.00	$65.80	$131.60	$394.80
$95.00	$69.40	$138.80	$416.40
$100.00	$73.00	$146.00	$438.00

MONTREAL SUMMER OLYMPIC GAMES — SERIES II

1974 $10 Obverse
Designer: Arnold Machin
Engraver: Patrick Brindley

Coin No. 5
Head of Zeus
Patrick Brindley

Coin No. 7
Temple of Zeus
Walter Ott

1974 $5 Obverse
Designer: Arnold Machin
Engraver: Patrick Brindley

Coin No. 6
Athlete with Torch
Patrick Brindley

Coin No. 8
Olympic Rings and Wreath
Walter Ott

Theme: Olympic Motifs
Official Release Date: September 16, 1974
Designer of Reverse: Anthony Mann, winner of an invitational competition.
Reverse Engravers: See above
Issue Price: See page 180
Finish: Proof and circulation

DATE	DESCRIPTION	QUANTITY SOLD	FINISH	MS-65	MS-66	MS-67/PR-68	PR-69
1974	$5 Athlete with Torch	1,990,570	Circulation	20.	25.	—	*
1974	$5 Athlete with Torch	Included	Proof	—	—	25.	—
1974	$5 Olympic Rings and Wreath	Included	Circulation	20.	25.	—	*
1974	$5 Olympic Rings and Wreath	Included	Proof	—	—	25.	—
1974	$10 Head of Zeus	1,974,939	Circulation	40.	50.	—	*
1974	$10 Head of Zeus	Included	Proof	—	—	50.	—
1974	$10 Temple of Zeus	Included	Circulation	40.	50.	—	*
1974	$10 Temple of Zeus	Included	Proof	—	—	50.	—

MONTREAL SUMMER OLYMPIC GAMES — SERIES III

1974 $10 Obverse
Designer: Arnold Machin
Engraver: Patrick Brindley

Coin No. 9
Lacrosse
Walter Ott

Coin No. 11
Cycling
Ago Aarand

1974 $5 Obverse
Designer: Arnold Machin
Engraver: Patrick Brindley

Coin No. 10
Canoeing
Patrick Brindley

Coin No. 12
Rowing
Terrence Smith

Theme:	Early Canadian Sports
Official Release Date:	April 16, 1975
Designer of Reverse:	Ken Danby, winner of an invitational competition.
Engravers:	See above
Issue Price:	See page 180
Finish:	Proof and circulation

DATE	DESCRIPTION	QUANTITY SOLD	FINISH	MS-65	MS-66	MS-67/PR-68	PR-69
1974	$5 Canoeing	1,990,570	Circulation	20.	25.	—	*
1974	$5 Canoeing	Included	Proof	—	—	25.	—
1974	$5 Rowing	Included	Circulation	20.	25.	—	*
1974	$5 Rowing	Included	Proof	—	—	25.	—
1974	$10 Lacrosse	1,974,939	Circulation	40.	50.	—	*
1974	$10 Lacrosse	Included	Proof	—	—	50.	—
1974	$10 Cycling	Included	Circulation	40.	50.	—	*
1974	$10 Cycling	Included	Proof	—	—	50.	—

MONTREAL SUMMER OLYMPIC GAMES — SERIES IV

1975 $10 Obverse
Designer: Arnold Machin
Engraver: Patrick Brindley

Coin No. 13
Men's Hurdles
Patrick Brindley

Coin No. 15
Women's Shot Put
Patrick Brindley

1975 $5 Obverse
Designer: Arnold Machin
Engraver: Patrick Brindley

Coin No. 14
Marathon
Walter Ott

Coin No. 16
Women's Javelin
Walter Ott

Theme: Olympic Track and Field Sports
Official Release Date: August 12, 1975
Designer of Reverse: Leo Yerxa, winner of an invitational competition.
Engravers: See above
Issue Price: See page 180
Finish: Proof and circulation

DATE	DESCRIPTION	QUANTITY SOLD	FINISH	MS-65	MS-66	MS-67/PR-68	PR-69
1975	$5 Marathon	1,985,000	Circulation	20.	25.	—	*
1975	$5 Marathon	Included	Proof	—	—	25.	—
1975	$5 Women's Javelin	Included	Circulation	20.	25.	—	*
1975	$5 Women's Javelin	Included	Proof	—	—	25.	—
1975	$10 Men's Hurdles	2,476,217	Circulation	40.	50.	—	*
1975	$10 Men's Hurdles	Included	Proof	—	—	50.	—
1975	$10 Women's Shot Put	Included	Circulation	40.	50.	—	*
1975	$10 Women's Shot Put	Included	Proof	—	—	50.	—

MONTREAL SUMMER OLYMPIC GAMES — SERIES V

| 1975 $10 Obverse
Designer: Arnold Machin
Engraver: Patrick Brindley | Coin No. 17
Paddling
Reverse design was
photochemically etched | Coin No. 19
Sailing
Reverse design was
photochemically etched |

| 1975 $5 Obverse
Designer: Arnold Machin
Engraver: Patrick Brindley | Coin No. 18
Diving
Reverse design was
photochemically etched | Coin No. 20
Swimming
Reverse design was
photochemically etched |

Theme: Olympic Summer Sports
Official Release Date: December 1, 1975
Designer of Reverse: Lynda Cooper, winner of an open national competition.
Engravers: See above
Issue Price: See page 180
Finish: Proof and circulation

DATE	DESCRIPTION	QUANTITY SOLD	FINISH	MS-65	MS-66	MS-67/PR-68	PR-69
1975	$5 Diving	1,985,000	Circulation	20.	25.	—	*
1975	$5 Diving	Included	Proof	—	—	25.	—
1975	$5 Swimming	Included	Circulation	20.	25.	—	*
1975	$5 Swimming	Included	Proof	—	—	25.	—
1975	$10 Paddling	2,476,216	Circulation	40.	50.	—	*
1975	$10 Paddling	Included	Proof	—	—	50.	—
1975	$10 Sailing	Included	Circulation	40.	50.	—	*
1975	$10 Sailing	Included	Proof	—	—	50.	—

MONTREAL SUMMER OLYMPIC GAMES — SERIES VI

1976 $10 Obverse
Designer: Arnold Machin
Engraver: Patrick Brindley

Coin No. 21
Field Hockey
Reverse design was
photochemically etched

Coin No. 23
Soccer
Reverse design was
photochemically etched

1976 $5 Obverse
Designer: Arnold Machin
Engraver: Patrick Brindley

Coin No. 22
Fencing
Reverse design was
photochemically etched

Coin No. 24
Boxing
Reverse design was
photochemically etched

Theme: Olympic Team and Body Contact Sports
Official Release Date: March 1, 1976
Designer of Reverse: Shigeo Fukada, winner of an open international competition.
Engravers: See above
Issue Price: See page 180
Finish: Proof and circulation

DATE	DESCRIPTION	QUANTITY SOLD	FINISH	MS-65	MS-66	MS-67/PR-68	PR-69
1976	$5 Fencing	1,887,630	Circulation	20.	25.	—	*
1976	$5 Fencing	Included	Proof	—	—	25.	—
1976	$5 Boxing	Included	Circulation	20.	25.	—	*
1976	$5 Boxing	Included	Proof	—	—	25.	—
1976	$10 Field Hockey	1,985.257	Circulation	40.	50.	—	*
1976	$10 Field Hockey	Included	Proof	—	—	50.	—
1976	$10 Soccer	Included	Circulation	40.	50.	—	*
1976	$10 Soccer	Included	Proof	—	—	50.	—

MONTREAL SUMMER OLYMPIC GAMES — SERIES VII

1976 $10 Obverse Designer: Arnold Machin Engraver: Patrick Brindley	**Coin No. 25** Olympic Stadium Ago Aarand	**Coin No. 27** Olympic Velodrome Terrence Smith

1976 $5 Obverse Designer: Arnold Machin Engraver: Patrick Brindley	**Coin No. 26** Olympic Village Sheldon Beveridge	**Coin No. 28** Olympic Flame Walter Ott

Theme: Olympic Games Souvenir Designs
Official Release Date: June 1, 1976
Designer of Reverse: Elliott John Morrison, winner of an invitational competition.
Engravers: See above
Issue Price: See page 180
Finish: Proof and circulation

DATE	DESCRIPTION	QUANTITY SOLD	FINISH	MS-65	MS-66	MS-67/PR-68	PR-69
1976	$5 Olympic Village	1,887,629	Circulation	20.	25.	—	*
1976	$5 Olympic Village	Included	Proof	—	—	25.	—
1976	$5 Olympic Flame	Included	Circulation	20.	25.	—	*
1976	$5 Olympic Flame	Included	Proof	—	—	25.	—
1976	$10 Olympic Stadium	1,985,257	Circulation	40.	50.	—	*
1976	$10 Olympic Stadium	Included	Proof	—	—	50.	—
1976	$10 Olympic Velodrome	Included	Circulation	40.	50.	—	*
1976	$10 Olympic Velodrome	Included	Proof	—	—	50.	—

EIGHT DOLLARS

EIGHT DOLLARS, GREAT GRIZZLY, 2004.

Designers:	
Obv.:	Susanna Blunt
Rev.:	Alain Leduc
Composition:	99.99% Ag
Silver content:	28.8 g, 0.925 tr oz
Weight:	28.8 g
Diameter:	39.0 mm
Thickness:	2.8 mm
Case of Issue:	See Derivatives, page 195

Engravers:	
Obv.:	Susan Taylor
Rev.:	Susan Taylor
Edge:	Reeded
Die Axis:	↑↑
Finish:	Proof

DATE	DESCRIPTION	QUANTITY SOLD	ISSUE PRICE	FINISH	PR-69	PR-70
2004	Great Grizzly	12,942	N.I.I.	Proof	65.	—

EIGHT DOLLARS, 120TH ANNIVERSARY OF THE CANADIAN PACIFIC RAILWAY, 2005.

A set of two eight-dollar coins was issued in 2005. One honours the Chinese workers in Canada for their enormous contributions; the other commemorates the opening of the Transcontinental Railway in 1885.

Railway Bridge   **Chinese Memorial**

Designers:	
Obv.:	Susanna Blunt
Rev.:	RCM Staff
Composition:	99.99% Ag with gold plated inner core
Silver content:	32.15 g, 1.03 tr oz
Weight:	32.15 g
Diameter:	40.0 mm
Thickness:	3.0 mm
Case of Issue:	Two-hole maroon leatherette clam style case, black flocked insert, encapsulated coin, COA

Engravers:	
Obv.:	Susan Taylor
Rev.:	José Osio
Edge:	Reeded
Die Axis:	↑↑
Finish:	Proof

DATE	DESCRIPTION	QUANTITY SOLD	ISSUE PRICE	FINISH	PR-69	PR-70
2005	Railway Bridge	—	N.I.I.	Proof	50.	—
2005	Chinese Memorial	—	N.I.I.	Proof	50.	—
2005	Set of 2 coins	9,892	120.00	Proof	80.	*

EIGHT DOLLARS, THE SHAPE OF TRADE IN ANCIENT CHINA, 2007.

Designers:	
Obv.:	Susanna Blunt
Rev.:	Harvey Chan
Composition:	99.99% Ag
Silver content:	25.18 g, 0.81 tr oz
Weight:	25.18 g
Diameter:	36.1 mm
Thickness:	2.9 mm
Case of Issue:	Maroon clam style case, black flocked insert, encapsulated coin, COA

Engravers:	
Obv.:	Susan Taylor
Rev.:	Cecily Mok
Edge:	Reeded
Die Axis:	↑↑
Finish:	Proof

DATE	DESCRIPTION	RCM ITEM #	QUANTITY SOLD	ISSUE PRICE	FINISH	PR-69	PR-70
2007	Ancient China	623417	19,996	49.95	Proof	45.	—

CHINESE HISTORY AND TRADITIONS SERIES

EIGHT DOLLARS, MAPLE OF LONG LIFE, 2007.

Designers and Engravers:

Obv.:	Susanna Blunt, Susan Taylor
Rev.:	Jianping Yan, RCM Staff
Composition:	99.99% Ag, Hologram
Silver content:	25.18 g, 0.81 tr oz
Weight:	25.18 g
Diameter:	36.1 mm
Thickness:	2.9 mm
Edge:	Reeded
Die Axis:	↑↑
Finish:	Proof
Case of Issue:	Maroon clam style case, black flocked insert, encapsulated coin, COA

EIGHT DOLLARS, MAPLE OF WISDOM, 2009.

Designers and Engravers:

Obv.:	Susanna Blunt, Susan Taylor
Rev.:	Simon Ng, RCM Staff
Composition:	92.5% Ag, 7.5% Cu, Hologram and crystal
Silver content:	23.40 g, 0.752 tr oz
Weight:	25.3 g
Diameter:	36.1 mm
Thickness:	3.0 mm
Edge:	Reeded
Die Axis:	↑↑
Finish:	Proof
Case of Issue:	Maroon clam style case, black flocked insert, encapsulated coin, COA

EIGHT DOLLARS, MAPLE OF STRENGTH, 2010.

Designers and Engravers:

Obv.:	Susanna Blunt, Susan Taylor		
Rev.:	Simon Ng, Cecily Mok		
Composition:	92.5% Ag, 7.5% Cu, Hologram		
Silver content:	23.40 g, 0.752 tr oz		
Weight:	25.3 g		
Diameter:	36.1 mm	**Edge:**	Reeded
Thickness:	3.0 mm	**Die Axis:**	↑↑
Finish:	Proof		
Case of Issue:	Maroon clam style case, black flocked insert, encapsulated coin, COA		

DATE	DESCRIPTION	RCM ITEM #	QUANTITY SOLD	ISSUE PRICE	FINISH	PR-69	PR-70
2007	Maple of Long Life	N/A	12,427	45.95	Proof	45.	—
2009	Maple of Wisdom	107785	7,273	88.88	Proof	90.	—
2010	Maple of Strength	110932	5,138	88.88	Proof	90.	—

Note: For other coins in the Chinese History and Traditions Series see page 235.

CANADIAN WILDLIFE SERIES, 2013-2017

EIGHT DOLLARS (1½ ounce), CANADIAN WILDLIFE SERIES, 2013-2017.

Obverse
2013-2014

2013 Polar Bear
Designer: A. Germain
Engraver: S. Stewart

2014 Arctic Fox
Designer: Maurice Gervais
Engraver: Konrad Wachelko

2015-2017
Obverse
With Radial Lines (RL)

2015 Polar Bear and Cub
Designer: G. Arnaktauyok
Engraver: RCM Staff

2016 Snow Falcon
Designer: Stan Witten
Engraver: RCM Staff

2017 Grizzly Bear
Designer: Pierre Leduc
Engraver: RCM Staff

Designers:		**Engravers:**	
Obv.:	Susanna Blunt	Obv.:	Susan Taylor
Rev.:	See reverse illustrations	Rev.:	See reverse illustrations
Composition:	99.99% Ag		
Weight:	46.65 g, 1.5 tr oz	**Edge:**	Reeded
Diameter:	38.1 mm	**Die Axis:**	↑↑
Thickness:	4.5 mm	**Finish:**	See pricing table
Case of Issue:	Bullion: Plastic tubes		
	Proof: Maroon leatherette clam style case, black flocked insert, encapsulated coin, COA		

DATE	DESCRIPTION	RCM ITEM #	QUANTITY SOLD	ISSUE PRICE	FINISH	MS-65	MS-66	PR-69	PR-70
2013	$8 (1½ oz) Polar Bear, Bullion	N/A	N/A	BV	Bullion	45.	—	*	*
2013	$8 (1½ oz) Polar Bear, Proof	N/A	9,684	124.95	Proof	—	—	110.	—
2014	$8 (1½ oz) Arctic Fox, Bullion	N/A	N/A	BV	Bullion	45.	—	*	*
2014	$8 (1½ oz) Arctic Fox, Proof	N/A	7,500	124.95	Proof	—	—	110.	—
2015	$8 (1½ oz) Polar Bear and Cub, Bullion	N/A	N/A	BV	Bullion	45.	—	*	*
2015	$8 (1½ oz) Polar Bear and Cub, Proof	N/A	N/A	134.95	Proof	—	—	110.	—
2016	$8 (1½ oz), Snow Falcon	N/A	N/A	BV	Bullion	45.	—	*	*
2017	$8 (1½ oz), Grizzly Bear, Bullion	N/A	N/A	BV	Bullion	45.	—	*	*

EIGHT DOLLARS (1¼ ounce), CANADIAN SILVER BISON, 2015-2016.

| Common Obverse | 2015 Canadian Silver Bison | 2016 Canadian Silver Bison |

Designers:
    Rev.:   RCM Staff
Composition: 99.99% Ag
Weight: 38.88 g, 1.25 tr oz
Thickness: 4.1 mm
Diameter: 38.0 mm
Case of Issue: Plastic tubes

Engravers:

Edge: Reeded
Die Axis: ↑↑
Finish: Bullion, Radial lines

DATE	DESCRIPTION	RCM ITEM #	QUANTITY SOLD	ISSUE PRICE	FINISH	MS-65	MS-66
2015	(1¼ oz), Canadian Silver Bison	N/A	500,000	BV	Bullion	35.	—
2016	(1¼ oz), Canadian Silver Bison	N/A	N/A	BV	Bullion	35.	—

EIGHT DOLLARS, DRAGON DANCE, 2016.

Designers and Engravers:
    Obv.:   Susanna Blunt, Susan Taylor
    Rev.:   Harvey Chan
Composition: 99.99% Ag
Silver content: 7.96 g, 0.25 tr oz
Weight: 7.96
Diameter: 27 mm   **Edge:**   Reeded
Thickness: N/A   **Die Axis:** ↑↑
Finish: Matte Proof
Case of Issue: Maroon clam style case, black flocked insert, encapsulated coin, COA

EIGHT DOLLARS, TIGER AND DRAGON YN AND YANG, 2016.

Designers and Engravers:
    Obv.:   Susanna Blunt, Susan Taylor
    Rev.:   Charles Vinh
Composition: 99.99% Ag
Silver content: 20.86 g, 0.67 tr oz
Weight: 20.86 g
Diameter: 36 mm   **Edge:**   Reeded
Thickness: N/A   **Die Axis:** ↑↑
Finish: Proof
Case of Issue: Maroon clam style case, black flocked insert, encapsulated coin, COA

DATE	DESCRIPTION	RCM ITEM #	QUANTITY SOLD	ISSUE PRICE	FINISH	PR-69	PR-70
2016	Dragon Dance	149744	19,990	29.95	Matte Proof	30.	—
2016	Tiger and Dragon Yin and Yang	151873	6,886	98.88	Proof	100.	—

EIGHT DOLLARS, LION DANCE, 2017.

Designers:
Obv.: Susanna Blunt
Rev.: Simon Ng
Composition: 99.99% Ag
Silver content: 7.96 g, 0.25 tr oz
Weight: 7.96 g
Diameter: 27 mm
Thickness: N/A
Case of Issue: Maroon clamshell with black beauty box.

Engravers:
Obv. Susan Taylor
Edge: Reeded
Die Axis: ↑↑
Finish: Matte Proof

DATE	DESCRIPTION	RCM ITEM #	MINTAGE	ISSUE PRICE	FINISH	PR-69	PR-70
2017	Lion Dance	154669	30,000	29.95	Matte Proof	30.	—

EIGHT DOLLARS, *FENG SHUI* GOOD LUCK CHARMS, 2017.

Designers:
Obv.: Susanna Blunt
Rev.: Charles Vinh
Composition: 99.99% Ag
Silver content: 20.86 g, 0.67 tr oz
Weight: 20.86 g
Diameter: 36 mm
Thickness: N/A
Case of Issue: Maroon clam style case, black flocked insert, encapsulated coin, COA

Engravers:
Obv. Susan Taylor
Edge: Reeded
Die Axis: ↑↑
Finish: Proof

DATE	DESCRIPTION	RCM ITEM #	MINTAGE	ISSUE PRICE	FINISH	PR-69	PR-70
2017	*Feng Shui* Good Luck Charms	160831	6,888	98.88	Proof	100.	—

EIGHT DOLLARS, DRAGON LUCK, 2018.

Designers:
Obv.: Susanna Blunt
Rev.: Simon Ng
Composition: 99.99% Ag
Silver content: 7.96 g, 0.25 tr oz
Weight: 7.96
Diameter: 27 mm
Thickness: N/A
Case of Issue: Maroon clamshell with black beauty box, COA

Engravers:
Obv. Susan Taylor
Edge: Reeded
Die Axis: ↑↑
Finish: Matte Proof

DATE	DESCRIPTION	RCM ITEM #	MINTAGE	ISSUE PRICE	FINISH	PR-69	PR-70
2018	Dragon Luck	164448	20,000	29.95	Matte Proof	30.	—

EIGHT DOLLARS, GOOD LUCK CHARMS – FIVE BLESSINGS, 2018.

Designers:
Obv.: Susanna Blunt
Rev.: Simon Ng
Composition: 99.99% Ag
Silver content: 20.86 g, 0.67 tr oz
Weight: 20.86
Diameter: 36 mm
Thickness: N/A
Case of Issue: Maroon clamshell with black beauty box, COA

Engravers:
Obv. Susan Taylor
Edge: Reeded
Die Axis: ↑↑
Finish: Matte Proof

DATE	DESCRIPTION	RCM ITEM #	MINTAGE	ISSUE PRICE	FINISH	PR-69	PR-70
2018	Good Luck Charms – Five Blessings	165914	6888	98.88	Proof	100.	—

EIGHT DOLLARS, CHINESE BLESSEINGS, 2018.

Designers:
Obv.: Susanna Blunt
Rev.: Aries Cheung
Composition: 99.99% Ag
Silver content: 47.35 g, 1.52 tr oz
Weight: 47.35 g
Diameter: 49.8 x 28.6 mm
Thickness: N/A
Case of Issue: Maroon clamshell with black beauty box, COA

Engravers:
Obv. Susan Taylor

Edge: Reeded
Die Axis: ↑↑
Finish: Proof

DATE	DESCRIPTION	RCM ITEM #	MINTAGE	ISSUE PRICE	FINISH	PR-69	PR-70
2018	Chinese Blessings	164614	5,888	159.95	Proof	160.	—

EIGHT DOLLARS, THE PEACEFUL PANDA, A GIFT OF FRIENDSHIP, 2018.

Designers:
Obv.: Susanna Blunt
Rev.: RCM Staff
Composition: 99.99% Ag
Silver content: 7.96 g, 0.25 tr oz
Weight: 7.96
Diameter: 27 mm
Thickness: N/A
Case of Issue: Custom folder and envelope

Engravers:
Obv. Susan Taylor

Edge: Reeded
Die Axis: ↑↑
Finish: Modified specimen

DATE	DESCRIPTION	RCM ITEM #	MINTAGE	ISSUE PRICE	FINISH	SP-68	SP-69
2018	The Peaceful Panda	167250	WSL	29.95	Modified SP	30.	—

EIGHT DOLLARS, BRILLIANT CHERRY BLOSSOMS: A GIFT OF BEAUTY, 2019

Designers:
Obv.: Susanna Blunt
Rev.: Anna Bucciarelli
Composition: 99.99% Ag
Silver content: 7.96 g, 0.25 tr oz
Weight: 7.96
Diameter: 27 mm
Thickness: N/A
Case of Issue: Folder with easel back

Engravers:
Obv. Susan Taylor

Edge: Reeded
Die Axis: ↑↑
Finish: Specimen

DATE	DESCRIPTION	RCM ITEM #	MINTAGE	ISSUE PRICE	FINISH	SP-68	SP-69
2019	Brilliant Cherry Blossoms	169907	WSL	29.95	Specimen	30.	—

EIGHT DOLLARS, PANDAS: A GOLDEN GIFT OF FRIENDSHIP, 2019

Designers:		Engravers:	
Obv.:	Susanna Blunt	Obv.	Susan Taylor
Rev.:	Simon Ng		

Composition: 99.99% Ag, fully gold plated
Silver content: 7.96 g, 0.25 tr oz

Weight:	7.96	**Edge:**	Reeded
Diameter:	27 mm	**Die Axis:**	↑↑
Thickness:	N/A	**Finish:**	Modified Specimen

Case of Issue: Custom folder and envelope with three different Chinese calligraphy cards

DATE	DESCRIPTION	RCM ITEM #	MINTAGE	ISSUE PRICE	FINISH	SP-68	SP-69
2019	Pandas: A Golden Gift of Friendship	171201	88,888	39.95	Modified Specimen	30.	—

EIGHT DOLLAR DERIVATIVES

DATE	DESCRIPTION	QUANTITY SOLD	ISSUE PRICE	ISSUER	FINISH	MARKET PRICE
2004	**Eight Dollar Great Grizzly**; Two postage stamps; Wooden presentation case	12,942	48.88	RCM, CP	Proof	65.

TEN DOLLARS

TEN DOLLARS, YEAR OF THE VETERAN, 2005.

Designers:		Engravers:	
Obv.:	Susanna Blunt	Obv.	Susan Taylor
Rev.:	Elaine Goble		
Composition:	99.99% Ag		
Silver content:	25.175 g, 0.81 tr oz		
Weight:	25.175 g	**Edge:**	Reeded
Diameter:	36.1 mm	**Die Axis:**	↑↑
Thickness:	3.1 mm	**Finish:**	Proof
Case of Issue:	Maroon plastic case, black plastic insert, encapsulated coin, COA		

DATE	DESCRIPTION	QUANTITY SOLD	ISSUE PRICE	FINISH	PR-69	PR-70
2005	Year of the Veteran	6,549	49.95	Proof	35.	—

TEN DOLLARS, COMMEMORATING THE VISIT OF POPE JOHN PAUL II TO CANADA, 2005.

Designers:		Engravers:	
Obv.:	Susanna Blunt	Obv.	Susan Taylor
Rev.:	Susan Taylor		
Composition:	99.99% Ag		
Silver content:	25.175 g, 0.81 tr oz		
Weight:	25.175 g	**Edge:**	Reeded
Diameter:	36.1 mm	**Die Axis:**	↑↑
Thickness:	3.1 mm	**Finish:**	Proof
Case of Issue:	Maroon plastic case, black plastic insert, encapsulated coin, COA		

DATE	DESCRIPTION	QUANTITY SOLD	ISSUE PRICE	FINISH	PR-69	PR-70
2005	Pope John Paul II	24,716	49.95	Proof	55.	—

Note: In 2005 a set containing both the $10 silver and $75 gold (see page 426) coins was issued to commemorate the visit to Canada of Pope John Paul II. This may have been a special presentation set as only nine were issued.

TEN DOLLARS, FORTRESS OF LOUISBOURG, NATIONAL HISTORIC SERIES, 2006.

Designers:		Engravers:	
Obv.:	Susanna Blunt	Obv.	Susan Taylor
Rev.:	Marcos Hallam		
Composition:	99.99% Ag		
Silver content:	25.175 g, 0.81 tr oz		
Weight:	25.175 g	**Edge:**	Reeded
Diameter:	36.1 mm	**Die Axis:**	↑↑
Thickness:	3.1 mm	**Finish:**	Proof
Case of Issue:	Maroon plastic case, black plastic insert, encapsulated coin, COA		

DATE	DESCRIPTION	QUANTITY SOLD	ISSUE PRICE	FINISH	PR-69	PR-70
2006	Fortress of Louisbourg	5,544	49.95	Proof	40.	—

TEN DOLLARS, BLUE WHALE, 2010.

This is the last coin and stamp set in the Canadian Wildlife Series which was co-produced by the Royal Canadian Mint and Canada Post.

Designers:		Engravers:	
Obv.:	Susanna Blunt	Obv.	Susan Taylor
Rev.:	Pierre Ledu	Rev:	Stan Witten
Composition:	92.50% Ag, 7.50% Cu		
Silver content:	25.70 g, 0.826 tr oz		
Weight:	27.78 g	**Edge:**	Reeded
Diameter:	40.0 mm	**Die Axis:**	↑↑
Thickness:	2.7 mm	**Finish:**	Proof
Case of Issue:	See Derivatives page 229		

DATE	DESCRIPTION	RCM ITEM #	QUANTITY SOLD	ISSUE PRICE	FINISH	PR-69	PR-70
2010	Blue Whale	111991	9,719	N.I.I.	Proof	70.	—

TEN DOLLARS, 75TH ANNIVERSARY OF THE FIRST BANK NOTES ISSUED BY THE BANK OF CANADA, 1935-2010.

The reverse design on this coin is a reproduction of the allegory that appeared on the original 1935 ten-dollar bank note; a seated woman surrounded by a variety of farm produce to symbolise the harvest.

Designers:
Obv.: Susanna Blunt
Rev.: Susan Taylor
Composition: 99.99% Ag
Silver content: 15.90 g, 0.511 tr oz
Weight: 15.90 g
Diameter: 34.0 mm
Thickness: 2.2 mm
Case of Issue: Maroon leatherette clam style case, black flock insert, encapsulated coin, COA

Engravers:
Obv. Susan Taylor
Die Axis: ↑↑
Finish: Proof
Edge: Reeded

DATE	DESCRIPTION	RCM ITEM #	QUANTITY SOLD	ISSUE PRICE	FINISH	PR-69	PR-70
2010 (1935-)	75th Anniv. of First Notes Issued by Bank of Canada	110592	6,818	54.95	Proof	50.	—

TEN DOLLARS, HIGHWAY OF HEROES, 2011.

Designers:
Obv.: Susanna Blunt
Rev.: Major C. Gauthier/S. Witten
Composition: 99.99% Ag
Silver content: 15.87 g, 0.510 tr oz
Weight: 15.87 g
Diameter: 34.0 mm
Thickness: 2.0 mm
Case of Issue: Maroon leatherette clam style case, black flocked insert, encapsulated coin, COA

Engravers:
Obv. Susan Taylor
Rev: S. Witten
Die Axis: ↑↑
Finish: Proof
Edge: Reeded

DATE	DESCRIPTION	RCM ITEM #	QUANTITY SOLD	ISSUE PRICE	FINISH	PR-69	PR-70
2011	Highway of Heroes	116742	7,732	69.95	Proof	50.	—

TEN DOLLARS, WINTER TOWN, 2011.

Designers:
Obv.: Susanna Blunt
Rev.: Virginia Boulay
Composition: 99.99% Ag, Coloured
Silver content: 15.87 g, 0.510 tr oz
Weight: 15.87 g
Diameter: 34.0 mm
Thickness: 2.0 mm
Case of Issue: Maroon leatherette clam style case, black flocked insert, encapsulated coin, COA

Edge: Reeded
Die Axis: ↑↑
Finish: Proof

DATE	DESCRIPTION	RCM ITEM #	QUANTITY SOLD	ISSUE PRICE	FINISH	PR-69	PR-70
2011	Winter Town	115967	4,103	69.95	Proof	40.	—

TEN DOLLARS, LITTLE SKATERS, 2011.

Designers:
Obv.: Susanna Blunt
Rev.: Virginia Boulay
Composition: 99.99% Ag, Coloured
Silver content: 15.87 g, 0.510 tr oz
Weight: 15.87 g
Diameter: 34.0 mm
Thickness: 2.0 mm
Case of Issue: Maroon leatherette clam style case, black flocked insert, encapsulated coin, COA

Engravers:
Obv. Susan Taylor
Rev: Christie Paquet
Edge: Reeded
Die Axis: ↑↑
Finish: Proof

DATE	DESCRIPTION	RCM ITEM #	QUANTITY SOLD	ISSUE PRICE	FINISH	PR-69	PR-70
2011	Little Skaters	115999	3,663	69.95	Proof	40.	—

BOREAL FOREST SET

TEN DOLLARS, BOREAL FOREST SET, 2011.

The year 2011 was declared the International Year of Forests by the United Nations, a time to celebrate the important role forests play in our lives.

Common Obverse	Orca Whale Eng.: Cecily Mok	Peregrine Falcon Eng.: Marcos Hallam	Wood Bison Eng.: Konrad Wachelko	Boreal Forest Eng.: Marcos Hallam

Designers:
Obv.:   Susanna Blunt
Rev.:   Corrine Hunt
Composition: 99.99% Ag
Silver content: 15.87 g, 0.510 tr oz
Weight: 15.87 g
Diameter: 34.0 mm
Thickness: 2.0 mm
Case of Issue: Maroon leatherette clam style case, black flocked insert encapsulated coin, COA

Engravers:
Obv.:   Susan Taylor
Rev.:   See reverse illustrations

Edge: Reeded
Die Axis: ↑↑
Finish: Proof

DATE	DESCRIPTION	RCM ITEM #	QUANTITY SOLD	ISSUE PRICE	FINISH	PR-69	PR-70
2011	Orca Whale	115548	3,131	69.95	Proof	45.	—
2011	Peregrine Falcon	115555	3,014	69.95	Proof	45.	—
2011	Wood Bison	114821	3,063	69.95	Proof	45.	—
2011	Boreal Forest	116061	3,292	69.95	Proof	45.	—

TEN DOLLARS, YEAR OF THE DRAGON, 2012.

Designers:
Obv.:   Susanna Blunt
Rev.:   Three Degrees Creative Group Inc.,

Engravers:
Obv.:   Susan Taylor
Rev.:   Konrad Wachelko

Composition: 99.99% Ag
Silver content: 15.87 g, 0.510 tr oz
Weight: 15.87 g   **Edge:**   Reeded
Diameter: 33.9 mm   **Die Axis:**   ↑↑
Thickness: 2.0 mm   **Finish:**   Specimen
Case of Issue: Red cardboard pocket, red envelope, encapsulated coin, COA

DATE	DESCRIPTION	RCM ITEM #	QUANTITY SOLD	ISSUE PRICE	FINISH	SP-68	SP-69
2012	Year of the Dragon	119213	51,128	29.95	Specimen	25.	—

TEN DOLLARS, *RMS TITANIC*, 2012.

This coin was issued for the 100th anniversary of the sinking of *RMS Titanic* on her maiden voyage.

Designers:
Obv.:   Susanna Blunt
Rev.:   Yves Bérubé
Composition: 99.99% Ag
Silver content: 15.87 g, 0.510 tr oz
Weight: 15.87 g
Diameter: 33.9 mm
Thickness: 2.0 mm
Case of Issue: Maroon leatherette clam style case, black flocked insert, encapsulated coin, COA

Engravers:
Obv.   Susan Taylor
Rev: Konrad Wachelko

Edge: Reeded
Die Axis: ↑↑
Finish: Proof

DATE	DESCRIPTION	RCM ITEM #	QUANTITY SOLD	ISSUE PRICE	FINISH	PR-69	PR-70
2012	*RMS Titanic*	118110	20,000	64.95	Proof	55.	—

TEN DOLLARS, *HMS SHANNON*, 1812-2012.

The Leda-class frigate, *HMS Shannon*, was launched from Finsbury, England, in 1806. Captain Philip Broke led his vessel to many victories against the French during the Napoleonic Wars. When tensions rose in the autumn of 1811, *HMS Shannon* sailed to North America.

Designers:		**Engravers:**
Obv.:	Susanna Blunt	Obv.	Susan Taylor
Rev.:	Bonnie Ross	Rev:	Christie Paquet
Composition:	99.99% Ag, Selectively gold plated		
Silver content:	15.87 g, 0.510 tr oz		
Weight:	15.87 g	**Edge:**	Reeded
Diameter:	34.0 mm	**Die Axis:**	↑↑
Thickness:	2.1 mm	**Finish:**	Proof
Case of Issue:	Black leatherette clam style case, black insert, encapsulated coin, COA, custom coloured box		

DATE	DESCRIPTION	RCM ITEM #	QUANTITY SOLD	ISSUE PRICE	FINISH	PR-69	PR-70
2012 (1812-)	*HMS Shannon*	119227	9,970	64.95	Proof	60.	—

TEN DOLLARS, PRAYING MANTIS, 2012.

Designers:		**Engravers:**
Obv.:	Susanna Blunt	Obv.	Susan Taylor
Rev.:	Robert Ganz	Rev:	Konrad Wachelko
Composition:	99.99% Ag		
Silver content:	15.87 g, 0.510 tr oz		
Weight:	15.87 g	**Edge:**	Reeded
Diameter:	34.0 mm	**Die Axis:**	↑↑
Thickness:	2.1 mm	**Finish:**	Proof
Case of Issue:	Black leatherette clam style case, black flocked insert, encapsulated coin, COA, custom coloured sleeve		

DATE	DESCRIPTION	RCM ITEM #	QUANTITY SOLD	ISSUE PRICE	FINISH	PR-69	PR-70
2012	Praying Mantis	118885	5,727	69.95	Proof	40.	—

TEN DOLLARS, WELCOME TO THE WORLD, 2012-2019.

This design is also featured on the twenty-five-cent coins contained in the Baby Gift Sets for 2011 and 2013 (see pages 33-34). It is also featured on the $4 silver issue of 2011 (see page 162).

Designers:		**Engravers:**
Obv.:	Susanna Blunt	Obv.	Susan Taylor
Rev.:	José Osio	Rev:	Matt Bowan
Composition:	99.99% Ag		
Silver content:	15.87 g, 0.510 tr oz		
Weight:	15.87 g	**Edge:**	Reeded
Diameter:	34.0 mm	**Die Axis:**	↑↑
Thickness:	2.1 mm	**Finish:**	See pricing table
Case of Issue:	Maroon leatherette clam style case, black flocked insert, encapsulated coin, COA, custom sleeve		

DATE	DESCRIPTION	RCM ITEM #	QUANTITY SOLD	ISSUE PRICE	FINISH	PR-69	PR-70
2012	Welcome to the World	118596	9,999	59.95	Rev Proof	110.	—
2013	Welcome to the World	121169	14,916	59.95	Proof	90.	—
2014	Welcome to the World	127562	14,994	59.95	Matte Proof	90.	—
2015	Welcome to the World	134847	14,996	59.95	Rev Proof	90.	—
2016	Welcome to the World	148314	19,905	59.95	Rev. Proof	90.	—
2017	Welcome to the World	154645	6,505	59.95	Rev. Proof	70.	—
2018	Welcome to the World	163154	20,000	59.95	Rev. Proof	60.	—
2019	Welcome to the World	169956	20,000	59.95	Rev. Proof	60.	—

TEN DOLLARS, YEAR OF THE SNAKE, 2013.

Designers:		**Engravers:**	
Obv.:	Susanna Blunt	Obv.	Susan Taylor
Rev.:	Aries Chung	Rev:	Stan Witten
Composition:	99.99% Ag		
Silver content:	15.87 g, 0.510 tr oz		
Weight:	15.87 g	**Edge:**	Reeded
Diameter:	34.0 mm	**Die Axis:**	↑↑
Thickness:	2.1 mm	**Finish:**	Specimen
Case of Issue:	Maroon leatherette clam style case,		
	black flocked insert, encapsulated coin, COA		

DATE	DESCRIPTION	RCM ITEM #	QUANTITY SOLD	ISSUE PRICE	FINISH	SP-68	SP-69
2013	Year of the Snake	119943	22,986	39.95	Specimen	30.	—

TEN DOLLARS, YEAR OF THE SNAKE (CHINESE CHARACTER), 2013.

The Snake personality is graceful and soft-spoken. It has a hypnotic beauty and never gives itself totally away. The mysterious Snake is a strategic planner that has everyone guessing its next move. The Snake is a strong individual and is usually destined for great success. This is a special edition Year of the Snake.

Designers:		**Engravers:**	
Obv.:	Susanna Blunt	Obv.	Susan Taylor
Rev.:	Simon Ng	Rev:	Konrad Wachelko
Composition:	99.99% Ag		
Silver content:	15.87 g, 0.510 tr oz		
Weight:	15.87 g	**Edge:**	Reeded
Diameter:	34.0 mm	**Die Axis:**	↑↑
Thickness:	2.1 mm	**Finish:**	Specimen
Case of Issue:	Maroon leatherette clam style case,		
	black flocked insert, encapsulated coin, COA		

DATE	DESCRIPTION	RCM ITEM #	QUANTITY SOLD	ISSUE PRICE	FINISH	SP-68	SP-69
2013	Year of the Snake	123958	5,647	43.88	Specimen	35.	—

TEN DOLLARS, WINTER SCENE, 2013.

Designers:		**Engravers:**	
Obv.:	Susanna Blunt	Obv.	Susan Taylor
Rev.:	Rémi Clark	Rev:	José Osio
Composition:	99.99% Ag, Coloured		
Silver content:	15.87 g, 0.510 tr oz		
Weight:	15.87 g	**Edge:**	Reeded
Diameter:	34.0 mm	**Die Axis:**	↑↑
Thickness:	2.1 mm	**Finish:**	Proof
Case of Issue:	Maroon leatherette clam style case,		
	black flocked insert, encapsulated coin, COA		

DATE	DESCRIPTION	RCM ITEM #	QUANTITY SOLD	ISSUE PRICE	FINISH	PR-69	PR-70
2013	Winter Scene	120227	8,001	69.95	Proof	50.	—

TEN DOLLARS, 75TH ANNIVERSARY OF SUPERMAN™: VINTAGE, 2013.

Designers:		**Engravers:**	
Obv.:	Susanna Blunt	Obv.:	Susan Taylor
Rev.:	DC Comics/Warner Brothers	Rev.:	Konrad Wachelko
Composition:	99.99% Ag		
Silver content:	7.96 g, 0.25 tr oz		
Weight:	7.96 g	**Edge:**	Reeded
Diameter:	27.0 mm	**Die Axis:**	↑↑
Thickness:	1.8 mm	**Finish:**	Proof
Case of Issue:	Clear plastic cover, black plastic coin display,		
	encapsulated coin, COA, custom box		

DATE	DESCRIPTION	RCM ITEM #	QUANTITY SOLD	ISSUE PRICE	FINISH	PR-69	PR-70
2013	75th Anniv. of Superman™: Vintage	125838	14,972	44.75	Proof	45.	—

O CANADA SET ONE

TEN DOLLARS, O CANADA SET ONE, 2013.

Common Obverse

Designers and Engravers:
Obv.:   Susanna Blunt, Susan Taylor
Rev.:   See reverse illustrations
Composition: 99.99% Ag
Silver content: 15.87 g, 0.51 tr oz
Weight: 15.87 g   **Edge:**   Reeded
Diameter: 34.0 mm   **Die Axis:**   ↑↑
Thickness: 2.2 mm   **Finish:**   Matte Proof
Case of Issue:
Single: Maroon leatherette clam style case, black flocked insert, encapsulated coin, COA, custom coloured box
Subscription: 12-hole wooden case, red flocked top insert, black flocked bottom insert, encapsulated coins, COA, custom box

The Inukshuk
Designer: Tony Bianco
Engraver: Samantha Strath

The Beaver
Designer: Pierre Leduc
Engraver: Stan Witten

The Royal Canadian Mounted Police
Designer: Tony Bianco
Engraver: Konrad Wachelko

The Polar Bear
Designer: Pierre Leduc
Engraver: Steven Stewart

Summer Fun
Designer: Claudio D'Angelo
Engraver: Christie Paquet

The Wolf
Designer: Pierre Leduc
Engraver: Eric Boyer

Niagara Falls
Designer: Emily Damstra
Engraver: Konrad Wachelko

The Caribou
Designer: Pierre Leduc
Engraver: Stan Witten

Hockey
Designer: Tony Bianco
Engraver: Cecily Mok

The Orca
Designer: Pierre Leduc
Engraver: Alex Tirabasso

The Maple Leaf (with colour)
Designer: Emily Damstra
Engraver: Steven Stewart

Canadian Holiday Season
Designer: Doug Geldart
Engraver: Eric Boyer

TEN DOLLARS, O CANADA SET ONE, 2013, PRICING TABLE.

DATE	DESCRIPTION	RCM ITEM #	QUANTITY SOLD	ISSUE PRICE	FINISH	PR-69	PR-70
2013	The Inukshuk	121745	38,843	39.95	Proof	25.	—
2013	The Beaver	121795	38,560	39.95	Proof	25.	—
2013	The Royal Canadian Mounted Police	123610	36,914	39.95	Proof	25.	—
2013	The Polar Bear	121628	38,555	39.95	Proof	25.	—
2013	Summer Fun	123829	34,867	39.95	Proof	25.	—
2013	The Wolf	123820	34,899	39.95	Proof	25.	—
2013	Niagara Falls	124098	33,544	39.95	Proof	25.	—
2013	The Caribou	123195	33,522	39.95	Proof	25.	—
2013	Hockey	123859	33,325	39.95	Proof	25.	—
2013	The Orca	124067	30,834	39.95	Proof	25.	—
2013	The Maple Leaf (with colour)	121962	42,551	54.95	Proof	30.	—
2013	Canadian Holiday Season	124107	31,022	39.95	Proof	25.	—
2013	Set of 12 Coins	123567	—	479.40	Proof	300.	*

TEN DOLLARS, O CANADA SET ONE, SELECTIVELY GOLD PLATED, 2013.

The coins in this set are the same as the O Canada Set issued in 2013, however each coin is framed by a ring of gold plating. Single coins were not available from the Mint, and can only be obtained from the break up of sets.

Designers and Engravers: See O Canada Set
Specifications: As O Canada Set except the coins are selectively gold plated

Case of Issue: Wooden case, red flocked insert at top, black flocked insert at bottom, encapsulated coins, COA, custom beauty box

DATE	DESCRIPTION	RCM ITEM #	QUANTITY SOLD	ISSUE PRICE	FINISH	PR-69	PR-70
2013	The Inukshuk, Selectively gold plated	N/A	—	N.I.I.	Proof	70.	—
2013	The Beaver, Selectively gold plated	N/A	—	N.I.I.	Proof	70.	—
2013	The Royal Canadian Mounted Police, Selectively gold plated	N/A	—	N.I.I.	Proof	70.	—
2013	The Polar Bear, Selectively gold plated	N/A	—	N.I.I.	Proof	70.	—
2013	Summer Fun, Selectively gold plated	N/A	—	N.I.I.	Proof	70.	—
2013	The Wolf, Selectively gold plated	N/A	—	N.I.I.	Proof	70.	—
2013	Niagara Falls, Selectively gold plated	N/A	—	N.I.I.	Proof	70.	—
2013	The Caribou, Selectively gold plated	N/A	—	N.I.I.	Proof	70.	—
2013	Hockey, Selectively gold plated	N/A	—	N.I.I.	Proof	70.	—
2013	The Orca, Selectively gold plated	N/A	—	N.I.I.	Proof	70.	—
2013	Maple Leaf (with colour), Selectively gold plated	N/A	—	N.I.I.	Proof	70.	—
2013	Canadian Holiday Season, Selectively gold plated	N/A	—	N.I.I.	Proof	70.	—
2013	Set of 12 coins	125403	637	899.95	Proof	750.	*

Note: For other coins in the O Canada, Series One, see pages 344 and 418.

DUCKS OF CANADA SERIES

TEN DOLLARS, DUCKS OF CANADA SERIES, 2013-2016.

| Common Obverse | Mallard
Des.: Trevor Tennant | Wood Duck
Des.: Trevor Tennant | Northern Pintail
Des.: Samantha Strath |

| Harlequin Duck
Des.: Trevor Tennant | Cinnamon Teal
Des.: Denis Mayer Jr. | Canvasback
Des.: Glen Scrimshaw |

Designers:
Obv.: Susanna Blunt
Rev.: See reverse illustrations
Composition: 99.99% Ag, Coloured
Silver content: 15.87 g, 0.510 tr oz
Weight: 15.87 g
Diameter: 34.0 mm
Thickness: 2.1 mm
Case of Issue: Maroon leatherette clam style case, black flocked insert, encapsulated coin, COA

Engravers:
Obv.: Susan Taylor
Rev.: RCM Staff

Edge: Reeded
Die Axis: ↑↑
Finish: Proof

DATE	DESCRIPTION	RCM ITEM #	QUANTITY SOLD	ISSUE PRICE	FINISH	PR-69	PR-70
2013	Mallard	120087	8,998	69.95	Proof	50.	—
2013	Wood Duck	123014	9,866	69.95	Proof	50.	—
2014	Northern Pintail	127545	9,919	69.95	Proof	50.	—
2014	Harlequin Duck	130587	5,837	69.95	Proof	50.	—
2015	Cinnamon Teal	141289	2,944	69.95	Proof	50.	—
2016	Canvasback	142650	3,017	69.95	Proof	50.	—

TEN DOLLARS, DREAMCATCHER, 2013.

Many variations exist across the First Nations cultures, but they all exercise the same tradition of stopping bad dreams, and letting good draw through to the mind of the dreamer.

Designers:
Obv.: Susanna Blunt
Rev.: Darlene Gait
Composition: 99.99% Ag, Hologram, with colour
Silver content: 15.87 g, 0.510 tr oz
Weight: 15.87 g
Diameter: 34.0 mm
Thickness: 2.1 mm
Case of Issue: Maroon leatherette clam style case, black flocked insert, encapsulated coin, COA

Engravers:
Obv. Susan Taylor
Rev: Samantha Strath

Edge: Reeded
Die Axis: ↑↑
Finish: Proof

DATE	DESCRIPTION	RCM ITEM #	QUANTITY SOLD	ISSUE PRICE	FINISH	PR-69	PR-70
2013	Dreamcatcher	125828	9,957	74.95	Proof	65.	—

DRAGONFLY SERIES

TEN DOLLARS, DRAGONFLY SERIES, 2013-2015.

These coins were issued to commemorate Canada's dragonfly species and their habitats.

| Common Obverse | Twelve-Spotted Skimmer | Green Darner | Pygmy Snaketail |

Designers:
- Obv.: Susanna Blunt
- Rev.: Celia Godkin

Composition: 99.99% Ag, Hologram with colour
Silver content: 15.87 g, 0.510 tr oz
Weight: 15.87 g
Diameter: 34.0 mm
Thickness: 2.1 mm
Case of Issue: Maroon leatherette clam style case, black flocked insert, encapsulated coin, COA

Engravers:
- Obv.: Susan Taylor
- Rev.: Samantha Strath

Edge: Reeded
Die Axis: ↑↑
Finish: Proof

DATE	DESCRIPTION	RCM ITEM #	QUANTITY SOLD	ISSUE PRICE	FINISH	PR-69	PR-70
2013	Twelve-Spotted Skimmer Dragonfly	123746	9,923	79.95	Proof	50.	—
2014	Green Darner Dragonfly	128863	7,471	79.95	Proof	50.	—
2015	Pygmy Snaketail		3,159	79.95	Proof	50.	—

TEN DOLLARS, A PARTRIDGE IN A PEAR TREE, 2013.

Designers:
- Obv.: Susanna Blunt
- Rev.: Risto Turlinen

Composition: 99.99% Ag, Coloured
Silver content: 15.87 g, 0.510 tr oz
Weight: 15.87 g
Diameter: 34.0 mm
Thickness: 2.1 mm
Case of Issue: Maroon leatherette clam style case, black flocked insert, encapsulated coin, COA

Engravers:
- Obv. Susan Taylor
- Rev. José Osio

Edge: Reeded
Die Axis: ↑↑
Finish: Proof

DATE	DESCRIPTION	RCM ITEM #	QUANTITY SOLD	ISSUE PRICE	FINISH	PR-69	PR-70
2013	A Partridge in a Pear Tree	123701	4,475	64.95	Proof	50.	—

TEN DOLLARS, HOLIDAY CANDLES, 2013.

Designers:
- Obv.: Susanna Blunt
- Rev.: Claudio D'Angelo

Composition: 99.99% Ag, Coloured
Silver content: 15.87 g, 0.510 tr oz
Weight: 15.87 g
Diameter: 34.0 mm
Thickness: 2.0 mm
Case of Issue: Maroon leatherette clam style case, black flocked insert, encapsulated coin, COA

Engravers:
- Obv. Susan Taylor
- Rev. RCM Staff

Edge: Reeded
Die Axis: ↑↑
Finish: Proof

DATE	DESCRIPTION	RCM ITEM #	QUANTITY SOLD	ISSUE PRICE	FINISH	PR-69	PR-70
2013	Holiday Candles	124874	3,188	74.95	Proof	55.	—

TEN DOLLARS, YEAR OF THE HORSE, 2014.

Designers:		**Engravers:**	
Obv.:	Susanna Blunt	Obv.	Susan Taylor
Rev.:	Simon Ng	Rev:	Samantha Strath
Composition:	99.99% Ag		
Silver content:	15.87 g, 0.510 tr oz		
Weight:	15.87 g	**Edge:**	Reeded
Diameter:	34.0 mm	**Die Axis:**	↑↑
Thickness:	2.0 mm	**Finish:**	Specimen
Case of Issue:	Maroon leatherette clam style case, black flocked insert, encapsulated coin, COA		

DATE	DESCRIPTION	RCM ITEM #	QUANTITY SOLD	ISSUE PRICE	FINISH	SP-68	SP-69
2014	Year of the Horse	124628	25,436	39.95	Specimen	40.	—

TEN DOLLARS, 2014 FIFA™ WORLD CUP, 2014.

Designers:		**Engravers:**	
Obv.:	Susanna Blunt	Obv.	Susan Taylor
Rev.:	Greg Banning	Rev:	José Osio
Composition:	99.99% Ag		
Silver content:	15.87 g, 0.510 tr oz		
Weight:	15.87 g	**Edge:**	Reeded
Diameter:	33.9 mm	**Die Axis:**	↑↑
Thickness:	2.0 mm	**Finish:**	Proof
Case of Issue:	Black and white clam style case, black flocked insert, encapsulated coin, COA, full colour sleeve		

DATE	DESCRIPTION	RCM ITEM #	QUANTITY SOLD	ISSUE PRICE	FINISH	PR-69	PR-70
2014	2014 FIFA™ World Cup	128158	7,674	54.95	Proof	50.	—

TEN DOLLARS, SKATING IN CANADA, 2014.

Designers:		**Engravers:**	
Obv.:	Susanna Blunt	Obv.	Susan Taylor
Rev.:	Tony Harris	Rev:	Matt Bowen
Composition:	99.99% Ag, Coloured		
Silver content:	15.87 g, 0.510 tr oz		
Weight:	15.87 g	**Edge:**	Reeded
Diameter:	34.0 mm	**Die Axis:**	↑↑
Thickness:	2.2 mm	**Finish:**	Proof
Case of Issue:	Maroon clam style case, black flocked insert, encapsulated coin, COA		

DATE	DESCRIPTION	RCM ITEM #	QUANTITY SOLD	ISSUE PRICE	FINISH	PR-69	PR-70
2014	Skating in Canada	129522	4,653	64.95	Proof	55.	—

TEN DOLLARS, THE MOBILISATION OF OUR NATION, 2014.

This coin was issued to commemorate the 100th anniversary of the declaration of World War One.

Designers:		**Engravers:**	
Obv.:	Susanna Blunt	Obv.	Susan Taylor
Rev.:	Maskull Lasserre	Rev:	Matt Bowen
Composition:	99.99% Ag		
Silver content:	15.87 g, 0.510 tr oz		
Weight:	15.87 g	**Edge:**	Reeded
Diameter:	34.0 mm	**Die Axis:**	↑↑
Thickness:	2.0 mm	**Finish:**	Matte proof
Case of Issue:	Maroon clam style case, black flocked insert, encapsulated coin, COA		

DATE	DESCRIPTION	RCM ITEM #	QUANTITY SOLD	ISSUE PRICE	FINISH	PR-69	PR-70
2014	The Mobilisation of our Nation	129457	7,313	44.95	Proof	45.	—

TEN DOLLARS, POPE JOHN PAUL II, 2014.

This coin celebrates the canonization of Pope John Paul II on April 27, 2014.

Designers:		**Engravers:**	
Obv.:	Susanna Blunt	Obv.	Susan Taylor
Rev.:	RCM Staff,	Rev:	Christie Paquet
Composition:	99.99% Ag		
Silver content:	15.87 g, 0.510 tr oz		
Weight:	15.87 g	**Edge:**	Reeded
Diameter:	34.0 mm	**Die Axis:**	↑↑
Thickness:	2.0 mm	**Finish:**	Matte proof
Case of Issue:	Maroon clam style case, black flocked insert, encapsulated coin, COA		

DATE	DESCRIPTION	RCM ITEM #	QUANTITY SOLD	ISSUE PRICE	FINISH	PR-69	PR-70
2014	Pope John Paul II	132483	8,499	69.95	Proof	70.	—

TEN DOLLARS, 70TH ANNIVERSARY OF D-DAY, 1944-2014.

Designers:		**Engravers:**	
Obv.:	Susanna Blunt	Obv.	Susan Taylor
Rev.:	Maskull Lasserre	Rev:	RCM Staff
Composition:	99.99% Ag		
Silver content:	15.87 g, 0.510 tr oz		
Weight:	15.87 g	**Edge:**	Reeded
Diameter:	34.0 mm	**Die Axis:**	↑↑
Thickness:	2.0 mm	**Finish:**	Proof
Case of Issue:	Maroon clam style case, black flocked insert, encapsulated coin, COA		

DATE	DESCRIPTION	RCM ITEM #	QUANTITY SOLD	ISSUE PRICE	FINISH	PR-69	PR-70
2014 (1944-)	70th Anniversary of D-Day	132484	8,003	49.95	Proof	55.	—

TEN DOLLARS, "WAIT FOR ME, DADDY", 2014.

Based on the iconic 1940 photograph taken in British Columbia by photographer Claude Dettloff, this coin commemorates the 75th anniversary of the declaration of the Second World War.

Designers:		**Engravers:**	
Obv.:	Susanna Blunt	Obv.	Susan Taylor
Rev.:	Claude Dettloff	Rev:	RCM Staff
Composition:	99.99% Ag, Selectively gold plated		
Silver content:	15.87 g, 0.510 tr oz		
Weight:	15.87 g	**Edge:**	Reeded
Diameter:	34.0 mm	**Die Axis:**	↑↑
Thickness:	N/A	**Finish:**	Proof
Case of Issue:	Maroon clam style case, black flocked insert, encapsulated coin, COA		

DATE	DESCRIPTION	RCM ITEM #	QUANTITY SOLD	ISSUE PRICE	FINISH	PR-69	PR-70
2014	"Wait For Me, Daddy"	132620	10,000	59.95	Proof	55.	—

TEN DOLLARS, ICONIC SUPERMAN™ COMIC BOOK COVERS #1 (1938), 2014.

This coin pays homage to the 1938 debut of Superman™ as seen on the cover of Action Comics.

Designers:		**Engravers:**	
Obv.:	Susanna Blunt	Obv.	Susan Taylor
Rev.:	DC Comics	Rev:	RCM Staff
Composition:	99.99% Ag		
Silver content:	15.87 g, 0.510 tr oz		
Weight:	15.87 g	**Edge:**	Reeded
Diameter:	34.0 mm	**Die Axis:**	↑↑
Thickness:	N/A	**Finish:**	Proof
Case of Issue:	Coloured custom case, black flocked insert, encapsulated coin, COA		

DATE	DESCRIPTION	RCM ITEM #	QUANTITY SOLD	ISSUE PRICE	FINISH	PR-69	PR-70
2014	Iconic Superman™ Comic Book Covers #1 (1938)	133872	9,999	69.95	Proof	70.	—

O CANADA SET TWO

TEN DOLLARS, O CANADA SET TWO, 2014.

Common Obverse

Designers and Engravers:

Obv.:	Susanna Blunt, Susan Taylor
Rev.:	See reverse illustrations

Composition: 99.99% Ag
Silver content: 15.87 g, 0.51 tr oz
Weight: 15.87 g
Diameter: 34.0 mm
Thickness: 2.1 mm
Case of Issue:

Edge: Reeded
Die Axis: ↑↑
Finish: Matte Proof

Singly: Maroon leatherette clam style case, black flocked insert, encapsulated coin, COA, custom coloured box

Subscription: 10-hole wooden case, red flocked top insert, black flocked bottom insert, encapsulated coins, COA, custom box

The Igloo	Grizzly Bear	Skiing Canada's Slopes	Moose	Down by the Old Maple Tree
Designer: Yves Bérubé	Designer: Glen Loates	Designer: Kendra Dixon	Designer: Claudio D'Angelo	Designer: Claudio D'Angelo
Engraver: Cecily Mok	Engraver: José Osio	Engraver: RCM Staff	Engraver: Stan Witten	Engraver: RCM Staff

Canada Goose	Canadian Cowboy	Bison	The Northern Lights	Canadian Holiday Scene
Des.: Jean Charles Daumas	Designer: Bernie Brown	Designer: Trevor Tennant	Designer: Julius Csotonyi	Designer: Doug Geldart
Engraver: Matt Bowen	Engraver: Cecily Mok	Engraver: RCM Staff	Engraver: RCM Staff	Engraver: Cecily Mok

DATE	DESCRIPTION	RCM ITEM #	QUANTITY SOLD	ISSUE PRICE	FINISH	PR-69	PR-70
2014	The Igloo	128967	20,736	39.95	Proof	30.	—
2014	Grizzly Bear	129121	20,933	39.95	Proof	30.	—
2014	Skiing Canada's Slopes	129045	17,384	39.95	Proof	30.	—
2014	Moose	129153	19,791	39.95	Proof	30.	—
2014	Down by the Old Maple Tree	129084	17,122	39.95	Proof	30.	—
2014	Canada Goose	129093	16,840	39.95	Proof	30.	—
2014	Canadian Cowboy	129327	16,521	39.95	Proof	30.	—
2014	Bison	129315	16,614	39.95	Proof	30.	—
2014	The Northern Lights (with colour)		19,058	54.95	Proof	40.	—
2014	Canadian Holiday Scene	129007	17,178	39.95	Proof	30.	—

TEN DOLLARS, O CANADA SET TWO, SELECTIVELY GOLD PLATED SET, 2014.

The coins in this set are the same as the O Canada Series issued in 2014, however each coin is framed by a ring of gold plating. Single coins were not available from the Mint, and can only be obtained from the break up of sets.

Common Obverse

Reverse
Moose

Designers and Engravers: See O Canada Set
Specifications: As O Canada Set except the coins are selectively gold plated
Case of Issue: Red wooden case, black flocked insert, encapsulated coins, COA, custom box

DATE	DESCRIPTION	RCM ITEM #	QUANTITY SOLD	ISSUE PRICE	FINISH	PR-69	PR-70
2014	The Igloo	N/A	—	N.I.I.	Matte Proof	90.	—
2014	Grizzly Bear	N/A	—	N.I.I.	Matte Proof	90.	—
2014	Skiing Canada's Slopes	N/A	—	N.I.I.	Matte Proof	90.	—
2014	Moose	N/A	—	N.I.I.	Matte Proof	90.	—
2014	Down by the Old Maple Tree,	N/A	—	N.I.I.	Matte Proof	90.	—
2014	Canada Goose	N/A	—	N.I.I.	Matte Proof	90.	—
2014	Canadian Cowboy	N/A	—	N.I.I.	Matte Proof	90.	—
2014	Bison	N/A	—	N.I.I.	Matte Proof	90.	—
2014	The Northern Lights (with colour)	N/A	—	N.I.I.	Matte Proof	90.	—
2014	Canadian Holiday Scene	N/A	—	N.I.I.	Matte Proof	90.	—
2014	Set of 10 coins	130638	637	849.95	Matte Proof	750.	*

FIRST NATIONS ART SERIES

TEN DOLLARS, FIRST NATIONS ART SERIES, 2014-2015.

This series celebrates the artwork of Kwaguilth artist Richard Hunt and Coast Salish artist Darlene Gait.

Designers and Engravers:
Obv.:	Susanna Blunt, Susan Taylor
Rev.:	See reverse illustrations, RCM Staff
Composition:	99.99% Ag, Hologram
Silver content:	15.87 g, 0.510 tr oz
Weight:	15.87 g
Diameter:	34.0 mm
Thickness:	N/A
Edge:	Reeded
Die Axis:	↑↑
Finish:	Proof
Case of Issue:	Maroon leatherette clam style case, black flocked insert, encapsulated coin, COA

Salmon
Des.: Darlene Gait

Mother Feeding Baby
Des.: Richard Hunt

DATE	DESCRIPTION	RCM ITEM #	QUANTITY SOLD	ISSUE PRICE	FINISH	PR-69	PR-70
2014	Salmon	130561	8,406	74.95	Proof	70.	—
2015	Mother Feeding Baby	N/A	2,054	79.95	Proof	70.	—

TEN DOLLARS, YEAR OF THE SHEEP, 2015.

An artistic rendering of bamboo fills the coin's field while the Chinese character for sheep or ram is seen in the sheep's shoulder.

Designers:		Engravers:	
Obv.:	Susanna Blunt	Obv.	Susan Taylor
Rev.:	Simon Ng	Rev:	RCM Staff
Composition:	99.99% Ag, Hologram, with colour		
Silver content:	15.87 g, 0.510 tr oz		
Weight:	15.87 g	**Edge:**	Reeded
Diameter:	34.0 mm	**Die Axis:**	↑↑
Thickness:	N/A	**Finish:**	Specimen
Case of Issue:	Maroon leatherette clam style case, black flocked insert, encapsulated coin, COA		

DATE	DESCRIPTION	RCM ITEM #	QUANTITY SOLD	ISSUE PRICE	FINISH	SP-68	SP-69
2015	Year of the Sheep	130568	15,223	39.88	Specimen	40.	—

TEN DOLLARS, CELEBRATING CANADA, 2015.

A symbolic map-like representation designed by Kwame Delfish depicts the Canadian Rocky Mountains, a white-tailed deer, the wheat growing provinces of Canada, the fishing industry, the Tower of Peace in Ottawa, a partial map of Nunavut, and the lighthouse at Peggy's Cove, Nova Scotia.

Designers:		Engravers:	
Obv.:	Susanna Blunt	Obv.	Susan Taylor
Rev.:	Kwame Delfish	Rev:	RCM Staff
Composition:	99.99% Ag, Selectively gold plated		
Silver content:	15.87 g, 0.510 tr oz		
Weight:	15.87 g	**Edge:**	Reeded
Diameter:	34.0 mm	**Die Axis:**	↑↑
Thickness:	N/A	**Finish:**	Proof
Case of Issue:	Maroon leatherette clam style case, black flocked insert, encapsulated coin, COA		

DATE	DESCRIPTION	RCM ITEM #	QUANTITY SOLD	ISSUE PRICE	FINISH	PR-69	PR-70
2015	Celebrating Canada	141689	2,469	69.95	Proof	75.	—

TEN DOLLARS, WINTER SCENE, 2015.

Designed by artist Remi Clark, this coin's reverse captures the iconic rolling hills and winter snowfall of Canada.

Designers:		Engravers:	
Obv.:	Susanna Blunt	Obv.	Susan Taylor
Rev.:	Louise Martineau	Rev:	RCM Staff
Composition:	99.99% Ag, Coloured		
Silver content:	15.87 g, 0.510 tr oz		
Weight:	15.87 g	**Edge:**	Reeded
Diameter:	34.0 mm	**Die Axis:**	↑↑
Thickness:	N/A	**Finish:**	Proof
Case of Issue:	Maroon leatherette clam style case, black flocked insert, encapsulated coin, COA		

DATE	DESCRIPTION	RCM ITEM #	QUANTITY SOLD	ISSUE PRICE	FINISH	PR-69	PR-70
2015	Winter Scene	130616	2,159	64.95	Proof	55.	—

TEN DOLLARS, 200TH ANNIVERSARY OF THE BIRTH OF SIR JOHN A. MACDONALD, 2015.

Designed by Joel Kimmel, this ten dollar coin celebrates the 200th anniversary of the birth of Canada's first Prime Minister.

Designers:		Engravers:	
Obv.:	Susanna Blunt	Obv.	Susan Taylor
Rev.:	Joel Kimmel	Rev:	RCM Staff
Composition:	99.99% Ag, Selectively gold plated		
Silver content:	15.87 g, 0.510 tr oz		
Weight:	15.87 g	**Edge:**	Reeded
Diameter:	34.0 mm	**Die Axis:**	↑↑
Thickness:	N/A	**Finish:**	Proof
Case of Issue:	Maroon leatherette clam style case, black flocked insert, encapsulated coin, COA		

DATE	DESCRIPTION	RCM ITEM #	QUANTITY SOLD	ISSUE PRICE	FINISH	PR-69	PR-70
2015	200th Anniv. Birth Sir John A. MacDonald	130630	2,886	69.95	Proof	65.	—

CANADIAN NHL SET

TEN DOLLARS, CANADIAN NHL SET, 2015.

This set of seven coins is comprised of the Canadian hockey teams of The National Hockey League (NHL).

Common Obverse

Calgary Flames

Edmonton Oilers

Montreal Canadiens

Ottawa Senators

Toronto Maple Leafs

Vancouver Canucks

Winnipeg Jets

Designers:	**Engravers:**
Obv.: Susanna Blunt	Obv.: Susan Taylor
Rev.: RCM Staff	Rev.: RCM Staff

Composition: 99.99% Ag, Hologram with colour
Silver content: 15.87 g, 0.510 tr oz
Weight: 15.87 g
Diameter: 34.0 mm   **Edge:**   Reeded
Thickness: N/A   **Die Axis:**   ↑↑
                                                Finish: Reverse Proof
Case of Issue: Maroon leatherette clam style case, black flocked insert, encapsulated coin, COA

DATE	DESCRIPTION	RCM ITEM #	QUANTITY SOLD	ISSUE PRICE	FINISH	PR-69	PR-70
2015	Calgary Flames	130932	4,510	74.95	Proof	50.	—
2015	Edmonton Oilers	130599	4,337	74.95	Proof	50.	—
2015	Montreal Canadiens	130603	5,997	74.95	Proof	60.	—
2015	Ottawa Senators	130932	4,874	74.95	Proof	50.	—
2015	Toronto Maple Leafs	130600	5,997	74.95	Proof	50.	—
2015	Vancouver Canucks	N/A	5,901	74.95	Proof	50.	—
2015	Winnipeg Jets	130598	4,553	74.95	Proof	50.	—

CANOE ACROSS CANADA SET

TEN DOLLARS, CANOE ACROSS CANADA SET, 2015.

Designed by Greg Banning, this set of six coins depicts some of Canada's most scenic spots to canoe, from canoeing down a river (coin one), to the Yukon River (coin two), the Bow River in Alberta (coin three), Ontario's Georgian Bay Islands National Park (coin four), and to a lake near Quebec's Laurentian Mountains (coin five).

Common Obverse

Splendid Surroundings

Wondrous West

Magnificent Mountains

Serene Scene

Mirror, Mirror

Exquisite Ending

Designers:
Obv.: Susanna Blunt
Rev.: Greg Banning
Composition: 99.99% Ag
Silver content: 15.87 g, 0.510 tr oz
Weight: 15.87 g
Diameter: 34.0 mm
Thickness: N/A

Engravers:
Obv.: Susan Taylor
Rev.: RCM Staff

Edge: Reeded
Die Axis: ↑↑
Finish: Proof

Case of Issue: Singly: Maroon leatherette clam style case, black flocked insert, encapsulated coin, COA
Subscription: Six-hole wooden canoe-shaped case, painted red exterior, black mount, encapsulated coins, COA

DATE	DESCRIPTION	RCM ITEM #	QUANTITY SOLD	ISSUE PRICE	FINISH	PR-69	PR-70
2015	Splendid Surroundings	142509	7,929	44.95	Proof	40.	—
2015	Wondrous West	141951	8,490	44.95	Proof	40.	—
2015	Magnificent Mountains	144242	7,847	44.95	Proof	40.	—
2015	Serene Scene	144504	7,466	44.95	Proof	40.	—
2015	Mirror, Mirror	N/A	7,298	44.95	Proof	40.	—
2015	Exquisite Ending	N/A	7,311	44.95	Proof	40.	—

FIFA WOMEN'S WORLD CUP™ SET

TEN DOLLARS, FIFA WOMEN'S WORLD CUP™ SET, 2015.

Celebrating the FIFA Women's World Cup hosted in Moncton, Montreal, Ottawa, Winnipeg, Edmonton and Vancouver, this set reflects the excitement of women's soccer. A set of three $75 gold coins was also issued for the FIFA Women's World Cup™ in 2015 (see page 428).

Common Obverse

Canada Welcomes The World

"Go Canada Go!"

The Goalie

Heading The Ball

The Kicker

Celebration

Designers:			**Engravers:**	
Obv.:	Susanna Blunt		Obv.:	Susan Taylor
Rev.:	Greg Banning		Rev.:	RCM Staff
Composition:	99.99% Ag			
Silver content:	15.87 g, 0.510 tr oz			
Weight:	15.87 g		**Edge:**	Reeded
Diameter:	34.0 mm		**Die Axis:**	↑↑
Thickness:	N/A		**Finish:**	Proof
Case of Issue:	Singly: Maroon leatherette clam style case, black flocked insert, encapsulated coin, COA, custom box			
	Subscription: Six-hole wooden case, black flocked insert, encapsulated coins, COA			

DATE	DESCRIPTION	RCM ITEM #	QUANTITY SOLD	ISSUE PRICE	FINISH	PR-69	PR-70
2015	Canada Welcomes The World, Coloured	145070	5,104	59.95	Proof	50.	—
2015	"Go Canada GO!", Coloured	145101	4,363	59.95	Proof	50.	—
2015	The Goalie	144404	5,103	54.95	Proof	50.	—
2015	Heading The Ball	144422	5,358	54.95	Proof	50.	—
2015	The Kicker	144476	5,498	54.95	Proof	50.	—
2015	Celebration	144413	5,038	54.95	Proof	50.	—

COLOURFUL SONGBIRDS OF CANADA SET

TEN DOLLARS, COLOURFUL SONGBIRDS OF CANADA SET, 2015.

This five-coin set captures the colourful beauty of some of Canada's songbirds.

Common Obverse

Designers:		Engravers:	
Obv.:	Susanna Blunt	Obv.:	Susan Taylor
Rev.:	See reverse illustrations	Rev.:	See reverse illustrations
Composition:	99.99% Ag		
Silver content:	15.87 g, 0.510 tr oz		
Weight:	15.87 g	**Edge:**	Reeded
Diameter:	34.0 mm	**Die Axis:**	↑↑
Thickness:	N/A	**Finish:**	Proof
Case of Issue:	Singly: Maroon leatherette clam style case, black flocked insert, encapsulated coin, COA		
	Subscription: Five-hole musical paperboard case, white flocked insert, custom case, encapsulated coins, COA		

The Northern Cardinal	The Magnolia Warbler	The Blue Jay	The Baltimore Oriole	The Violet-Green Swallow
Des.: Derek C. Wicks	Des.: Hélène Girard	Designer and Engraver:	Designer and Engraver:	Designer and Engraver:
Engr.: RCM Staff	Engr.: RCM Staff	RCM Staff	RCM Staff	RCM Staff

DATE	DESCRIPTION	RCM ITEM #	QUANTITY SOLD	ISSUE PRICE	FINISH	PR-69	PR-70
2015	The Northern Cardinal	141271	13,063	64.95	Proof	60.	—
2015	The Magnolia Warbler	142260	10,255	64.95	Proof	60.	—
2015	The Blue Jay	142400	12,109	64.95	Proof	60.	—
2015	The Baltimore Oriole	143122	9,469	64.95	Proof	60.	—
2015	The Violet-Green Swallow	142286	9,806	64.95	Proof	60.	—

ADVENTURE CANADA SERIES

TEN DOLLARS, ADVENTURE CANADA, 2015.

There's an endless variety of adventures to be found across Canada. Every season and every geographical region has something new and exciting to offer.

Common Obverse

Designers:		Engravers:	
Obv.:	Susanna Blunt	Obv.:	Susan Taylor
Rev.:	Ken Ryan	Rev.:	Ken Ryan
Composition:	99.99% Ag		
Silver content:	15.87 g, 0.510 tr oz		
Weight:	15.87 g	**Edge:**	Reeded
Diameter:	34.0 mm	**Die Axis:**	↑↑
Thickness:	N/A	**Finish:**	Matte Proof
Case of Issue:	Maroon leatherette clam style case, black flocked insert, encapsulated coin, COA		

Windsurfing	Whitewater Rafting	Mountain Bking	Ice Climbing	Dog Sledding

TEN DOLLARS, ADVENTURE CANADA, 2015, PRICING TABLE.

DATE	DESCRIPTION	RCM ITEM #	QUANTITY SOLD	ISSUE PRICE	FINISH	PR-69	PR-70
2015	Windsurfing	145552	1,449	44.95	Matte Proof	45.	—
2015	Whitewater Rafting	143351	1,104	44.95	Matte Proof	45.	—
2015	Mountain Biking	144702	2,248	44.95	Matte Proof	45.	—
2015	Ice Climbing	145587	1,162	44.95	Matte Proof	45.	—
2015	Dog Sledding	145539	1,109	44.95	Matte Proof	45.	—

DC COMICS™ ORIGINALS SET

TEN DOLLARS, *DC COMICS™ ORIGINALS*, 2015.

The *DC Comics Original*s series has a classic, slightly retro style, recalling the look most comic book fans grew up with and remember fondly. Basing itself on the DC Comics style of the 1980s, this series celebrates one of the most established looks for the DC Comics pantheon of Super Heroes, and a few of its villains too.

Common Obverse

Designers:
Obv.:   Susanna Blunt
Rev.:   DC Comics
Composition: 99.99% Ag
Silver content: 15.87 g, 0.510 tr oz
Weight: 15.87 g
Diameter: 34.0 mm
Thickness: N/A
Case of Issue: Premium graphic case.

Engravers:
Obv.:   Susan Taylor
Rev.:   DC Comics

Edge: Reeded
Die Axis: ↑↑
Finish: Matte Proof

Gauntlet

Strength

Unity

Legacy

DATE	DESCRIPTION	RCM ITEM #	QUANTITY SOLD	ISSUE PRICE	FINISH	PR-69	PR-70
2015	Gauntlet	148008	10,763	54.95	Matte Proof	50.	—
2015	Strength	148006	9,638	54.95	Matte Proof	50.	—
2015	Unity	148007	9,459	54.95	Matte Proof	50.	—
2015	Legacy	148005	11,158	54.95	Matte Proof	50.	—

LOONEY TUNES™ SET

TEN DOLLARS, LOONEY TUNES™, 2015.

Common Obverse

Bugs. Daffy. Tweety. Sylvester. For many Canadians, the mere mention of these names evoke fond childhood memories of spending Saturday mornings in front of a television, transfixed and spellbound as these characters—and many more—outsmarted each other in situations that could only exist in our imaginations.

"I Tawt I Taw A Putty Tat!"

"Suffering Succotash!"

"Where's The Kaboom?"

"Beep! Beep!"

"Wile E. Coyote – Super Genius"

"You're Despicable"

"What's Up, Doc?"

"That's All Folks!"

Designers:
Obv.: Susanna Blunt
Rev.: Warner Bros.
Composition: 99.99% Ag
Silver content: 15.87 g, 0.510 tr oz
Weight: 15.87 g
Diameter: 34.0 mm
Thickness: N/A
Case of Issue: Graphic paperboard box.

Engravers:
Obv.: Susan Taylor
Rev.: Warner Bros.

Edge: Reeded
Die Axis: ↑↑
Finish: Matte Proof

DATE	DESCRIPTION	RCM ITEM #	QUANTITY SOLD	ISSUE PRICE	FINISH	PR-69	PR-70
2015	"I Tawt I Taw A Putty Tat!"	144925	11,519	49.95	Matte Proof	40.	—
2015	"Suffering Succotash!"	144934	9,528	49.95	Matte Proof	40.	—
2015	"Where's The Kaboom?"	145447	9,710	49.95	Matte Proof	40.	—
2015	"Beep! Beep!"	145888	8,941	49.95	Matte Proof	40.	—
2015	"Wile E. Coyote – Super Genius"	145448	8,795	49.95	Matte Proof	40.	—
2015	"You're Despicable"	144916	8,849	49.95	Matte Proof	40.	—
2015	"What's Up, Doc?"	144904	8,891	49.95	Matte Proof	40.	—
2015	"That's All Folks!"	145449	8,899	49.95	Matte Proof	40.	—

GOALIES SET

TEN DOLLARS, GOALIES, 2015.

NHL® history comes alive! Relive the excitement of the Original Six™ era with this commemorative series of coins that celebrates legendary goaltenders from each team.

Common Obverse

Eddie Giacomin

Gerry Cheevers

Glenn Hall

Jaques Plante

Johnny Bower

Terry Sawchuk

Designers:		Engravers:	
Obv.:	Susanna Blunt	Obv.:	Susan Taylor
Rev.:	Steven Rosati	Rev.:	Steven Rosati

Composition: 99.99% Ag
Silver content: 15.87 g, 0.510 tr oz
Weight: 15.87 g
Diameter: 34.0 mm
Thickness: N/A
Case of Issue: Brown clamshell with graphic beauty box.

Edge: Reeded
Die Axis: ↑↑
Finish: Proof

DATE	DESCRIPTION	RCM ITEM #	QUANTITY SOLD	ISSUE PRICE	FINISH	PR-69	PR-70
2015	Goalies: Eddie Giacomin	146534	6,232	74.95	Proof	75.	—
2015	Goalies: Gerry Cheevers	146522	6,417	74.95	Proof	75.	—
2015	Goalies: Glenn Hall	146545	5,416	74.95	Proof	75.	—
2015	Goalies: Jacques Plante	146512	7,417	74.95	Proof	75.	—
2015	Goalies: Johnny Bower	146488	7,232	74.95	Proof	75.	—
2015	Goalies: Terry Sawchuk	146556	6,279	74.95	Proof	75.	—

TEN DOLLARS, WINTER FUN, 2016.

Designers:		Engravers:	
Obv.:	Susanna Blunt	Obv.	Susan Taylor
Rev.:	Maurade Baynton		

Composition: 99.99% Ag, Coloured
Silver content: 15.87 g, 0.510 tr oz
Weight: 15.87 g
Diameter: 34.0 mm
Thickness: N/A
Case of Issue: Maroon clamshell with black beauty box.

Edge: Reeded
Die Axis: ↑↑
Finish: Proof

DATE	DESCRIPTION	RCM ITEM #	QUANTITY SOLD	ISSUE PRICE	FINISH	PR-69	PR-70
2016	Winter Fun	146610	2,986	64.95	Proof	60.	—

TEN DOLLARS, CELEBRATION OF LOVE, 2016.

Designers and Engravers:

Obv.:	Susanna Blunt		
Rev.:	Anna Bucciarelli		
Composition:	99.99% Ag, Coloured		
Silver content:	7.96 g, 0.25 tr oz		
Weight:	7.96 g	**Edge:**	Reeded
Diameter:	27 mm	**Die Axis:**	↑↑
Thickness:	N/A	**Finish:**	Proof
Case of Issue:	Premium graphic box.		

DATE	DESCRIPTION	RCM ITEM #	QUANTITY SOLD	ISSUE PRICE	FINISH	PR-69	PR-70
2016	Celebration of Love	149027	14,888	49.95	Proof	55.	—

BATMAN V SUPERMAN: DAWN OF JUSTICE™ SERIES

TEN DOLLARS, *BATMAN V SUPERMAN: DAWN OF JUSTICE™*, 2016.

With the release of the highly anticipated movie *Batman v Superman: Dawn of Justice*, the Royal Canadian Mint is excited to introduce an unforgettable series of coins!

Common Obverse

Designers and Engravers:

Obv.:	Susanna Blunt, Susan Taylor		
Rev.:	DC Comics		
Composition:	99.99% Ag		
Silver content:	15.87 g, 0.510 tr oz		
Weight:	15.87 g	**Edge:**	Reeded
Diameter:	34.0 mm	**Die Axis:**	↑↑
Thickness:	N/A	**Finish:**	Matte Proof
Case of Issue:	Premium graphic case.		

Logo	Superman™	Batman™	Wonder Woman™

DATE	DESCRIPTION	RCM ITEM #	QUANTITY SOLD	ISSUE PRICE	FINISH	PR-69	PR-70
2016	Batman v Superman – Logo	149939	14,953	49.95	Matte Proof	50.	—
2016	Batman v Superman – Superman	149940	13,638	49.95	Matte Proof	50.	—
2016	Batman v Superman – Batman	149941	14,594	49.95	Matte Proof	50.	—
2016	Batman v Superma – Wonder Woman	150277	12,087	49.95	Matte Proof	50.	—

TEN DOLLARS, YEAR OF THE MONKEY, 2016.

Designers:		**Engravers:**	
Obv.:	Susanna Blunt	Obv.	Susan Taylor
Rev.:	Simon Ng		
Composition:	99.99% Ag		
Silver content:	15.87 g, 0.510 tr oz		
Weight:	15.87 g	**Edge:**	Reeded
Diameter:	34.0 mm	**Die Axis:**	↑↑
Thickness:	N/A	**Finish:**	Specimen
Case of Issue:	Maroon clamshell with black beauty box.		

DATE	DESCRIPTION	RCM ITEM #	QUANTITY SOLD	ISSUE PRICE	FINISH	SP-68	SP-69
2016	Year of the Monkey	145396	15,878	39.88	Specimen	40.	—

REFLECTIONS OF WILDLIFE SET

TEN DOLLARS, REFLECTIONS OF WILDLIFE, 2016.

The three-coin Reflections of Wildlife series continues its celebration of this natural beauty through depictions of a quiet, contemplative moment in the wild.

| Common Obverse | Grizzly Bear | Otter | Arctic Fox |

Designers:
Obv.:   Susanna Blunt
Rev.:   Maurade Baynton
Composition: 99.99% Ag
Silver content: 15.87 g, 0.510 tr oz
Weight: 15.87 g
Diameter: 34.0 mm
Thickness: N/A
Case of Issue: Maroon clamshell with black beauty box.

Engravers:
Obv.:   Susan Taylor
Rev.:   Maurade Baynton

Edge: Reeded
Die Axis: ↑↑
Finish: Proof

DATE	DESCRIPTION	RCM ITEM #	QUANTITY SOLD	ISSUE PRICE	FINISH	PR-69	PR-70
2016	Grizzly Bear	150127	11,078	39.95	Proof	40.	—
2016	Otter	150325	8,219	39.95	Proof	40.	—
2016	Arctic Fox		7,556	39.95	Proof	40.	—

DAY OF THE DINOSAURS SET

TEN DOLLARS, DAY OF THE DINOSAURS, 2016.

The prehistoric creatures that roamed the land before us inspire a mix of awe, curiosity and even fear.

| Common Obverse | The Spiked Lizard | Terror of the Sky | The Armoured Tank |
| | Designer: RCM Staff | Designer: Dino Pulera | Designer: Julius Csotonyi |

Designers:
Obv.:   Susanna Blunt
Rev.:   See reverse illustrations
Composition: 99.99% Ag, selective colour
Silver content: 15.87 g, 0.510 tr oz
Weight: 15.87 g
Diameter: 34.0 mm
Thickness: N/A
Case of Issue: Maroon clamshell with black beauty box.

Engravers:
Obv.:   Susan Taylor
Rev.:   See reverse illustrations

Edge: Reeded
Die Axis: ↑↑
Finish: Proof

DATE	DESCRIPTION	RCM ITEM #	QUANTITY SOLD	ISSUE PRICE	FINISH	PR-69	PR-70
2016	The Spiked Lizard	153615	7,297	44.95	Proof	45.	—
2016	Terror of the Sky	152729	7,333	44.95	Proof	45.	—
2016	The Armoured Tank	153585	7,217	44.95	Proof	45.	—

TEN DOLLARS, STAR TREK™ SERIES, 2016.

From warp drives to teleporters, *U.S.S. Enterprise* (NCC-1701) has offered us an exciting vision of what space travel could entail in the 23rd century. Her five-year mission under the command of Captain James Tiberius Kirk (played by Canadian actor William Shatner) made legends of both the ship and her captain, as featured together on this fine silver coin that celebrates the 50th anniversary of *Star Trek™*.

Common Obverse

Designers:			Engravers:	
Obv.:	Susanna Blunt		Obv.	Susan Taylor
Rev.:	RCM Staff			
Composition:	99.99% Ag, selective colour			
Silver content:	15.87 g, 0.510 tr oz			
Weight:	15.87 g		**Edge:**	Reeded
Diameter:	34.0 mm		**Die Axis:**	↑↑
Thickness:	N/A		**Finish:**	Proof
Case of Issue:	Colorful custom graphic box.			

Captain Kirk	**Scotty**	**Spock**	**Uhura**

DATE	DESCRIPTION	RCM ITEM #	QUANTITY SOLD	ISSUE PRICE	FINISH	PR-69	PR-70
2016	Star Trek™: Captain Kirk	153321	12,498	54.95	Proof	80.	—
2016	Star Trek™: Scotty	153256	12,080	54.95	Proof	50.	—
2016	Star Trek™: Spock	153230	11,460	54.95	Proof	50.	—
2016	Star Trek™: Uhura	153244	10,115	54.95	Proof	50.	—

TEN DOLLARS, ICONIC CANADA: INUKSHUK, 2016.

Designers:			Engravers:	
Obv.:	Susanna Blunt		Obv.	Susan Taylor
Rev.:	Tony Bianco			
Composition:	99.99% Ag, Reverse gold plating			
Silver content:	15.87 g, 0.510 tr oz			
Weight:	15.87 g		**Edge:**	Reeded
Diameter:	34.0 mm		**Die Axis:**	↑↑
Thickness:	N/A		**Finish:**	Proof
Case of Issue:	Maroon clamshell with black beauty box.			

DATE	DESCRIPTION	RCM ITEM #	QUANTITY SOLD	ISSUE PRICE	FINISH	PR-69	PR-70
2016	Iconic Canada: Inukshuk	149869	5,983	59.95	Proof	70.	—

TEN DOLLARS, MAPLE LEAF SILHOUETTE: CANADA GEESE (SHAPED), 2016.

Designers and Engravers:		
Obv.:	Susanna Blunt, Susan Taylor	
Rev.:	Trevor Tennant	
Composition:	99.99% Ag	
Silver content:	15.67 g, 0.504 tr oz	
Weight:	15.67 g	**Edge:** Plain
Diameter:	39.6 x 38 mm	**Die Axis:** ↑↑
Thickness:	N/A	**Finish:** Proof
Case of Issue:	Maroon clamshell with black beauty box.	

DATE	DESCRIPTION	RCM ITEM #	QUANTITY SOLD	ISSUE PRICE	FINISH	PR-69	PR-70
2016	Maple Leaf Silhouette: Canada Geese	154096	11.704	84.95	Proof	75.	—

PASSION TO PLAY SET

TEN DOLLARS, PASSION TO PLAY, 2017.

On the ice or in the streets, youth hockey is a timeless tradition that plays out year-round from coast to coast, and embodies the purest spirit of the sport! This fine silver coin set pays tribute to this nationwide passion to play that has endured for over 100 years, and celebrates fan loyalties to Canada's beloved NHL® teams.

Common Obverse

Edmonton Oilers

Ottawa Senators

Winnipeg Jets

Toronto Maple Leafs

Calgary Flames

Vancouver Canucks

Montreal Canadiens

Designers:	
Obv.:	Susanna Blunt
Rev.:	Silvia Pecota
Composition:	99.99% Ag
Silver content:	15.87 g, 0.510 tr oz
Weight:	15.87 g
Diameter:	34.0 mm
Thickness:	N/A
Case of Issue:	Maroon clamshell with custom graphic box.

Engravers:	
Obv.:	Susan Taylor
Rev.:	Silvia Pecota
Edge:	Reeded
Die Axis:	↑↑
Finish:	Matte Proof

DATE	DESCRIPTION	RCM ITEM #	QUANTITY SOLD	ISSUE PRICE	FINISH	PR-69	PR-70
2017	Edmonton Oilers	156128	3,676	74.95	Matte Proof	75.	—
2017	Ottawa Senators	156178	3,547	74.95	Matte Proof	75.	—
2017	Winnipeg Jets	156193	3,674	74.95	Matte Proof	75.	—
2017	Toronto Maple Leafs	156205	5,696	74.95	Matte Proof	75.	—
2017	Calgary Flames	156217	3,592	74.95	Matte Proof	75.	—
2017	Vancouver Canucks	156246	4,280	74.95	Matte Proof	75.	—
2017	Montreal Canadiens	125258	5,568	74.95	Matte Proof	75.	—

TEN DOLLARS, YEAR OF THE ROOSTER, 2017.

Designers:			**Engravers:**	
Obv.:	Susanna Blunt		Obv.	Susan Taylor
Rev.:	Three Degrees Creative Group			
Composition:	99.99% Ag			
Silver content:	15.87 g, 0.510 tr oz			
Weight:	15.87 g		**Edge:**	Reeded
Diameter:	34 mm		**Die Axis:**	↑↑
Thickness:	N/A		**Finish:**	Specimen
Case of Issue:	Maroon clamshell with black beauty box.			

DATE	DESCRIPTION	RCM ITEM #	QUANTITY SOLD	ISSUE PRICE	FINISH	SP-68	SP-69
2017	Year of the Rooster	154178	11,898	41.88	Specimen	42.	—

CELBRATING CANADA'S 150TH SET

TEN DOLLARS, CELBRATING CANADA'S 150TH, 2017.

From colourful flora to iconic fauna and landmarks, breathtaking images of Canada's landscapes reflect the diversity of the Canadian experience.

Designers:		Engravers:	
Obv.:	Susanna Blunt	Obv.	Susan Taylor
Rev.:	See reverse illustrations		
Composition:	99.99% Ag		
Silver content:	15.87 g, 0.510 tr oz		
Weight:	15.87 g	Edge:	Reeded
Diameter:	34.0 mm	Die Axis:	↑↑
Thickness:	N/A	Finish:	Matte Proof
Case of Issue:	Maroon clamshell with black beauty box.		

Common Obverse

Common Loon
Des.: Jim Cumming

Kayaking on the River
Des.: Daniel Dagenais

Lighthouse at Peggy's Cove
Des.: Dale Wilson

Great Blue Heron
Des.: Claude Belanger

Canola Field
Des.: John Sylvester

Float Planes
on the Mackenzie River
Des.: Adam Hill

Grizzly Bear
Des.: "Jenny" Janet Stevens

Panmure Island
Des.: Robert Hamilton

Aurora Borealis
at McIntyre Creek
Des.: Peter Mather

Wild Swift Fox and Pups
Des.: John E. Marriott

Peyto Lake
Des.: Missy Mandel

Iceberg at Dawn
Des.: Dale Wilson

Drum Dancing
Des.: Michelle Valberg

TEN DOLLARS, CELBRATING CANADA'S 150TH, 2017, PRICING TABLE.

DATE	DESCRIPTION	RCM ITEM #	QUANTITY SOLD	ISSUE PRICE	FINISH	PR-69	PR-70
2017	Common Loon	153714	10,967	44.95	Matte Proof	50.	—
2017	Kayaking on the River	154302	9,710	44.95	Matte Proof	50.	—
2017	Lighthouse at Peggy's Cove	154502	10,177	44.95	Matte Proof	50.	—
2017	Great Blue Heron	156308	8,781	44.95	Matte Proof	50.	—
2017	Canola Field	155060	8,369	44.95	Matte Proof	50.	—
2017	Float Planes on the Mackenzie River	155062	7,214	44.95	Matte Proof	50.	—
2017	Grizzly Bear	155064	1,005	51.95	Matte Proof	50.	—
2017	Panmure Island	155066	25,000	51.95	Matte Proof	50.	—
2017	Aurora Borealis at McIntyre Creek	155068	25,000	51.95	Matte Proof	50.	—
2017	Wild Swift Fox and Pups	155070	25,000	51.95	Matte Proof	50.	—
2017	Peyto Lake	155072	25,000	51.95	Matte Proof	50.	—
2017	Iceberg at Dawn	155074	25,000	51.95	Matte Proof	50.	—
2017	Drum Dancing	155076	25,000	51.95	Matte Proof	50.	—

ICONIC CANADA SERIES, 2017

TEN DOLLARS, ICONIC CANADA SERIES, 2017.

Each coin in this five-coin subscription is a visual celebration of a nation and its spirit, through the richly varied images that have come to represent the Canadian experience.

Common Obverse

Dog Sledding Under The Northern Lights
Dss.: Claudio D'Angelo

The Sugar Shack
Des.: Tony Bianco

Spring Sightings
Des.: Silvia Pecota

The Beaver
Des.: Glen Loates

Autumn's Palette
Des.: Tony Bianco

Designers:
Obv.: Susanna Blunt
Rev.: See reverse illustrations
Composition: 99.99% Ag, Coloured
Weight: 15.87 g
Diameter: 34 mm
Thickness: N/A
Case of Issue: Maroon clamshell with black beauty box.

Engravers:
Obv.: Susan Taylor

Silver content: 15.87 g, 0.510 tr oz
Edge: Reeded
Die Axis: ↑↑
Finish: Matte Proof

DATE	DESCRIPTION	RCM ITEM #	MINTAGE	ISSUE PRICE	FINISH	PR-69	PR-70
2017	Dog Sledding Under The Northern Lights	158955	15,000	51.95	Matte Proof	52.	—
2017	The Sugar Shack	159304	15,000	51.95	Matte Proof	52.	—
2017	Spring Sightings	159928	15,000	51.95	Matte Proof	52.	—
2017	The Beaver	159891	15,000	51.95	Matte Proof	52.	—
2017	Autumn's Palette	161055	15,000	51.95	Matte Proof	52.	—

BIRDS AMONG NATURE'S COLOURS SERIES

TEN DOLLARS, BIRDS AMONG NATURE'S COLOURS, 2017.

Among the many species of birds that breed in Canada, where their interactions with the environment leaves us with a greater appreciation for the beauty that surrounds us – as beautifully showcased in this unique five-coin set.

Common Obverse

Chickadee
Des.: Jean-Charles Daumas

Designers:		Engravers:	
Obv.:	Susanna Blunt	Obv.	Susan Taylor
Rev.:	See reverse illustrations		
Composition:	99.99% Ag, Coloured		
Silver content:	15.87 g, 0.510 tr oz		
Weight:	15.87 g	Edge:	Reeded
Diameter:	34.0 mm	Die Axis:	↑↑
Thickness:	N/A	Finish:	Proof
Case of Issue:	Maroon clamshell with black beauty box, COA.		

Northern Flicker
Des.: Jean-Chares Daumas

Tufted Titmouse
Des.: Derek C. Wicks

Purple Martin
Des.: Derek C. Wicks

Nuthatch
Des.: Derek C. Wicks

DATE	DESCRIPTION	RCM ITEM #	MINTAGE	ISSUE PRICE	FINISH	PR-69	PR-70
2017	Chickadee	156230	15,000	64.95	Proof	65.	—
2017	Northern Flicker	156232	15,000	64.95	Proof	65.	—
2017	Tufted Titmouse	156234	15,000	64.95	Proof	65.	—
2017	Purple Martin	156236	15,000	64.95	Proof	65.	—
2017	Nuthatch	156238	15,000	64.95	Proof	65.	—

TEN DOLLARS, YEAR OF THE DOG, 2018.

Designers:		Engravers:	
Obv.:	Susanna Blunt	Obv.	Susan Taylor
Rev.:	Simon Ng		
Composition:	99.99% Ag		
Silver content:	15.87 g, 0.510 tr oz		
Weight:	15.87 g	Edge:	Reeded
Diameter:	34.0 mm	Die Axis:	↑↑
Thickness:	N/A	Finish:	Specimen
Case of Issue:	Maroon clamshell with black beauty box, COA.		

DATE	DESCRIPTION	RCM ITEM #	MINTAGE	ISSUE PRICE	FINISH	SP-68	SP-69
2018	Year of the Dog	162185	15,888	41.88	Specimen	42.	—

LEARNING TO PLAY SERIES

TEN DOLLARS, LEARNING TO PLAY SERIES, 2018.

Celebrate Canadian hockey and family togetherness with this series of seven exclusive coins that feature the Canadian NHL teams, and celebrate children learning to play.

Common Obverse

Calgary Flames

Edmonton Oilers

Montreal Canadiens

Ottawa Senators

(Toronto Maple Leafs)

Toronto Maple Leafs

Vancouver Canucks

Winnipeg Jets

Designers:		**Engravers:**	
Obv.:	Susanna Blunt	Obv.:	Susan Taylor
Rev.:	John Mantha	Rev.:	RCM Staff
Composition:	99.99% Ag, with colour		
Silver content:	15.87 g, 0.510 tr oz		
Weight:	15.87 g	**Edge:**	Reeded
Diameter:	34.0 mm	**Die Axis:**	↑↑
Thickness:	N/A	**Finish:**	Matte Proof
Case of Issue:	Maroon clamshell with black beauty box, COA		

DATE	DESCRIPTION	RCM ITEM #	MINTAGE	ISSUE PRICE	FINISH	PR-69	PR-70
2018	Calgary Flames	161407	7,000	74.95	Matte Proof	75.	—
2018	Edmonton Oilers	161414	7,000	74.95	Matte Proof	75.	—
2018	Montreal Canadiens	161435	7,000	74.95	Matte Proof	75.	—
2018	Ottawa Senators	161421	7,000	74.95	Matte Proof	75.	—
2018	Toronto Maple Leafs	161392	7,000	74.95	Matte Proof	75.	—
2018	Vancouver Canucks	161400	7,000	74.95	Matte Proof	75.	—
2018	Winnipeg Jets	161428	7,000	74.95	Matte Proof	75.	—

TEN DOLLARS, THE COMMON LOON: BEAUTY AND GRACE, 2018.

Designers:		**Engravers:**	
Obv.:	Susanna Blunt	Obv.	Susan Taylor
Rev.:	Arnold Nogy		
Composition:	99.99% Ag		
Silver content:	23.17 g, 0.75 tr oz		
Weight:	23.17 g	**Edge:**	Reeded
Diameter:	36.07 mm	**Die Axis:**	↑↑
Thickness:	N/A	**Finish:**	Proof
Case of Issue:	Maroon clamshell with black beauty box, COA.		

DATE	DESCRIPTION	RCM ITEM #	MINTAGE	ISSUE PRICE	FINISH	PR-69	PR-70
2018	The Common Loon: Beauty and Grace	161488	7,500	69.95	Proof	70.	—

TEN DOLLARS, *YIN* AND *YANG* - TIGER AND DRAGON, 2018.

These amazing *yin* and *yang*-shaped coins feature two heroes of Chinese tradition — the Tiger and the Dragon — fit together to form a perfect whole. The theme of balance is fully realized in their stunning imagery, rich colour, and singular design.

Designers:		Engravers:	
Obv.:	Susanna Blunt	Obv.	Susan Taylor
Rev.:	Three Degrees Creative Group		
Composition:	99.99% Ag		
Silver content:	15.87 g, 0.510 tr oz		
Weight:	15.87 g (per coin)	Edge:	Plain
Diameter:	39 mm (combined)	Die Axis:	↑↑
Thickness:	N/A	Finish:	Proof
Case of Issue:	Maroon clamshell with black beauty box, COA.		

TEN DOLLARS, BLACK AND WHITE *YIN* AND *YANG* - TIGER AND DRAGON, 2018.

Designers:		Engravers:	
Obv.:	Susanna Blunt	Obv.	Susan Taylor
Rev.:	Simon Ng		
Composition:	99.99% Ag		
Silver content:	15.87 g, 0.510 tr oz		
Weight:	15.87 g (per coin)	Edge:	Plain
Diameter:	39 mm (combined)	Die Axis:	↑↑
Thickness:	N/A	Finish:	Proof
Case of Issue:	Maroon clamshell with black beauty box, COA.		

DATE	DESCRIPTION	RCM ITEM #	MINTAGE	ISSUE PRICE	FINISH	PR-69	PR-70
2018	*Yin* and *Yang* — Tiger and Dragon	161488	6,000	164.95	Proof	165.	—
2018	Black and White *Yin* and *Yang* — Tiger and Dragon	165868	6,000	164.95	Proof	165.	—

STAR TREK™ STARSHIPS SERIES

TEN DOLLARS, STAR TREK™ STARSHIPS, 2018.

Collect all three coins of the most famous starships in the Star Trek universe.

Common Obverse	**Enterprise-D** *(Star Trek - The Next Generation)*	**Voyager** *(Star Trek - Voyager)*	**Enterprse NX-01** *(Star Trek - Enterprise)*

Designers:		Engravers:	
Obv.:	Susanna Blunt	Obv.:	Susan Taylor
Rev.:	RCM Staff	Rev.:	RCM Staff
Composition:	99.99% Ag		
Silver content:	15.87 g, 0.510 tr oz		
Weight:	15.87 g	Edge:	Reeded
Diameter:	34.0 mm	Die Axis:	↑↑
Thickness:	N/A	Finish:	Proof
Case of Issue:	Graphic beauty box, COA.		

DATE	DESCRIPTION	RCM ITEM #	MINTAGE	ISSUE PRICE	FINISH	PR-69	PR-70
2018	*Enterprise-D*	164115	10,000	64.95	Proof	65.	—
2018	*Voyager*	164127	10,000	64.95	Proof	65.	—
2018	*Enterprise* NX-01	164103	10,000	64.95	Proof	65.	—

TEN DOLLARS, ARMISTICE, 2018.

The 2018 $10 Armistice fine silver coin commemorates the centennial of the Armistice of 1918, an agreement for peace after the four long, mud-soaked years of the First World War (1914-1918).

Designers:		Engravers:	
Obv.:	Susanna Blunt	Obv.	Susan Taylor
Rev.:	Laurie McGraw		
Composition:	99.99% Ag		
Silver content:	15.87 g, 0.51 tr oz		
Weight:	15.87 g	**Edge:**	Reeded
Diameter:	34 mm	**Die Axis:**	↑↑
Thickness:	N/A	**Finish:**	Specimen
Case of Issue:	Encapsulated coin packaged in a custom folder.		

DATE	DESCRIPTION	RCM ITEM #	MINTAGE	ISSUE PRICE	FINISH	SP-68	SP-69
2018	Armstice	169348	WSL	34.95	Specimen	35.	—

TEN DOLLARS, LUNAR YEAR OF THE PIG, 2019.

Designers:		Engravers:	
Obv.:	Susanna Blunt	Obv.	Susan Taylor
Rev.:	Simon Ng		
Composition:	99.99% Ag		
Silver content:	15.87 g, 0.51 tr oz		
Weight:	15.87 g	**Edge:**	Reeded
Diameter:	34 mm	**Die Axis:**	↑↑
Thickness:	N/A	**Finish:**	Specimen
Case of Issue:	Maroon clamshell with black beauty box, COA.		

DATE	DESCRIPTION	RCM ITEM #	MINTAGE	ISSUE PRICE	FINISH	SP-68	SP-69
2019	Lunar Year of the Pig	167550	45,888	41.88	Specimen	42.	—

TEN DOLLARS, EQUALITY, 2019.

Designers:		Engravers:	
Obv.:	Susanna Blunt	Obv.	Susan Taylor
Rev.:	Joe Average		
Composition:	99.99% Ag		
Silver content:	15.87 g, 0.51 tr oz		
Weight:	15.87 g	**Edge:**	Reeded
Diameter:	34 mm	**Die Axis:**	↑↑
Thickness:	N/A	**Finish:**	Matte Proof
Case of Issue:	Maroon clamshell with black beauty box, COA.		

DATE	DESCRIPTION	RCM ITEM #	MINTAGE	ISSUE PRICE	FINISH	SP-68	SP-69
2019	Equality	172533	15,000	49.95	Matte Proof	50.	—

TEN DOLLAR DERIVATIVES

DATE	DESCRIPTION	MINTAGE	ISSUE PRICE	ISSUER	FINISH	MARKET PRICE
2010	**Ten Dollar Blue Whale;** Souvenir sheet of two $10 Blue Whale postage stamps; Booklet; Maple wood case	9,719	79.95	RCM, CP	Proof	75.

FIFTEEN DOLLARS

FIFTEEN DOLLARS, 100TH ANNIVERSARY OF THE OLYMPIC MOVEMENT, 1992-1996.

The International Olympic Committee initiated a commemorative coin programme to mark the centennial of the modern Olympic movement in 1996. Five mints, those of Canada, Australia, France, Austria and Greece, participated by each issuing one gold and two silver coins over a five year period. The total collection comprises five gold and ten silver coins.

The Royal Canadian Mint issued the first three coins in 1992. The silver fifteen dollar coins are listed here, the 1992 $175 gold coin on page 438.

The Standard Catalogue lists only the coins issued by the Royal Canadian Mint.

Common Obverse
Designer and Engraver:
Dora de Pédery-Hunt

Coin No. 1
Speed Skater,
Pole Vaulter, Gymnast
Designer: David Craig
Engraver: Sheldon Beveridge

Coin No. 2
The Spirit Of the Generations
Designer: Stewart Sherwood
Engraver: Terry Smith

Composition:	92.5% Ag, 7.5% Cu		
Silver content:	31.108 g, 1.00 tr oz		
Weight:	33.63 g	**Edge: Lettering:**	Citius, Altius, Fortius
Diameter:	40.0 mm	**Die Axis:**	↑↑
Thickness:	3.1 mm	**Finish:**	Proof
Case of Issue:	Singly: Burgundy leatherette case		
	Set: Wooden display case		

DATE	DESCRIPTION	QUANTITY SOLD	ISSUE PRICE	FINISH	PR-68	PR-69
1992	Speed Skater, with edge lettering	105,645	46.95	Proof	50.	—
1992	Speed Skater, without edge lettering	Included	46.95	Proof	375.	—
1992	Spirit of the Generations, with edge lettering	Included	46.95	Proof	50.	—
1992	Spirit of the Generations, without edge lettering	Included	46.95	Proof	375.	—

NOTE TO COLLECTORS

When the initials N.I.I. appear in the pricing table it indicates the coin was part of a set issued by the Royal Canadian Mint, and not issued individually. Coin designs that are found only in sets offered by the Royal Canadian Mint are listed individually by denomination, and date in Volume Two.

SP-68 / PR-69	This price is based on the item still being in the original package as sold by the Mint.
SP-69 / PR-70	This price is based on the item being graded by a reputable third-party grading company.
	Prices are generally not listed due to the low number of sales of certified products in these grades.
	Price should be based on population reports and market demand.

CHINESE LUNAR CALENDAR SERIES

FIFTEEN DOLLARS, CHINESE LUNAR CALENDAR STERLING SILVER COIN SERIES, 1998-2009.

Common Obverse except for date

Starting in 1998 with the year of the Tiger, the Royal Canadian Mint embarked on a twelve-year series of Chinese Lunar calendar coins which ended in 2009. The twelve sterling silver coins were issued one per year to commemorate the start of each new year of the twelve-year cycle. The coins were available singly or by subscription. The subscription was for a five-year period beginning in 1999 and ending in 2003. The five coins, shipped one per year, were offered at a fixed price of $428.28 including a sterling silver medallion housed in a 13-hole presentation box made of embossed red velvet and gold moiré. The single presentation box is a smaller version of the larger one, red and gold moiré.

Note: Coins illustrated smaller than actual size.

Year of the Tiger 1998	**Year of the Rabbit 1999**	**Year of the Dragon 2000**	**Year of the Snake 2001**
Designer: Harvey Chan	Designer: Harvey Chan	Designer: Harvey Chan	Designer: Harvey Chan
Engraver: Stan Witten	Engraver: José Osio	Engraver: José Osio	Engraver: José Osio

Year of the Horse 2002	**Year of the Ram 2003**	**Year of the Monkey 2004**	**Year of the Rooster 2005**
Designer: Harvey Chan	Designer: Harvey Chan	Designer: Harvey Chan	Designer: Harvey Chan
Engraver: José Osio	Engraver: José Osio	Engraver: Stan Witten	Engraver: José Osio

Year of the Dog 2006	**Year of the Pig 2007**	**Year of the Rat 2008**	**Year of the Ox 2009**
Designer: Harvey Chan	Designer: Harvey Chan	Designer: Harvey Chan	Designer: Harvey Chan
Engraver: José Osio	Engraver: José Osio	Engraver: José Osio	Engraver: José Osio

FIFTEEN DOLLARS, CHINESE LUNAR CALENDAR STERLING SILVER COIN SERIES, 1998-2009 (cont.).

Designers:
  Obv.: Dora de Pédery-Hunt
  Rev.: See reverse illustrations
Composition: 92.5% Ag, 7.5% Cu,
    24-karat gold plated cameo
Silver content: 30.71 to 31.45 g, 0.987 to 1.011 tr oz
Weight: 33.2 to 34.0 g
Diameter: 40.0 mm
Thickness: 3.0 to 3.35 mm

Engravers:
  Obv.: Dora de Pédery-Hunt
  Rev.: See reverse illustrations

Edge: Reeded
Die Axis: ↑↑
Finish: Proof

Case of Issue:
  Set: A thirteen-hole embossed red velvet presentation box with goldmoiré sides. Included is a sterling silver medallion carrying the twelve signs of the zodiac.
  Singly: Embossed red velvet presentation box as above, encapsulated, COA

DATE	DESCRIPTION	RCM ITEM #	QUANTITY SOLD	ISSUE PRICE	FINISH	PR-69	PR-70
1998	Empty case to hold 12 sterling silver coins and a sterling silver medallion	N/A	—	—	—	125.	*
1998	Year of the Tiger	N/A	68,888	68.88	Proof	150.	—
1999	Year of the Rabbit	N/A	77,791	72.88	Proof	70.	—
2000	Year of the Dragon	N/A	88,634	72.88	Proof	90.	—
2001	Year of the Snake	N/A	60,754	94.88	Proof	60.	—
2002	Year of the Horse	N/A	59,395	94.88	Proof	60.	—
2003	Year of the Ram	N/A	53,714	94.88	Proof	60.	—
2004	Year of the Monkey	N/A	46,175	105.88	Proof	75.	—
2005	Year of the Rooster	N/A	44,690	105.88	Proof	60.	—
2006	Year of the Dog	N/A	41,634	112.88	Proof	60.	—
2007	Year of the Pig	N/A	10,752	88.88	Proof	60.	—
2008	Year of the Rat	N/A	9,209	88.88	Proof	60.	—
2009	Year of the Ox	6241009	7,096	88.88	Proof	60.	—

FIFTEEN DOLLARS, CHINESE LUNAR CALENDAR DERIVATIVES

DATE	DESCRIPTION	MINTAGE	ISSUE PRICE	ISSUER	FINISH	MARKET PRICE
1998	**Year of the Tiger**, Fifteen dollar coin; Souvenir stamp sheet; Presentation album	8,000	88.88	RCM, CP	Proof	150.
1999	**Year of the Rabbit**, as 1998	8,000	88.88	RCM, CP	Proof	70.
2000	**Year of the Dragon**, as 1998	10,000	88.88	RCM, CP	Proof	90.
2000	**Year of the Dragon**, 18kt gold stamp, Mint stamp, Presentation case	N/A	N/A	RCM, CP	Proof	550.
2001	**Year of the Snake**, as 1998	8,000	94.88	RCM, CP	Proof	60.
2002	**Year of the Horse**, as 1998	8,000	98.88	RCM, CP	Proof	60.
2003	**Year of the Ram**, as 1998	8,000	98.88	RCM, CP	Proof	60.
2004	**Year of the Monkey**, as 1998	8,000	105.88	RCM, CP	Proof	75.
2005	**Year of the Rooster**, as 1998	8,000	105.88	RCM, CP	Proof	60.
2006	**Year of the Dog**, as 1998	8,000	112.88	RCM, CP	Proof	60.
2007	**Year of the Pig**, as 1998	8,000	112.88	RCM, CP	Proof	60.
2008	**Year of the Rat**, as 1998	8,000	112.88	RCM, CP	Proof	60.
2009	**Year of the Ox**, as 1998	8,000	112.88	RCM, CP	Proof	60.

VIGNETTES OF ROYALTY SERIES

FIFTEEN DOLLARS, VIGNETTES OF ROYALTY SERIES, 2008-2009.

Common Obverse

Victoria
Designer: Leonard C. Wyon
Engraver: RCM Staff

Edward VII
Designer: G. W. De Saulles
Engraver: RCM Staff

George V
Designer: E. B. MacKennal
Engraver: RCM Staff

George VI
Designer: T. H. Paget
Engraver: RCM Staff

Elizabeth II
Designer: Mary Gillick
Engraver: RCM Staff

Designers:		**Engravers:**	
Obv.:	Susanna Blunt	Obv.:	Susan Taylor
Rev.:	See reverse illustrations	Rev.:	See reverse illustrations
Composition:	92.5% Ag, 7.5% Cu		
Silver content:	27.75 g, 0.89 tr oz		
Weight:	30.0 g	**Edge:**	Plain
Diameter:	36.2 mm	**Die Axis:**	↑↑
Thickness:	3.2 mm	**Finish:**	Proof-like
Case of Issue:	Singly: Maroon leatherette clam style case, black flocked insert, encapsulated coin, COA		
	Set: Five-hole maroon clam style case to hold the series of coins.		

DATE	DESCRIPTION	ISSUE DATE	RCM ITEM #	QUANTITY SOLD	ISSUE PRICE	FINISH	PL-68	PL-69
2008	Victoria	Oct. 31, 2007	6244008	3,442	99.95	Proof-like	75.	—
2008	Edward VII	July 23, 2008	6244018	6,261	99.95	Proof-like	75.	—
2008	George V	Oct. 1, 2008	6244028	—	99.95	Proof-like	75.	—
2009	George VI	Apr. 15, 2009	6244009	10,045	99.95	Proof-like	75.	—
2009	Elizabeth II	Oct. 1, 2009	6244019	2,643	99.95	Proof-like	75.	—
—	Vignettes of Royalty Set, 5 coins	—	N/A	N/A	499.95	Proof-like	325.	—

NOTES FOR COLLECTORS

1. The RCM Report of 2009 does not break down the "quantity sold" figures for the George V and George VI coins, but group all under George VI.
2. It is interesting to note that after 55 years the Royal Canadian Mint recognises a Proof-like finish. The vignettes are struck in ultra high relief on a Proof-like background.

PLAYING CARD MONEY SERIES

FIFTEEN DOLLARS, PLAYING CARD MONEY SERIES, 2008-2009.

This series was issued to commemorate the issue of playing cards used as money during times of chronic shortages in the 17th- and 18th- centuries in New France.

2008 Obverse

Jack of Hearts

Queen of Spades

2009 Obverse

King of Hearts

Ten of Spades

Designers:		Engravers:	
Obv.:	Susanna Blunt	Obv.:	Susan Taylor
Rev.:	Original artwork by Henry Beau	Rev.:	José Osio
	Public Archives of Canada		

Composition:	92.5% Ag, 7.5% Cu, Painted; Gold plate on edge		
Silver content:	29.193 g, 0.938 tr oz		
Weight:	31.56 g	**Edge:**	Plain
Size:	49.8 x 28.6 mm	**Die Axis:**	↑↑
Thickness:	2.4 to 2.7 mm	**Finish:**	Proof
Case of Issue:	Singly: Maroon leatherette clam style case, black flocked insert, encapsulated coin, COA		
	Set: Four-hole maroon clam style case, black flocked insert, encapsulated coins		

DATE	DESCRIPTION	ISSUE DATE	RCM ITEM #	QUANTITY SOLD	ISSUE PRICE	FINISH	PL-68	PL-69
2008	Jack of Hearts	July 23, 2008	101427	11,362	89.95	Proof	75.	—
2008	Queen of Spades	Oct. 1, 2008	101428	8,714	89.95	Proof	75.	—
2009	King of Hearts	Apr. 15, 2009	101430	5,798	89.95	Proof	75.	—
2009	Ten of Spades	July 22, 2009	101029	5,921	89.95	Proof	75.	—
—	Playing Card Money Set	—	107185	278	359.80	Proof	275.	*

LUNAR LOTUS SERIES

FIFTEEN DOLLARS, SILVER LUNAR LOTUS SERIES, 2010-2019.

**Common Obverse
except for date**

A new Lunar Calendar series was introduced in 2010. The new series, beginning with the 2010 Year of the Tiger, will run for twelve years. The scalloped coin is reminiscent of a lotus flower.

   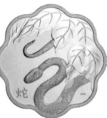 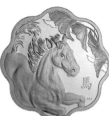

| 2010 Year of the Tiger | 2011 Year of the Rabbit | 2012 Year of the Dragon | 2013 Year of the Snake | 2014 Year of the Horse |
| Eng.: José Osio | Eng.: Konrad Wachelko | Eng.: Cecily Mok | Eng.: Christie Paquet | Eng.: Eric Boyer |

| 2015 Year of the Sheep | 2016 Year of the Monke | 2017 Year of the Rooster | 2018 Year of the Dog | 2019 Year of the Pig |
| Eng.: RCM Staff | Eng.: RCM Staff | Eng.: RCM Staff | Eng.: RCM Staff | Eng.: RCM Staff |

Designers:
Obv.:   Susanna Blunt
Rev.:   Three Degrees Creative Group Inc.
Composition: 2010-2012: 92.5% Ag, 7.5% Cu
2013-2019: 99.99% Ag
Weight: 26.3 to 26.51 g
Diameter (scalloped): 38.0 mm
Thickness: 2.9 mm

Engravers:
Obv.:   Susan Taylor
Rev.:   See reverse illustrations
Silver content: 2010-2012: 24.327 g, 0.782 tr oz
2013-2019: 26.7 g, 0.858 tr oz
Edge: Plain
Die Axis: ↑↑
Finish: Proof

Case of Issue: Singly: Silver satin-like covered case, black flocked insert, encapsulated coin, COA
Set: Hardwood exterior with high-gloss finish and silk-screened paper. Interior has high-gloss finish in Chinese red with a silver design. Wooden insert accommodates 12 coins.

DATE	DESCRIPTION	RCM ITEM #	QUANTITY SOLD	ISSUE PRICE	FINISH	PR-69	PR-70
2010	Year of the Tiger	107655	10,268	88.88	Proof	120.	—
2011	Year of the Rabbit	109604	19,888	88.88	Proof	130.	—
2012	Year of the Dragon	109605	25,216	98.88	Proof	100.	—
2013	Year of the Snake	109606	21,906	98.88	Proof	100.	—
2014	Year of the Horse	109607	20,575	98.88	Proof	100.	—
2015	Year of the Sheep	109608	16,056	98.88	Proof	100.	—
2016	Year of the Monkey	109609	13,391	98.88	Proof	100.	—
2017	Year of the Rooster	109610	11,668	101.88	Proof	100.	—
2018	Year of the Dog	109611	18,888	101.88	Proof	100.	—
2019	Year of the Pig	109612	15,888	101.88	Proof	102.	—

Note: Coins illustrated smaller than actual size.

CLASSIC CHINESE ZODIAC SERIES

FIFTEEN DOLLARS, CLASSIC CHINESE ZODIAC SERIES, 2010-2019.

Common Obverse

A second Lunar Calendar series was introduced in 2010. This new series is distributed by the Asian Business Centre and the Royal Canadian Mint. The proposed quantity was 9,999 units.

2010 Year of the Tiger
Eng.: Konrad Wachelko

2011 Year of the Rabbit
Eng.: William Woodruff

2012 Year of the Dragon
Eng.: Stan Witten

2013 Year of the Snake
Eng.: Stan Witten

2014 Year of the Horse
Eng.: Konrad Wachelko

2015 Year of the Sheep
Eng.: RCM Staff

2016 Year of the Monkey
Eng.: RCM Staff

2017 Year of the Rooster
Eng.: RCM Staff

2018 Year of the Dog
Eng.: RCM Staff

2019 Year of the Pig
Eng.: RCM Staff

Designers:		**Engravers:**
Obv.: Susanna Blunt		Obv.: Susan Taylor
Rev.: Aries Cheung		Rev.: See reverse illustrations
Composition: 99.99% Ag		**Silver content:** 31.39 g, 1.01 tr oz
Weight: 31.39 g		**Edge:** Reeded
Diameter: 38.0 mm		**Die Axis:** ↑↑
Thickness: 3.2 mm		**Finish:** Proof

Case of Issue: Singly: Silver satin-like covered case, black flocked insert, encapsulated coin, COA
Set: Hardwood exterior with high-gloss finish and silk-screened paper. Interior has high-gloss finish in Chinese red with a silver design. Wooden insert accommodates 12 coins.

DATE	DESCRIPTION	RCM ITEM #	QUANTITY SOLD	ISSUE PRICE	FINISH	PR-69	PR-70
2010	Year of the Tiger	106644	N/A	88.88	Proof	130.	—
2011	Year of the Rabbit	111194	9,999	98.88	Proof	150.	—
2012	Year of the Dragon	114067	19,644	98.88	Proof	100.	—
2013	Year of the Snake	119715	14,213	98.88	Proof	100.	—
2014	Year of the Horse	124036	15,738	98.88	Proof	100.	—
2015	Year of the Sheep	129849	9,256	98.88	Proof	100.	—
2016	Year of the Monkey	142479	9,817	98.88	Proof	100.	—
2017	Year of the Rooster	144057	8,256	101.88	Proof	100.	—
2018	Year of the Dog	144058	10,888	101.88	Proof	100.	—
2019	Year of the Pig	144059	15,888	101.88	Proof	100.	—

CONTINUITY OF THE CROWN SET

FIFTEEN DOLLARS, CONTINUITY OF THE CROWN SET, 2011.

Common Obverse	HRH Prince Henry of Wales Engraver: Stan Witten	HRH Prince William of Wales Engraver: Konrad Wachelko	HRH The Prince of Wales Engraver: William Woodruff

Designers:
   Obv.:   Susanna Blunt
   Rev.:   Laurie McGaw
Composition: 92.5% Ag, 7.5% Cu
Silver content: 23.29 g, 0.75 tr oz
Weight: 25.175 g
Diameter: 36.2 mm
Thickness: 3.0 mm

Engravers:
   Obv.:   Susan Taylor
   Rev.:   See reverse illustrations

Edge: Plain
Die Axis: ↑↑
Finish: Proof-like

Case of Issue: Singly: Maroon clam style case, black flocked insert, encapsulated coin, COA
                 Set: Three-hole maroon clam style case to hold the coins.

DATE	DESCRIPTION	RCM ITEM #	QUANTITY SOLD	ISSUE PRICE	FINISH	PR-69	PR-70
2011	HRH Prince Henry of Wales	110617	5,751	109.95	Proof-like	50.	—
2011	HRH Prince William of Wales	112244	6,217	109.95	Proof-like	50.	—
2011	HRH The Prince of Wales	113119	4,788	109.95	Proof-like	50.	—
2011	Set of 3 coins	115207	—	329.85	Proof-like	130.	—

CHINESE HISTORY AND TRADITIONS SERIES

FIFTEEN DOLLARS, CHINESE HISTORY AND TRADITIONS SERIES, 2011-2015.

Featuring a hologram on the coins' reverses, this series celebrates the history and traditions of Chinese culture with depictions of a magpie and lotus flower (Maple of Happiness), two deer (Maple of Good Fortune), an elephant decorated with a chrysanthemum (Maple of Peace), two cranes (Maple of Longevity), and three fish (Maple of Prosperity).

Common Obverse

Maple of Happiness
Designer: Simon Ng
Engraver: Stan Witten

Maple of Good Fortune
Designer: Three Degree
Creative Group
Engraver: Cecily Mok

Maple of Peace
Designer: Simon Ng
Engraver: Steven Stewart

Maple of Longevity
Designer: Simon Ng
Engraver: RCM Staff

Maple of Prosperity
Designer: Albert Ng
Engraver: RCM Staff

Designers:		**Engravers:**	
Obv.:	Susanna Blunt	Obv.:	Susan Taylor
Rev.:	See reverse illustrations	Rev.:	See reverse illustrations

Composition: 99.99% Ag, Hologram
Silver content: 31.1 g, 1.0 tr oz
Weight: 31.1 g   **Edge:** Reeded
Diameter: 38.0 mm   **Die Axis:** ↑↑
Thickness: 3.1 mm   **Finish:** Proof
Case of Issue: Maroon leatherette clam style case, black flocked insert, encapsulated coin, COA

DATE	DESCRIPTION	RCM ITEM #	QUANTITY SOLD	ISSUE PRICE	FINISH	PR-69	PR-70
2011	Maple of Happiness	113879	8,209	98.88	Proof	90.	—
2012	Maple of Good Fortune	119078	8,866	98.88	Proof	90.	—
2013	Maple of Peace	123302	8,510	98.88	Proof	90.	—
2014	Maple of Longevity	130304	9,821	98.88	Proof	75.	—
2015	Maple of Prosperity	143809	3,483	98.88	Proof	90.	—

Note: For the other coins in the Chinese History and Traditions Series see page 190.

SUPERMAN™ SERIES

FIFTEEN DOLLARS, 75TH ANNIVERSARY OF SUPERMAN™: MODERN DAY, 2013.

Depicting a modern rendering of Superman™, Superman's™ native Kryptonian language encircles the outside rim and reads "75 Years of Superman".

Designers and Engravers:

Obv.:	Susanna Blunt, Susan Taylor
Rev.:	DC Comics/Warner Brothers, Samantha Strath

Composition: 99.99% Ag, Painted
Silver content: 15.87 g, 0.510 tr oz

Weight:	15.87 g	**Edge:**	Reeded
Diameter:	34.0 mm	**Die Axis:**	↑↑
Thickness:	2.1 mm	**Finish:**	Matte Proof

Case of Issue: Clear plastic cover, black plastic coin display, encapsulated coin, COA, custom beauty box

DATE	DESCRIPTION	RCM ITEM #	QUANTITY SOLD	ISSUE PRICE	FINISH	PR-69	PR-70
2013	75th Anniv. of Superman™: Modern Day	128225	14,962	69.75	Proof	75.	—

FIFTEEN DOLLARS, ICONIC SUPERMAN™ COMIC BOOK COVERS: ACTION COMICS #419 (1972), 2014.

Based on the 1972 iconic comic book cover, this coin commemorates Superman's strength as he fights the evils that lurk within Metropolis.

Designers and Engravers:

Obv.:	Susanna Blunt, Susan Taylor
Rev.:	DC Comics/Warner Brothers, RCM Staff

Composition: 99.99% Ag, Painted
Silver content: 23.17 g, 0.75 tr oz

Weight:	23.17 g	**Edge:**	Reeded
Diameter:	36.07 mm	**Die Axis:**	↑↑
Thickness:	2.1 mm	**Finish:**	Proof

Case of Issue: Custom case, black flocked insert, encapsulated coin, COA

DATE	DESCRIPTION	RCM ITEM #	QUANTITY SOLD	ISSUE PRICE	FINISH	PR-69	PR-70
2014	Action Comics #419 (1972)	133880	10,000	89.95	Proof	75.	—

EXPLORING CANADA SERIES

Common
Obverse

FIFTEEN DOLLARS, EXPLORING CANADA SERIES, 2014-2015.
This set celebrates the adventurous and courageous spirit of Canada's pioneering explorers.

| The Voyageurs | The Gold Rush | The Arctic Expedition | The Vikings | The West Coast Exploration |

| The Pioneering Mapmakers | The Wild Rivers Exploration | Building the Canadian Pacific Railway | Scientific Exploration | Space Exploration |

Designers:
Obv.: Susanna Blunt
Rev.: John Mantha
Composition: 99.99% Ag
Silver content: 23.17 g, 0.75 tr oz
Weight: 23.17 g
Diameter: 36.07 mm
Thickness: N/A

Engravers:
Obv.: Susan Taylor
Rev.: RCM Staff

Edge: Reeded
Die Axis: ↑↑
Finish: Matte Proof

Case of Issue: Singly: Maroon leatherette clam style case, black flocked insert, encapsulated coin, COA, custom case
Subscription: 10-hole graphic paperboard case, encapsulated coins, COA

DATE	DESCRIPTION	RCM ITEM #	QUANTITY SOLD	ISSUE PRICE	FINISH	PR-69	PR-70
2014	The Voyageurs	132670	7,907	54.95	Proof	50.	—
2014	The Gold Rush	132675	8,001	54.95	Proof	50.	—
2014	The Arctic Expedition	132677	3,103	54.95	Proof	50.	—
2014	The Vikings	132689	6,601	54.95	Proof	50.	—
2014	The West Coast Exploration	132691	6,202	54.95	Proof	50.	—
2014	The Pioneering Mapmakers	132693	5,775	54.95	Proof	50.	—
2015	The Wild Rivers Exploration	135221	5,625	54.95	Proof	50.	—
2015	Building the Canadian Pacific Railway	135223	6,144	54.95	Proof	50.	—
2015	Scientific Exploration	135225	5,574	54.95	Proof	50.	—
2015	Space Exploration	135227	5,529	54.95	Proof	50.	—

ARTWORK BY FRANKLIN CARMICHAEL

FIFTEEN DOLLARS, ARTWORK BY FRANKLIN CARMICHAEL, 2015.

Celebrating the artwork of Canada's youngest member of the Group of Seven on the 125th anniversary of Franklin Carmichael's birth, this set of coins features three of Carmichael's most famous works.

| Common Obverse | The Upper Ottawa, Near Mattawa (c. 1924) | Cranberry Lake (c. 1934) | Landscape |

Designers:
Obv.:   Susanna Blunt
Rev.:   Franklin Carmichael
Composition: 99.99% Ag, Hologram
Silver content: 23.17 g, 0.75 tr oz
Weight: 23.17 g
Diameter: 36.07 mm
Thickness: N/A
Case of Issue: Maroon leatherette clam style case to hold three coins, black flocked insert, encapsulated coin, COA

Engravers:
Obv.:   Susan Taylor
Rev.:   RCM Staff

Edge: Reeded
Die Axis: ↑↑
Finish: Proof

DATE	DESCRIPTION	RCM ITEM #	QUANTITY SOLD	ISSUE PRICE	FINISH	PR-69	PR-70
2015	*The Upper Ottawa, Near Mattawa* (c. 1924)	N/A	385	N.I.I.	Proof	70.	—
2015	*Cranberry Lake* (c. 1934)	N/A	381	N.I.I.	Proof	70.	—
2015	*Landscape*	N/A	—	N.I.I.	Proof	70.	—
2015	Set of 3 coins	142218	2,601	199.95	Proof	180.	*

CELEBRATION OF SPRING SERIES

FIFTEEN DOLLARS, CELEBRATION OF SPRING, 2016-2017.

Designers and Engravers:
Obv.:   Susanna Blunt,
             Susan Taylor
Rev.:   Jan Poynter
Composition: 99.99% Ag, Painted
Silver content: 23.17 g, 0.75 tr oz
Weight: 23.17 g
Diameter: 36.07 mm
Thickness: N/A
Edge: Reeded
Die Axis: ↑↑
Finish: Proof
Case of Issue: Maroon clamshell with
             graphic beauty box, COA.

| Common Obverse | Cherry Blossoms | Lilac Blossoms |

DATE	DESCRIPTION	RCM ITEM #	QUANTITY SOLD	ISSUE PRICE	FINISH	PR-69	PR-70
2016	Celebration of Spring: Cherry Blossoms	150432	6,499	64.95	Proof	100.	—
2017	Celebration of Spring: Lilac Blossoms	159083	10,000	69.95	Proof	70.	—

NATIONAL HEROES SERIES

FIFTEEN DOLLARS, NATIONAL HEROES, 2016.

Bravery in its purest form is the willingness to save another's life despite personal risk. The Royal Canadian Mint proudly honours everyday heroes.

| Common Obverse | Firefighters | Paramedics | Police | Military |

Designers :
Obv.: Susanna Blunt
Rev.: Ken Ryan
Composition: 99.99% Ag, Painted
Silver content: 23.17 g, 0.75 tr oz
Weight: 23.17 g
Diameter: 36.07 mm
Thickness: N/A
Case of Issue: Maroon leatherette clam style case, black flocked insert, encapsulated coin, COA, custom case

Engravers:
Obv.: Susan Taylor

Edge: Reeded
Die Axis: ↑↑
Finish: Proof

DATE	DESCRIPTION	RCM ITEM #	QUANTITY SOLD	ISSUE PRICE	FINISH	PR-69	PR-70
2016	National Heroes: Firefighters	152180	9,997	69.95	Proof	100.	—
2016	National Heroes: Paramedics	152928	8,435	69.95	Proof	55.	—
2016	National Heroes: Police	153190	8,132	69.95	Proof	55.	—
2016	National Heroes: Military	152300	8,163	69.95	Proof	55.	—

Note: Coins illustrated smaller than actual size.

GREAT CANADIAN OUTDOORS SERIES

FIFTEEN DOLLARS, GREAT CANADIAN OUTDOORS, 2017.

Canadians have a deep, enduring connection with nature that is evidenced by the many activities we enjoy outside thorughout the year — summer, winter, rain or sun! This four-coin series explores a nation at play in our favourite playground, the Canadian landscape. The reverse design is made possible by combining photo-luminescent (glow-in-the-dark) technology, a full colour application, *and* traditional engraving.

| Common Obverse | Night Skiing | Sunset Canoeing | Around the Campfire | Nature Walk at Sunrise |

Designers :
Obv.: Susanna Blunt
Rev.: Joel Kimmel
Composition: 99.99% Ag, Painted
Silver content: 23.17 g, 0.75 tr oz
Weight: 23.17 g
Diameter: 36.07 mm
Thickness: N/A
Case of Issue: Maroon clamshell with black beauty box. COA

Engravers:
Obv.: Susan Taylor

Edge: Reeded
Die Axis: ↑↑
Finish: Proof

FIFTEEN DOLLARS, GREAT CANADIAN OUTDOORS, 2017, PRICING PANEL.

DATE	DESCRIPTION	RCM ITEM #	MINTAGE	ISSUE PRICE	FINISH	PR-69	PR-70
2017	Night Skiing	158360	15,000	69.95	Proof	70.	—
2017	Sunset Canoeing	160612	15,000	69.95	Proof	70.	—
2017	Around the Campfire	160613	15,000	69.95	Proof	70.	—
2017	Nature Walk at Sunrise	160614	15,000	69.95	Proof	70.	—

IN THE EYES OF... SERIES

FIFTEEN DOLLARS, IN THE EYES OF..., 2017.

The eyes are the focus of this new series in which an innovative enamel effect provides like-like colour, while glow-in-the-dark allows the animal eyes to peer out from the dark.

| Common Obverse | In The Eyes of the Great Horned Owl | In The Eyes of the Lynx | In The Eyes of the Wolf |

Designers:
Obv.:   Susanna Blunt
Rev.:   Curtis Atwater
Composition: 99.99% Ag
Silver content: 23.17 g, 0.75 tr oz
Weight: 23.17 g
Diameter: 36 mm
Thickness: N/A
Case of Issue: Maroon clamshell with black beauty box, encapsulated coin, COA

Engravers:
Obv.:   Susan Taylor
Rev.:   RCM Staff

Edge: Reeded
Die Axis: ↑↑
Finish: Proof

DATE	DESCRIPTION	RCM ITEM #	MINTAGE	ISSUE PRICE	FINISH	PR-69	PR-70
2017	In The Eyes of the Great Horned Owl	162949	6,500	79.95	Proof	80.	—
2017	In The Eyes of the Lynx	163463	6,500	79.95	Proof	80.	—
2017	In The Eyes of the Wolf	163452	6,500	79.95	Proof	80.	—

FIFTEEN DOLLARS, MAGNIFICENT BALD EAGLES, 2018.

Designers and Engravers:
Obv.:   Susanna Blunt, Susan Taylor
Rev.:   Tony Bianco
Composition: 99.99% Ag
Silver content: 31.39 g, 1.01 tr oz
Weight: 31.39 g   **Edge:**   Reeded
Diameter: 38 mm   **Die Axis:**   ↑↑
Thickness: N/A   **Finish:**   Proof
Case of Issue: Maroon clamshell with black beauty box, COA.

DATE	DESCRIPTION	RCM ITEM #	MINTAGE	ISSUE PRICE	FINISH	PR-69	PR-70
2018	Magnificent Bald Eagles	166955	5,500	94.95	Proof	95.	—

FIFTEEN DOLLARS, BLESSINGS OF HARMONY, 2018.

Designers and Engravers:
    Obv.:   Susanna Blunt, Susan Taylor
    Rev.:   Aries Cheung

Composition:	99.99% Ag			
Silver content:	26.51 g, 0.85 tr oz			
Weight:	26.51 g	**Edge:**	Plain	
Diameter:	38 mm	**Die Axis:**	↑↑	
Thickness:	N/A	**Finish:**	Proof	
Case of Issue:	Maroon clamshell with black beauty box, COA.			

DATE	DESCRIPTION	RCM ITEM #	MINTAGE	ISSUE PRICE	FINISH	PR-69	PR-70
2018	Blessings of Harmony	166850	4,888	118.88	Proof	120.	—

TWENTY DOLLARS
CALGARY OLYMPIC WINTER GAMES

TWENTY DOLLARS, CALGARY OLYMPIC WINTER GAMES, 1985-1988.

In 1988, Calgary, Alberta, hosted the XV Olympic Winter Games. To commemorate the event, and assist in the financing, the Federal Government, through the Royal Canadian Mint, agreed to produce a series of ten sterling silver coins and one gold coin. The silver coins were issued in sets of two $20.00 coins over the period September 1985 through September 1987. Unlike the 1976 Olympic coins, the Calgary Winter Olympic coins were issued in proof quality only.

The date on the coins (obverse) is the year of minting while the reverse carries the date 1988, the year of the games. Mintage was limited to a total of 5,000,000 coins, resulting if minted in equal numbers, in 500,000 complete sets of the ten coins. The first offering of the coins for sale by the Royal Canadian Mint was based on 350,000 complete sets at $370.00 per set. By the fifth series the complete set was being offered at $420.00.

Edge lettering was used for the first time on Canadian silver coins. "XV OLYMPIC WINTER GAMES - JEUX OLYMPIQUES D'HIVER" appeared on all ten silver coins. There are existing varieties that have missed the edge lettering process.

Designers:	See each coin	**Engravers:**	See each coin
Composition:	92.5% Ag, 7.5% Cu	**Thickness:**	3.0 mm
Silver content:	31.51 g, 1.01 tr oz	**Edge:**	Lettered
Weight:	34.07 g	**Die Axis:**	↑↑
Diameter:	40.0 mm	**Finish:**	Proof
Case of Issue:	Green velvet, Olympic Logo, one or two coin display.		

SERIES ONE

1985 Reverse
Arnold Machin

Coin No. 1 Downhill Skiing
Ian Stewart, Terrence Smith

Coin No. 2 Speed Skating
Friedrich Peter, Ago Aarand

SERIES TWO

1986 Obverse
Arnold Machin

Coin No. 3 Hockey
Ian Stewart, Victor Coté

Coin No. 4 Biathlon
John Mardon, Sheldon Beveridge

DATE	DESCRIPTION	ISSUE DATE	QUANTITY SOLD	ISSUE PRICE	FINISH	PR-68	PR-69
1985	Downhill Skiing	Sept. 15, 1985	406,360	37.00	Proof	30.	—
1985	Speed Skating	Sept. 15, 1985	354,222	37.00	Proof	30.	—
1985	Speed Skating, no edge lettering	Sept. 15, 1985	Included	37.00	Proof	225.	—
1985	Set of 2 Series One coins	Sept. 15, 1985	Included	74.00	Proof	60.	*
1986	Hockey	Feb. 25, 1986	396,602	37.00	Proof	30.	—
1986	Hockey, no edge lettering	Feb. 25, 1986	Included	37.00	Proof	225.	—
1986	Biathlon	Feb. 25, 1986	308,086	37.00	Proof	30.	—
1986	Biathlon, no edge lettering	Feb. 25, 1986	Included	37.00	Proof	225.	—
1986	Set of 2 Series Two coins		Included	79.00	Proof	60.	*

CALGARY OLYMPIC WINTER GAMES (cont.).

SERIES THREE

1986 Obverse
Arnold Machin

Coin No. 5 Cross-Country Skiing
Ian Stewart, Terrence Smith

Coin No. 6 Free-Style Skiing
Walter Ott, Walter Ott

SERIES FOUR

1987 Obverse
Arnold Machin

Coin No. 7 Figure Skating
Raymond Taylor, Walter Ott

Coin No. 8 Curling
Walter Ott, Sheldon Beveridge

SERIES FIVE

1987 Obverse
Arnold Machin

Coin No. 9 Ski-Jumping
Raymond Taylor, David Kierans

Coin No. 10 Bobsleigh
John Mardon, Victor Coté

DATE	DESCRIPTION	ISSUE DATE	QUANTITY SOLD	ISSUE PRICE	FINISH	PR-68	PR-69
1986	Cross-Country Skiing	Aug. 18, 1986	303,199	39.50	Proof	30.	—
1986	Free-Style Skiing	Aug. 18, 1986	294,322	39.50	Proof	30.	—
1986	Free-Style Skiing, no edge lettering	Aug. 18, 1986	Included	39.50	Proof	225.	—
1986	Set of 2 Series Three coins	Aug. 18, 1986	Included	79.00	Proof	60.	*
1987	Figure Skating	Mar. 14, 1987	334,875	39.50	Proof	30.	—
1987	Figure Skating, no edge lettering	Mar. 14, 1987	Included	39.50	Proof	225.	—
1987	Curling	Mar. 14, 1987	286,457	39.50	Proof	30.	—
1987	Set of 2 Series Four coins	Mar. 14, 1987	Included	79.00	Proof	60.	*
1987	Ski-Jumping	Aug. 11, 1987	290,954	42.00	Proof	30.	—
1987	Bobsleigh	Aug. 11, 1987	274,326	42.00	Proof	30.	—
1987	Set of 2 Series Five coins	Aug. 11, 1987	Included	84.00	Proof	60.	*

AVIATION COMMEMORATIVES

TWENTY DOLLARS, AVIATION COMMEMORATIVES, SERIES ONE, 1990-1994.

Canada's aviation heroes and achievements are commemorated on this series of twenty dollar sterling silver coins. The series consists of ten coins issued two per year over five years. For the first time each coin design contains a 24-karat gold covered oval cameo portrait of the aviation hero commemorated. All coins were issued in proof quality and a maximum of 50,000 of each coin was offered for sale during the program. The issue price of the ten-coin case was $37.00.

Designers:		**Engravers:**	
Obv. and Rev.: See each coin		Obv. and Rev.: See each coin	
Composition:	92.5% Ag, 7.5% Cu, 24-karat gold-covered cameo		
Silver content:	28.77 g, 0.925 tr oz	**Edge:**	Interrupted serrations
Weight:	31.103 g	**Die Axis:**	↑↑
Diameter:	38.0 mm	**Finish:**	Proof
Thickness:	3.5 mm		
Case of Issue:	Aluminum case in the shape of a wing. Single and ten coin display cases made from recycled Canadian airplanes.		

1990 Obverse
Designer and Engraver:
Dora de Pédery-Hunt

Coin No. 1
Avro Anson and the North
American Harvard
Robert Leckie
Rev. Designer: Geoff Bennett
Rev. Engraver: S. Beveridge
Portrait Engr.: Terrence Smith

Coin No. 2
Avro Lancaster
J. E. Fauquier
Rev. Designer: R.R. Carmichael
Rev. Engraver: Ago Aarand
Portrait Engr.: S. Beveridge

1991 Obverse
Designer and Engraver:
Dora de Pédery-Hunt

Coin No. 3
A.E.A. Silver Dart
F.W. Baldwin / J.A.D. McCurdy
Rev. Designer: George Velinger
Rev. Engraver: S. Beveridge
Portrait Engr.: Terrence Smith

Coin No. 4
de Havilland Beaver
Phillip C. Garratt
Rev. Designer: Peter Mossman
Rev. Engraver: Ago Aarand
Portrait Engr.: William Woodruff

DATE	DESCRIPTION	SERIES	ISSUE DATE	QUANTITY SOLD	ISSUE PRICE	FINISH	PR-68	PR-69
1990	Avro Anson/N.A. Harvard	One	Sept. 15/90	41,844	55.50	Proof	50.	—
1990	Avro Lancaster	One	Sept. 15/90	43,596	55.50	Proof	120.	—
1991	A.E.A. Silver Dart	One	May 16/91	35,202	55.50	Proof	50.	—
1991	de Havilland Beaver	One	May 16/91	36,197	55.50	Proof	50.	—

TWENTY DOLLARS, AVIATION COMMEMORATIVES, SERIES ONE, 1990-1994 (cont.).

1992 Obverse
Designer and Engraver:
Dora de Pédery-Hunt

Coin No. 5
Curtiss JN-4 (Canuck)
Sir Frank Wilton Baillie
Rev. Designer: George Velinger
Rev. Engr.: Sheldon Beveridge
Portrait Engr.: Terrence Smith

Coin No. 6
de Havilland Gipsy Moth
Murton A. Seymour
Rev. Designer: John Mardon
Rev. Engraver: Ago Aarand
Portrait Engr.: Susan Taylor

1993 Obverse
Designer and Engraver:
Dora de Pédery-Hunt

Coin No. 7
Fairchild 71c
James A. Richardson
Rev. Designer: R. R. Carmichael
Rev. Engraver: Susan Taylor
Portrait Engr.: Susan Taylor

Coin No. 8
Lockheed 14 Super Electra
Zebulon Lewis Leigh
Rev. Designer: R. R. Carmichael
Rev. Engraver: S. Beveridge
Portrait Engr.: S. Beveridge

1994 Obverse
Designer and Engraver:
Dora de Pédery-Hunt

Coin No. 9
Curtiss HS-2L
Stuart Graham
Rev. Designer: John Mardon
Rev. Engraver: S. Beveridge
Portrait Engr.: Susan Taylor

Coin No. 10
Canadian Vickers Vedette
Wilfred T. Reid
Rev. Designer: R. R. Carmichael
Rev. Engraver: S. Beveridge
Portrait Engr.: S. Beveridge

DATE	DESCRIPTION	SERIES	ISSUE DATE	QUANTITY SOLD	ISSUE PRICE	FINISH	PR-68	PR-69
1992	Curtiss JN-4 (Canuck)	One	Aug. 13/92	33,105	55.50	Proof	50.	—
1992	de Havilland Gipsy Moth	One	Aug. 13/92	32,537	55.50	Proof	50.	—
1993	Fairchild 71c	One	May 3/93	32,199	55.50	Proof	50.	—
1993	Lockheed 14 Super Electra	One	May 3/93	32,550	55.50	Proof	50.	—
1994	Curtiss HS-2L	One	Mar. 24/94	31,242	55.50	Proof	50.	—
1994	Canadian Vickers Vedette	One	Mar. 24/94	30,880	55.50	Proof	50.	—
1990-94	Set of 10 Series One coins	One	—	—	—	Proof	400.	*

TWENTY DOLLARS, AVIATION COMMEMORATIVES, SERIES TWO, 1995-1999.

This is the second series of the aviation cameo coins of Canada. The theme of this series is "Powered Flight in Canada — Beyond World War II." The obverses, physical and chemical specifications are the same as the first series.

SERIES TWO

1995 Obverse
Designer and Engraver:
Dora de Pédery-Hunt

Coin No. 1
Fleet 80 Canuck
J. Omer (Bob) Noury
Rev. Designer: Robert Bradford
Rev. Engraver: Cosme Saffioti
Portrait Engr.: Cosme Saffioti

Coin No. 2
DHC-1 Chipmunk
W. C. Russell Bannock
Rev. Designer: Robert Bradford
Rev. Engraver: William Woodruff
Portrait Engr.: Ago Aarand

1996 Obverse
Designer and Engraver:
Dora de Pédery-Hunt

Coin No. 3
Avro Canada CF-100 Canuck
Janus Zurakowski
Rev. Designer: Jim Bruce
Rev. Engraver: Stan Witten
Portrait Engr.: Cosme Saffioti

Coin No. 4
Avro Canada CF-105 Arrow
James A. Chamberlin
Rev. Designer: Jim Bruce
Rev. Engraver: William Woodruff
Portrait Engr.: S. Beveridge

1997 Obverse
Designer and Engraver:
Dora de Pédery-Hunt

Coin No. 5
Canadair F-86 Sabre
Fern Villeneuve
Rev. Designer: Ross Buckland
Rev. Engraver: William Woodruff
Portrait Engr.: Cosme Saffioti

Coin No. 6
Canadair CT-114 Tutor Jet
Edward Higgins
Rev. Designer: Ross Buckland
Rev. Engraver: Stan Witten
Portrait Engr.: Ago Aarand

TWENTY DOLLARS, AVIATION COMMEMORATIVES, SERIES TWO, 1995-1999 (cont.).

1998 Obverse
Designer and Engraver:
Dora de Pédery-Hunt

Coin No. 7
Canadair CP-107 Argus
William S. Longhurst
Rev. Designer: Peter Mossman
Rev. Engraver: Sheldon
Beveridge

Coin No. 8
Canadair CL-215 Waterbomber
Paul Gagnon
Rev. Designer: Peter Mossman
Rev. Engraver: Stan Witten
Portrait Engr.: William Woodruff

1999 Obverse
Designer and Engraver:
Dora de Pédery-Hunt

Coin No. 9
de Havilland DHC-6 Twin Otter
George A. Neal
Rev. Designer: Neil Aird
Rev. Engraver: Cosme Saffioti
Portrait Engr.: Cosme Saffioti

Coin No. 10
de Havilland DHC-8 Dash 8
Robert H. (Bob) Fowler
Rev. Designer: Neil Aird
Rev. Engraver: William Woodruff
Portrait Engr.: Cosme Saffioti

DATE	DESCRIPTION	SERIES	ISSUE DATE	QUANTITY SOLD	ISSUE PRICE	FINISH	PR-68	PR-69
1995	Fleet 80 Canuck	Two	Sept. 16/95	17,438	57.95	Proof	50.	—
1995	DHC-1 Chipmunk	Two	Sept. 16/95	17,722	57.95	Proof	60.	—
1996	CF-100 Canuck	Two	July 25/96	18,508	57.95	Proof	50.	—
1996	CF-105 Arrow	Two	July 25/96	27,163	57.95	Proof	120.	—
1997	F86 Sabre	Two	Aug. 15/97	16,440	57.95	Proof	50.	—
1997	Tutor Jet	Two	Aug. 15/97	18,414	57.95	Proof	50.	—
1998	Argus	Two	June 5/98	14,711	57.95	Proof	50.	—
1998	Waterbomber	Two	June 5/98	15,237	57.95	Proof	50.	—
1999	Twin Otter	Two	April 15/99	14,173	57.95	Proof	75.	—
1999	Dash 8	Two	April 15/99	14,138	57.95	Proof	75.	—
1995-99	Set of 10 Series Two coins	Two	—	—	—	Proof	400.	*

Note: In 1998 a special issue two-coin set (coins 7 and 8) boxed with a cardboard model was offered to collectors.
See Derivatives, page 341.

TRANSPORTATION ON LAND, SEA AND RAIL SERIES

TWENTY DOLLARS, TRANSPORTATION ON LAND, SEA AND RAIL, 2000-2003.

Canada's first sterling silver hologram cameo twenty dollar coins were issued in 2000. This series of twelve coins commemorates Canadian achievements in transportation. Each coin bears a holographic cameo of famous Canadian methods of transportation.

Designers:		**Engravers:**
Obv. and Rev.: See each coin		Obv. and Rev.: See each coin
Composition:	92.5% Ag, 7.5% Cu, Holographic cameo; 2003 Selectively gold plated	
Silver content:	28.77 g, 0.925 tr oz	
Weight:	31.103 g	**Edge:** Interrupted serrations
Diameter:	38.0 mm	**Die Axis:** ↑↑
Thickness:	3.5 mm	**Finish:** Proof
Case of Issue:	Charcoal coloured anodized aluminum case with RCM logo, black flocked insert, COA	

TRANSPORTATION ON LAND, SEA AND RAIL, 2000.

2000 Obverse	Coin No. 1	Coin No. 2	Coin No. 3
Designer and Engraver	H.S. Taylor Steam Buggy	The Bluenose	The Toronto
Dora de Pédery-Hunt	John Mardon	J. Franklin Wright	J. Mardon, Stan Witten
	Cosme Saffioti	Stan Witten	Cosme Saffioti

DATE	DESCRIPTION	ISSUE DATE	QUANTITY SOLD	ISSUE PRICE	FINISH	PR-69	PR-70
2000	H.S. Taylor Steam Buggy	Apr.18/2000	Total	59.95	Proof	50.	—
2000	The Bluenose	Apr.18/2000	mintage	59.95	Proof	110.	—
2000	The Toronto	Apr.18/2000	all coins	59.95	Proof	50.	—
2000	Set of 3 coins	—	44,367	179.85	Proof	180.	*

TRANSPORTATION ON LAND, SEA AND RAIL, 2001.

2001 Obverse	Coin No. 4	Coin No. 5	Coin No. 6
Designer and Engraver	The Russell "Light Four"	The Marco Polo	The Scotia
Dora de Pédery-Hunt	Model L Touring Car	J. Franklin Wright	Don Curley
	John Mardon, José Osio	Stan Witten	William Woodruff

DATE	DESCRIPTION	ISSUE DATE	QUANTITY SOLD	ISSUE PRICE	FINISH	PR-69	PR-70
2001	The Russell "Light Four"	Apr.17/2001	Total	59.95	Proof	50.	—
2001	The Marco Polo	Apr.17/2001	mintage	59.95	Proof	50.	—
2001	The Scotia	Apr.17/2001	all coins	59.95	Proof	50.	—
2001	Set of 3 coins	—	41,828	179.85	Proof	130.	*

TRANSPORTATION ON LAND, SEA AND RAIL SERIES (cont.).

TWENTY DOLLARS, TRANSPORTATION ON LAND, SEA AND RAIL, 2002.

2002 Obverse **Designer and Engraver** **Dora de Pédery-Hunt**	**Coin No. 7** **The Gray-Dort** **John Mardon** **Cosme Saffioti**	**Coin No. 8** **The William Lawrence** **Bonnie Ross** **William Woodruff**	**Coin No. 9** **D-10 Locomotive** **Dan Fell** **William Woodruff**

DATE	DESCRIPTION	ISSUE DATE	QUANTITY SOLD	ISSUE PRICE	FINISH	PR-69	PR-70
2002	The Gray-Dort	Apr.17/2002	Total	59.95	Proof	50.	—
2002	The William Lawrence	Apr.17/2002	mintage	59.95	Proof	50.	—
2002	D-10 Locomotive	Apr.17/2002	all coins	59.95	Proof	50.	—
2002	Set of 3 coins	—	35,944	195.00	Proof	130.	*

TWENTY DOLLARS, TRANSPORTATION ON LAND, SEA AND RAIL, 2003.

2003 Obverse **Designer and Engraver** **Dora de Pédery-Hunt**	**Coin No. 10** **HMCS Bras d'Or** **Hydrofoil designed by** **DeHavilland in 1967** **Donald Curley, Stan Witten**	**Coin No. 11** **C.N.R. FA-1 Diesel Electric** **Locomotive - No. 9400** **John Mardon** **William Woodruff**	**Coin No. 12** **Bricklin SV-1 (Land)** **designed by Malcolm in 1974** **Brian Hughes** **José Osio**

DATE	DESCRIPTION	ISSUE DATE	QUANTITY SOLD	ISSUE PRICE	FINISH	PR-69	PR-70
2003	HMCS Bras d'Or	Apr.7/2003	Total	59.95	Proof	60.	—
2003	C.N.R. FA-1 Diesel Electric Locomotive	Apr.7/2003	mintage	59.95	Proof	60.	—
2003	Bricklin SV-1	Apr.7/2003	all coins	59.95	Proof	60.	—
2003	Set of 3 coins	—	31,997	195.00	Proof	150.	*

Note: 1. The 2002 Land, Sea and Rail collection was offered with matching COA in a limited edition of 2,500.
2. Coins illustrated smaller than actual size.

NATURAL WONDERS SERIES

TWENTY DOLLARS, NATURAL WONDERS SERIES, 2003-2005.

The Royal Canadian Mint, in 2003, introduced a new series of twenty dollar commemorative coins. Each coin carries a holographic, decal, or a selectively gold plated image of one of Canada's natural wonders.

2003 Obverse
Designer and Engraver:
Dora de Pédery-Hunt

2004-2005 Obverse
Designer: Susanna Blunt
Engraver: Susan Taylor

Designers and Engravers: See illustrations
Composition: 99.99% Ag
Silver content: 31.39 g, 1.01 tr oz
Weight: 31.39 g   **Edge:** Reeded
Diameter: 38.0 mm   **Die Axis:** ↑↑
Thickness: 3.5 mm
Finish: Proof
Case of Issue:
(A) Veneer, wooden clam style case, light brown flocked interior, encapsulated coin, COA
(B) Red leatherette clam style case, flocked black insert, encapsulated coin, COA

Niagara Falls
Designer and Engraver:
Gary Corcoran

Rocky Mountains
Designer and Engraver:
José Osio

Icebergs
Designer and Engraver:
RCM Staff

Northern Lights
Designer: Gary Corcoran
Engraver: Stan Witten

Hopewell Rocks
Designer and Engraver:
Stan Witten

Diamonds
Designer and Engraver:
José Osio

DATE	DESCRIPTION	QUANTITY SOLD	ISSUE PRICE	FINISH	PR-69	PR-70
2003	Niagara Falls, Hologram	29,967	79.95	Proof	70.	—
2003	Rocky Mountains, Decal	28,793	69.95	Proof	50.	—
2004	Icebergs, Hologram	24,879	69.95	Proof	50.	—
2004	Northern Lights, Double Image Hologram	34,135	79.95	Proof	50.	—
2004	Hopewell Rocks, Selectively gold plated	16,918	69.95	Proof	50.	—
2005	Diamonds, Double Image Hologram	35,000	69.95	Proof	50.	—

CANADIAN LIGHTHOUSE SERIES

TWENTY DOLLARS (1 ounce), CANADIAN LIGHTHOUSE SERIES, 2004-2005.

Sambro Island Lighthouse
Designer: Hedley Doty   Engraver: William Woodruff

Toronto Island Lighthouse
Designer: Brian Hughes   Engraver: William Woodruff

Designers:
  Obv.:   Susanna Blunt
  Rev.:   See reverse illustrations
Composition: 99.99% Ag
Weight: 31.1035 g, 1 oz
Diameter: 38.0 mm
Thickness: 3.2 mm
Finish: Proof, Frosted relief against a mirror background
Case of Issue: Maroon leatherette clam style case, black insert, encapsulated coin, COA

Engravers:
  Obv.:   Susan Taylor
  Rev.:   See reverse illustraitons

Edge: Reeded
Die Axis: ↑↑

DATE	DESCRIPTION	QUANTITY SOLD	ISSUE PRICE	FINISH	PR-69	PR-70
2004	Sambro Island Lighthouse	18,476	69.95	Proof	40.	—
2005	Toronto Island Lighthouse	14,006	69.95	Proof	50.	—

Note: See page 592 for Sambro Island Lighthouse derivative.

TALL SHIPS SERIES

TWENTY DOLLARS, TALL SHIPS SERIES, 2005-2007.

2005 Obverse
2006 Obverse

Designers and Engravers:
  Obv.:   Susanna Blunt, Susan Taylor
  Rev.:   See reverse illustrations
Composition: 99.99% Ag, Hologram
Silver content: 31.39 g, 1.01 tr oz
Weight: 31.39 g   **Edge:** Reeded
Diameter: 38.0 mm   **Die Axis:** ↑↑
Thickness: 3.0 mm   **Finish:** Proof
Case of Issue: Maroon plastic slide case, black
      plastic insert, encapsulated coin, COA

2007 Obverse

Three-Masted Ship
Designer: Bonnie Ross
Engraver: William Woodruff

Ketch
Designer: John M. Horton
Engraver: Susan Taylor

Brigantine
Designer: Bonnie Ross
Engraver: William Woodruff

TWENTY DOLLARS, TALL SHIPS SERIES, 2005-2007, PRICING PANEL.

DATE	DESCRIPTION	RCM ITEM #	QUANTITY SOLD	ISSUE PRICE	FINISH	PR-69	PR-70
2005	Three-Masted Ship, Hologram	N/A	18,276	69.95	Proof	55.	—
2006	Ketch, Hologram	N/A	10,299	69.95	Proof	65.	—
2007	Brigantine, Hologram	623047	7,935	74.95	Proof	65.	—

NATIONAL PARKS SERIES

TWENTY DOLLARS, NATIONAL PARKS SERIES, 2005-2006.

2005 Obverse	North Pacific Rim National	Mingan Archipelago National
Designer: Susanna Blunt	Park Reserve of Canada (QC)	Park Reserve of Canada (QC)
Engraver: Susan Taylor	Designer: Susanna Blunt	Designer: Pierre Leduc
	Engraver: Stan Witten	Engraver: José Osio

2006 Obverse	Georgian Bay Islands	Nahanni National Park	Jasper National Park of
Designer: Susanna Blunt	National Park (ON)	Reserve of Canada (NWT)	Canada (AL)
Engraver: Susan Taylor	Designer: Tony Bianco	Designer: Virginia Boulay	Designer: Michelle Grant
	Engraver: William Woodruff	Engraver: William Woodruff	Engraver: William Woodruff

Designers:	See illustrations		Engravers:	See illustrations
Composition:	99.99% Ag			
Silver content:	31.39 g, 1.01 tr oz			
Weight:	31.39 g		Edge:	Reeded
Diameter:	38.0 mm		Die Axis:	↑↑
Thickness:	3.0 mm		Finish:	Proof
Case of Issue:	Maroon plastic slide case, black plastic insert, encapsulated coin, COA			

DATE	DESCRIPTION	QUANTITY SOLD	ISSUE PRICE	FINISH	PR-69	PR-70
2005	North Pacific Rim National Park Reserve of Canada (QC)	21,695	69.95	Proof	50.	—
2005	Mingan Archipelago National Park Reserve of Canada (QC)	Included	69.95	Proof	50.	—
2006	Georgian Bay Islands National Park (ON)	20,218	69.95	Proof	50.	—
2006	Nahanni National Park Reserve of Canada (NWT)	Included	69.95	Proof	70.	—
2006	Jasper National Park of Canada (AL)	Included	69.95	Proof	70.	—

Note: 1. National Parks single quantities were not recorded in the RCM Reports of 2005 and 2006 as individual entries, but only as totals sold for those years. There will be a difference between the projected issue as noted on the certificate of authenticity and the actual number sold.

2. Coins illustrated smaller than actual size.

CANADIAN ARCHITECTURAL SET

TWENTY DOLLARS, CANADIAN ARCHITECTURAL SET, 2006.

Common Obverse

Notre Dame Basilica

30th Anniversary CN Tower

Pengrowth Saddledome

Designers:		**Engravers:**	
Obv.:	Susanna Blunt	Obv.:	Susan Taylor
Rev.:	Jianping Yan	Rev.:	RCM Staff
Composition:	99.99% Ag, Photographic hologram		
Silver content:	31.1 g, 1.0 tr oz		
Weight:	31.1 g	**Edge:**	Reeded
Diameter:	38.0 mm	**Die Axis:**	↑↑
Thickness:	3.0 mm	**Finish:**	Proof
Case of Issue:	Maroon plastic slide case, black plastic insert, encapsulated coin, COA		

DATE	DESCRIPTION	QUANTITY SOLD	ISSUE PRICE	FINISH	PR-69	PR-70
2006	Notre Dame Basilica, Photographic Hologram	30,906	69.95	Proof	60.	—
2006	30th Anniv. CN Tower, Photographic Hologram	Included	69.95	Proof	60.	—
2006	Pengrowth Saddledome, Photographic Hologram	Included	69.95	Proof	60.	—

TWENTY DOLLARS, 125TH ANNIVERSARY OF THE FIRST INTERNATIONAL POLAR YEAR, 2007.

Common Obverse

Silver

Blue Plasma

Designers:		**Engravers:**	
Obv.:	Susanna Blunt	Obv.:	Susan Taylor
Rev.:	Laurie McGaw	Rev.:	Susan Taylor
Composition:	92.5% Ag, 7.5% Cu		
Silver content:	25.70 g, 0.826 tr oz		
Weight:	27.78 g	**Edge:**	Reeded
Diameter:	40.0 mm	**Die Axis:**	↑↑
Thickness:	2.5 mm	**Finish:**	Proof and Proof Plasma
Case of Issue:	Maroon clam style case, black flocked insert, encapsulated coin, COA		

DATE	DESCRIPTION	QUANTITY SOLD	ISSUE PRICE	FINISH	PR-69	PR-70
2007	125th Anniv. First Int'l Polar Year, Silver	9,164	64.95	Proof	50.	—
2007	125th Anniv. First Int'l Polar Year, Blue Plasma	3,005	249.95	Proof	170.	—

Note: Coins illustrated smaller than actual size.

HOLIDAY SERIES

TWENTY DOLLARS, HOLIDAY SERIES, 2007-2011.

| Obverse
2007-2008
With RCM Logo | Obverse
2010-2011
Without RCM Logo | 2007
Holiday Sleigh Ride
Designer: Tony Bianco
Engraver: RCM Staff | 2008
Holiday Carols
Designer: Tony Bianco
Engravers: C. Mok, K. Wachelko |

2010
Holiday Pine Cones, Moonlight
Designer: Susan Taylor
Engraver: RCM Staff

2010
Holiday Pine Cones, Ruby
Designer: Susan Taylor
Engraver: RCM Staff

2011
Christmas Tree
Designer: Tony Bianco
Engraver: José Osio

Designers:
  Obv.:   Susanna Blunt
  Rev.:   See reverse illustrations
Composition: 99.99% Ag
Silver content: 31.39 g, 1.01 tr oz
Weight: 31.39 g
Diameter: 38.0 mm
Thickness: 3.1 to 3.3 mm
Finish: 2007-2008: Proof; 2010-2011: Proof, with crystallised Swarovski elements
Case of Issue: Maroon clam style case, black flocked insert, encapsulated coin, COA

Engravers:
  Obv.:   Susan Taylor

Edge: Reeded
Die Axis: ↑↑

DATE	DESCRIPTION	RCM ITEM #	MINTAGE	ISSUE PRICE	FINISH	PR-69	PR-70
2007	Holiday Sleigh Ride	N/A	6,804	69.95	Proof	65.	—
2008	Holiday Carols	102352	5,224	69.95	Proof	55.	—
2010	Holiday Pine Cones, Moonlight	111164	4,754	99.95	Proof	90.	—
2010	Holiday Pine Cones, Ruby	111163	4,907	99.95	Proof	90.	—

CRYSTAL SNOWFLAKE SERIES

TWENTY DOLLARS, CRYSTAL SNOWFLAKE SERIES, 2007-2013.

Designers:
Obv.:   Susanna Blunt
Rev.:   Konrad Wachelko

Composition: 2007: 92.5% Ag, 7.5% Cu
2008-2013: 99.99% Ag,
with crystallised Swarovski elements

Weight: 2007: 50.0 g; 2008-2013: 31.0 to 31.39 g
Diameter: 38.0 mm
Thickness: 2007: 4.8 mm; 2008-2013: 3.0 to 3.2 mm
Case of Issue: Maroon clam style case, black flocked insert, encapsulated coin, COA

Engravers:
Obv.:   Susan Taylor
Rev.:   Konrad Wachelko

Silver content: 2007: 46.34 g, 1.490 tr oz
2008-2011: 31.39 g, 1.01 tr oz
2012-2013: 31.0 g, 1.0 tr oz

Edge: Reeded
Die Axis: ↑↑
Finish: Proof

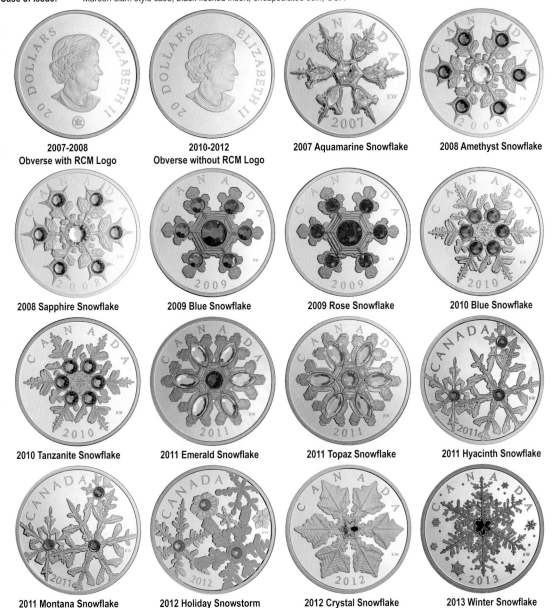

2007-2008
Obverse with RCM Logo

2010-2012
Obverse without RCM Logo

2007 Aquamarine Snowflake

2008 Amethyst Snowflake

2008 Sapphire Snowflake

2009 Blue Snowflake

2009 Rose Snowflake

2010 Blue Snowflake

2010 Tanzanite Snowflake

2011 Emerald Snowflake

2011 Topaz Snowflake

2011 Hyacinth Snowflake

2011 Montana Snowflake

2012 Holiday Snowstorm

2012 Crystal Snowflake

2013 Winter Snowflake

TWENTY DOLLARS, CRYSTAL SNOWFLAKE SERIES, 2007-2013, PRICING PANEL.

DATE	DESCRIPTION	RCM ITEM #	QUANTITY SOLD	ISSUE PRICE	FINISH	PR-69	PR-70
2007	Crystal Snowflake, Aquamarine	N/A	4,989	94.95	Proof	300.	—
2007	Crystal Snowflake, Iridescent	N/A	4,980	94.95	Proof	200.	—
2008	Crystal Snowflake, Amethyst	103033	7,172	94.95	Proof	120.	—
2008	Crystal Snowflake, Sapphire	103034	7,765	94.95	Proof	120.	—
2009	Crystal Snowflake, Blue	105674	7,477	94.95	Proof	90.	—
2009	Crystal Snowflake, Rose	105672	7,004	94.95	Proof	90.	—
2010	Crystal Snowflake, Blue	110809	7,390	94.95	Proof	90.	—
2010	Crystal Snowflake, Tanzanite	110816	7,241	94.95	Proof	90.	—
2011	Crystal Snowflake, Emerald	115617	6,586	114.95	Proof	90.	—
2011	Crystal Snowflake, Topaz	115618	6,041	114.95	Proof	90.	—
2011	Small Crystal Snowflakes, Hyacinth	115852	5,660	114.95	Proof	90.	—
2011	Small Crystal Snowflakes, Montana	115846	5,822	114.95	Proof	90.	—
2012	Holiday Snowstorm	N/A	4,886	114.95	Proof	90.	—
2012	Crystal Snowflake	119921	4,896	114.95	Proof	90.	—
2013	Winter Snowflake	126249	4,166	114.95	Proof	90.	—

CRYSTAL RAINDROP SERIES

TWENTY DOLLARS, CRYSTAL RAINDROP SERIES, 2008-2012.

| 2008
Obverse
With RCM Logo | 2009-2012
Obverse
Without RCM Logo | 2008 Crystal Raindrop
Designer: Celia Godkin
Engraver: Cecily Mok | 2009 Autumn Crystal Raindrop
Designer: Celia Godkin
Engraver: RCM Staff |

| 2010 Maple Leaf with Crystal Raindrop
Designer: Celia Godkin
Engraver: Susan Taylor | 2011 Crystal Raindrop and Maple Leaf
Designer: Celia Godkin
Engraver: Cecily Mok | 2012 The Sugar Maple
Designer: Celia Godkin
Engraver: RCM Staff |

Designers:
Obv.:   Susanna Blunt
Rev.:   See reverse illustrations
Composition: 99.99% Ag, Colourised, Crystallised
            Swarovski element
Silver content: 31.39 g, 1.01 tr oz
Weight: 31.39 g
Diameter: 38.0 mm
Thickness: 3.1 mm
Case of Issue: Maroon clam style case, black flocked insert, encapsulated coin, COA

Engravers:
Obv.:   Susan Taylor

Edge: Reeded
Die Axis: ↑↑
Finish: Proof

DATE	DESCRIPTION	RCM ITEM #	MINTAGE	ISSUE PRICE	FINISH	PR-69	PR-70
2008	Crystal Raindrop	102773	13,122	89.95	Proof	120.	—
2009	Autumn Crystal Raindrop	106670	9,998	94.95	Proof	140.	—
2010	Maple Leaf with Crystal Raindrop	110214	9,659	104.95	Proof	110.	—
2011	Crystal Raindrop and Maple Leaf	113847	9,594	109.95	Proof	110.	—
2012	The Sugar Maple	118373	9,933	119.95	Proof	110.	—

GREAT CANADIAN LOCOMOTIVES SERIES

TWENTY DOLLARS, GREAT CANADIAN LOCOMOTIVES SERIES, 2008-2011

The Hudson, Locomotive 2850 was chosen to transport King George VI and Queen Elizabeth from Quebec City to Vancouver, during their royal visit of 1939. The royal crest was mounted on the engine and tender, and remained after the visit, thus The Royal Hudson.

The Jubilee was introduced in 1936 for the CPR's 50th anniversary of the completion of the Transcontinental Railway in 1886. Classed as a 2-10-4 engine, The Selkirk engines were built by Montreal Locomotive Works for Canadian Pacific Railway to handle the steep grades of the Selkirk Mountains in British Columbia.

The D-10-class ten wheeler type 4-6-0 locomotive was a typical Canadian Pacific Railway steam locomotive. Five hundred and eight locomotives were built between 1905 and 1913 and formed the backbone of CPR's freight locomotive fleet. Most burned coal, but 28 were converted to oil.

2008	2008
Obverse	The Royal Hudson
With RCM Logo	Konrad Wachelko

2009-2011	2009	2010	2011
Obverse	The Jubilee	The Selkirk	D-10
Without RCM Logo	William Woodruff	William Woodruff	Marcos Hallam

Designers:		**Engravers:**	
Obv.:	Susanna Blunt	Obv.:	Susan Taylor
Rev.:	RCM Engravers (from Canadian Canadian Pacific Railway Archives)	Rev.:	See reverse illustrations
Composition:	99.99% Ag		
Silver content:	31.39 g, 1.01 tr oz	**Edge:**	Plain, edge lettering "ROYAL HUDSON",
Weight:	31.39 g		"JUBILEE", "SELKIRK" or "D-10"
Diameter:	38.0 mm	**Die Axis:**	↑↑
Thickness:	3.2 mm	**Finish:**	Proof
Case of Issue:	Maroon leatherette clam style case, black flocked insert, encapsulated coin, COA		

DATE	DESCRIPTION	RCM ITEM #	MINTAGE	ISSUE PRICE	FINISH	PR-69	PR-70
2008	The Royal Hudson	101483	8,345	69.95	Proof	70.	—
2009	The Jubilee	105269	6,036	69.95	Proof	70.	—
2010	The Selkirk	110154	5,874	79.95	Proof	70.	—
2011	D-10	110579	8,662	79.95	Proof	70.	—

Note: Coins illustrated smaller than actual size.

CANADIAN INDUSTRY SERIES

TWENTY DOLLARS, CANADIAN INDUSTRY SERIES, 2008-2009.

Common Obverse

Agriculture Trade
Engraver: José Osio

Coal Mining Trade
Engraver: Christie Paquet

Designers:		**Engravers:**	
Obv.:	Susanna Blunt	Obv.:	Susan Taylor
Rev.:	John Mardon	Rev.:	See reverse illustrations
Composition:	99.99% Ag		
Silver content:	31.39 g, 1.01 tr oz		
Weight:	31.39 g	**Edge:**	Reeded
Diameter:	38.0 mm	**Die Axis:**	↑↑
Thickness:	3.1 mm	**Finish:**	Proof
Case of Issue:	Maroon clam style case, black flocked insert, encapsulated coin, COA		

DATE	DESCRIPTION	RCM ITEM #	MINTAGE	ISSUE PRICE	FINISH	PR-69	PR-70
2008	Agriculture Trade	101044	5,802	69.95	Proof	70.	—
2009	Coal Mining Trade	103729	3,349	74.95	Proof	70.	—

TWENTY DOLLARS, SUMMER MOON MASK, 2009.

Designers and Engravers:			
Obv.:	Susanna Blunt, Susan Taylor		
Rev.:	Jody Broomfield, Susan Taylor		
Composition:	99.99% Ag		
Silver content:	31.39 g, 1.01 tr oz		
Weight:	31.39 g	**Edge:**	Reeded
Diameter:	38.0 mm	**Die Axis:**	↑↑
Thickness:	3.2 mm	**Finish:**	Proof
Case of Issue:	Maroon leatherette clam style case, black flocked insert, encapsulated coin, COA		

DATE	DESCRIPTION	RCM ITEM #	QUANTITY SOLD	ISSUE PRICE	FINISH	PR-69	PR-70
2009	Summer Moon Mask	102693	2,834	69.95	Proof	170.	—

TWENTY DOLLARS, 475TH ANNIVERSARY JACQUES CARTIER'S ARRIVAL AT GASPÉ, 1534-2009.

Designers and Engravers:			
Obv.:	Susanna Blunt, Susan Taylor		
Rev.:	John Mardon, Stan Witten		
Composition:	99.99% Ag		
Silver content:	31.39 g, 1.01 tr oz		
Weight:	31.39 g	**Edge:**	Reeded
Diameter:	38.0 m	**Die Axis:**	↑↑
Thickness:	3.2 mm	**Finish:**	Proof
Case of Issue:	Maroon leatherette clam style case, black flocked insert, encapsulated coin, COA		

DATE	DESCRIPTION	RCM ITEM #	QUANTITY SOLD	ISSUE PRICE	FINISH	PR-69	PR-70
2009 (1534-)	475th Anniversary of Jacques Cartier's Arrival at Gaspé	108027	1,516	169.95	Proof	225.	—

2008-2009 CANADIAN NHL TEAM GOALIE MASKS SET

TWENTY DOLLARS, 2008-2009 CANADIAN NHL TEAM GOALIE MASKS SET, 2009.

| Common Obverse | Calgary Flames | Edmonton Oilers |

| Montreal Canadiens | Ottawa Senators | Toronto Maple Leafs | Vancouver Canucks |

Designers:
Obv.:   Susanna Blunt
Rev.:   Marcos Hallam
Composition: 92.5% Ag, 7.5% Cu, Painted
Weight: 27.78 g
Diameter: 40.0 mm
Thickness: 2.6 mm
Case of Issue: Lucite stand, encapsulated coin, COA, cardboard outer box

Engravers:
Obv.:   Susan Taylor

Silver content: 25.70 g, 0.826 tr oz
Edge: Reeded
Die Axis: ↑↑
Finish: Proof

DATE	DESCRIPTION	RCM ITEM #	MINTAGE	ISSUE PRICE	FINISH	PR-69	PR-70
2009	Calgary Flames	102834	125	74.95	Proof	120.	—
2009	Edmonton Oilers	102835	147	74.95	Proof	120.	—
2009	Montreal Canadiens	102831	748	74.95	Proof	130.	—
2009	Ottawa Senators	102832	95	74.95	Proof	120.	—
2009	Toronto Maple Leafs	102833	244	74.95	Proof	120.	—
2009	Vancouver Canucks	102836	129	74.95	Proof	120.	—

Note: Quantity Sold numbers are those for 2009. The Royal Mint Annual Report for 2010 did not report additional units sold.

TWENTY DOLLARS, 75TH ANNIVERSARY OF THE FIRST BANK NOTES ISSUED BY BANK OF CANADA, 1935-2010.

Designers and Engravers:
Obv.:   Susanna Blunt, Susan Taylor
Rev.:   Konrad Wachelko
Composition: 99.99% Ag
Silver content: 31.39 g, 1.01 tr oz
Weight: 31.39 g   **Edge:**   Reeded
Diameter: 38.0 mm   **Die Axis:**   ↑↑
Thickness: 3.2 mm   **Finish:**   Proof
Case of Issue: Maroon clam style case, black flocked insert, encapsulated coin, COA

DATE	DESCRIPTION	RCM ITEM #	QUANTITY SOLD	ISSUE PRICE	FINISH	PR-69	PR-70
2010 (1935-)	75th Anniversary of First Notes Issued by Bank of Canada	110595	6,720	79.95	Proof	65.	—

PAINTED WILDFLOWER SERIES

TWENTY DOLLARS, PAINTED WILDFLOWER SERIES, 2010-2015.

| Common Obverse | 2010
Water Lily
Designer: Claudio D'Angelo
Engraver: Cecily Mok | 2011
Crystal Dewdrop and Wild Rose
Designer: Margaret Dest
Engraver: José Osio | 2012
Rhododendron
Designer: Claudio D'Angelo
Engraver: RCM Staff |

| 2013
Blue Flag Iris
Designer: Celia Godkin
Engraver: RCM Staff | 2014
Red Trillium
Designer: Margaret Best
Engraver: RCM Staff | 2015
Black-Eyed Susan
Designer: Laurie Koss
Engraver: RCM Staff |

Designers:
  Obv.:   Susanna Blunt
  Rev.:   See reverse illustrations
Composition: 99.99% Ag, Painted, crystallised Swarovski elements
Silver content: 31.39 g, 1.01 tr oz
Weight: 31.39 g
Diameter: 38.0 mm
Thickness: 3.1 mm
Case of Issue: Maroon leatherette clam style case, black flocked insert, encapsulated coin, COA

Engravers:
  Obv.:   Susan Taylor
  Rev.:   See reverse illustrations
Edge: Reeded
Die Axis: ↑↑
Finish: Proof

DATE	DESCRIPTION	RCM ITEM #	MINTAGE	ISSUE PRICE	FINISH	PR-69	PR-70
2010	Water Lily	108405	9,990	104.95	Proof	100.	—
2011	Crystal Dewdrop and Wild Rose	112465	9,989	109.95	Proof	100.	—
2012	Rhododendron	117486	9,991	119.95	Proof	100.	—
2013	Blue Flag Iris	122136	9,953	119.95	Proof	100.	—
2014	Red Trillium	130403	7,453	119.95	Proof	100.	—
2015	Black-Eyed Susan	145322	3,768	119.95	Proof	100.	—

Note: Coins illustrated smaller than actual size.

TWENTY DOLLARS, HRH PRINCE WILLIAM OF WALES AND MISS CATHERINE MIDDLETON, 2011.

This coin is embedded with a sapphire colour Swarovski element.

Designers and Engravers:

Obv.:	Susanna Blunt, Susan Taylor
Rev.:	Laurie McGaw, José Osio
Composition:	99.99% Ag, Swarovski element
Silver content:	31.39 g, 1.01 tr oz
Weight:	31.39 g **Die Axis:** ↑↑
Diameter:	38.0 mm **Thickness:** 3.2 mm
Edge:	Plain (laser engraved HRH PRINCE WILLIAM MISS CATHERINE MIDDLETON SAR LE PRINCE WILLIAM ET MLLE CATHERINE MIDDLETON)
Finish:	Proof
Case of Issue:	Maroon clam style case, black flocked insert, encapsulated coin, COA

DATE	DESCRIPTION	RCM ITEM #	QUANTITY SOLD	ISSUE PRICE	FINISH	PR-69	PR-70
2011	HRH Prince William of Wales / Miss Catherine Middleton	114249	24,858	104.95	Proof	50.	—

TWENTY DOLLARS, WINTER SCENE, 2011.

Designers and Engravers:

Obv.:	Susanna Blunt, Susan Taylor
Rev.:	Rémi Clark, José Osio
Composition:	92.50% Ag, 0.75% Cu
Silver content:	25.70 g, 0.826 tr oz
Weight:	27.78 g **Edge:** Reeded
Diameter:	40.0 mm **Die Axis:** ↑↑
Thickness:	2.5 mm **Finish:** Proof
Case of Issue:	Maroon leatherette clam style case, black flocked insert, encapsulated coin, COA

DATE	DESCRIPTION	RCM ITEM #	QUANTITY SOLD	ISSUE PRICE	FINISH	PR-69	PR-70
2011	Winter Scene	1151548	5,287	69.95	Proof	60.	—

CANADIAN GARDEN FLORA AND FAUNA SERIES

TWENTY DOLLARS, CANADIAN GARDEN FLORA AND FAUNA SERIES, 2011-2015.

This series of coins feature a hand-crafted Venetian glass detail by master glassmaker Giuliano Donaggio from Murano, Italy, atop a coloured background designed by Maurice Gervais. This series was also issued in a gold $250 set (see page 455 and a 25¢ series of coins (see page 48).

Common Obverse

2011
Tulip with Ladybug
Designer: Cosme Saffioti
Engraver: RCM Staff
Ladybug: Giuliano Donnagio

2012
Aster with Bumble Bee
Designer: Cosme Saffioti
Engraver: Cecily Mok
Bumble Bee: Giuliano Donnagio

2013
Purple Coneflower and
Eastern Tailed Blue Butterfly
Designer: Maurice Gervais
Engraver: Konrad Wachelko
Butterfly: Giuliano Donnagio

2014
Water-lily and Leopard Frog
Designer: Maurice Gervaiso
Engraver: Konrad Wachelko
Leopard Frog: Giuliano Donnagio

2015
Turtle with Broadleaf
Arrowhead Flower
Designer: Maurice Gervais
Engraver: RCM Staff
Turtle: Giuliano Donnagio

Designers:		**Engravers:**	
Obv.:	Susanna Blunt	Obv.:	Susan Taylor
Rev.:	See reverse illustrations	Rev.:	See reverse illustrations
Composition:	99.99% Ag, Coloured, Murano glass insect		
Silver content:	31.39 g, 1.01 tr oz		
Weight:	31.39 g	**Edge:**	Reeded
Diameter:	38.0 mm	**Die Axis:**	↑↑
Thickness:	3.1 mm	**Finish:**	Proof
Case of Issue:	Maroon clam style case, black flocked insert, encapsulated coin, COA		

DATE	DESCRIPTION	RCM ITEM #	MINTAGE	ISSUE PRICE	FINISH	PR-69	PR-70
2011	Tulip with Ladybug	114346	4,985	139.95	Proof	1,100.	—
2012	Aster with Bumble Bee	117583	9,991	139.95	Proof	220.	—
2013	Purple Coneflower and Eastern Tailed Blue Butterfly	121899	9,994	149.95	Proof	220.	—
2014	Water-lily and Leopard Frog	130503	12,500	149.95	Proof	130.	—
2015	Turtle with Broadleaf Arrowhead Flower	143220	12,500	149.95	Proof	130.	—

TWENTY FOR TWENTY SERIES

TWENTY DOLLARS (¼ OUNCE), FINE SILVER, TWENTY FOR TWENTY SERIES, 2011-2016.

Common Obverse
2011-2012

2011 - Five Maple Leaves
Des.: Cosme Saffioti
Engr.: RCM Staff

2011 - Canoe
Des.: Jason Bouwman
Engr.: William Woodruff

2012 - Polar Bear
Des.: Emily Damsta
Engr.: Stan Witten

2012 - Farewell to the Penny
Des.: Jesse Koreck
Engr.: José Osio

2012 - Magical Reindeer
Des.: Virginia Boulay
Engr.: José Osio

2012 - Obverse:
Queen's Diamond Jubilee
Des.: Mary Gilllick
Engr.: RCM Staff

2012 - Reverse:
Queen's Diamond Jubilee
Des.: Laurie McGaw
Engr.: RCM Staff

Common Obverse
2013-2015

2013 - Hockey
Des.: Greg Banning
Engr.: José Osio

2013 - Wolf
Des.: Glen Loates
Engr.: Eric Boyer

2013 - Iceberg
Des.: Emily Damstra
Engr.: Christie Paquet

Designers:
- Obv.: Susanna Blunt
- Rev.: See reverse illustrations

Composition: 99.99% Ag
Weight: 7.96 g, 0.25 tr oz
Diameter: 27.0 mm
Thickness: 1.8 mm
Case of Issue: 2011 Five Maple leaves: Vinyl pouch
2011-2013: Vinyl pouch, encapsulated coin, coloured folder

Engravers:
- Obv.: Susan Taylor
- Rev.: See reverse illustrations

Edge: Reeded
Die Axis: ↑↑
Finish: Specimen

DATE	DESCRIPTION	RCM ITEM #	MINTAGE	ISSUE PRICE	FINISH	SP-68	SP-69
2011	$20, Five Maple Leaves		198,000	20.00	Specimen	35.	—
2011	$20, Canoe	115885	244,000	20.00	Specimen	25.	—
2012	$20, Polar Bear	118006	174,474	20.00	Specimen	25.	—
2012	$20, Farewell to the Penny	118938	192,010	20.00	Specimen	25.	—
2012	$20, Magical Reindeer	122206	162,620	20.00	Specimen	25.	—
2012 (1952-)	$20, Queen's Diamond Jubilee	118932	180,020	20.00	Specimen	25.	—
2013	$20, Hockey	121733	245,325	20.00	Specimen	25.	—
2013	$20, Wolf	122289	248,779	20.00	Specimen	25.	—
2013	$20, Iceberg	127158	222,741	20.00	Specimen	25.	—

TWENTY DOLLARS (¼ ounce), FINE SILVER, TWENTY FOR TWENTY SERIES, 2011-2016 (cont.).

2013 - Santa
Des.: Jesse Koreck
Engr.: Eric Boyer

2014 - Canada Goose
Des.: Trevor Tennant
Engr.: Cecily Mok

2014 - Bobcat
Des.: Ken Ryan
Engr.: RCM Staff

2014 - Summertime
Des.: RCM Staff
Engr.: RCM Staff

2014 - Snowman
Des.: J. Koreck
Engr.: RCM Staff

2015 - FIFA Women's
World Cup™
Des.: Joel Kimmel
Engr.: RCM Staff

2015 - Gingerbread Man
Des.: Chris & Rosina Reid
Engr.: RCM Staff

2015 - Bugs Bunny©
Des.: Warner Bros.
Entertainment Inc.
Engr.: RCM Staff

2015
DC Comics Originals™:
Superman
Des.: DC Comics
Engr.: RCM Staff

2016
Tyrannosaurus Rex
Des.: Julius Cstonyi
Engr.: RCM Staff

2016
Star Trek: Enterprise
Des.: RCM Staff
Engr.: RCM Staff

2016
Batman V Superman:
Dawn of Justice™
Des.: DC Comics
Engr.: RCM Staff

Designers:
Obv.: Susanna Blunt
Rev.: See reverse illustrations
Composition: 99.99% Ag
Weight: 7.96 g, 0.25 tr oz
Diameter: 26.9 mm
Thickness: 1.8 mm
Case of Issue: Vinyl pouch, encapsulated coin, coloured folder

Engravers:
Obv.: Susan Taylor
Rev.: See reverse illustrations

Edge: Reeded
Die Axis: ↑↑
Finish: Specimen

DATE	DESCRIPTION	RCM ITEM #	MINTAGE	ISSUE PRICE	FINISH	SP-68	SP-69
2013	$20, Santa	122292	221,922	20.00	Specimen	25.	—
2014	$20, Canada Goose	129259	223,706	20.00	Specimen	25.	—
2014	$20, Bobcat	130498	223,496	20.00	Specimen	25.	—
2014	$20, Summertime	130531	197,937	20.00	Specimen	25.	—
2014	$20, Snowman	135154	208,333	20.00	Specimen	25.	—
2015	$20, FIFA Women's World Cup™	144566	168,086	20.00	Specimen	25.	—
2015	$20, Gingerbread Man	149289	174,978	20.00	Specimen	25.	—
2015	$20, Bugs Bunny©	145083	270,194	20.00	Specimen	25.	—
2015	$20, DC Comics™ Originals: Superman™	118023	257,315	20.00	Specimen	25.	—
2016	$20, *Tyrannosaurus Rex*	149723	155,657	20.00	Specimen	25.	—
2016	$20, *Star Trek™: Enterprise*	152206	207,287	20.00	Specimen	30.	—
2016	$20, *Batman v Superman: Dawn of Justice™*	150137	159,790	20.00	Specimen	25.	—

THE QUEEN'S DIAMOND JUBILEE SERIES

TWENTY DOLLARS, DIAMOND JUBILEE WITH CRYSTAL, 1952-2012.

Designers and Engravers:
Obv.:	Susanna Blunt, Susan Taylor
Rev.:	Laurie McGaw, Susan Taylor
Composition:	99.99% Ag, Swarovski element
Silver content:	31.39 g, 1.01 tr oz
Weight:	31.39 g **Edge:** Reeded
Diameter:	38.0 mm **Die Axis:** ↑↑
Thickness:	3.1 mm **Finish:** Proof
Case of Issue:	Maroon clam style case, black flocked insert, encapsulated coin, COA

TWENTY DOLLARS, QUEEN ELIZABETH II AND PRINCE PHILIP, 1952-2012.

This twenty-dollar silver coin is also found in the Queen's Diamond Jubilee Royal Silver Set.

Designers and Engravers:
Obv.:	Susanna Blunt, Susan Taylor
Rev.:	Laurie McGaw, Susan Taylor
Composition:	99.99% Ag
Silver content:	31.39 g, 1.01 tr oz
Weight:	31.39 g **Edge:** Reeded
Diameter:	38.0 mm **Die Axis:** ↑↑
Thickness:	3.1 mm **Finish:** Proof
Case of Issue:	Black clam style case, black flocked insert, encapsulated coin, COA

TWENTY DOLLARS, ROYAL CYPHER, 60TH JUBILEE, 1952-2012.

Designers and Engravers:
Obv.:	Susanna Blunt, Susan Taylor
Rev.:	Christie Paquet
Composition:	99.99% Ag
Silver content:	31.39 g, 1.01 tr oz
Weight:	31.39 g **Edge:** Reeded
Diameter:	38.0 mm **Die Axis:** ↑↑
Thickness:	3.1 mm **Finish:** Proof
Case of Issue:	Maroon clam style case, black flocked insert, encapsulated coin, COA

TWENTY DOLLARS, THE QUEEN'S PORTRAIT, 2012.

Designers and Engravers:
Obv.:	Susanna Blunt, Susan Taylor
Rev.:	Laurie McGaw, Christie Paquet
Composition:	99.99% Ag
Silver content:	30.75 g, 0.99 tr oz
Weight:	30.75 g **Edge:** Plain
Diameter:	36.0 mm **Die Axis:** ↑↑
Thickness:	3.0 mm **Finish:** Proof
Case of Issue:	Maroon clam style case, black flocked insert, encapsulated coin, COA

DATE	DESCRIPTION	RCM ITEM #	QUANTITY SOLD	ISSUE PRICE	FINISH	PR-69	PR-70
2012 (1952-)	Diamond Jubilee With Crystal	114565	10,780	104.95	Proof	90.	—
2012 (1952-)	Queen Elizabeth II and Prince Philip	114550	5,627	84.95	Proof	75.	—
2012 (1952-)	Royal Cypher, 60th Jubilee	114556	3,568	84.95	Proof	75.	—
2012	The Queen's Portrait	118581	7,473	129.95	Proof	90.	—

THE QUEEN'S DIAMOND JUBILEE SERIES (cont.).

TWENTY DOLLARS, THE QUEEN'S VISIT TO CANADA, 2012.

Queen Elizabeth II has been an Honourary Commissioner of the RCMP since 1953. During a visit to England in 1969 to participate in the Royal Windsor Horse Show, the RCMP presented the Queen with one of their finest horses Burmese. The RCMP has presented a further five horses since then, each to commemorate an important milestone.

Designers and Engravers:
Obv.:	Susanna Blunt, Susan Taylor
Rev.:	Bonnie Ross, Cecily Mok
Composition:	99.99% Ag
Silver content:	31.39 g, 1.01 tr oz

Weight:	31.39 g	**Edge:**	Reeded
Diameter:	38.0 mm	**Die Axis:**	↑↑
Thickness:	3.1 mm	**Finish:**	Proof
Case of Issue:	Maroon clam style case, black flocked insert, encapsulated coin, COA		

DATE	DESCRIPTION	RCM ITEM #	QUANTITY SOLD	ISSUE PRICE	FINISH	PR-69	PR-70
2012	The Queen's Visit to Canada	118539	11,113	89.95	Proof	75.	—

TWENTY DOLLARS, WINNIPEG JETS, 2011.

The Winnipeg Jets is a professional (NHL) ice hockey team based in Winnipeg, Manitoba. The team plays its home games at the MTS Centre and takes their name after Winnipeg's original WHA/NHL team.

Designers and Engravers:
Obv.:	Susanna Blunt, Susan Taylor
Rev.:	William Woodruff, RCM Staff
Composition:	99.99% Ag
Silver content:	31.39 g, 1.01 tr oz

Weight:	31.39 g	**Edge:**	Reeded
Diameter:	37.8 mm	**Die Axis:**	↑↑
Thickness:	3.1 mm	**Finish:**	Proof
Case of Issue:	Maroon leatherette clam style case, black flocked insert, encapsulated coin, COA		

DATE	DESCRIPTION	RCM ITEM #	QUANTITY SOLD	ISSUE PRICE	FINISH	PR-69	PR-70
2011	Winnipeg Jets	117570	5,536	94.95	Proof	75.	—

TWENTY DOLLARS, 50 YEARS OF THE CANADIAN COAST GUARD, 1962-2012.

During a 1994 science expedition the CCGS Louis S. St. Laurent navigated through 3,700 kilometres of Arctic Ice visiting the North Pole as it made the first crossing of the Arctic Ocean from the Pacific to the Atlantic. It was a joint Canada-US expedition with the USCGC Polar Sea. On August 22nd, 1994, the Louis S. St. Laurent was the first Canadian ship to reach the North Pole.

Designers and Engravers:
Obv.:	Susanna Blunt, Susan Taylor
Rev.:	Yves Bérubé, Stan Witten
Composition:	99.99% Ag
Silver content:	31.39 g, 1.01 tr oz

Weight:	31.39 g	**Edge:**	Reeded
Diameter:	38.0 mm	**Die Axis:**	↑↑
Thickness:	3.0 mm	**Finish:**	Proof
Case of Issue:	Canadian maple wood case, black flocked insert, encapsulated coin, COA		

DATE	DESCRIPTION	RCM ITEM #	QUANTITY SOLD	ISSUE PRICE	FINISH	PR-69	PR-70
2012 (1962-)	50 Years of the Canadian Coast Guard	118282	6,696	129.95	Proof	80.	—

TWENTY DOLLARS, THE THREE WISE MEN, 2012.

Designers and Engravers:

Obv.:	Susanna Blunt, Susan Taylor
Rev.:	Jason Bouwman, Stan Witten
Composition:	99.99% Ag, Crystal element
Silver content:	28.1 g, 0.9 tr oz
Weight:	28.1 g **Edge:** Reeded
Diameter:	40.0 mm **Die Axis:** ↑↑
Thickness:	2.6 mm **Finish:** Proof
Case of Issue:	Maroon clam style case, black flocked insert, encapsulated coin, COA

DATE	DESCRIPTION	RCM ITEM #	QUANTITY SOLD	ISSUE PRICE	FINISH	PR-69	PR-70
2012	The Three Wise Men	120100	3,916	114.95	Proof	80.	—

THE GROUP OF SEVEN SERIES

TWENTY DOLLARS, THE GROUP OF SEVEN SERIES, 2012-2013.

The Group of Seven were a group of Canadian landscape artists from the 1920-1933 period, who believed that a distinct Canadian art movement could be developed through direct contact with nature.

Common Obverse	*Stormy Weather, Georgian Bay*	**Nova Scotia Fishing Village**	*Houses, Cobalt (1931-1932)*
	Designer: F. H. Varley	Designer: Arthur Lismer	Designer: Franklin Carmichael
	Engraver: Marcos Hallam	Engraver: Stan Witten	Engraver: Susan Taylor

Toronto Street Winter Morning (1920)	*The Guardian of the Gorge*	*Sumacs*	*Saint-Tite-des-Caps*
Designer: Lawren S. Harris	Designer: Franz Johnston	Designer: J. E. H. MacDonald	Designer: A. Y. Jackson
Engraver: Susan Taylor	Engraver: Cecily Mok	Engraver: Steven Stewart	Engraver: Christie Paquet

Designers:

Obv.:	Susanna Blunt
Rev.:	See reverse illustrations
Composition:	99.99% Ag
Silver content:	31.39 g, 1.01 tr oz
Weight:	31.39 g
Diameter:	38.0 mm
Thickness:	3.1 mm

Engravers:

Obv.:	Susan Taylor

Edge:	Reeded
Die Axis:	↑↑
Finish:	Proof

Case of Issue: Singly: Maroon leatherette clam style case, black flocked insert, encapsulated coin, COA

Subscription: Seven-hole wooden case, black flocked insert. encapsulated coins, COA

TWENTY DOLLARS, THE GROUP OF SEVEN SERIES, 2012-2013, PRICING PANEL.

DATE	DESCRIPTION	RCM ITEM #	QUANTITY SOLD	ISSUE PRICE	FINISH	PR-69	PR-70
2012	Stormy Weather, Georgian Bay, F. H. Varley	117728	6,962	89.95	Proof	90.	—
2012	Nova Scotia Fishing Village, Arthur Lismer	117951	6,985	89.95	Proof	70.	—
2012	Houses, Cobalt (1931-1932), Franklin Carmichael	116516	6,946	89.95	Proof	70.	—
2013	Toronto Street, Winter Morning (1920), Lawren S. Harris	115728	6,694	89.95	Proof	70.	—
2013	The Guardian of the Gorge, Franz Johnston	118516	6,795	89.95	Proof	70.	—
2013	Sumacs, J. E. H. MacDonald	118525	6,479	89.95	Proof	70.	—
2013	Saint-Tite-des-Caps, A. Y. Jackson	115721	6,409	89.95	Proof	70.	—

TWENTY DOLLARS, BULL MOOSE FROM THE MOOSE FAMILY, ROBERT BATEMAN MOOSE COIN, 1962-2012.

The reverse design on this coin features a bull moose's head and antlers taken from Robert Bateman's painting The Moose Family. The coin was issued to commemorate the 50th anniversary of the Canadian Wildlife Federation.

Designers and Engravers:
Obv.: Susanna Blunt, Susan Taylor
Rev.: Robert Bateman, Stan Witten
Composition: 99.99% Ag
Silver content: 31.39 g, 1.01 tr oz
Weight: 31.39 g **Edge:** Reeded
Diameter: 38.0 mm **Die Axis:** ↑↑
Thickness: 3.1 mm **Finish:** Proof
Case of Issue: Maroon clam style case, black flocked insert, encapsulated coin, COA

DATE	DESCRIPTION	RCM ITEM #	QUANTITY SOLD	ISSUE PRICE	FINISH	PR-69	PR-70
2012 (1962-)	Bull Moose	120887	7,499	94.95	Proof	100.	—

Note: For other coins in the Robert Bateman Moose Coin Series see pages 398, 443, and 474.

TWENTY DOLLARS, THE BEAVER, 2013.

Designers and Engravers:
Obv.: Susanna Blunt, Susan Taylor
Rev.: Glen Loates, José Osio
Composition: 99.99% Ag
Silver content: 31.39 g, 1.01 tr oz
Weight: 31.39 g **Edge:** Reeded
Diameter: 38.0 mm **Die Axis:** ↑↑
Thickness: 3.1 mm **Finish:** Proof
Case of Issue: Maroon clam style case, black flocked insert, encapsulated coin, COA

DATE	DESCRIPTION	RCM ITEM #	QUANTITY SOLD	ISSUE PRICE	FINISH	PR-69	PR-70
2013	The Beaver	123784	8,498	99.95	Proof	80.	—

TWENTY DOLLARS, 300TH ANNIVERSARY OF LOUISBOURG, 1713-2013.

This coin celebrates the 300th anniversary of the founding of Louisbourg by French colonists and the contributions that the thriving community played in Nova Scotia.

Designers and Engravers:
Obv.: Susanna Blunt, Susan Taylor
Rev.: John Horton, Christie Paquet
Composition: 99.99% Ag
Silver content: 31.6 g, 1.01 tr oz
Weight: 31.6 g
Diameter: 40.0 mm **Die Axis:** ↑↑
Thickness: 3.0 mm **Finish:** Proof
Edge: Plain, Edge lettering "LOUISBOURG 300"
Case of Issue: Maroon clam style case, black flocked insert, encapsulated coin, COA

DATE	DESCRIPTION	RCM ITEM #	QUANTITY SOLD	ISSUE PRICE	FINISH	PR-69	PR-70
2013 (1713-)	300th Anniversary of Louisbourg	125259	4,976	89.95	Proof	80.	—

WORLD BASEBALL CLASSIC SET

TWENTY DOLLARS, WORLD BASEBALL CLASSIC SET, 2013.

These coins were issued to celebrate the World Baseball Classic Tournament held March 2nd to 19th, 2013. For other coins in this set see pages 428 and 438.

| Common Obverse | Fielder | Hitter | Pitcher | Runner |

Designers:
Obv.:   Susanna Blunt
Rev.:   Steve Hepburn
Composition: 99.99% Ag
Silver content: 31.1 g, 1.0 tr oz
Weight: 31.1 g
Diameter: 38.0 mm
Thickness: 3.2 mm
Case of Issue: Maroon leatherette clam style case, black flocked insert, encapsulated coin, COA, custom sleeve

Engravers:
Obv.:   Susan Taylor
Rev.:   Christie Paquet

Edge: Reeded
Die Axis: ↑↑
Finish: Proof

DATE	DESCRIPTION	RCM ITEM #	QUANTITY SOLD	ISSUE PRICE	FINISH	PR-69	PR-70
2013	Fielder	122369	866	114.95	Proof	90.	—
2013	Hitter	122359	1,405	114.95	Proof	90.	—
2013	Pitcher	122363	938	114.95	Proof	90.	—
2013	Runner	122343	864	114.95	Proof	90.	—

TWENTY DOLLARS, CANADIAN CONTEMPORARY ART, 2013.

Designers and Engravers:
Obv.:   Susanna Blunt, Susan Taylor
Rev.:   Carlito Dalceggio, Alex Tirabasso
Composition: 99.99% Ag
Silver content: 31.39 g, 1.01 tr oz
Weight: 31.39 g   **Edge:** Reeded
Diameter: 38.0 mm   **Die Axis:** ↑↑
Thickness: 3.1 mm   **Finish:** Proof
Case of Issue: Maroon clam style case, black flocked insert, encapsulated coin, COA

DATE	DESCRIPTION	RCM ITEM #	QUANTITY SOLD	ISSUE PRICE	FINISH	PR-69	PR-70
2013	Canadian Contemporary Art	126492	3,814	89.95	Proof	90.	—

TWENTY DOLLARS, HOLIDAY WREATH, 2013.

Designers and Engravers:
Obv.:   Susanna Blunt, Susan Taylor
Rev.:   Maurice Gervais, Samantha Strath
Composition: 99.99% Ag, Swarovski elements
Silver content: 31.2 g, 1.0 tr oz
Weight: 31.2 g   **Edge:** Reeded
Diameter: 37.9 mm   **Die Axis:** ↑↑
Thickness: 3.0 mm   **Finish:** Proof
Case of Issue: Maroon clam style case, black flocked insert, encapsulated coin, COA

DATE	DESCRIPTION	RCM ITEM #	QUANTITY SOLD	ISSUE PRICE	FINISH	PR-69	PR-70
2013	Holiday Wreath	124348	4,671	114.95	Proof	90.	—

TWENTY DOLLARS, CANDY CANE, 2013.

Designers: and Engravers:

Obv.:	Susanna Blunt, Susan Taylor
Rev.:	Steven Stewart, RCM Staff
Composition:	99.99% Ag, Coloured Murano glass
Silver content:	31.2 g, 1.0 tr oz
Weight:	31.2 g
Diameter:	37.9 mm
Thickness:	3.0 mm
Case of Issue:	Maroon clam style case, black flocked insert, encapsulated coin, COA

Edge:	Reeded
Die Axis:	↑↑
Finish:	Proof

DATE	DESCRIPTION	RCM ITEM #	QUANTITY SOLD	ISSUE PRICE	FINISH	PR-69	PR-70
2013	Candy Cane	125498	9,983	149.95	Proof	100.	—

TWENTY DOLLARS, YEAR OF THE SNAKE, 2013.

Designers: and Engravers:

Obv.:	Susanna Blunt, Susan Taylor
Rev.:	RCM Staff
Composition:	99.99% Ag,
Silver content:	7.96 g, 0.25 tr oz
Weight:	7.96 g
Diameter:	27 mm
Thickness:	N/A
Case of Issue:	Maroon clam style case, black flocked insert, encapsulated coin, COA

Edge:	Reeded
Die Axis:	↑↑
Finish:	Proof

DATE	DESCRIPTION	RCM ITEM #	QUANTITY SOLD	ISSUE PRICE	FINISH	SP-68	SP-69
2013	Year of the Snake	122860	56,798	31.95	Specimen	30.	—

TWENTY DOLLARS, BIRTH OF THE ROYAL INFANT SET, 2013.

This three-coin set commemorates the birth of Prince George of Cambridge on July 22nd, 2013.

Common Obverse	Baby Bears Des.: Laurie McGaw Engr.: Eric Boyer, Cecily Mok	Baby Crib Des.: Laurie McGaw Engr.: RCM Staff	Hands Des.: Laurie McGaw Engr.: Alex Tirabasso

Designers:

Obv.:	Susanna Blunt
Rev.:	See reverse illustrations
Composition:	99.99% Ag
Weight:	31.1 to 31.3 g
Diameter:	38.0 mm
Thickness:	3.2 mm
Case of Issue:	Maroon clam style case, 3-hole black flocked insert, encapsulated coin, COA, custom box

Engravers:

Obv.:	Susan Taylor

Silver content:	31.1 g, 1.0 tr oz
Edge:	Reeded
Die Axis:	↑↑
Finish:	Proof

DATE	DESCRIPTION	RCM ITEM #	QUANTITY SOLD	ISSUE PRICE	FINISH	PR-69	PR-70
2013	Baby Bears	N/A	—	N.I.I.	Proof	75.	—
2013	Baby Crib	N/A	—	N.I.I.	Proof	75.	—
2013	Hands	N/A	—	N.I.I.	Proof	75.	—
—	Set of 3 coins	153557	5,306	249.95	Proof	180.	*

THE BALD EAGLE SET

TWENTY DOLLARS, THE BALD EAGLE SET, 2013.

Common Obverse	Portrait of Power Engraver: Eric Boyer	Lifelong Mates Engraver: RCM Staff	Returning From the Hunt Engraver: RCM Staff	Mother Protecting Her Eaglets Engraver: Eric Boyer

Designers:
  Obv.: Susanna Blunt
  Rev.: Claudio D'Angelo, See illustrations
Composition: 99.99% Ag
Weight: 31.39 g

Diameter: 38.0 mm
Thickness: 3.1 mm
Case of Issue: Maroon clam style case, black flocked insert, encapsulated coin, COA, custom box

Engravers:
  Obv.: Susan Taylor

Silver content: 31.39 g, 1.01 tr oz
Edge: Plain, Edge lettering "1oz FINE SILVER"
"1 oz ARGENT PUR"
Die Axis: ↑↑
Finish: Proof

DATE	DESCRIPTION	RCM ITEM #	QUANTITY SOLD	ISSUE PRICE	FINISH	PR-69	PR-70
2013	Portrait of Power	125483	7,500	99.95	Proof	75.	—
2013	Portrait of Power, No Edge Lettering	N/A	Incl. above	99.95	Proof	225.	—
2013	Lifelong Mates	125565	7,499	99.95	Proof	75.	—
2013	Returning From the Hunt	125574	7,498	99.95	Proof	75.	—
2013	Mother Protecting Her Eaglets	125585	7,495	99.95	Proof	75.	—

SUPERMAN™ SERIES

TWENTY DOLLARS, 75TH ANNIVERSARY OF SUPERMAN™ SET, 2013.

Common Obverse	Man of Steel Engraver: Samantha Strath	Metropolis Engraver: Samantha Strath	The Shield Engraver: Susan Taylor

Designers:
  Obv.: Susanna Blunt
  Rev.: DC Comics/Warner Brothers
Composition: 99.99% Ag
Weight: 31.0 to 31.2 g
Diameter: 38.0 mm
Thickness: 3.1 mm
Case of Issue: Clear plastic cover, black plastic coin display, encapsulated coin, COA, custom box

Engravers:
  Obv.: Susan Taylor
  Rev.: See reverse illustrations
Silver content: 31.0 g, 1.0 tr oz
Edge: Reeded
Die Axis: ↑↑
Finish: Proof

DATE	DESCRIPTION	RCM ITEM #	QUANTITY SOLD	ISSUE PRICE	FINISH	PR-69	PR-70
2013	Man of Steel™, Painted	125850	9,984	109.75	Proof	130.	—
2013	Metropolis, Achromatic Hologram	125997	9,994	129.75	Proof	130.	—
2013	The Shield, Dual Enamel	126007	9,976	119.75	Proof	130.	—

UNTAMED CANADA SERIES, 2013-2014

TWENTY DOLLARS, THE ARCTIC FOX, 2013.

The Arctic Fox also known as the white fox, polar fox or snow fox, is a small fox native to the Arctic regions. It has fur on the bottom of its feet to protect it from the cold while digging. A $25 gold version of this series was issued in 2013-2014 (see page 423).

Designers and Engravers:

Obv.:	Susanna Blunt, Susan Taylor
Rev.:	Tivadar Bote, Steven Stewart

Composition: 99.99% Ag
Silver content: 28.02 g, 0.90 tr oz
Weight: 28.02 g   **Edge:** Reeded-
Diameter: 40.0 mm   **Die Axis:** ↑↑
Thickness: 2.5 mm   **Finish:** Proof
Case of Issue: Maroon clam style case, black flocked insert, encapsulated coin, COA

TWENTY DOLLARS, PRONGHORN, 2013.

The Pronghorn is fleet-footed and one of the fastest animals in North America. They can run more than 85 kilometres an hour, outrunning coyotes and bobcats.

Designers and Engravers:

Obv.:	Susanna Blunt, Susan Taylor
Rev.:	Tivadar Bote, Steven Stewart

Composition: 99.99% Ag
Silver content: 31.6 g, 1.01 tr oz
Weight: 31.60 g   **Edge:** Reeded
Diameter: 40.0 mm   **Die Axis** ↑↑
Thickness: 2.9 mm   **Finish:** Proof
Case of Issue: Maroon clam style case, black flocked insert, encapsulated coin, COA

TWENTY DOLLARS, WOLVERINE, 2014.

The wolverine is the largest member of the weasel family and resembles a small bear.

Designers and Engravers:

Obv.:	Susanna Blunt, Susan Taylor
Rev.:	Tivadar Bote, Steven Stewart

Composition: 99.99% Ag
Silver content: 31.6 g, 1.01 tr oz
Weight: 31.60 g   **Edge:** Reeded-
Diameter: 40.0 mm   **Die Axis:** ↑↑
Thickness: 2.9 mm   **Finish:** Proof
Case of Issue: Maroon clam style case, black flocked insert, encapsulated coin, COA

DATE	DESCRIPTION	RCM ITEM #	QUANTITY SOLD	ISSUE PRICE	FINISH	PR-69	PR-70
2013	The Arctic Fox	123231	7,538	84.95	Proof	80.	—
2013	Pronghorn	123136	4,181	89.95	Proof	80.	—
2014	Wolverine	128911	3,905	89.95	Proof	80.	—

CANADIAN MAPLE CANOPY SERIES

TWENTY DOLLARS, CANADIAN MAPLE CANOPY SERIES, 2013-2014.

The Maple Canopy Series features the changing foliage of a Canadian maple tree as it passes through the seasons.

Common Obverse	Spring	Autumn	Spring Splendour	Autumn Allure
	Designer: Emily Damstra	Designer: Margaret Best	Designer: Margaret Best	Designer: Emily Damstra
	Engraver: Matt Bowen	Engraver: Matt Bowen	Engraver: Alex Tirabasso	Engraver: RCM Staff

Designers:
Obv.: Susanna Blunt
Rev.: See reverse illustrations
Composition: 99.99% Ag, Coloured
Silver content: 31.2 g, 1.0 tr oz
Weight: 31.2 g
Diameter: 38.0 mm
Thickness: 3.1 mm
Case of Issue: Maroon clam style case, black flocked insert, encapsulated coin, COA

Engravers:
Obv.: Susan Taylor

Edge: Reeded
Die Axis: ↑↑
Finish: Proof

DATE	DESCRIPTION	RCM ITEM #	QUANTITY SOLD	ISSUE PRICE	FINISH	PR-69	PR-70
2013	Spring	123251	7,494	99.95	Proof	80.	—
2013	Autumn	125177	7,426	99.95	Proof	80.	—
2014	Spring Splendour	130513	7,498	99.95	Proof	80.	—
2014	Autumn Allure	130581	7,501	99.95	Proof	80.	—

TWENTY DOLLARS, MAPLE LEAF IMPRESSION, 2013-2014.

Common Obverse	Maple Leaf Impression - Red	Maple Leaf Impression - Green

Designers:
Obv.: Susanna Blunt
Rev.: José Osio
Composition: 99.99% Ag, Enamelled
Weight: 31.39 g
Diameter: 38.0 mm
Thickness: 3.1 mm
Case of Issue: Maroon clam style case, black flocked insert, encapsulated coin, COA

Engravers:
Obv.: Susan Taylor
Rev.: José Osio
Silver content: 31.39 g, 1.01 tr oz
Edge: Reeded
Die Axis: ↑↑
Finish: Proof

DATE	DESCRIPTION	RCM ITEM #	QUANTITY SOLD	ISSUE PRICE	FINISH	PR-69	PR-70
2013	Maple Leaf Impression - Red	127062	9,176	114.95	Proof	90.	—
2014	Maple Leaf Impression - Green	130315	5,562	114.95	Proof	90.	—

BUTTERFLIES OF CANADA SERIES

TWENTY DOLLARS, BUTTERFLIES OF CANADA SERIES, 2013-2015.

Featuring a slight "shimmer effect", this series of coins depicts a few of Canada's butterflies.

Common Obverse	2013	2014	2015
	Canadian Tiger Swallowtail	Red-Spotted Purple	Giant Sulphur *(Colias Gigantea)*
	Engraver: Samantha Strath	Engraver: RCM Staff	Designer: Celia Godkin
			Engraver: RCM Staff

Designers:		**Engravers:**	
Obv.:	Susanna Blunt	Obv.:	Susan Taylor
Rev.:	Celia Godkin	Rev.:	See reverse illustrations
Composition:	99.99% Ag, Coloured	**Silver content:**	28.02 g, 0.90 tr oz
Weight:	2013-2014: 28.02 g; 2015: 31.83 g	**Edge:**	Reeded
Diameter:	40.0 mm	**Die Axis:**	↑↑
Thickness:	N/A.	**Finish:**	Proof
Case of Issue:	Maroon clam style case, black flocked insert, encapsulated coin, COA, custom box		

DATE	DESCRIPTION	RCM ITEM #	QUANTITY SOLD	ISSUE PRICE	FINISH	PR-69	PR-70
2013	Canadian Tiger Swallowtail		9,024	99.95	Proof	90.	—
2014	Red-Spotted Purple		6,018	99.95	Proof	90.	—
2015	Giant Sulphur *(Colias Gigantea)*		3,901	99.95	Proof	90.	—

DINOSAURS OF CANADA SERIES

TWENTY DOLLARS, DINOSAURS OF CANADA SERIES, 2013-2015.

This series, whose renderings have been verified by the Royal Tyrrell Museum of Palaeontology, features prehistoric dinosaurs discovered in Canada.

Common Obverse	Bathygnathus Borealis	Scutellosaurus	Xenoceratops Foremostensis	Albertosaurus

Designers:		**Engravers:**	
Obv.:	Susanna Blunt	Obv.:	Susan Taylor
Rev.:	Julius Csotonyi	Rev.:	Steven Stewart
Composition:	99.99% Ag	**Silver content:**	31.39 g, 1.0 tr oz
Weight:	31.39 g	**Edge:**	Reeded
Diameter:	38.0 mm	**Die Axis:**	↑↑
Thickness:	3.1 mm	**Finish:**	Proof
Case of Issue:	Maroon clam style case, black flocked insert, encapsulated coin, COA		

DATE	DESCRIPTION	RCM ITEM #	QUANTITY SOLD	ISSUE PRICE	FINISH	PR-69	PR-70
2013	Bathygnathus Borealis	126591	7,973	89.95	Proof	75.	—
2014	Scutellosaurus	127200	5,245	89.95	Proof	75.	—
2014	Xenoceratops Foremostensis	130562	4,321	89.95	Proof	75.	—
2015	Albertosaurus	130634	1,970	89.95	Proof	75.	—

A STORY OF THE NORTHERN LIGHTS SERIES

TWENTY DOLLARS, A STORY OF THE NORTHERN LIGHTS SERIES, 2013-2015.

| Common Obverse | 2013 - The Great Hare
Designer: Nathalie Bertin
Engraver: Samantha Strath | 2014 - Howling Wolf
Designer: Nathalie Bertin
Engraver: RCM Staff | 2015 - The Raven
Designer: Nathalie Bertin
Engraver: RCM Staff |

Designers:		Engravers:	
Obv.:	Susanna Blunt	Obv.:	Susan Taylor
Rev.:	Nathalie Bertin	Rev.:	See reverse illustrations
Composition:	99.99% Ag, Hologram	Silver content:	30.4 g, 0.98 tr oz
Weight:	2013-2014: 30.4 g; 2015: 31.39 g	Edge:	Reeded
Diameter:	2013-2014: 37.8 mm; 2015: 38 mm	Die Axis:	↑↑
Thickness:	3.0 mm	Finish:	Proof
Case of Issue:	Maroon clam style case, black flocked insert, encapsulated coin, COA		

DATE	DESCRIPTION	RCM ITEM #	QUANTITY SOLD	ISSUE PRICE	FINISH	PR-69	PR-70
2013	The Great Hare	124763	8,492	109.95	Proof	90.	—
2014	Howling Wolf	129299	8,500	109.95	Proof	90.	—
2015	The Raven	141577	6,886	109.95	Proof	90.	—

CANADIAN AUTUMN SERIES

TWENTY DOLLARS, CANADIAN AUTUMN, 2013-2016.

| Common Obverse | 2013 - Autumn Bliss
Designer: Tony Bianco
Engraver: Matt Bowen | 2014 - Autumn Falls
Designer: Tony Bianco
Engraver: RCM Staff | 2015 - Autumn Allure
Designer: Emily Damstra
Engraver: RCM Staff | 2016 - Autumn Tranquility
Designer: Tony Bianco
Engraver: RCM Staff |

Designers:		Engravers:	
Obv.:	Susanna Blunt	Obv.:	Susan Taylor
Rev.:	See reverse illustrations		
Composition:	99.99% Ag, Coloured	Silver content:	31.39 g, 1.01 tr oz
Weight:	31.39 g	Edge:	Reeded
Diameter:	38.0 mm	Die Axis:	↑↑
Thickness:	3.1 mm	Finish:	Proof
Case of Issue:	Maroon clam style case, black flocked insert, encapsulated coin, COA custom box		

DATE	DESCRIPTION	RCM ITEM #	QUANTITY SOLD	ISSUE PRICE	FINISH	PR-69	PR-70
2013	Autumn Bliss	126023	7,498	99.95	Proof	90.	—
2014	Autumn Falls	132488	7,469	99.95	Proof	90.	—
2015	Autumn Express	143187	5,315	109.95	Proof	90.	—
2016	Autumn Tranquility	153557	3,998	102.95	Proof	90.	*

TWENTY DOLLARS, 50TH ANNIVERSARY OF CANADIAN PEACEKEEPING IN CYPRUS, 2014.

Designers and Engravers:
Obv.: Susanna Blunt, Susan Taylor
Rev.: Sylvia Pecota, Matt Bowen
Composition: 99.99% Ag, Blue enamel
Silver content: 31.39 g, 1.01 tr oz
Weight: 31.39 g **Edge:** Reeded
Diameter: 37.9 mm **Die Axis:** ↑↑
Thickness: 3.0 mm **Finish:** Proof
Case of Issue: Maroon clam style case, black flocked insert, encapsulated coin, COA

DATE	DESCRIPTION	RCM ITEM #	QUANTITY SOLD	ISSUE PRICE	FINISH	PR-69	PR-70
2014	50th Anniv. of Canadian Peacekeeping in Cyprus	126640	3,511	114.95	Proof	90.	—

TWENTY DOLLARS, POND HOCKEY, 2014.

Designers and Engravers:
Obv.: Susanna Blunt, Susan Taylor
Rev.: Richard DeWolfe, Matt Bowen
Composition: 99.99% Ag, Coloured
Silver content: 31.2 g, 1.0 tr oz
Weight: 31.2 g **Edge:** Reeded
Diameter: 37.9 mm **Die Axis:** ↑↑
Thickness: 3.1 mm **Finish:** Proof
Case of Issue: Maroon clam style case, black flocked insert, encapsulated coin, COA

DATE	DESCRIPTION	RCM ITEM #	QUANTITY SOLD	ISSUE PRICE	FINISH	PR-69	PR-70
2014	Pond Hockey	125548	8,488	99.95	Proof	80.	—

TWENTY DOLLARS, VENETIAN GLASS SNOWMAN, 2014.

Designers and Engravers:
Obv.: Susanna Blunt, Susan Taylor
Rev.: Julius Csotonyi, RCM Staff
Composition: 99.99% Ag, Coloured Murano glass
Silver content: 31.2 g, 1.0 tr oz
Weight: 31.2 g **Edge:** Reeded
Diameter: 37.9 mm **Die Axis:** ↑↑
Thickness: 3.0 mm **Finish:** Proof
Case of Issue: Maroon clam style case, black flocked insert, encapsulated coin, COA

DATE	DESCRIPTION	RCM ITEM #	QUANTITY SOLD	ISSUE PRICE	FINISH	PR-69	PR-70
2014	Venetian Glass Snowman	130617	10,000	149.95	Proof	130.	—

TWENTY DOLLARS, THE WOODLAND CARIBOU, 2014.

Designers and Engravers:
Obv.: Susanna Blunt, Susan Taylor
Rev.: Trevor Tennant, Samantha Strath
Composition: 99.99% Ag, Coloured
Silver content: 31.2 g, 1.0 tr oz
Weight: 31.2 g **Edge:** Reeded
Diameter: 38.0 mm **Die Axis:** ↑↑
Thickness: 3.1 mm **Finish:** Proof
Case of Issue: Maroon clam style case, black flocked insert, encapsulated coin, COA

DATE	DESCRIPTION	RCM ITEM #	QUANTITY SOLD	ISSUE PRICE	FINISH	PR-69	PR-70
2014	The Woodland Caribou	128955	8,493	99.95	Proof	90.	—

TWENTY DOLLARS, ICONIC POLAR BEAR, 2014.

Designers and Engravers:

Obv.:	Susanna Blunt, Susan Taylor
Rev.:	Glen Loates, Alex Tirabasso
Composition:	99.99% Ag, Coloured
Silver content:	31.2 g, 1.0 tr oz

Weight:	31.2 g	**Edge:**	Reeded
Diameter:	38.0 mm	**Die Axis:**	↑↑
Thickness:	3.1 mm	**Finish:**	Proof
Case of Issue:	Maroon clam style case, black flocked insert, encapsulated coin, COA		

DATE	DESCRIPTION	RCM ITEM #	QUANTITY SOLD	ISSUE PRICE	FINISH	PR-69	PR-70
2014	Iconic Polar Bear	128979	8,500	99.95	Proof	100.	—

TWENTY DOLLARS, 100TH ANNIVERSARY OF THE ROYAL ONTARIO MUSEUM, 2014.

Celebrating the centennial of the Royal Ontario Museum, this coin's reverse features the Statue of Cleopatra VII, purchased in the early 1900s by the museum's first director, with Michael-Lee Chin's crystalline shaped architectural design.

Designers and Engravers:

Obv.:	Susanna Blunt, Susan Taylor
Rev.:	Cecily Mok, Christie Paquet
Composition:	99.99% Ag, Sel.gold plated
Silver content:	31.39 g, 1.01 tr oz

Weight:	31.39 g	**Edge:**	Reeded
Diameter:	38.0 mm	**Die Axis:**	↑↑
Thickness:	3.0 mm	**Finish:**	Proof
Case of Issue:	Maroon clam style case, black flocked insert, encapsulated coin, COA		

DATE	DESCRIPTION	RCM ITEM #	QUANTITY SOLD	ISSUE PRICE	FINISH	PR-69	PR-70
2014	100th Anniv. of the Royal Ontario Museum	129273	6,299	114.95	Proof	90.	—

TWENTY DOLLARS, RIVER RAPIDS, 2014.

This coin celebrates Canadian artist E. Robert Ross' painting depicting a set of rapids on the Madawaska River in Algonquin Provincial Park.

Designers and Engravers:

Obv.:	Susanna Blunt, Susan Taylor
Rev.:	E. Robert Ross, RCM Staff
Composition:	99.99% Ag, Painted, Engraved
Silver content:	31.39 g, 1.0 tr oz

Weight:	31.39 g	**Edge:**	Reeded
Diameter:	38.0 mm	**Die Axis:**	↑↑
Thickness:	3.1 mm	**Finish:**	Proof
Case of Issue:	Maroon clam style case, black flocked insert, encapsulated coin, COA		

DATE	DESCRIPTION	RCM ITEM #	QUANTITY SOLD	ISSUE PRICE	FINISH	PR-69	PR-70
2014	River Rapids	132482	14,086	99.95	Proof	85.	—

TWENTY DOLLARS, ROYAL GENERATIONS, 2014.

Designed from an interpretation of a press photograph taken by Cathy Bursey-Sabourin, four generations of the Royal Family are depicted on the coin's reverse: Queen Elizabeth II, Prince Charles, Prince William and Prince George.

Designers and Engravers:

Obv.:	Susanna Blunt, Susan Taylor
Rev.:	C. Bursey-Sabourin, RCM Staff
Composition:	99.99% Ag
Silver content:	31.39 g, 1.01 tr oz
Weight:	31.39 g **Edge:** Reeded
Diameter:	38.0 mm **Die Axis:** ↑↑
Thickness:	N/A **Finish:** Proof
Case of Issue:	Maroon clam style case, black flocked insert, encapsulated coin, COA

DATE	DESCRIPTION	RCM ITEM #	QUANTITY SOLD	ISSUE PRICE	FINISH	PR-69	PR-70
2014	Royal Generations	130574	5,732	89.95	Proof	80.	—

THE WOOD BISON SET

TWENTY DOLLARS, THE WOOD BISON SET, 2014.

Common Obverse	A Portrait	The Bull and His Mate	The Fight	A Family at Rest
	Designer: Doug Comeau	Designer: Doug Comeau	Designer: Claudio D'Angelo	Designer: Claudio D'Angelo
	Engraver: Alex Tirabasso	Engraver: Matt Bowen	Engraver: Samantha Strath	Engraver: RCM Staff

Designers:

Obv.:	Susanna Blunt
Rev.:	See reverse illustrations
Composition:	99.99% Ag
Weight:	31.39 g
Diameter:	38.0 mm
Thickness:	3.1 mm
Case of Issue:	Maroon clam style case, black flocked insert, encapsulated coin, COA

Engravers:

Obv.:	Susan Taylor
Silver content:	31.39 g, 1.01 tr oz
Edge:	Plain, Edge lettering "1 OZ FINE SILVER 1 OZ ARGENT PUR"
Die Axis:	↑↑
Finish:	Proof

DATE	DESCRIPTION	RCM ITEM #	QUANTITY SOLD	ISSUE PRICE	FINISH	PR-69	PR-70
2014	A Portrait	128106	7,480	99.95	Proof	80.	—
2014	The Bull and his Mate	127939	7,500	99.95	Proof	80.	—
2014	The Fight	127948	7,501	99.95	Proof	80.	—
2014	A Family at Rest	128012	7,498	99.95	Proof	80.	—

THE LEGEND OF NANABOOZHOO SET

TWENTY DOLLARS, THE LEGEND OF NANABOOZHOO SET, 2014.

Nanaboozhoo is an important cultural character of the Anishinaase. He is a shape-shifting spirit that teaches right from wrong through his adventures.

| Common Obverse | Nanaboozhoo and the Thunderbird's Nest Engraver: José Osio | Nanaboozhoo and the Thunderbird Engraver: José Osio | Legend of Nanaboozhoo Engraver: Steven Stewart |

Designers:
Obv.: Susanna Blunt
Rev.: Cyril Assiniboine
Composition: 99.99% Ag
Weight: 31.39 g
Diameter: 38.0 mm
Thickness: 3.1 mm
Case of Issue: Maroon clam style case, black flocked insert, encapsulated coin, COA

Engravers:
Obv.: Susan Taylor
Rev.: See reverse illustrations
Silver content: 31.39 g, 1.01 tr oz
Edge: Reeded
Die Axis: ↑↑
Finish: Proof

DATE	DESCRIPTION	RCM ITEM #	QUANTITY SOLD	ISSUE PRICE	FINISH	PR-69	PR-70
2014	Nanaboozhoo and the Thunderbird's Nest	130507	5,500	89.95	Proof	80.	—
2014	Nanaboozhoo and the Thunderbird, S electively gold plated	130509	5,500	114.95	Proof	90.	—
2014	Legend of Nanaboozhoo, Coloured	130508	6,856	99.95	Proof	80.	—

STAINED GLASS SET

TWENTY DOLLARS, STAINED GLASS SET, 2014.

Covered in translucent enamel, the Stained Glass set replicates memorable stained glass pieces in Canada from the windows of Craigdarroch Castle in Victoria, British Columbia, to the McCausland stained glass dome in Casa Loma.

 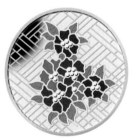 

| Common Obverse | Craigdarroch Castle | Casa Loma |

Designers:
Obv.: Susanna Blunt
Rev.: RCM Staff
Composition: 99.99% Ag, Coloured
Weight: 31.39 g
Diameter: 38.0 mm
Thickness: N/A
Case of Issue: Maroon clam style case, black flocked insert, encapsulated coin, COA

Engravers:
Obv.: Susan Taylor
Rev.: RCM Staff
Silver content: 31.39 g, 1.01 tr oz
Edge: Reeded
Die Axis: ↑↑
Finish: Proof

DATE	DESCRIPTION	RCM ITEM #	QUANTITY SOLD	ISSUE PRICE	FINISH	PR-69	PR-70
2014	Craigdarroch Castle	132481	4,980	129.95	Proof	100.	—
2014	Casa Loma	129110	3,238	129.95	Proof	100.	—

THE BALD EAGLE SET

TWENTY DOLLARS, THE BALD EAGLE SET, 2014.

| Common Obverse | Bald Eagle with Fish
Designer: Claudio D'Angelo
Engraver: Steven Stewart | Perched Bald Eagle
Selectively gold plated
Designer: Claudio D'Angelo
Engraver: Steven Stewart | Soaring Bald Eagle
Coloured
Designer: Claudio D'Angelo
Engraver: Eric Boyer |

Designers:
- Obv.: Susanna Blunt
- Rev.: See reverse illustrations

Composition: 99.99% Ag
Silver content: 31.83 g, 1.01 tr oz
Weight: 31.83 g
Diameter: 38.0 mm
Thickness: 3.1 mm
Case of Issue: Maroon clam style case, black flocked insert, encapsulated coin, COA

Engravers:
- Obv.: Susan Taylor

Edge: Reeded
Die Axis: ↑↑
Finish: Proof

DATE	DESCRIPTION	RCM ITEM #	QUANTITY SOLD	ISSUE PRICE	FINISH	PR-69	PR-70
2014	Bald Eagle with Fish, Proof	130524	7,582	89.95	Proof	80.	—
2014	Perched Bald Eagle, Proof, Selectively gold plated	130526	8,500	114.95	Proof	80.	—
2014	Soaring Bald Eagle, Proof with colour	130525	8,498	99.95	Proof	80.	—

TWENTY DOLLARS, 75TH ANNIVERSARY OF THE ROYAL WINNIPEG BALLET, 2014.

Celebrating the 75th anniversary of the Royal Winnipeg ballet's inception, the coin comes in a music box that plays Tchaikovsky's Sleeping Beauty, for a short period of time.

Designers and Engravers:
- Obv.: Susanna Blunt, Susan Taylor
- Rev.: David Cooper, RCM Staff

Composition: 99.99% Ag
Silver content: 31.6 g, 1.02 tr oz
Weight: 31.6 g
Diameter: 40.0 mm
Thickness: N/A
Case of Issue: Grey and peach paperboard case, grey insert, encapsulated coin, COA

Edge: Reeded
Die Axis: ↑↑
Finish: Proof

DATE	DESCRIPTION	RCM ITEM #	QUANTITY SOLD	ISSUE PRICE	FINISH	PR-69	PR-70
2014	75th Anniversary of the Royal Winnipeg Ballet	130586	7,499	99.95	Proof	90.	—

TWENTY DOLLARS, CELEBRATING EMILY CARR: TOTEM FOREST, 2014.

As one of Canada's most important artists, this coin features Emily Carr's iconic 1930 painting, Totem Forest. This coin was also issued in a three coin set which includes a $200 gold (page 443) and a $300 platinum coin (page 485).

Designers and Engravers:	
Obv.:	Susanna Blunt, Susan Taylor
Rev.:	Emily Carr, RCM Staff
Composition:	99.99% Ag
Silver content:	31.39 g, 1.01 tr oz
Weight:	31.39 g **Die Axis:** ↑↑
Diameter:	38.0 mm **Edge:** Reeded
Thickness:	N/A **Finish:** Proof
Case of Issue:	Maroon clam style case, black flocked insert, encapsulated coin, COA, graphic, box

DATE	DESCRIPTION	RCM ITEM #	QUANTITY SOLD	ISSUE PRICE	FINISH	PR-69	PR-70
2014	Celebrating Emily Carr: Totem Forest	133647	4,459	89.95	Proof	90.	—

INTERCONNECTIONS SET

TWENTY DOLLARS, INTERCONNECTIONS SET, 2014.

Featuring the artwork of Andy Everson, the set celebrates the interconnectedness between landscape and nature.

Common Obverse	Land - The Beaver	Air - The Thunderbird	Sea - The Orca

Designers:		**Engravers:**	
Obv.:	Susanna Blunt	Obv.:	Susan Taylor
Rev.:	Andy Everson	Rev.:	RCM Staff
Composition:	99.99% Ag, Hologram		
Silver content:	31.39 g, 1.01 tr oz		
Weight:	31.39 g	**Edge:**	Reeded
Diameter:	38.0 mm	**Die Axis:**	↑↑
Thickness:	N/A	**Finish:**	Proof
Case of Issue:	Maroon clam style case, black flocked insert, encapsulated coin, COA		

DATE	DESCRIPTION	RCM ITEM #	QUANTITY SOLD	ISSUE PRICE	FINISH	PR-69	PR-70
2014	Land - The Beaver	132674	4,415	105.00	Proof	105.	—
2014	Air - The Thunderbird	143475	2,754	105.00	Proof	105.	—
2014	Sea - The Orca	143475	2,343	105.00	Proof	105.	—

TWENTY DOLLARS, CHICKADEE WITH WINTER BERRIES, 2014.

Designers and Engravers:
Obv.:	Susanna Blunt, Susan Taylor
Rev.:	Steve Hepburn, RCM Staff

Composition: 99.99% Ag, Swarovski Crystals
Silver content: 31.39 g, 1.01 tr oz

Weight:	31.39 g	**Edge:**	Reeded
Diameter:	38.0 mm	**Die Axis:**	↑↑
Thickness:	N/A	**Finish:**	Proof

Case of Issue: Maroon clam style case, black flocked insert, encapsulated coin, COA

DATE	DESCRIPTION	RCM ITEM #	QUANTITY SOLD	ISSUE PRICE	FINISH	PR-69	PR-70
2014	Chickadee with Winter Berries	130618	5,724	114.95	Proof	105.	—

THE WHITE-TAILED DEER SET

TWENTY DOLLARS, THE WHITE-TAILED DEER SET, 2014.

Common Obverse	Portrait	A Challenge	Mates	A Doe and Her Fawns
	Des.: Desmond McCaffrey	Des.: Desmond McCaffrey	Des.: Claudio D'Angelo	Des.: Trevor Tennant
	Eng.: RCM Staff	Eng.: RCM Staff	Eng.: RCM Staff	Eng.: RCM Staff

Designers:
Obv.:	Susanna Blunt
Rev.:	See reverse illustrations

Composition: 99.99% Ag
Silver content: 31.39 g, 1.01 tr oz
Weight: 31.39 g

Engravers:
Obv.:	Susan Taylor

Diameter: 38.0 mm
Thickness: 3.1 mm
Case of Issue: Maroon clam style case, black flocked insert, encapsulated coin, COA, custom box

Edge: Plain Edge Lettering "1OZ FINE SILVER 9999 1OZ ARGENT PUR 9999"
Die Axis: ↑↑
Finish: Proof

DATE	DESCRIPTION	RCM ITEM #	QUANTITY SOLD	ISSUE PRICE	FINISH	PR-69	PR-70
2014	Portrait	130578	6,503	99.95	Proof	80.	—
2014	A Challenge	130596	6,682	99.95	Proof	80.	—
2014	Mates	130623	5,212	99.95	Proof	80.	—
2014	A Doe and Her Fawns	130635	4,960	99.95	Proof	80.	—

TWENTY DOLLARS, 100TH ANNIVERSARY OF HOCKEY CANADA, 2014.

Featuring a red and black enamel application, this coin celebrates the 100th anniversary of the founding of the Canadian Amateur Hockey Association (CAHA), a precursor to Hockey Canada.

Designers and Engravers:
Obv.:	Susanna Blunt, Susan Taylor
Rev.:	Team Canada Logo™, RCM Staff

Composition: 99.99% Ag, Enamelled
Silver content: 31.39 g, 1.01 tr oz
Weight: 31.39 g   **Edge:** Reeded
Diameter: 38.0 mm   **Die Axis:** ↑↑
Thickness: N/A   **Finish:** Proof
Case of Issue: Red paperboard case, black flocked insert, encapsulated coin, COA

DATE	DESCRIPTION	RCM ITEM #	QUANTITY SOLD	ISSUE PRICE	FINISH	PR-69	PR-70
2014	100th Anniversary of Hockey Canada	130626	7,489	119.95	Proof	110.	—

THE COUGAR SET

TWENTY DOLLARS, THE COUGAR SET, 2014.

Common Obverse	Atop A Mountain Designer: Glen Loates Engraver: RCM Staff	Perched On A Maple Tree Designer: Glen Loates Engraver: RCM Staff	Obverse Selectively Gold Plated	Pouncing In The Snow Designer: Maurade Bayton Engraver: RCM Staff

Designers:
Obv.:	Susanna Blunt
Rev.:	See reverse illustrations

Composition: 99.99% Ag
Silver content: 31.39 g, 1.01 tr oz
Weight: 31.39 g
Diameter: 38.0 mm
Thickness: N/A
Case of Issue:
Singly:	Maroon clam style case, black flocked insert, encapsulated coin, COA
Subscription:	3-hole wood case, black flocked insert, encapsulated coins, COA

Engravers:
Obv.:	Susan Taylor

Edge: Reeded
Die Axis: ↑↑
Finish: Proof

DATE	DESCRIPTION	RCM ITEM #	QUANTITY SOLD	ISSUE PRICE	FINISH	PR-69	PR-70
2014	Atop A Mountain	N/A	4,884	89.95	Proof	90.	—
2014	Perched On A Maple Tree, Coloured	N/A	3,845	99.95	Proof	90.	—
2014	Poucing In The Snow, Selectively Gold Plated	N/A	3,605	114.95	Proof	90.	—
2014	3-Coin Set	141318	N/A	N/A	Proof	N/A	N/A

THE SEVEN SACRED TEACHINGS SET

TWENTY DOLLARS, THE SEVEN SACRED TEACHINGS SET, 2014.

Reflecting the wisdom gleaned by the Anishinaabe people, this seven coin set features the Woodland style artwork of Métis artist Nathalie Bertin.

Common Obverse

Love
Engraver: Konrad Wachelko

Respect
Engraver: A. Tirabasso, E. Boyer

Courage
Engraver: Steven Stewart

Wisdom
Engraver: RCM Staff

Honesty
Engraver: RCM Staff

Humility
Engraver: RCM Staff

Truth
Engraver: RCM Staff

Designers:		Engravers:	
Obv.:	Susanna Blunt	Obv.:	Susan Taylor
Rev.:	Nathalie Bertin	Rev.:	See reverse illustrations
Composition:	99.99% Ag, Selectively gold plated		
Silver content:	31.83 g, 1.02 tr oz		
Weight:	31.83 g	Edge:	Reeded
Diameter:	40.0 mm	Die Axis:	↑↑
Thickness:	2.9 mm	Finish:	Proof
Case of Issue:	Maroon clam style case, black flocked insert, encapsulated coin, with custom beauty box, COA		

DATE	DESCRIPTION	RCM ITEM #	QUANTITY SOLD	ISSUE PRICE	FINISH	PR-69	PR-70
2014	Love	132621	6,761	109.95	Proof	90.	—
2014	Respect	132623	5,404	109.95	Proof	90.	—
2014	Courage	132625	3,443	109.95	Proof	90.	—
2014	Wisdom	132628	4,211	109.95	Proof	90.	—
2014	Honesty	132626	4,000*	109.95	Proof	90.	—
2014	Humility	132630	4,121	109.95	Proof	90.	—
2014	Truth	132632	4,337	109.95	Proof	90.	—

* The actual mintage figure for Honesty is missing in the 2014 Annual Report. The mintage shown is an estimate.

TWENTY DOLLARS, 75TH ANNIVERSARY OF THE FIRST ROYAL VISIT, 1939-2014.

Engraved from an archival photograph, the coin depicts King George VI and Queen Elizabeth standing on a train's platform.

Designers and Engravers:

Obv.:	Susanna Blunt, Susan Taylor
Rev.:	RCM Staff

Composition: 99.99% Ag
Silver content: 31.39 g, 1.01 tr oz
Weight: 31.39 g   **Edge:** Reeded
Diameter: 38.0 mm   **Die Axis:** ↑↑
Thickness: N/A   **Finish:** Proof, Antique
Case of Issue: Maroon clam style case, black flocked insert, encapsulated coin, COA, custom box

DATE	DESCRIPTION	RCM ITEM #	QUANTITY SOLD	ISSUE PRICE	FINISH	PR-69	PR-70
2014 (1939-)	75th Anniversary of the First Royal Visit	130052	4,995	139.95	Proof	110.	—

TWENTY DOLLARS, 25TH ANNIVERSARY OF THE CANADIAN SPACE AGENCY, 1989-2014.

This coin features an achromatic hologram showcasing a Canadian astronaut anchored to the Canadarm2.

Designers and Engravers:

Obv.:	Susanna Blunt, Susan Taylor
Rev.:	RCM Staff

Composition: 99.99% Ag, Hologram
Silver content: 31.39 g, 1.01 tr oz
Weight: 31.39 g   **Die Axis:** ↑↑
Diameter: 38.0 mm   **Finish:** Proo
Thickness: N/A   **Edge:** Reeded f
Case of Issue: Maroon clam style case, black flocked insert, encapsulated coin, COA, custom box

DATE	DESCRIPTION	RCM ITEM #	QUANTITY SOLD	ISSUE PRICE	FINISH	PR-69	PR-70
2014 (1989-)	25th Ann. of the Canadian Space Agency	140443	4,042	119.95	Proof	110.	—

LOST SHIPS IN CANADIAN WATERS SERIES

TWENTY DOLLARS, LOST SHIPS IN CANADIAN WATERS, 2014-2015.

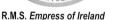

Common Obverse	R.M.S. *Empress of Ireland*	Franklin's Lost Expedition	S.S. *Edmund Fitzgerald*

Designers:

Obv.:	Susanna Blunt
Rev.:	John Horton

Composition: 99.99% Ag, Coloured
Weight: 31.39 g
Diameter: 38.0 mm
Thickness: N/A
Finish: Proof
Case of Issue: Maroon clam style case, black flocked insert, encapsulated coin, COA, custom box

Engravers:

Obv.:	Susan Taylor
Rev.:	RCM Staff

Silver content: 31.39 g, 1.01 tr oz
Edge: 2014: Plain with edge lettering
        2015: Plain with edge lettering
Die Axis: ↑↑

DATE	DESCRIPTION	RCM ITEM #	QUANTITY SOLD	ISSUE PRICE	FINISH	PR-69	PR-70
2014	R.M.S. *Empress of Ireland*	130532	7,003	109.95	Proof	90.	—
2015	Franklin's Lost Expedition	144687	6,994	109.95	Proof	90.	—
2015	S.S. *Edmund Fitzgerald*	147668	5,215	109.95	Proof	90.	—

BABY ANIMALS SERIES

TWENTY DOLLARS, BABY ANIMALS SERIES, 2014-2016.

Common Obverse

2014 - The Beaver
Designer: Glen Loates

2014 - Atlantic Puffin
Designer: Glen Loates

2015 - Burrowing Owl
Designer: Arnold Nogy

2015 - Black Bear
Designer: Clinton Jammer

2015 - Mountain Goat
Designer: Glen Loates

2015 - White-Tailed Deer
Designer: Glen Loates

2015 - Porcupine
Designer: Trevor Tennant

2016 - Raccoon
Designer: Trevor Tennant

2016 - Common Loon
Designer: Glen Loates

2016 - Caribou
Designer: Glen Loates

2016 - Woodchuck
Designer: Michelle Grant

Designers:		Engravers:	
Obv.:	Susanna Blunt	Obv.:	Susan Taylor
Rev.:	See reverse illustrations		
Composition:	99.99% Ag, Coloured	**Silver content:**	31.39 g, 1.01 tr oz
Weight:	31.39 g	**Edge:**	Reeded
Diameter:	38.0 mm	**Die Axis:**	↑↑
Thickness:	N/A	**Finish:**	Proof
Case of Issue:	Maroon clam style case, black flocked insert, encapsulated coin, COA		

TWENTY DOLLARS, BABY ANIMALS SERIES, 2014-2016, PRICING TABLE.

DATE	DESCRIPTION	RCM ITEM #	QUANTITY SOLD	ISSUE PRICE	FINISH	PR-69	PR-70
2014	The Beaver	130548	7,500	99.95	Proof	80.	—
2014	Atlantic Puffin	131336	7,500	99.95	Proof	80.	—
2015	Burrowing Owl	141715	7,716	99.95	Proof	80.	—
2015	Black Bear	143404	7,502	99.95	Proof	80.	—
2015	Mountain Goat	144365	7,482	99.95	Proof	80.	—
2015	White-Tailed Deer	144572	7,448	99.95	Proof	80.	—
2015	Porcupine	147582	6,961	99.95	Proof	80.	—
2016	Raccoon	154210	4,004	99.95	Proof	90.	—
2016	Common Loon	151607	3,908	99.95	Proof	90.	—
2016	Caribou	150055	3,500	99.95	Proof	90.	—
2016	Woodchuck	153776	3,383	99.95	Proof	90.	—

ICONIC SUPERMAN™ COMIC BOOK COVERS

TWENTY DOLLARS, *ICONIC SUPERMAN*™ COMIC BOOK COVERS, 2014-2015.

Common Obverse:

Designers and Engravers:
Obv.:	Susanna Blunt, Susan Taylor
Rev.:	DC Comics/Warner Bros., RCM Staff
Composition:	99.99% Ag, Coloured
Silver content:	31.39 g, 1.0 tr oz
Weight:	31.39 g
Diameter:	38.0 mm
Thickness:	N/A
Edge:	Reeded
Die Axis:	↑↑
Finish:	Proof
Case of Issue:	Custom case, black flocked insert, encapsulated coin, COA

Superman Annual #1 (2012)   *Action Comics #1 (2011)*   *Superman Unchained #2 (2013)*   *Superman #28 (2014)*

DATE	DESCRIPTION	RCM ITEM #	QUANTITY SOLD	ISSUE PRICE	FINISH	PR-69	PR-70
2014	Iconic Superman™ Comic Book Covers: Superman Annual #1 (2012)	133888	9,999	109.95	Proof	90.	—
2015	Iconic Superman™ Comic Book Covers: *Action Comics #1 (2011)*	146342	10,000	109.95	Proof	90.	—
2015	Iconic Superman™ Comic Book Covers: *Superman Unchained #2 (2013)*	146330	9,988	109.95	Proof	90.	—
2015	Iconic Superman™ Comic Book Covers: *Superman #28 (2014)*	146364	9,990	109.95	Proof	90.	—

PREHISTORIC ANIMALS SERIES

TWENTY DOLLARS (1 OUNCE), PREHISTORIC ANIMALS, 2014-2015.

This $20 Woolly Mammoth was also issued in a set of two coins (see page 481), the second coin being the 1/10 ounce $5 gold maple (see page 419).

Common Obverse

The Woolly Mammoth
Designer: M. Skrepnick

American Scimitar Sabre-Tooth Cat
Designer: Julius Csotonyi

Designers:
  Obv.:   Susanna Blunt
  Rev.:   See reverse illustrations
Composition: 99.99% Ag
Weight: 31.39 g
Diameter: 38.0 mm
Thickness: N/A
Case of Issue: Maroon leatherette clam style case, black flocked insert, encapsulated coin, COA

Engravers:
  Obv.:   Susan Taylor

Silver content: 31.39 g, 1.0 tr oz
Edge: Reeded
Die Axis: ↑↑
Finish: Proof

DATE	DESCRIPTION	RCM ITEM #	QUANTITY SOLD	ISSUE PRICE	FINISH	PR-69	PR-70
2014	The Woolly Mammoth (1 oz)	132487	7,502	89.95	Proof	80.	—
2015	American Scimitar Sabre-Tooth Cat	149166	4,086	89.95	Proof	80.	—

THE GREAT LAKES SERIES

TWENTY DOLLARS, THE GREAT LAKES SERIES, 2014-2015.

Bathymetric maps of the five Great Lakes are detailed by a raised image on these twenty dollar silver coins.

Designers:
  Obv.:   Susanna Blunt
  Rev.:   RCM Staff
Composition: 99.99% Ag, Enamelled
Silver content: 31.1 g, 1.0 tr oz
Weight: 31.1 g
Diameter: 37.9 mm
Thickness: 3.1 mm
Case of Issue: Singly: Maroon clam style case, black flocked insert, encapsulated coin, COA
    Subscription: Five-hole maple wood display case, black flocked insert, encapsulated coins, COA

Engravers:
  Obv.: Susan Taylor
  Rev.: Eric Boyer

Edge: Reeded
Die Axis: ↑↑
Finish: Proof

Common Obverse

Lake Superior

Lake Ontario

Lake Erie

Lake Huron

Lake Michigan

TWENTY DOLLARS, THE GREAT LAKES SERIES, 2014-2015, PRICING PANEL.

DATE	DESCRIPTION	RCM ITEM #	QUANTITY SOLD	ISSUE PRICE	FINISH	PR-69	PR-70
2014	Lake Superior	129333	9,992	114.95	Proof	100.	—
2014	Lake Ontario	129404	9,680	114.95	Proof	100.	—
2014	Lake Erie	130533	9,842	114.95	Proof	90.	—
2015	Lake Huron	129825	8,071	114.95	Proof	100.	—
2015	Lake Michigan	132475	8,284	114.95	Proof	100.	—

MAJESTIC MAPLE LEAVES SERIES

TWENTY DOLLARS, MAJESTIC MAPLE LEAVES, 2014-2017.

The 2014 Majestic Maple Leaves were also issued as part of a five-coin subscription. Please see the $5 Gold coin (page 416) and $5 Platinum coin (page 483).

| 2014 Common Obverse | 2014 Majestic Maple Leaves
Designer: Pierre Leduc | 2014 Majestic Maple Leaves,
Coloured
Designer: Pierre Leduc | 2014 Majestic Maple Leaves,
With Jade
Designer: Pierre Leduc |

| 2016 Obverse | 2016 Majestic Maple Leaves,
With Drusy Stone
Designer: Tony Bianco | 2017 Obverse | 2017 Majestic Maple Leaves
With Drusy Stone
Designer: Lisa Thomson-Khan |

Designers:
Obv.: Susanna Blunt
Rev.: See reverse illustrations
Composition: 99.99% Ag
Weight: 31.39 g
Diameter: 38.0 mm
Thickness: N/A
Case of Issue: Singly: Maroon clam style case, black flocked insert, encapsulated coin, COA; 2014 Set: 3-hole wood case, black flocked insert

Engravers:
Obv.: Susan Taylor

Silver content: 31.39 g, 1.01 tr oz
Edge: Reeded
Die Axis: ↑↑
Finish: Proof

DATE	DESCRIPTION	RCM ITEM #	QUANTITY SOLD	ISSUE PRICE	FINISH	PR-69	PR-70
2014	Majestic Maple Leaves	131197	6,519	89.95	Proof	80.	—
2014	Majestic Maple Leaves, Coloured	131198	6,021	99.95	Proof	80.	—
2014	Majestic Maple Leaves, With Jade	131199	5,116	114.95	Proof	80.	—
2016	Majestic Maple Leaves, With Drusy Stone	150359	3,999	159.95	Proof	140.	—
2017	Majestic Maple Leaves, With Drusy Stone	161583	4,000	161.95	Proof	155.	—

TWENTY DOLLARS, THE WOLF, 2015.

Designers and Engravers:

Obv.:	Susanna Blunt, Susan Taylor
Rev.:	Pierre Leduc, RCM Staff

Composition: 99.99% Ag

Silver content: 31.39 g, 1.01 tr oz

Weight:	31.39 g	**Edge:**	Reeded
Diameter:	38.0 mm	**Die Axis:**	↑↑
Thickness:	N/A	**Finish:**	Proof

Case of Issue: Maroon clam style case, black flocked insert, encapsulated coin, COA

DATE	DESCRIPTION	RCM ITEM #	QUANTITY SOLD	ISSUE PRICE	FINISH	PR-69	PR-70
2015	The Wolf	133912	7,497	99.95	Proof	100.	—

MAJESTIC ANIMALS SERIES

TWENTY DOLLARS, THE MAJESTIC MOOSE, 2015.

Designers and Engravers:

Obv.:	Susanna Blunt, Susan Taylor
Rev.:	Claudio D'Angelo, RCM Staff

Composition: 99.99% Ag, Coloured

Silver content: 31.39 g, 1.01 tr oz

Weight:	31.39 g	**Edge:**	Reeded
Diameter:	38.0 mm	**Die Axis:**	↑↑
Thickness:	N/A	**Finish:**	Proof

Case of Issue: Maroon clam style case, black flocked insert, encapsulated coin, COA

TWENTY DOLLARS, BIGHORN SHEEP, 2015.

Designers and Engravers:

Obv.:	Susanna Blunt, Susan Taylor
Rev.:	Maurade Baynton, RCM Staff

Composition: 99.99% Ag, Coloured

Silver content: 31.39 g, 1.01 tr oz

Weight:	31.39 g	**Edge:**	Reeded
Diameter:	38.0 mm	**Die Axis:**	↑↑
Thickness:	N/A	**Finish:**	Proof

Case of Issue: Maroon clam style case, black flocked insert, encapsulated coin, COA

TWENTY DOLLARS, MISTY MORNING MULE DEER, 2015.

Designers and Engravers:

Obv.:	Susanna Blunt, Susan Taylor
Rev.:	Trevor Tennant

Composition: 99.99% Ag, Coloured

Silver content: 31.83 g, 1.02 tr oz

Weight:	31.39 g	**Edge:**	Reeded
Diameter:	38 mm	**Die Axis:**	↑↑
Thickness:	N/A	**Finish:**	Proof

Case of Issue: Maroon clamshell with custom beauty box, COA

DATE	DESCRIPTION	RCM ITEM #	QUANTITY SOLD	ISSUE PRICE	FINISH	PR-69	PR-70
2015	The Majestic Moose	131203	7,492	99.95	Proof	90.	—
2015	Bighorn Sheep	141824	6,500	99.95	Proof	90.	—
2015	Misty Morning Mule Deer	143319	6,500	99.95	Proof	90.	—

MAJESTIC ANIMALS SERIES (cont.)

TWENTY DOLLARS, MAJESTIC ELK, 2015.

Designers and Engravers:

Obv.:	Susanna Blunt, Susan Taylor
Rev.:	Maurade Baynton

Composition:	99.99% Ag		
Silver content:	31.39 g, 1.01 tr oz		
Weight:	31.39 g	**Edge:**	Reeded
Diameter:	38 mm	**Die Axis:**	↑↑
Thickness:	N/A	**Finish:**	Proof
Case of Issue:	Maroon clamshell with custom beauty box, COA		

TWENTY DOLLARS, IMPOSING ALPHA WOLF, 2015.

Designers and Engravers:

Obv.:	Susanna Blunt, Susan Taylor
Rev.:	Maurade Baynton

Composition:	99.99% Ag, Coloured		
Silver content:	31.39 g, 1.01 tr oz		
Weight:	31.39 g	**Edge:**	Reeded
Diameter:	38 mm	**Die Axis:**	↑↑
Thickness:	N/A	**Finish:**	Proof
Case of Issue:	Maroon clamshell with custom beauty box, COA		

DATE	DESCRIPTION	RCM ITEM #	QUANTITY SOLD	ISSUE PRICE	FINISH	PR-69	PR-70
2015	Majestic Elk	144305	6,501	99.95	Proof	100.	—
2015	Imposing Alpha Wolf	143726	6,499	99.95	Proof	100.	—

TWENTY DOLLARS, ICE DANCER, 2015.

Designers and Engravers:

Obv.:	Susanna Blunt, Susan Taylor
Rev.:	Douglas R. Laird, RCM Staff

Composition:	99.99% Ag, Coloured		
Silver content:	31.39 g, 1.01 tr oz		
Weight:	31.39 g	**Edge:**	Reeded
Diameter:	38.0 mm	**Die Axis:**	↑↑
Thickness:	N/A	**Finish:**	Proof
Case of Issue:	Maroon clam style case, black flocked insert, encapsulated coin, COA		

DATE	DESCRIPTION	RCM ITEM #	QUANTITY SOLD	ISSUE PRICE	FINISH	PR-69	PR-70
2015	Ice Dancer	132489	6,357	99.95	Proof	90.	—

TWENTY DOLLARS, BEAVER AT WORK, 2015.

Designers and Engravers:

Obv.:	Susanna Blunt, Susan Taylor
Rev.:	John Mardon, RCM Staff

Composition:	99.99% Ag, Coloured		
Silver content:	31.39 g, 1.01 tr oz		
Weight:	31.39 g	**Edge:**	Reeded
Diameter:	38.0 mm	**Die Axis:**	↑↑
Thickness:	N/A	**Finish:**	Proof
Case of Issue:	Maroon clam style case, black flocked insert, encapsulated coin, COA		

DATE	DESCRIPTION	RCM ITEM #	QUANTITY SOLD	ISSUE PRICE	FINISH	PR-69	PR-70
2015	Beaver At Work	130637	6,538	99.95	Proof	90.	—

TWENTY DOLLARS, GEORGE-ÉTIENNE CARTIER, 2015.

Commemorating Canada's first Minister of Militia and Defence, George-Étienne Cartier is depicted in front of Province House, in Charlottetown, the site of the 1864 Charlottetown Conference.

Designers and Engravers:

Obv.:	Susanna Blunt, Susan Taylor
Rev.:	William Lazos, RCM Staff

Composition: 99.99% Ag
Silver content: 31.39 g, 1.01 tr oz
Weight: 31.39 g   **Edge:** Reeded
Diameter: 38.0 mm   **Die Axis:** ↑↑
Thickness: N/A   **Finish:** Proof
Case of Issue: Maroon clam style case, black flocked insert, encapsulated coin, COA

DATE	DESCRIPTION	RCM ITEM #	QUANTITY SOLD	ISSUE PRICE	FINISH	PR-69	PR-70
2015	George-Étienne Cartier	142691	1,268	89.95	Proof	90.	—

TWENTY DOLLARS, SIR JOHN A. MACDONALD, 2015.

Designers and Engravers:

Obv.:	Susanna Blunt, Susan Taylor
Rev.:	William Lazos, RCM Staff

Composition: 99.99% Ag
Silver content: 31.39 g, 1.01 tr oz
Weight: 31.39 g   **Edge:** Reeded
Diameter: 38.0 mm   **Die Axis:** ↑↑
Thickness: N/A   **Finish:** Proof
Case of Issue: Maroon clam style case, black flocked insert, encapsulated coin, COA

DATE	DESCRIPTION	RCM ITEM #	QUANTITY SOLD	ISSUE PRICE	FINISH	PR-69	PR-70
2015	Sir John A. MacDonald	142709	2,865	89.95	Proof	90.	—

TWENTY DOLLARS, HOLIDAY REINDEER, 2015.

Designers and Engravers:

Obv.:	Susanna Blunt, Susan Taylor
Rev.:	Lisa Thomson-Khan

Composition: 99.99% Ag
Silver content: 31.39 g, 1.01 tr oz
Weight: 31.39 g   **Edge:** Reeded
Diameter: 38.0 mm   **Die Axis:** ↑↑
Thickness: N/A   **Finish:** Proof
Case of Issue: Maroon clam style case, black flocked insert, encapsulated coin, COA

DATE	DESCRIPTION	RCM ITEM #	QUANTITY SOLD	ISSUE PRICE	FINISH	PR-69	PR-70
2015	Holiday Reindeer	148169	4,579	114.95	Proof	100.	—

TWENTY DOLLARS, WEDDING, 2015.

Designers and Engravers:

Obv.:	Susanna Blunt, Susan Taylor
Rev.:	Joel Kimmel, RCM Staff

Composition: 99.99% Ag, Sel. gold plated
Silver content: 31.83 g, 1.02 tr oz
Weight: 31.83 g   **Edge:** Reeded
Diameter: 40.0 mm   **Die Axis:** ↑↑
Thickness: N/A   **Finish:** Proof
Case of Issue: Maroon clam style case, black flocked insert, encapsulated coin, COA

DATE	DESCRIPTION	RCM ITEM #	QUANTITY SOLD	ISSUE PRICE	FINISH	PR-69	PR-70
2015	Wedding	143936	7,414	109.95	Proof	100.	—

TWENTY DOLLARS, 100TH ANNIVERSARY OF *IN FLANDERS FIELDS*, 2015.

Featuring the effigy of King George V, this coin pays tribute to John McCrae's poem.

Designers and Engravers:

Obv.:	Sir E.B. MacKennal, RCM Staff
Rev.:	Lauric McGaw, RCM Staff
Composition:	99.99% Ag
Silver content:	31.39 g, 1.01 tr oz
Weight:	31.39 g
Diameter:	38.0 mm
Thickness:	N/A
Case of Issue:	Maroon clam style case, black flocked insert, encapsulated coin, COA, custom box

Die Axis : ↑↑
Finish: Proof
Edge: Reeded

DATE	DESCRIPTION	RCM ITEM #	QUANTITY SOLD	ISSUE PRICE	FINISH	PR-69	PR-70
2015	100th Anniv. of *In Flanders Fields*	144527	5,367	89.95	Proof	90.	—

NORTH AMERICAN SPORTFISH SERIES

TWENTY DOLLARS, NORTH AMERICAN SPORTFISH SET, 2015.

Designers and Engravers:

Obv.:	Susanna Blunt, Susan Taylor
Rev.:	Curtis Atwater, RCM Staff
Composition:	99.99% Ag
Silver content:	31.39 g, 1.01 tr oz
Weight:	31.39 g
Diameter:	38.0 mm
Thickness:	3.1 mm
Edge:	Plain Edge Lettering, "9999 FINE SILVER 1OZ 9999 ARGENT PUR 1 OZ"

Die Axis: ↑↑
Finish: Proof

Common Obverse   **Largemouth Bass**

Northern Pike   **Walleye**   **Rainbow Trout**

Case of Issue: Singly: Maroon clam style case, black flocked insert, encapsulated coin, COA, custom box
Subscription: Four coin walnut wooden case, black flocked insert, encapsulated coins, COA

DATE	DESCRIPTION	RCM ITEM #	QUANTITY SOLD	ISSUE PRICE	FINISH	PR-69	PR-70
2015	Largemouth Bass	142202	6,490	99.95	Proof	90.	—
2015	Northern Pike	142210	6,409	99.95	Proof	90.	—
2015	Walleye	143995	6,375	99.95	Proof	90.	—
2015	Rainbow Trout	143947	6,612	99.95	Proof	90.	—

FORESTS OF CANADA SERIES

TWENTY DOLLARS, FORESTS OF CANADA SERIES, 2015.

The Forests of Canada Series was also offered as an 4-coin subscription.

Common Obverse

Designers and Engravers:

Obv.:	Susanna Blunt, Susan Taylor
Rev.:	See reverse illustrations, RCM Staff

Composition: 99.99% Ag, Coloured
Silver content: 31.39 g, 1.01 tr oz
Weight: 31.39 g **Edge:** Reeded
Diameter: 38.0 mm **Die Axis:** ↑↑
Thickness: N/A **Finish:** Proof
Case of Issue: Maroon clam style case, black flocked insert, encapsulated coin, COA

Carolinian Tulip-Tree
Designer: Julius Csotonyi

Coast Shore Pine
Designer: Margaret Best

Columbian Yew Tree
Designer: Julius Csotonyi

Boreal Balsam Poplar
Designer: Margaret Best

DATE	DESCRIPTION	RCM ITEM #	QUANTITY SOLD	ISSUE PRICE	FINISH	PR-69	PR-70
2015	Carolinian Tulip-Tree	142684	3,100	99.95	Proof	90.	—
2015	Coast Shore Pine	143360	3,117	99.95	Proof	90.	—
2015	Columbian Yew Tree	143131	2,781	99.95	Proof	90.	—
2015	Boreal Balsam Poplar	143297	2,271	99.95	Proof	90.	—

TWENTY DOLLARS, CANADIAN ICONS: POLAR BEAR, 2015.

Designers and Engravers:

Obv.:	Susanna Blunt, Susan Taylor
Rev.:	Cindy Deborah Sorley-Keichinger

Composition: 99.99% Ag, with Jade
Silver content: 31.39 g, 1.01 tr oz
Weight: 31.39 g **Edge:** Reeded
Diameter: 38 mm **Die Axis:** ↑↑
Thickness: N/A **Finish:** Proof with jade
Case of Issue: Maroon clamshell with custom beauty box, COA

DATE	DESCRIPTION	RCM ITEM #	QUANTITY SOLD	ISSUE PRICE	FINISH	PR-69	PR-70
2015	Canadian Icons: Polar Bear	144553	4,910	114.95	Proof	100.	—

UNESCO AT HOME & ABROAD SET

TWENTY DOLLARS, UNESCO AT HOME & ABROAD, 2015.

In 2015, a $50 gold version of the Mount Fuji & The Canadian Rockies was also issued (see page 424)

| Common Obverse | Wood Buffalo National Park
and Sichuan Giant Panda Santuaries
Designer: Lauren Crawshaw | Mount Fuji & The Canadian Rockies
Designer: Trevor Tennant |

Designers:
- Obv.: Susanna Blunt
- Rev.: See reverse illustrations
- Composition: 99.99% Ag
- Weight: 31.39 g
- Diameter: 38.0 mm
- Thickness: N/A
- Case of Issue: Maroon clamshell with custom beauty box, COA.

Engravers:
- Obv.: Susan Taylor
- Rev.: See reverse illustrations
- Silver content: 31.39 g, 1.01 tr oz
- Edge: Reeded
- Die Axis: ↑↑
- Finish: Proof

DATE	DESCRIPTION	RCM ITEM #	QUANTITY SOLD	ISSUE PRICE	FINISH	PR-69	PR-70
2015	Wood Buffalo National Park and Sichuan Giant Panda Sanctuaries	146686	2,157	89.95	Proof	80.	—
2015	Mount Fuji & The Canadian Rockies	142315	3,373	89.95	Proof	80.	—

TORONTO 2015™ PAN AM/PARAPAN AM GAMES SET

TWENTY DOLLARS, TORONTO 2015™ PAN AM/PARAPAN AM GAMES, 2015.

| Common Obverse | Toronto 2015™ Pan Am/Parapan Am Games:
In the Spirit of Sports
Designer: Tony Bianco | Toronto 2015™ Pan Am/Parapan Am Games:
United We Play!™
Designer: Christi Belcourt |

Designers:
- Obv.: Susanna Blunt
- Rev.: See reverse illustrations
- Composition: 99.99% Ag
- Weight: 31.39 g
- Diameter: 38.0 mm
- Thickness: N/A
- Case of Issue: Maroon clamshell with custom beauty box. COA.

Engravers:
- Obv.: Susan Taylor
- Rev.: See reverse illustrations
- Silver content: 31.39 g, 1.01 tr oz
- Edge: Reeded
- Die Axis: ↑↑
- Finish: Proof

DATE	DESCRIPTION	RCM ITEM #	QUANTITY SOLD	ISSUE PRICE	FINISH	PR-69	PR-70
2015	Toronto 2015™ Pan Am/Parapan Am Games: In The Spirit of Sports	144462	1,779	124.95	Proof	125.	—
2015	Toronto 2015™ Pan Am/Parapan Am Games: United We Play!™	143492	1,857	124.95	Proof	125.	—

TWENTY DOLLARS, 70TH ANNIVERSARY OF THE END OF THE ITALIAN CAMPAIGN, 2015.

Designers and Engravers:

Obv.:	Susanna Blunt, Susan Taylor
Rev.:	Joel Kimmel

Composition: 99.99% Ag
Silver content: 31.39 g, 1.01 tr oz

Weight:	31.39 g	Edge:	Reeded
Diameter:	38 mm	Die Axis:	↑↑
Thickness:	N/A	Finish:	Proof

Case of Issue: Paper diorama with custom beauty box, COA

DATE	DESCRIPTION	RCM ITEM #	QUANTITY SOLD	ISSUE PRICE	FINISH	PR-69	PR-70
2015	70th Ann. End of the Italian Campaign	144042	3,996	109.95	Proof	110.	—

TWENTY DOLLARS, MAPLE LEAF REFLECTION, 2015.

Designers and Engravers:

Obv.:	Susanna Blunt, Susan Taylor
Rev.:	Lilyane Caulombe

Composition: 99.99% Ag
Silver content: 31.39 g, 1.01 tr oz

Weight:	31.39 g	Edge:	Reeded
Diameter:	38 mm	Die Axis:	↑↑
Thickness:	N/A	Finish:	Proof

Case of Issue: Maroon clamshefll with custom beauty box, COA

DATE	DESCRIPTION	RCM ITEM #	QUANTITY SOLD	ISSUE PRICE	FINISH	PR-69	PR-70
2015	Maple Leaf Reflection	142738	5,502	99.95	Proof	90.	—

TWENTY DOLLARS, THE CANADIAN MAPLE LEAF (SHAPED), 2015.

Designers and Engravers:

Obv.:	Susanna Blunt, Susan Taylor
Rev.:	Marcos Hallam

Composition: 99.99% Ag
Silver content: 31.5 g, 1.01 tr oz

Weight:	31.5 g	Edge:	Reeded
Diameter:	40.0 mm	Die Axis:	↑↑
Thickness:	N/A	Finish:	Proof

Case of Issue: Custom Maple leaf shaped presentation case, COA

DATE	DESCRIPTION	RCM ITEM #	QUANTITY SOLD	ISSUE PRICE	FINISH	PR-69	PR-70
2015	The Canadian Maple Leaf	143627	14,939	149.95	Proof	150.	—

TWENTY DOLLARS, TOM THOMSON: SPRING ICE (1916), 2015.

Designers and Engravers:

Obv.:	Susanna Blunt, Susan Taylor
Rev.:	Tom Thomson, RCM Staff

Composition: 99.99% Ag, Selective gold plating
Silver content: 31.39 g, 1.01 tr oz

Weight:	31.39 g	Edge:	Reeded
Diameter:	38 mm	Die Axis:	↑↑
Thickness:	N/A	Finish:	Proof

Case of Issue: Maroon clamshefll with standard beauty box, COA

DATE	DESCRIPTION	RCM ITEM #	QUANTITY SOLD	ISSUE PRICE	FINISH	PR-69	PR-70
2015	Tom Thomson: Spring Ice (1916)	150535	1,572	114.95	Proof	115.	—

TWENTY DOLLARS, A HISTORIC REIGN, 2015.

Designers and Engravers:

Obv.:	Susanna Blunt, Susan Taylor
Rev.:	Cathy Bursey Sabourin
Composition:	99.99% Ag, Coloured
Silver content:	31.39 g, 1.01 tr oz

Weight:	31.39 g	Edge:	Reeded
Diameter:	38 mm	Die Axis:	↑↑
Thickness:	N/A	Finish:	Proof
Case of Issue:	Maroon clamshell with black beauty box, COA		

DATE	DESCRIPTION	RCM ITEM #	QUANTITY SOLD	ISSUE PRICE	FINISH	PR-69	PR-70
2015	A Historic Reign		7,472	109.95	Proof	90.	—

TWENTY DOLLARS, LOONEY TUNES™: MERRIE MELODIES, 2015.

Designers and Engravers:

Obv.:	Susanna Blunt, Susan Taylor
Rev.:	Warner Bros.
Composition:	99.99% Ag
Silver content:	31.39 g, 1.01 tr oz

Weight:	31.39 g	Edge:	Reeded
Diameter:	38 mm	Die Axis:	↑↑
Thickness:	N/A	Finish:	Proof
Case of Issue:	ACME Crate with custom beauty box, COA.		

DATE	DESCRIPTION	RCM ITEM #	QUANTITY SOLD	ISSUE PRICE	FINISH	PR-69	PR-70
2015	Merrie Melodies	144947	12,275	109.95	Proof	90.	—

LOONEY TUNES™ SET

TWENTY DOLLARS, LOONEY TUNES™, 2015.

Common Obverse	Sylvester	Bugs Bunny	Daffy Duck	Tweety

Designers:

Obv.:	Susanna Blunt
Rev.:	Warner Bros.
Composition:	99.99% Ag
Weight:	31.39 g
Diameter:	40.0 mm
Thickness:	N/A
Case of Issue:	Wooden box with custom beauty box, COA.

Engravers:

Obv.:	Susan Taylor

Silver content:	31.39 g, 1.01 tr oz
Edge:	Reeded
Die Axis:	↑↑
Finish:	Proof

DATE	DESCRIPTION	RCM ITEM #	QUANTITY SOLD	ISSUE PRICE	FINISH	PR-69	PR-70
2015	Sylvester, Bugs, Daffy, Tweety (4-coin set only)	144879	4,568	419.95	Proof	350.	—
2015	Looney Tunes: Sylvester		3,556				
2015	Looney Tunes: Bugs Bunny		11,390				
2015	Looney Tunes: Daffy Duck		3,627				
2015	Looney Tunes: Tweety		3,686				

Note: These coins were sold as a 4-coin set, though mintages indicate otherwise.

THE CANADIAN HOME FRONT SERIES

TWENTY DOLLARS, THE CANADIAN HOME FRONT, 2015-2016.

Featuring the effigy of King George V, this coin pays tribute to the contribution facilitated by the railways during the war effort.

2015 Obverse

2016 Obverse

Designers and Engravers:
Obv.:	Susanna Blunt, Susan Taylor
Rev.:	See reverse illustrations

Composition: 99.99% Ag
Silver content: 31.39 g, 1.01 tr oz
Weight: 31.39 g   **Edge:** Reeded
Diameter: 38.0 mm   **Die Axis:** ↑↑
Thickness: N/A   **Finish:** Proof
Case of Issue: Maroon clam style case, black flocked insert, encapsulated coin, COA, custom box

Transcontinental Railroad
Designer: David A. Oram

Canada's First Submarine During The First World War
Designer: Yves Bérubé

British Commonwealth Air Training Plan
Designer: David A. Oram

Patrol Against U-Boats
Designer: Bonnie Ross

DATE	DESCRIPTION	RCM ITEM #	QUANTITY SOLD	ISSUE PRICE	FINISH	PR-69	PR-70
2015	Transcontinental Railroad	144429	4,490	89.95	Proof	90.	—
2015	Canada's First Submarine During the First World War	133224	3,193	89.95	Proof	90.	—
2016	British Commonwealth Air Training Plan	145881	3,206	89.95	Proof	90.	—
2016	Patrol Against U-Boats	145882	2,819	89.95	Proof	90.	—

Note: Coins illustrated smaller than actual size.

GRIZZLY BEAR SERIES

TWENTY DOLLARS, GRIZZLY BEAR, 2015-2016.

| The Catch | Togetherness | Family | The Battle |

Designers:
Obv.: Susanna Blunt
Rev.: Lauren Crawshaw
Composition: 99.99% Ag
Weight: 31.39 g
Diameter: 38.0 mm
Thickness: N/A
Case of Issue: Maroon clamshell with custom beauty box, COA

Engravers:
Obv.: Susan Taylor

Silver content: 31.39 g, 1.01 tr oz
Edge: Plain, with edge lettering
Die Axis: ↑↑
Finish: Proof

DATE	DESCRIPTION	RCM ITEM #	QUANTITY SOLD	ISSUE PRICE	FINISH	PR-69	PR-70
2015	Grizzly Bear: The Catch	143765	5,280	99.95	Proof	90.	—
2015	Grizzly Bear: Togetherness	145355	5,145	99.95	Proof	90.	—
2015	Grizzly Bear: Family	145456	4,617	99.95	Proof	90.	—
2016	Grizzly Bear: The Battle	145335	3,418	99.95	Proof	90.	—

WEATHER PHENOMENON SERIES

TWENTY DOLLARS, WEATHER PHENOMENON, 2015-2017.

| Common Obverse | Summer Storm | Winter Freeze | Radiant Rainbow | Fiery Sky |

Designers:
Obv.: Susanna Blunt
Rev.: Tony Bianco
Composition: 99.99% Ag
Weight: 31.39 g
Diameter: 38.0 mm
Thickness: N/A
Case of Issue: Maroon clamshell with black beauty box COA.

Engravers:
Obv.: Susan Taylor
Rev.: Arnold Nogy
Silver content: 31.39 g, 1.01 tr oz
Edge: Reeded
Die Axis: ↑↑
Finish: Proof

DATE	DESCRIPTION	RCM ITEM #	QUANTITY SOLD	ISSUE PRICE	FINISH	PR-69	PR-70
2015	Weather Phenomenon: Summer Storm	146667	7,983	99.95	Proof	90.	—
2015	Weather Phenomenon: Winter Freeze	148300	7,043	99.95	Proof	90.	—
2016	Weather Phenomenon: Radiant Rainbow	152317	7,890	99.95	Proof	90.	—
2017	Weather Phenomenon: Fiery Sky	154020	7,643	99.95	Proof	90	—

MASTERS CLUB EXCLUSIVE SCALLOP-EDGE SERIES

TWENTY DOLLARS, MASTERS CLUB EXCLUSIVE, 2015-2017.

Designers and Engravers:

Obv.:	Susanna Blunt, Susan Taylor
Rev.:	Tony Bianco
Composition:	99.99% Ag
Silver content:	26.51 g, 0.85 tr oz
Weight:	26.51 g
Diameter:	38 mm
Thickness:	N/A
Edge:	Plain
Die Axis:	↑↑
Finish:	Proof
Case of Issue:	Wooden box with graphic beauty box, COA

2015 Master of the Sky: Canada Goose

2016 Master of the Sea: The Orca

2017 Master of the Land: The Timber Wolf

DATE	DESCRIPTION	RCM ITEM #	QUANTITY SOLD	ISSUE PRICE	FINISH	PR-69	PR-70
2015	Master of the Sky: Canada Goose	147349	5,972	99.95	Proof	80.	—
2016	Master of the Sea: The Orca	152165	5,660	99.95	Proof	100.	—
2017	Master of the Land: The Timber Wolf	160602	6,000	102.95	Proof	100.	—

Note: This series was exclusively sold to the Mint Master's Club Members only.

FIRST WORLD WAR: BATTLEFRONT SERIES

TWENTY DOLLARS, FIRST WORLD WAR: BATTLEFRONT SET, 2015-2018.

Featuring the effigy of King George V, the Battlefront Series commemorates the contributions of Canadians during the First World War. It was after the Second Battle of Ypres that John McCrae penned *In Flanders Fields*.

Common Obverse

Designers		Engravers:	
Obv.:	Sir E.B. Mackennal	Obv.:	RCM Staff
Rev.:	See reverse illustrations	Rev.:	RCM Staff
Composition:	99.99% Ag, Selectively gold plated		
Silver content:	31.39 g, 1.01 tr oz		
Weight:	31.39 g		
Diameter:	38.0 mm	Edge:	Reeded
Thickness:	N/A	Die Axis:	↑↑
Finish:	Proof with selective gold plating		
Case of Issue:	Maroon clam style case, black flocked insert, encapsulated coin, COA, custom box		

The Battle of Neuve-Chapelle
Designer: Joel Kimmel

The Second Battle of Ypres
Designer: Silvia Pecota

The Battle of Beaumont-Hamel
Designer: Silvia Pecota

The Somme Offensive
Designer: Glen Loates

The Battle of Vimy Ridge
Designer: Pandora Young

The Battle of Passchendaele
Designer: Pandora Young

Canada's Hundred Days
Designer: Joel Kimmel

Armistice of Compiègne
Designer: William McMillan

DATE	DESCRIPTION	RCM ITEM #	QUANTITY SOLD	ISSUE PRICE	FINISH	PR-69	PR-70
2015	The Battle of Neuve-Chapelle	133229	3,224	109.95	Proof	110.	—
2015	The Second Battle of Ypres	140830	3,397	109.95	Proof	110.	—
2016	The Battle of Beaumont-Hamel	147827	3,517	109.95	Proof	110.	—
2016	The Somme Offensive	147828	3,247	109.95	Proof	110.	—
2017	The Battle of Vimy Ridge	147829	10,000	112.95	Proof	115.	—
2017	The Battle of Passchendaele	147830	10,000	112.95	Proof	115.	—
2018	Canada's Hundred Days	147831	10,000	114.95	Proof	115.	—
2018	Armistice of Compiègne	147832	10,000	114.95	Proof	115.	—

SECOND WORLD WAR: BATTLEFRONT SERIES

TWENTY DOLLARS, SECOND WORLD WAR: BATTLEFRONT SERIES, 2015-2018.

The Second World War Battlefront series honours Canada's participation in key battles during the Second World War. A 10-coin subscription, ending in 2020.

Common Obverse

The Battle of Britain 2015 (1940-)
Designer: Ardell Bourgeois
Engraver: T.H. Paget

Designers and Engravers:

Obv.:	See reverse illustrations
Rev.:	See reverse illustrations
Composition:	99.99% Ag
Silver content:	31.39 g, 1.01 tr oz
Weight:	31.39 g
Diameter:	38.0 mm
Thickness:	N/A
Case of Issue:	Maroon clam style case, black flocked insert, encapsulated coin, COA

Edge:	Reeded
Die Axis:	↑↑
Finish:	Proof

The Battle of Hong Kong
Des.: Joel Kimmel
Engraver: T.H. Paget

The Battle of Dieppe
Des.: Alan Daneil
Engraver: T.H. Paget

The Bombing War
Des.: Glen Loates
Engraver: T.H. Paget

The Battle of the Atlantic
Des.: Neil Hamelin
Engraver: T.H. Paget

The Invasion of Sicily
Des.: Valentine De Landro
Engraver: T.H. Paget

DATE	DESCRIPTION	RCM ITEM #	QUANTITY SOLD	ISSUE PRICE	FINISH	PR-69	PR-70
2015 (1940-)	The Battle of Britain	142025	6,543	89.95	Proof	90.	—
2016	The Battle of Hong Kong	147818	4,110	89.95	Proof	90.	—
2017	The Battle of Dieppe	147819	7,500	92.95	Proof	95.	—
2017	The Bombing War	147820	7,500	92.95	Proof	95.	—
2018	The Battle of the Atlantic	147821	7,500	94.95	Proof	95.	—
2018	The Invasion of Sicily	147822	7,500	94.95	Proof	95.	—

TWENTY DOLLARS, A CELEBRATION OF HER MAJESTY'S 90TH BIRTHDAY, 2016.

Designers and Engravers:

Obv.:	Susanna Blunt, Susan Taylor
Rev.:	Tony Bianco
Composition:	99.99% Ag,
Silver content:	31.39 g, 1.02 tr oz
Weight:	31.39 g
Diameter:	38 mm
Thickness:	N/A
Case of Issue:	Maroon clamshell with black beauty box, COA

Edge:	Reeded
Die Axis:	↑↑
Finish:	Proof

DATE	DESCRIPTION	RCM ITEM #	QUANTITY SOLD	ISSUE PRICE	FINISH	PR-69	PR-70
2016	A Celebration of Her Majesty's 90th Birthday	153794	7,006	99.95	Proof	100.	—

THE UNIVERSE SET

TWENTY DOLLARS, THE UNIVERSE, 2016.

Common Obverse	**The Universe: Observatoire du Mont-Mégantic, Quebec** Designer: Loïc Beaumont-Tremblay	**The Universe: The Burke-Gaffney Observatory, N.S.** Glow-in-the-Dark Glass with Opal Designer: Joel Kimmel and Loic Beaumont-Tremblay	**The Universe: NRC Dominion Radio Astrophysical Observatory (DRAO), B.C.** Glow-in-the-Dark Glass with Silver Fume Designer: Ardell Bourgeois

Designers:
Obv.: Susanna Blunt
Rev.: See reverse illustrations
Composition: 99.99% Ag, Coloured, Glow paint
Silver content: 31.39 g, 1.01 tr oz
Weight: 31.39 g
Diameter: 38.0 mm
Thickness: N/A
Case of Issue: Maroon clamshell with black beauty box, COA.

Engravers:
Obv.: Susan Taylor
Rev.: See reverse illustrations

Edge: Reeded
Die Axis: ↑↑
Finish: Proof, colour and borosilicate glass

DATE	DESCRIPTION	RCM ITEM #	QUANTITY SOLD	ISSUE PRICE	FINISH	PR-69	PR-70
2016	The Universe: Observatoire du Mont-Mégantic, Quebec	147000	8,311	149.95	Proof	150.	—
2016	The Universe: The Burke-Gaffney Observatory, N.S.	149878	5,536	149.95	Proof	150.	—
2016	The Universe: NRC Dominion Radio Astrophysical Observatory (DRAO), B.C.	149879	4,471	149.95	Proof	125.	—

TWENTY DOLLARS, VENETIAN GLASS ANGEL, 2016.

Designers and Engravers:
Obv.: Susanna Blunt
Rev.: Julius Csotonyi
Composition: 99.99% Ag
Silver content: 31.39 g, 1.01 tr oz
Weight: 31.39 g   **Edge:** Reeded
Diameter: 38 mm   **Die Axis:** ↑↑
Thickness: N/A   **Finish:** Proof with Murano glass
Case of Issue: Maroon clamshell with graphic beauty box, COA.

DATE	DESCRIPTION	RCM ITEM #	QUANTITY SOLD	ISSUE PRICE	FINISH	PR-69	PR-70
2016	Venetian Glass Angel	147315	7,973	149.95	Proof	125.	—

CANADIAN LANDSCAPE SERIES

TWENTY DOLLARS, CANADIAN LANDSCAPE, 2016

Common Obverse   **The Rockies**   **The Lake**   **Ski Chalet**   **Reaching the Top**

Designers:
Obv.: Susanna Blunt
Rev.: Stéphanie Gauvin
Composition: 99.99% Ag, with Colour
Weight: 31.83 g
Diameter: 40.0 mm
Thickness: N/A
Case of Issue: Maroon clamshell with standard beauty box, COA.

Engravers:
Obv.: Susan Taylor
Silver content: 31.83 g, 1.02 tr oz
Edge: Reeded
Die Axis: ↑↑
Finish: Proof

DATE	DESCRIPTION	RCM ITEM #	QUANTITY SOLD	ISSUE PRICE	FINISH	PR-69	PR-70
2016	Canadian Landscape Series: The Rockies		3,005	99.95	Proof	100.	—
2016	Canadian Landscape Series: The Lake	147335	2,673	99.95	Proof	100.	—
2016	Canadian Landscape Series: Ski Chalet	149875	2,479	99.95	Proof	100.	—
2016	Canadian Landscape Series: Reaching the Top	149876	2,136	99.95	Proof	100.	—

TWENTY DOLLARS, SNOWY OWL, 2016.

Designers and Engravers:
Obv.: Susanna Blunt, Susan Taylor
Rev.: Douglas Laird
Composition: 99.99% Ag,
Silver content: 31.39 g, 1.02 tr oz
Weight: 31.39 g   **Edge:** Reeded
Diameter: 38 mm   **Die Axis:** ↑↑
Thickness: N/A   **Finish:** Proof
Case of Issue: Maroon clamshell with black beauty box, COA

DATE	DESCRIPTION	RCM ITEM #	QUANTITY SOLD	ISSUE PRICE	FINISH	PR-69	PR-70
2016	Snowy Owl	147324	6,498	99.95	Proof	100.	—

TWENTY DOLLARS, MOTHER EARTH, 2016.

Designers and Engravers:
Obv.: Susanna Blunt, Susan Taylor
Rev.: Alexandra Lefort
Composition: 99.99% Ag,
Silver content: 31.39 g, 1.02 tr oz
Weight: 31.39 g   **Edge:** Reeded
Diameter: 38 mm   **Die Axis:** ↑↑
Thickness: N/A   **Finish:** Proof
Case of Issue: Maroon clamshell with black beauty box, COA

DATE	DESCRIPTION	RCM ITEM #	QUANTITY SOLD	ISSUE PRICE	FINISH	PR-69	PR-70
2016	Mother Earth	151837	6,989	104.95	Proof	170.	—

GEOMETRY IN ART SET

TWENTY DOLLARS, GEOMETRY IN ART, 2016.

Common Obverse

Designers:
Obv.:   Susanna Blunt
Rev.:   Calder Moore
Composition: 99.99% Ag, Coloured
Silver content: 31.83 g, 1.02 tr oz
Weight: 31.83 g
Diameter: 40.0 mm
Thickness: N/A
Case of Issue: Maroon clamshell with graphic beauty box.
Also available as a subscription with black wooden box, COA.

Engravers:
Obv.:   Susan Taylor
Rev.:   Calder Moore

Edge: Reeded
Die Axis: ↑↑
Finish: Proof

| The Loon | The Polar Bear | The Caribou | The Beaver | The Maple Leaf |

DATE	DESCRIPTION	RCM ITEM #	QUANTITY SOLD	ISSUE PRICE	FINISH	PR-69	PR-70
2016	Geometry in Art: The Loon	148871	6,671	99.95	Proof	100.	—
2016	Geometry in Art: The Polar Bear	148062	6,838	99.95	Proof	100.	—
2016	Geometry in Art: The Caribou	150055	6,459	99.95	Proof	100.	—
2016	Geometry in Art: The Beaver	151004	5,471	99.95	Proof	100.	—
2016	Geometry in Art: The Maple Leaf		5,678	99.95	Proof	100.	—

TWENTY DOLLARS, FOUR-LEAF CLOVER, 2016.

Designers and Engravers:
Obv.:   Susanna Blunt, Susan Taylor
Rev.:   Lilyane Coulombe
Composition: 99.99% Ag, Enameled
Silver content: 31.83 g, 1.02 tr oz
Weight: 31.39 g
Diameter: 38 mm
Thickness: N/A
Case of Issue: Maroon clamshell with black beauty box, COA

Edge: Reeded
Die Axis: ↑↑
Finish: Proof

DATE	DESCRIPTION	RCM ITEM #	QUANTITY SOLD	ISSUE PRICE	FINISH	PR-69	PR-70
2016	Four-Leaf Clover	149886	5,888	109.95	Proof	100.	—

AIRCRAFT OF THE FIRST WORLD WAR SET

TWENTY DOLLARS, AIRCRAFT OF THE FIRST WORLD WAR, 2016.

| Common Obverse | The Royal Aircraft Factory S.E.5A | The Sopwith Triplane | Curtiss H-12 |

Designers:
Obv.: Susanna Blunt
Rev.: David A. Oram
Composition: 99.99% Ag, Coloured
Weight: 31.83 g
Diameter: 40.0 mm
Thickness: N/A
Case of Issue: Maroon clamshell with black beauty box, COA.

Engravers:
Obv.: Susan Taylor
Rev.: David A. Oram
Silver content: 31.83 g, 1.02 tr oz
Edge: Reeded
Die Axis: ↑↑
Finish: Proof

DATE	DESCRIPTION	RCM ITEM #	QUANTITY SOLD	ISSUE PRICE	FINISH	PR-69	PR-70
2016	The Royal Aircraft Factory S.E.5A	149426	7,253	99.95	Proof	100.	—
2016	The Sopwith Triplane	150230	5,643	99.95	Proof	100.	—
2016	Curtiss H-12	150240	5,013	99.95	Proof	100.	—

CANADIAN SALMONIDS SET

TWENTY DOLLARS, CANADIAN SALMONIDS, 2016

| Common Obverse | Atlantic Salmon | Arctic Char | Sockeye Salmon |

Designers:
Obv.: Susanna Blunt
Rev.: Curtis Atwater
Composition: 99.99% Ag, with Colour
Weight: 31.83 g
Diameter: 40.0 mm
Thickness: N/A
Case of Issue: Maroon clamshell with black beauty box. Available as a subscription, with fishing lure, COA.

Engravers:
Obv.: Susan Taylor
Rev.: Curtis Atwater
Silver content: 31.83 g, 1.02 tr oz
Die Axis: ↑↑
Edge: Reeded
Finish: Proof

DATE	DESCRIPTION	RCM ITEM #	QUANTITY SOLD	ISSUE PRICE	FINISH	PR-69	PR-70
2016	Canadian Salmonids: Atlantic Salmon		4,520	99.95	Proof	100.	—
2016	Canadian Salmonids: Arctic Char	150524	4,535	99.95	Proof	100.	—
2016	Canadian Salmonids: Sockeye Salmon	150699	4,059	99.95	Proof	100.	—

TWENTY DOLLARS, *BATMAN V SUPERMAN: DAWN OF JUSTICE*™ – THE TRINITY, 2016.

Designers and Engravers:

Obv.:	Susanna Blunt, Susan Taylor
Rev.:	DC Comics
Composition:	99.99% Ag, Coloured
Silver content:	31.83 g, 1.02 tr oz

Weight:	31.83 g	**Edge:**	Reeded
Diameter:	40 mm	**Die Axis:**	↑↑
Thickness:	N/A	**Finish:**	Proof
Case of Issue:	Premium presentation case, COA		

DATE	DESCRIPTION	RCM ITEM #	QUANTITY SOLD	ISSUE PRICE	FINISH	PR-69	PR-70
2016	*Batman v Superman: Dawn of Justice*™ – The Trinity	150397	8,302	109.95	Proof	100.	—

TWENTY DOLLARS, CELEBRATING THE 40TH SEASON OF THE *TORONTO BLUE JAYS*™, 2016.

Designers and Engravers:

Obv.:	Susanna Blunt, Susan Taylor
Rev.:	Joel Kimmel
Composition:	99.99% Ag, Coloured
Silver content:	31.39 g, 1.01 tr oz

Weight:	31.39 g	**Edge:**	Reeded
Diameter:	38 mm	**Die Axis:**	↑↑
Thickness:	N/A	**Finish:**	Proof
Case of Issue:	Maroon clamshell with full colour beauty box, COA		

DATE	DESCRIPTION	RCM ITEM #	QUANTITY SOLD	ISSUE PRICE	FINISH	PR-69	PR-70
2016	40th Anniversary *Toronto Blue Jays*™	154360	11,507	99.95	Proof	100.	—

TWENTY DOLLARS, *STAR TREK*™: ENTERPRISE, 2016.

Designers and Engravers:

Obv.:	Susanna Blunt, Susan Taylor
Rev.:	RCM Staff
Composition:	99.99% Ag, Coloured
Silver content:	31.39 g, 1.01 tr oz

Weight:	31.39 g	**Edge:**	Reeded
Diameter:	38 mm	**Die Axis:**	↑↑
Thickness:	N/A	**Finish:**	Proof
Case of Issue:	Maroon clamshell with graphic beauty box, COA		

DATE	DESCRIPTION	RCM ITEM #	QUANTITY SOLD	ISSUE PRICE	FINISH	PR-69	PR-70
2016	*Star Trek*™: Enterprise	152114	11,491	109.95	Proof	110.	—

TWENTY DOLLARS, CANADA'S COLOURFUL MAPLE LEAF (SHAPED), 2016.

Designers and Engravers:

Obv.:	Susanna Blunt, Susan Taylor
Rev.:	Maurice Gervais
Composition:	99.99% Ag, Coloured
Silver content:	31.5 g, 1.01 tr oz

Weight:	31.5 g	**Edge:**	Plain
Diameter:	42 mm x 43 mm	**Die Axis:**	↑↑
Thickness:	N/A	**Finish:**	Proof
Case of Issue:	Custom Maple leaf shaped presentation case, COA		

DATE	DESCRIPTION	RCM ITEM #	QUANTITY SOLD	ISSUE PRICE	FINISH	PR-69	PR-70
2016	Canada's Colourful Maple Leaf		11,407	154.95	Proof	130.	—

THE MIGRATORY BIRDS CONVENTION SET

TWENTY DOLLARS, THE MIGRATORY BIRDS CONVENTION, 2016

| Common Obverse | The Mountain Bluebird | The American Avocet | The American Goldfinch | The Pileated Woodpecker |

Designers:
Obv.: Susanna Blunt
Rev.: Claudio D'Angelo
Composition: 99.99% Ag, with Colour
Weight: 31.39 g
Diameter: 38 mm
Thickness: N/A
Case of Issue: Maroon clamshell with custom beauty box, COA.

Engravers:
Obv.: Susan Taylor

Silver content: 31.83 g, 1.0 tr oz
Edge: Reeded
Die Axis: ↑↑
Finish: Proof

DATE	DESCRIPTION	RCM ITEM #	QUANTITY SOLD	ISSUE PRICE	FINISH	PR-69	PR-70
2016	The Mountain Bluebird	149540	5,353	99.95	Proof	100.	—
2016	The American Avocet	150993	4,138	99.95	Proof	100.	—
2016	The American Goldfinch	152048	4,599	99.95	Proof	100.	—
2016	The Pileated Woodpecker	152988	4,480	99.95	Proof	100.	—

DC COMICS™ ORIGINALS SERIES

TWENTY DOLLARS, *DC COMICS™ ORIGINALS*, 2016

| Common Obverse | DC Comics™ Originals: The Man of Steel™ | DC Comics™ Originals: The Amazing Amazon | DC Comics™ Originals: The Dark Knight™ | DC Comics™ Originals: The Trinity |

Designers:
Obv.: Susanna Blunt
Rev.: DC Comics
Composition: 99.99% Ag, with Colour
Weight: 31.83 g
Diameter: 40.0 mm
Thickness: N/A
Case of Issue: One-of-a-kind collector case features a glow-in-the-dark BATMAN™ emblem!, COA

Engravers:
Obv.: Susan Taylor
Rev.: RCM Staff

Silver content: 31.83 g, 1.02 tr oz
Edge: Reeded
Die Axis: ↑↑
Finish: Proof

DATE	DESCRIPTION	RCM ITEM #	QUANTITY SOLD	ISSUE PRICE	FINISH	PR-69	PR-70
2016	The Man of Steel™	150266	3,088	109.95	Proof	110.	—
2016	The Amazing Amazon	150288	4,396	109.95	Proof	110.	—
2016	The Dark Knight™	150418	2,889	109.95	Proof	110.	—
2016	The Trinity	150882	2,132	112.95	Proof	110.	—

TWENTY DOLLARS, MAPLE LEAF MAZE, 2016.

Designers and Engravers:

Obv.:	Susanna Blunt, Susan Taylor
Rev.:	Maurice Gervais
Composition:	99.99% Ag, Coloured
Silver content:	31.39 g, 1.01 tr oz
Weight:	31.39 g
Diameter:	38 mm
Thickness:	N/A
Case of Issue:	Maroon clamshell with black beauty box, COA

Edge:	Reeded
Die Axis:	↑↑
Finish:	Proof

DATE	DESCRIPTION	RCM ITEM #	QUANTITY SOLD	ISSUE PRICE	FINISH	PR-69	PR-70
2016	Maple Leaf Maze	153437	6,647	114.95	Proof	100.	—

TWENTY DOLLARS, DIWALI: FESTIVAL OF LIGHTS, 2016.

A $200 gold coin with the same design was issued in 2015 (see page 446).

Designers and Engravers:

Obv.:	Susanna Blunt, Susan Taylor
Rev.:	Sarindar Dhaliwal
Composition:	99.99% Ag, Coloured
Silver content:	31.39 g, 1.01 tr oz
Weight:	31.39 g
Diameter:	38 mm
Thickness:	N/A
Case of Issue:	Maroon clamshell with black beauty box, COA

Edge:	Reeded
Die Axis:	↑↑
Finish:	Proof

DATE	DESCRIPTION	RCM ITEM #	QUANTITY SOLD	ISSUE PRICE	FINISH	PR-69	PR-70
2016	Diwali: Fesitval of Lights		2,981	91.95	Proof	90.	—

TWENTY DOLLARS, A ROYAL TOUR, 2016.

Designers and Engravers:

Obv.:	Susanna Blunt, Susan Taylor
Rev.:	Chris Jelf
Composition:	99.99% Ag, Coloured
Silver content:	31.39 g, 1.01 tr oz
Weight:	31.39 g
Diameter:	38 mm
Thickness:	N/A
Case of Issue:	Maroon clamshell with black beauty box, COA

Edge:	Reeded
Die Axis:	↑↑
Finish:	Proof

DATE	DESCRIPTION	RCM ITEM #	QUANTITY SOLD	ISSUE PRICE	FINISH	PR-69	PR-70
2016	A Royal Tour	158945	6,542	109.95	Proof	110.	—

TWENTY DOLLARS, THE COLOURFUL WINGS OF A BUTTERFLY, 2016.

Designers and Engravers:

Obv.:	Susanna Blunt, Susan Taylor
Rev.:	Bonnie Ross
Composition:	99.99% Ag, Coloured
Silver content:	31.39 g, 1.01 tr oz
Weight:	31.39 g
Diameter:	38 mm
Thickness:	N/A
Case of Issue:	Maroon clamshell with black beauty box, COA

Edge:	Reeded
Die Axis:	↑↑
Finish:	Proof

DATE	DESCRIPTION	RCM ITEM #	QUANTITY SOLD	ISSUE PRICE	FINISH	PR-69	PR-70
2016	The Colourful Wings of a Butterfly	157872	2,682	158.95	Proof	140.	—

ICONIC STAR TREK™ SCENES

TWENTY DOLLARS, ICONIC *STAR TREK*™ SCENES, 2016

Part of the Royal Canadian Mint's celebration of the 50th Anniversary of *Star Trek* — a television series that is beloved by generations of Canadians, and whose vision of the future helped inspire innovation in our time!

Common Obverse

**Star Trek™:
The City on the Edge of Forever**

**Star Trek™:
Mirror Mirror**

**Star Trek™:
The Trouble With Tribbles**

Designers:
Obv.: Susanna Blunt
Rev.: RCM Staff
Composition: 99.99% Ag, with Colour
Weight: 31.39 g
Diameter: 38.0 mm
Thickness: N/A
Case of Issue: Graphic beauty box.

Engravers:
Obv.: Susan Taylor
Rev.: RCM Staff
Silver content: 31.39 g, 1.01 tr oz
Edge: Reeded
Die Axis: ↑↑
Finish: Proof

DATE	DESCRIPTION	RCM ITEM #	QUANTITY SOLD	ISSUE PRICE	FINISH	PR-69	PR-70
2016	*Star Trek™:* The City on the Edge of Forever	152125	5,204	109.95	Proof	110.	—
2016	*Star Trek™:* Mirror Mirror	152136	5,093	109.95	Proof	110.	—
2016	*Star Trek™:* The Trouble With Tribbles	152151	5,245	109.95	Proof	110.	—

ICONIC CANADA SERIES

TWENTY DOLLARS, ICONIC CANADA, 2016-2017.

2016 Obverse

**2016: The Polar Bear
Designer: Julius Csotonyi**

2017 Obverse

**2017: The Grizzly Bear
Designer: W. Allan Hancock**

Designers:
Obv.: Susanna Blunt
Rev.: See reverse illustrations
Composition: 99.99% Ag, Coloured
Weight: 31.39 g
Diameter: 38 mm
Thickness: N/A
Case of Issue: Maroon clamshell with custom beauty box, COA

Engravers:
Rev.: Susan Taylor

Silver content: 31.39 g, 1.01 tr oz
Edge: Reeded
Die Axis: ↑↑
Finish: Proof

DATE	DESCRIPTION	RCM ITEM #	QUANTITY SOLD	ISSUE PRICE	FINISH	PR-69	PR-70
2016	Iconic Canada: The Polar Bear	N/A	3,958	109.95	Proof	110.	—
2017	Iconic Canada: The Grizzly Bear	N/A	4,000	113.95	Proof	110.	—

Note: These coins were exclusively sold to the Mint Master's Club Members only.

MAJESTIC ANIMAL SERIES

TWENTY DOLLARS, MAJESTIC ANIMAL, 2016-2017.

Common
Obverse

Designers:
Obv.: Susanna Blunt
Rev.: See reverse illustrations
Composition: 99.99% Ag, Coloured
Weight: 31.83 g
Diameter: 38 mm
Thickness: N/A
Case of Issue: Maroon clamshell with custom beauty box.
Also sold as a subscription, with black beauty box, COA.

Engravers:
Obv.: Susan Taylor

Silver content: 31.83 g, 1.02 tr oz
Edge: Reeded
Die Axis: ↑↑
Finish: Proof

Regal Red-Tailed Hawk
Designer: Emily S. Damstra

The Commanding
Canadian Lynx
Designer: Denis Mayer Jr.

The Baronial Bald Eagle
Designer: Glen Loates

The Benevolent Bison
Designer: Doug Comeau

The Bold Black Bear
Designer: Pierre Leduc

DATE	DESCRIPTION	RCM ITEM #	QUANTITY SOLD	ISSUE PRICE	FINISH	PR-69	PR-70
2016	Regal Red-Tailed Hawk	150199	5,648	99.95	Proof	90.	—
2016	The Commanding Canadian Lynx	151794	5,821	99.95	Proof	90.	—
2016	The Baronial Bald Eagle	151780	5,545	99.95	Proof	90.	—
2016	The Benevolent Bison	151927	4,965	99.95	Proof	90.	—
2017	The Bold Black Bear	151942	5,145	99.95	Proof	90.	—

TWENTY DOLLARS, JEWEL OF THE RAIN, 2016-2017.

2016 Obverse

Jewel of the Rain:
Bigleaf Maple
Des.: Caren Heine

2017 Obverse

Jewel of the Rain:
Sugar Maple Leaves
Des.: Lisa Thomson-Khan

Designers:
Obv.: Susanna Blunt
Rev.: See reverse illustrations
Composition: 99.99% Ag, Coloured
Weight: 31.39 g
Diameter: 38 mm
Thickness: N/A
Case of Issue: Maroon clamshell with black beauty box, COA

Engravers:
Obv.: Susan Taylor

Silver content: 31.39 g, 1.01 tr oz
Edge: Reeded
Die Axis: ↑↑
Finish: Proof

DATE	DESCRIPTION	RCM ITEM #	QUANTITY SOLD	ISSUE PRICE	FINISH	PR-69	PR-70
2016	Jewel of the Rain: Bigleaf Maple	152064	4,482	124.95	Proof	125.	—
2017	Jewel of the Rain: Sugar Maple Leaves	158128	4,500	129.95	Proof	130.	—

LANDSCAPE ILLUSION SERIES

TWENTY DOLLARS, LANDSCAPE ILLUSION, 2016-2017.

Common
Obverse

Designers:		Engravers:	
Obv.:	Susanna Blunt	Obv.:	Susan Taylor
Rev.:	Julius T. Csotonyi		
Composition:	99.99% Ag, Coloured	**Silver content:**	31.83 g, 1.02 tr oz
Weight:	31.83 g	**Edge:**	Reeded
Diameter:	38 mm	**Die Axis:**	↑↑
Thickness:	N/A	**Finish:**	Proof
Case of Issue:	sold as a subscription, white box with custom beauty box, COA.		

Mountain Goat	Butterfly	Salmon	Pronghorn Antelope	Snowy Owl

DATE	DESCRIPTION	RCM ITEM #	QUANTITY SOLD	ISSUE PRICE	FINISH	PR-69	PR-70
2016	Mountain Goat	150385	3,517	90.00	Proof	90.	—
2016	Butterfly	149552	3,871	90.00	Proof	90.	—
2016	Salmon	150479	3,121	90.00	Proof	90.	—
2017	Pronhorn Antelope	150494	2,903	90.00	Proof	90.	—
2017	Snowy Owl	150509	2,794	90.00	Proof	90.	—

CANADIAN KALEIDOSCOPE SERIES

TWENTY DOLLARS, CANADIANA KALEIDSCOPE: 2016-2017.

Tumbled glass and coloured shapes create amazing patterns inside a kaleidoscope, and this breakthrough new series explores the incredible designs that can be achieved when great Canadian icons become the focus of the kaleidoscope's reflective magic.

Common Obverse	Canadiana Kaleidoscope: Polar Bear	Canadiana Kaleidoscope: The Loon	Canadiana Kaleidoscope: Maple Leaf

Designers:		Engravers:	
Obv.:	Susanna Blunt	Obv.:	Susan Taylor
Rev.:	Calder Moore	Rev.:	Calder Moore
Composition:	99.99% Ag	**Silver content:**	31.85 g, 1.02 tr oz
Weight:	31.85 g	**Edge:**	Plain
Diameter:	60.0 mm	**Die Axis:**	↑↑
Thickness:	N/A	**Finish:**	Proof
Case of Issue:	Maroon clamshell with black beauty box.		

DATE	DESCRIPTION	RCM ITEM #	QUANTITY SOLD	ISSUE PRICE	FINISH	PR-69	PR-70
2016	Canadiana Kaleidoscope: Polar Bear		3,626	117.95	Proof	120.	—
2017	Canadiana Kaleidoscope: The Loon	157447	7,500	117.95	Proof	120.	—
2017	Canadiana Kaleidoscope: Maple Leaf	157645	7,500	117.95	Proof	120.	—

LITTLE CREATURES SERIES

TWENTY DOLLARS, LITTLE CREATURES: SNAIL, 2016-2018.

Common Obverse

2016 Snail

2017 Dogbane Beetle

2018 Monarch Caterpillar

Designers:		**Engravers:**	
Obv.:	Susanna Blunt	Obv.:	Susan Taylor
Rev.:	Maurice Gervais		
Composition:	99.99% Ag, Coloured	**Silver content:**	31.39 g, 1.01 tr oz
Weight:	31.39 g	**Edge:**	Reeded
Diameter:	38 mm	**Die Axis:**	↑↑
Thickness:	N/A	**Finish:**	Proof
Case of Issue:	Maroon clamshell with black beauty box, COA		

DATE	DESCRIPTION	RCM ITEM #	QUANTITY SOLD	ISSUE PRICE	FINISH	PR-69	PR-70
2016	Little Creatures: Snail	150905	8,007	149.95	Proof	130.	—
2017	Little Creatures: Dogbane Beetle	156050	8,500	151.95	Proof	150.	—
2018	Little Creatures: Monarch Caterpillar	164404	5,000	154.95	Proof	155.	—

TRADITIONAL UKRAINIAN PYSANKA

TWENTY DOLLARS, TRADITIONAL UKRAINIAN PYSANKA, 2016-2019.

Though many cultures regard the egg as one of spring's most enduring symbols, few do so as beautifully as the Ukrainian people, whose pysanka is a reminder of life's beginnings and the potential inherent in every living thing.

Designers:		**Engravers:**	
Obv.:	Susanna Blunt	Rev.:	Ann C. Morash
Composition:	99.99% Ag, Coloured		
Silver content:	31.39 g, 1.01 tr oz		
Weight:	31.39 g - 31.82 g	**Die Axis:**	↑↑
Diameter:	45 mm long x 33 mm wide	**Edge:**	Interrupted reeding
Thickness:	N/A	**Finish:**	2016-2017, 2019: Proof
Case of Issue:	Maroon clamshell with black beauty box, COA		2018: Proof with reverse gold plating

2016-2017, 2019 Common Obverse

2016 Traditional Pysanka

2017 Traditional Pysanka

2018 Obverse

2018 Golden Spring Pysanka

2019 Vegreville Pysanka

TWENTY DOLLARS, TRADITIONAL UKRAINIAN PYSANKA, 2016-2019, PRICING PANEL.

DATE	DESCRIPTION	RCM ITEM #	QUANTITY SOLD	ISSUE PRICE	FINISH	PR-69	PR-70
2016	Traditional Ukrainian Pysanka	150664	4,000	114.95	Proof	700.	—
2017	Traditional Ukrainian Pysanka	158380	5,000	114.95	Proof	200.	—
2018	Golden Spring Pysanka	164675	5,000	129.95	Proof	150.	—
2019	Vegreville Pysanka	170739	5,000	129.95	Proof	130.	—,

TWENTY DOLLARS, NATURE'S ADORNMENTS: DRAGONFLY, 2017.

Designers and Engravers:
Obv.:   Susanna Blunt, Susan Taylor
Rev.:   Emily Damstra
Composition: 99.99% Ag, Coloured
Silver content: 31.39 g, 1.01 tr oz
Weight: 31.39 g   **Edge:**   Reeded
Diameter: 38 mm   **Die Axis:**   ↑↑
Thickness: N/A   **Finish:**   Proof
Case of Issue: Maroon clamshell with graphic beauty box, COA

DATE	DESCRIPTION	RCM ITEM #	QUANTITY SOLD	ISSUE PRICE	FINISH	PR-69	PR-70
2017	Nature's Adornments: Dragonfly	155015	2,749	148.95	Proof	150.	—

UNDER THE SEA SERIES

TWENTY DOLLARS, UNDER THE SEA, 2017.

This three-coin series features unique marine species found in Canadian waters.

Common Obverse   Seahorse   Sea Star   Sea Turtle

Designers:
Obv.:   Susanna Blunt
Rev.:   Maurice Gervais
Composition: 99.99% Ag, Coloured
Weight: 31.39 g
Diameter: 38 mm
Thickness: N/A
Case of Issue: Maroon clamshell with black beauty box, COA

Engravers:
Obv.:   Susan Taylor

Silver content: 31.39 g, 1.01 tr oz
Edge: Reeded
Die Axis: ↑↑
Finish: Proof

DATE	DESCRIPTION	RCM ITEM #	QUANTITY SOLD	ISSUE PRICE	FINISH	PR-69	PR-70
2017	Under the Sea: Seahorse	154338	3,360	151.95	Proof	150.	—
2017	Under the Sea: Sea Star	156870	7,500	151.95	Proof	150.	—
2017	Under the Sea: Sea Turtle	156871	7,500	151.95	Proof	150.	—

TWENTY DOLLARS, SNOWFLAKE, 2017.

Designers and Engravers:

Obv.:	Susanna Blunt, Susan Taylor
Rev.:	Don Komarechka

Composition: 99.99% Ag, Coloured
Silver content: 31.39 g, 1.01 tr oz

Weight:	31.39 g	**Edge:**	Reeded
Diameter:	38 mm	**Die Axis:**	↑↑
Thickness:	N/A	**Finish:**	Proof

Case of Issue: Maroon clamshell with black beauty box, COA

DATE	DESCRIPTION	RCM ITEM #	QUANTITY SOLD	ISSUE PRICE	FINISH	PR-69	PR-70
2017	Snowflake	162196	5,026	113.95	Proof	115.	—

TWENTY DOLLARS, SNOW-COVERED TREES, 2017.

Designers and Engravers:

Obv.:	Susanna Blunt, Susan Taylor
Rev.:	Tony Bianco

Composition: 99.99% Ag, Coloured
Silver content: 31.39 g, 1.01 tr oz

Weight:	31.39 g	**Edge:**	Reeded
Diameter:	38 mm	**Die Axis:**	↑↑
Thickness:	N/A	**Finish:**	Proof

Case of Issue: Maroon clamshell with black beauty box, COA

DATE	DESCRIPTION	RCM ITEM #	QUANTITY SOLD	ISSUE PRICE	FINISH	PR-69	PR-70
2017	Snow-Covered Trees	162268	3,114	152.95	Proof	150.	—

TWENTY DOLLARS, BRILLIANT BIRCH LEAVES WITH DRUSY STONE, 2017.

Designers and Engravers:

Obv.:	Susanna Blunt, Susan Taylor
Rev.:	Tony Bianco

Composition: 99.99% Ag, Coloured
Silver content: 31.39 g, 1.01 tr oz

Weight:	31.39 g	**Edge:**	Reeded
Diameter:	38 mm	**Die Axis:**	↑↑
Thickness:	N/A	**Finish:**	Proof

Case of Issue: Maroon clamshell with black beauty box, COA

DATE	DESCRIPTION	RCM ITEM #	QUANTITY SOLD	ISSUE PRICE	FINISH	PR-69	PR-70
2017	Brilliant Birch Leaves with Drusy Stone	156983	1,878	161.95	Proof	160.	—

TWENTY DOLLARS, THE NUTTY SQUIRREL AND THE MIGHTY OAK, 2017.

Designers and Engravers:

Obv.:	Susanna Blunt, Susan Taylor
Rev.:	Tony Bianco

Composition: 99.99% Ag, Coloured
Silver content: 31.39 g, 1.01 tr oz

Weight:	31.39 g	**Edge:**	Reeded
Diameter:	38 mm	**Die Axis:**	↑↑
Thickness:	N/A	**Finish:**	Proof

Case of Issue: Maroon clamshell with black beauty box, COA

DATE	DESCRIPTION	RCM ITEM #	QUANTITY SOLD	ISSUE PRICE	FINISH	PR-69	PR-70
2017	The Nutty Squirrel and the Mighty Oak	157604	2,131	116.95	Proof	115.	—

GLISTENING NORTH SERIES

TWENTY DOLLARS, GLISTENING NORTH, 2017.

A collectible work of art that celebrates the beauty of Northern Canada and its wildlife! An RCM first — selective use of Diamond Glitter adds an intensely glittering effect that recreates the light-reflecting qualities of the coloured snow and ice.

Common Obverse	The Polar Bear Designer: Glen Loates	The Arctic Tern Designer: Derek C. Wicks	The Arctic Wolf Designer: Maurade Baynton

Designers:
Obv.:   Susanna Blunt
Rev.:   See reverse illustrations
Composition: 99.99% Ag
Silver content: 31.39 g, 1.01 tr oz
Weight: 31.39 g
Diameter: 38.0 mm
Thickness: N/A
Case of Issue: Maroon clamshell with black beauty box. COA.

Engravers:
Obv.:   Susan Taylor
Rev.:   See reverse illustrations

Edge: Reeded
Die Axis: ↑↑
Finish: Proof

DATE	DESCRIPTION	RCM ITEM #	QUANTITY SOLD	ISSUE PRICE	FINISH	PR-69	PR-70
2017	Glistening North: The Polar Bear	155735	4,595	114.95	Proof	115.	—
2017	Glistening North: The Arctic Tern	159135	7,500	114.95	Proof	115.	—
2017	Glistening North: The Arctic Wolf	160988	5,000	119.95	Proof	120.	—

TWENTY DOLLARS, CANADIAN UNDERWATER LIFE, 2017.

This unique coin takes you beneath the waves to discover the amazing underwater worlds that lie off Canada's coasts. The 3D "water" droplet on this coin highlights six of the ocean's residents who face significant challenges caused by human activity.

Designers and Engravers:
Obv.:   Susanna Blunt, Susan Taylor
Rev.:   Alexandra Lefort
Composition: 99.99% Ag, Coloured
Silver content: 31.39 g, 1.01 tr oz
Weight: 31.39 g   **Edge:**   Reeded
Diameter: 38 mm   **Die Axis:**   ↑↑
Thickness: N/A   **Finish:**   Proof
Case of Issue: Maroon clamshell with black beauty box, COA

DATE	DESCRIPTION	RCM ITEM #	QUANTITY SOLD	ISSUE PRICE	FINISH	PR-69	PR-70
2017	Canadian Underwater Life	157232	4,581	106.95	Proof	110.	—

AIRCRAFT OF THE SECOND WORLD WAR SERIES

TWENTY DOLLARS, AIRCRAFT OF THE SECOND WORLD WAR, 2017.

The Aircraft of the Second World War series salutes three of the most iconic aircraft flown between 1939 and 1945. Whether used to defend the homeland, in combat overseas or as part of the British Commonwealth Air Training Plan here in Canada, these aircraft are remembered as important symbols of Canadian valour and sacrifice.

Common Obverse	Hawker Hurricane	Avro Anson	Consolidated Canso

Designers:
Obv.:	Susanna Blunt
Rev.:	David A. Oram

Composition: 99.99% Ag
Weight: 31.83 g
Diameter: 40.0 mm
Thickness: N/A
Case of Issue: Maroon clamshell with black beauty box.COA.

Engravers:
Obv.:	Susan Taylor

Silver content: 31.83 g, 1.02 tr oz
Edge: Reeded
Die Axis: ↑↑
Finish: Proof

DATE	DESCRIPTION	RCM ITEM #	QUANTITY SOLD	ISSUE PRICE	FINISH	PR-69	PR-70
2017	Hawker Hurricane	155694	500	102.95	Proof	100.	—
2017	Avro Anson	156470	7,500	102.95	Proof	100.	—
2017	Consolidated Canso	156472	7,500	102.95	Proof	100.	—

TWENTY DOLLARS, PEARL FLOWERS, 2017.

Designers and Engravers:
Obv.:	Susanna Blunt
Rev.:	Margaret Best

Composition: 99.99% Ag, Coloured
Silver content: 31.39 g, 1.01 tr oz
Weight: 31.39 g   Edge: Reeded
Diameter: 38 mm   Die Axis: ↑↑
Thickness: N/A   Finish: Proof
Case of Issue: Maroon clamshell with black beauty box, COA

DATE	DESCRIPTION	RCM ITEM #	MINTAGE	ISSUE PRICE	FINISH	PR-69	PR-70
2017	Pearl Flowers	157047	6,000	119.95	Proof	120.	—

TWENTY DOLLARS, *STAR TREK*™: THE BORG, 2017.

Designers and Engravers:
Obv.:	Susanna Blunt
Rev.:	RCM Staff

Composition: 99.99% Ag, Coloured
Silver content: 31.39 g, 1.01 tr oz
Weight: 31.39 g   Edge: Reeded
Diameter: 38 mm   Die Axis: ↑↑
Thickness: N/A   Finish: Proof
Case of Issue: Maroon clamshell with graphic beauty box, COA

DATE	DESCRIPTION	RCM ITEM #	MINTAGE	ISSUE PRICE	FINISH	PR-69	PR-70
2017	*Star Trek*™: The Borg	159907	10,000	112.95	Proof	100.	—

EN PLEIN AIR SERIES

TWENTY DOLLARS, EN PLEIN AIR, 2017.

Common Obverse

Springtime Gifts

Maritime Memories

A Paddle Awaits

Designers:		**Engravers:**	
Obv.:	Susanna Blunt	Obv.:	Susan Taylor
Rev.:	Elizabeth Sim	Rev.:	RCM Staff
Composition:	99.99% Ag, Coloured	**Silver content:**	31.85 g, 1.02 tr oz
Weight:	31.85 g	**Edge:**	Plain
Diameter:	60 mm	**Die Axis:**	↑↑
Thickness:	N/A	**Finish:**	Proof
Case of Issue:	Maroon clamshell with black beauty box, COA		

DATE	DESCRIPTION	RCM ITEM #	MINTAGE	ISSUE PRICE	FINISH	PR-69	PR-70
2017	En Plein Air:Springtime Gifts	160935	5,500	119.95	Proof	120.	—
2017	En Plein Air: Maritime Memories	160969	5,500	119.95	Proof	120.	—
2017	En Plein Air: A Paddle Awaits	160977	5,500	119.95	Proof	120.	—

TWENTY DOLLARS, CANOE TO TRANQUIL TIMES, 2017.

Designers and Engravers:			
Obv.:	Susanna Blunt		
Rev.:	Margaret Best		
Composition:	99.99% Ag, Coloured		
Silver content:	31.39 g, 1.01 tr oz		
Weight:	31.39 g	**Edge:**	Reeded
Diameter:	38 mm	**Die Axis:**	↑↑
Thickness:	N/A	**Finish:**	Proof
Case of Issue:	Maroon clamshell with black beauty box, COA		

DATE	DESCRIPTION	RCM ITEM #	MINTAGE	ISSUE PRICE	FINISH	PR-69	PR-70
2017	Canoe to Tranquil Times	161911	4,500	124.95	Proof	125.	—

TWENTY DOLLARS, A PLATINUM CELEBRATION, 2017.

On November 20, 2017, Her Majesty Queen Elizabeth II and His Royal Highness Prince Philip, Duke of Edinburgh, celebrated their 70th wedding anniversary. The Royal Canadian Mint marked this occasion with a special keepsake coin that will be prized by royalty watchers, historians, collectors and art connoisseurs alike.

Designers and Engravers:			
Obv.:	Susanna Blunt		
Rev.:	Derek Wicks		
Composition:	99.99% Ag		
Silver content:	31.39 g, 1.01 tr oz		
Weight:	31.39 g	**Edge:**	Reeded
Diameter:	38 mm	**Die Axis:**	↑↑
Thickness:	N/A	**Finish:**	Proof
Case of Issue:	Maroon clamshell with black beauty box, COA		

DATE	DESCRIPTION	RCM ITEM #	MINTAGE	ISSUE PRICE	FINISH	PR-69	PR-70
2017	A Platinum Celebration	163560	7,500	104.95	Proof	105.	—

CANADA'S COASTS SERIES

TWENTY DOLLARS, CANADA'S COASTS SERIES, 2017.

Follow the setting sun across each coin in the series – each sunset features its own disctinct colours.

| Common Obverse | Pacific Coast | Atlantic Coast | Arctic Coast |

Designers:

Obv.:	Susanna Blunt
Rev.:	Curtis Atwater
Composition:	99.99% Ag, Coloured
Weight:	31.39 g
Diameter:	38 mm
Thickness:	N/A
Case of Issue:	Maroon clamshell with black beauty box, COA

Engravers:

Obv.:	Susan Taylor
Rev.:	RCM Staff
Silver content:	31.39 g, 1.01 tr oz
Edge:	Reeded
Die Axis:	↑↑
Finish:	Proof

DATE	DESCRIPTION	RCM ITEM #	MINTAGE	ISSUE PRICE	FINISH	PR-69	PR-70
2017	Pacific Coast	161310	7,500	109.95	Proof	110.	—
2017	Atlantic Coast	161321	7,500	109.95	Proof	110.	—
2017	Arctic Coast	162373	7,500	109.95	Proof	110.	—

TWENTY DOLLARS, GILDED SILVER MAPLE LEAF (SHAPED), 2017.

Designers and Engravers:

Obv.:	Susanna Blunt, Susan Taylor		
Rev.:	Joel Kimmel		
Composition:	99.99% Ag, Selective gold plating		
Silver content:	31.39 g, 1.01 tr oz		
Weight:	31.39 g	Edge:	Plain
Diameter:	42 mm x 43 mm	Die Axis:	↑↑
Thickness:	N/A	Finish:	Proof
Case of Issue:	Maroon clamshefll with black beauty box, COA		

DATE	DESCRIPTION	RCM ITEM #	MINTAGE	ISSUE PRICE	FINISH	PR-69	PR-70
2017	Gilded Silver Maple Leaf	157268	10,000	161.95	Proof	160.	—

LOCOMOTIVES ACROSS CANADA SERIES

TWENTY DOLLARS, LOCOMOTIVES ACROSS CANADA, 2017.

Common Obverse	**The 4-4-0** **Des.: David A. Oram**	**RS-20** **Des.: John Mantha**	**GE ES44AC** **Des.: John Mantha**

Designers:
  Obv.:   Susanna Blunt
  Rev.:   See reverse illustrations
Composition: 99.99% Ag, Selective gold plating
Weight: 31.39 g
Diameter: 38 mm
Thickness: N/A
Case of Issue: Maroon clamshell with black beauty box, COA

Engravers:
  Obv.:   Susan Taylor
  Rev.:   RCM Staff
Silver content: 31.39 g, 1.01 tr oz
Edge: Reeded
Die Axis: ↑↑
Finish: Proof

DATE	DESCRIPTION	RCM ITEM #	MINTAGE	ISSUE PRICE	FINISH	PR-69	PR-70
2017	Locomotives Across Canada: The 4-4-0	154858	7,500	112.95	Proof	115.	—
2017	Locomotives Across Canada: RS 20	155136	7,500	112.95	Proof	115.	—
2017	Locomotives Across Canada: GE ES44AC	155138	7,500	112.95	Proof	115.	—

BEJEWELED BUGS SERIES

TWENTY DOLLARS, BEJEWELED BUGS, 2017.

Common Obverse	**Bejeweled Bugs: Butterfly**	**Bejeweled Bugs: Bee**

Designers:
  Obv.:   Susanna Blunt
  Rev.:   Jori van der Linde
Composition: 99.99% Ag
Weight: 31.39 g
Diameter: 38.0 mm
Thickness: N/A
Case of Issue: Maroon clamshell with black beauty box, COA.

Engravers:
  Obv.:   Susan Taylor
  Rev.:   RCM Staff
Silver content: 31.39 g, 1.01 tr oz
Edge: Reeded
Die Axis: ↑↑
Finish: Proof

DATE	DESCRIPTION	RCM ITEM #	MINTAGE	ISSUE PRICE	FINISH	PR-69	PR-70
2017	Bejeweled Bugs: Butterfly	161986	4,000	174.95	Proof	175.	—
2017	Bejeweled Bugs: Bee	162253	4,000	174.95	Proof	175.	—

TWENTY DOLLARS, HOT AIR BALLOONS, 2017.

Designers and Engravers:

Obv.:	Susanna Blunt
Rev.:	Calder Moore
Composition:	99.99% Ag
Silver content:	31.82 g, 1.02 tr oz
Weight:	31.82 g
Diameter:	45 long x 33 wide mm
Thickness:	N/A
Edge:	Interrupted Reeding
Die Axis:	↑↑
Finish:	Proof
Case of Issue:	Maroon clamshell with black beauty box, COA

DATE	DESCRIPTION	RCM ITEM #	MINTAGE	ISSUE PRICE	FINISH	PR-69	PR-70
2017	Hot Air Balloons	161098	5,000	114.95	Proof	100.	—

TWENTY DOLLARS, PUZZLE COIN, CANADA 150, 2017.

Like a puzzle, Confederation came together piece by piece, every part clicking into place over time, the end result far greater than the sum of its parts. Diverse geographies, natural wonders and resources coming together from coast to coast to coast. A multitude of traditions, languages, and skills blurring distinct cultural lines. History may have recorded the beginning of Confederation 150 years ago, but for today's citizens, Canada can begin anywhere on this nation's ever-evolving continuum. This puzzle coin is an outstanding, first-ever achievement at the Mint, and a unique portrait of Canada that will be the highlight of the most distinctive collections.

Each piece of the puzzle has a face value of $50 (central coin) and $20 (each of the jigsaw pieces). See page 383 for the $50

Designers and Engravers:

Obv.:	Susanna Blunt
Rev.:	Cathy Bursey-Sabourin
Composition:	99.99% Ag, Selective gold plating, coloured
Silver content:	502.47 g, 16.16 tr oz
Weight:	502.47 g (complete puzzle set)
Diameter:	123.7 mm
Finished Size:	184 mm x 184 mm
Thickness:	N/A
Edge:	Interrupted Reeding
Die Axis:	↑↑
Finish:	Proof
Case of Issue:	Wood case with black beauty box, COA

DATE	DESCRIPTION	RCM ITEM #	MINTAGE	ISSUE PRICE	FINISH	PR-69	PR-70
2017	Puzzle Coin, Canada 150		800	1,867	Proof	2,200.	—

Note: This coin was only sold as a complete set of 14 puzzle pieces, plus a central coin.

TWENTY DOLLARS, 100TH ANNIVERSARY OF THE TORONTO MAPLE LEAFS®, 2017.

Designers and Engravers:

Obv.:	Susanna Blunt		
Rev.:	Steven Rosati		
Composition:	99.99% Ag		
Silver content:	31.39 g, 1.01 tr oz		
Weight:	31.39 g	**Edge:**	Reeded
Diameter:	38 mm	**Die Axis:**	↑↑
Thickness:	N/A	**Finish:**	Proof
Case of Issue:	Maroon clamshell with black beauty box, COA		

DATE	DESCRIPTION	RCM ITEM #	MINTAGE	ISSUE PRICE	FINISH	PR-69	PR-70
2017	100th Ann. Toronto Maple Leafs®	162085	15,000	119.95	Proof	120.	—

TWENTY DOLLARS, CANADA: PROTECTING OUR FUTURE, 2017.

Designers and Engravers:

Obv.:	Susanna Blunt		
Rev.:	Corrine Hunt		
Composition:	99.99% Ag, Hologram		
Silver content:	31.39 g, 1.01 tr oz		
Weight:	31.39 g	**Edge:**	Reeded
Diameter:	38 mm	**Die Axis:**	↑↑
Thickness:	N/A	**Finish:**	Proof
Case of Issue:	Maroon clamshell with black beauty box, COA		

DATE	DESCRIPTION	RCM ITEM #	MINTAGE	ISSUE PRICE	FINISH	PR-69	PR-70
2017	Canada: Protecting Our Future	162222	6,000	114.95	Proof	115.	—

THREE-DIMENSIONAL SERIES

TWENTY DOLLARS, THREE-DIMENSIONAL, 2017-2018.

Common Obverse	3-D Breaching Whale	3-D Leaping Cougar	3-D Approaching Canada Goose

Designers:

Obv.:	Susanna Blunt
Rev.:	Matt Bowen
Composition:	99.99% Ag, Coloured
Weight:	31.39 g
Diameter:	38 mm
Thickness:	N/A
Case of Issue:	Maroon clamshell with black beauty box, COA

Engravers:

Obv.:	Susan Taylor
Silver content:	31.39 g, 1.01 tr oz
Edge:	Reeded
Die Axis:	↑↑
Finish:	Proof

DATE	DESCRIPTION	RCM ITEM #	QUANTITY SOLD	ISSUE PRICE	FINISH	PR-69	PR-70
2017	Three-Dimensional Breaching Whale	156549	4,657	117.95	Proof	100.	—
2017	Three-Dimensional Leaping Cougar	160349	6,000	117.95	Proof	100.	—
2018	Three-Dimensional Approaching Canada Goose	161712	6,000	117.95	Proof	120.	—

NATURE'S IMPRESSIONS SERIES

TWENTY DOLLARS, NATURE'S IMPRESSIONS, 2017-2018.

Striking edge patterning features animal prints that are carefully engraved all along the coin's edge in a continuous pattern — a creative tie-in to the reverse image itself.

| Common Obverse | Woodland Caribou | Polar Bear | Wolf |

Designers:
- Obv.: Susanna Blunt
- Rev.: Claudio D'Angelo

Composition: 99.99% Ag
Weight: 31.39 g
Diameter: 38.0 mm
Thickness: N/A
Case of Issue: Maroon clamshell with custom beauty box. COA.

Engravers:
- Obv.: Susan Taylor
- Rev.: RCM Staff

Silver content: 31.39 g, 1.01 tr oz
Edge: Plain with edge pattern
Die Axis: ↑↑
Finish: Proof

DATE	DESCRIPTION	RCM ITEM #	QUANTITY SOLD	ISSUE PRICE	FINISH	PR-69	PR-70
2017	Nature's Impressions: Woodland Caribou	151652	2,696	102.95	Proof	100.	—
2017	Nature's Impressions: Polar Bear	154411	503	102.95	Proof	100.	—
2018	Nature's Impressions: Wolf	164846	5,500	104.95	Proof	105.	—

ANCIENT CANADA SERIES

TWENTY DOLLARS, ANCIENT CANADA, 2017-2018.

Millions of years ago, the Canadian landscape was teeming with prehistoric species whose remains lie in the rocks that bridge our era with theirs. This is Ancient Canada! Through unique striking techniques and an antique finish, takea closer look at life before us through its depiction of the fossilized remains.

| Common Obverse | Image based on fossil specimen TMP 1995.110.1 curated at the Royal Tyrrell Museum | Image based on fossil specimen TMP 1995.110.1 curated at the Royal Tyrrell Museum | Image based on fossil specimen curated at the Royal Tyrrell Museum |

Designers:
- Obv.: Susanna Blunt
- Rev.: See reverse illustration

Composition: 99.99% Ag
Weight: 31.39 g
Diameter: 38 mm (approx.)
Thickness: N/A
Case of Issue: Floating frame with black beaty box.

Engravers:
- Obv.: Susan Taylor
- Rev.: RCM Staff

Silver content: 31.39 g, 1.02 tr oz
Edge: Plain
Die Axis: ↑↑
Finish: Antique

TWENTY DOLLARS, ANCIENT CANADA, 2017-2018, PRICING PANEL.

DATE	DESCRIPTION	RCM ITEM #	MINTAGE	ISSUE PRICE	FINISH	PR-69	PR-70
2017	Ancient Canada: *Ornithomimus*	154259	5,500	134.95	Antique	135.	—
2017	Ancient Canada: *Ogygopsis*	154260	5,500	134.95	Antique	135.	—
2018	Ancient Canada: *Gorgosaurus*	163382	5,500	134.95	Antique	135.	—

CANADIAN HONOURS SERIES

TWENTY DOLLARS, CANADIAN HONOURS, 2017-2018.

A 5-coin series explores the highest honours in Canada's Honours System.

Common Obverse

Designers:
Obv.: Susanna Blunt
Rev.: Various artists
Composition: 99.99% Ag, Coloured
Silver content: 31.83 g, 1.02 tr oz
Weight: 31.83 g
Diameter: 40 mm
Thickness: N/A
Case of Issue: Maroon clamshell with black beauty box, COA

Engravers:
Obv.: Susan Taylor

Edge: Reeded
Die Axis: ↑↑
Finish: Proof

Sacrifice Medal	45th Anniversary of the Order of Military Merit	50th Anniversary of the Order of Canada	45th Anniversary of the Cross of Valour	25th Anniversary of the Star of Military Valour

DATE	DESCRIPTION	RCM ITEM #	MINTAGE	ISSUE PRICE	FINISH	PR-69	PR-70
2017	Canadian Honours: Sacrifice Medal	157648	5,500	109.95	Proof	110.	—
2017	Canadian Honours: 45th Anniversary of the Order of the Military Merit	157649	5,500	109.95	Proof	110.	—
2017	Canadian Honours 50th Anniversary of the Order of Canada	157647	5,500	109.95	Proof	110.	—
2017	Canadian Honours 45th Anniversary of the Cross of Valour	162045	5,500	109.95	Proof	110.	—
2018	Canadian Honours 25th Anniversary of the Star of Military Valour	164525	5,500	109.95	Proof	110.	—

MOTHER NATURE'S MAGNIFICATION SERIES

TWENTY DOLLARS, MOTHER NATURE'S MAGNIFICATION, 2017-2018.

Common Obverse	Beauty Under The Sun Des.: Alexandra Lefort	Morning Dew Des.: Margaret Best

Designers:
Obv.:	Susanna Blunt
Rev.:	See reverse illustrations
Composition:	99.99% Ag, Coloured
Weight:	31.39 g
Diameter:	38 mm
Thickness:	N/A
Case of Issue:	Maroon clamshell with black beauty box, COA

Engravers:
Obv.:	Susan Taylor
Rev.:	RCM Staff
Silver content:	31.39 g, 1.01 tr oz
Edge:	Reeded
Die Axis:	↑↑
Finish:	Proof

DATE	DESCRIPTION	RCM ITEM #	MINTAGE	ISSUE PRICE	FINISH	PR-69	PR-70
2017	Beauty Under The Sun	159265	7,500	106.95	Proof	110.	—
2018	Morning Dew	162163	7,500	106.95	Proof	100.	—

FROM SEA TO SEA TO SEA SERIES

TWENTY DOLLARS, FROM SEA TO SEA TO SEA, 2017-2018.

Canada's national motto pays tribute to the oceans that border our land, for these waters — and the life within them — have long nurtured, challenged and fascinated Canadians. The rich diversity of life in the Pacific, Arctic and Atlantic Oceans are an important part of Canada's maritime heritage, and is at the heart of a three-coin series.

Common Obverse	Atlantic Starfish	Pacific Salmon	Arctic Beluga Whale

Designers:
Obv.:	Susanna Blunt
Rev.:	Tony Bianca
Composition:	99.99% Ag, Selective gold plating
Weight:	31.39 g
Diameter:	38 mm
Thickness:	N/A
Case of Issue:	Maroon clamshell with black beauty box, COA.

Engravers:
Obv.:	Susan Taylor
Rev.:	RCM Staff
Silver content:	31.39 g, 1.01 tr oz
Edge:	Reeded
Die Axis:	↑↑
Finish:	Proof

DATE	DESCRIPTION	RCM ITEM #	MINTAGE	ISSUE PRICE	FINISH	PR-69	PR-70
2017	From Sea to Sea to Sea: Atlantic Starfish	154620	7,500	112.95	Proof	115.	—
2017	From Sea to Sea to Sea: Pacific Salmon	155336	7,500	112.95	Proof	115.	—
2018	From Sea to Sea to Sea: Arctic Beluga Whale	156967	7,500	112.95	Proof	115.	—

TWENTY DOLLARS, BEST WISHES ON YOUR WEDDING DAY!, 2017-2019.

Selective pink gold plating brings to life the intricately patterned heart on the reverse, as well as the effigy of Her Majesty Queen Elizabeth II on the obverse.

| Common Obverse | 2017 Best Wishes | 2018 Best Wishes | 2019 Best Wishes |

Designers:
Obv.: Susanna Blunt
Rev.: Sylvie Daigneault
Composition: 99.99% Ag, Coloured
Weight: 31.83 g
Diameter: 40 mm
Thickness: N/A
Case of Issue: Premium graphic box, COA.

Engravers:
Obv.: Susan Taylor
Rev.: RCM Staff
Silver content: 31.83 g, 1.02 tr oz
Edge: Reeded
Die Axis: ↑↑
Finish: Proof

DATE	DESCRIPTION	RCM ITEM #	QUANTITY SOLD	ISSUE PRICE	FINISH	PR-69	PR-70
2017	Best Wishes On Your Wedding Day!	157580	10,000	112.95	Proof	110.	—
2018	Best Wishes On Your Wedding Day!	163731	10,000	114.95	Proof	115.	—
2019	Best Wishes On Your Wedding Day!	170404	10,000	109.95	Proof	110.	—

NOCTURNAL BY NATURE SERIES

TWENTY DOLLARS, NOCTURNAL BY NATURE, 2017-2019.

An innovative RCM FIRST: The first-time use of black rhodium plating, one of Earth's rarest precious metals, lends itself perfectly to recreating the dark night sky, yet allows the moon's uniquely frosted finish to shine through.

| Common Obverse | The Barn Owl | The Little Brown Bat | The Howling Wolf | Cunning Cougar |
| | Des.: Jamie Desrochers | Des.: Calder Moore | Des.:Claude Thivierge | Des.: Tony Bianco |

Designers:
Obv.: Susanna Blunt
Rev.: See reverse illustration
Composition: 99.99% Ag
Weight: 31.39 g
Diameter: 38 mm
Thickness: N/A
Case of Issue: Maroon clamshell with black beauty box, COA.

Engravers:
Obv.: Susan Taylor
Rev.: RCM Staff
Silver content: 31.39 g, 1.02 tr oz
Edge: Plain
Die Axis: ↑↑
Finish: Matte Proof

DATE	DESCRIPTION	RCM ITEM #	MINTAGE	ISSUE PRICE	FINISH	PR-69	PR-70
2017	Nocturnal By Nature: The Barn Owl	156565	7,000	119.95	Matte Proof	120.	—
2017	Nocturnal By Nature: The Little Brown Bat	161270	7,000	119.95	Matte Proof	120.	—
2018	Nocturnal By Nature: The Howling Wolf	164652	7,000	119.95	Matte Proof	120.	—
2019	Nocturnal By Nature: Cunning Cougar	167127	7,000	119.95	Matte Proof	120.	—

TWENTY DOLLARS, ICE CRYSTALS, 2018.

Designers and Engravers:

Obv.:	Susanna Blunt
Rev.:	Don Komarechka

Composition:	99.99% Ag		
Silver content:	31.39 g, 1.01 tr oz		
Weight:	31.39 g	Edge:	Reeded
Diameter:	38 mm	Die Axis:	↑↑
Thickness:	N/A	Finish:	Proof
Case of Issue:	Maroon clamshell with black beauty box, COA		

DATE	DESCRIPTION	RCM ITEM #	MINTAGE	ISSUE PRICE	FINISH	PR-69	PR-70
2018	Ice Crystals	162196	6,000	113.95	Proof	115.	—

TWENTY DOLLARS, TREE OF LIFE, 2018.

Designers and Engravers:

Obv.:	Susanna Blunt
Rev.:	Steve Hepburn

Composition:	99.99% Ag		
Silver content:	31.39 g, 1.01 tr oz		
Weight:	31.39 g	Edge:	Reeded
Diameter:	38 mm	Die Axis:	↑↑
Thickness:	N/A	Finish:	Proof
Case of Issue:	Maroon clamshell with black beauty box, COA		

DATE	DESCRIPTION	RCM ITEM #	MINTAGE	ISSUE PRICE	FINISH	PR-69	PR-70
2018	Tree of Life	162055	6,500	119.95	Proof	120.	—

TWENTY DOLLARS, HOLIDAY REINDEER, 2018.

Designers and Engravers:

Obv.:	Susanna Blunt
Rev.:	Anna Bucciarelli

Composition:	99.99% Ag		
Silver content:	31.39 g, 1.01 tr oz		
Weight:	31.39 g	Edge:	Reeded
Diameter:	38 mm	Die Axis:	↑↑
Thickness:	N/A	Finish:	Proof
Case of Issue:	Maroon clamshell with black beauty box, COA		

DATE	DESCRIPTION	RCM ITEM #	MINTAGE	ISSUE PRICE	FINISH	PR-69	PR-70
2018	Holiday Reindeer	161737	5,000	152.95	Proof	155.	—

TWENTY DOLLARS, CANADA'S ICONIC INUKSHUK: GUIDING THE WAY, 2018.

Designers and Engravers:

Obv.:	Susanna Blunt
Rev.:	Tony Bianco

Composition:	99.99% Ag, Reverse gold plating		
Silver content:	31.39 g, 1.01 tr oz		
Weight:	31.39 g	Edge:	Reeded
Diameter:	38 mm	Die Axis:	↑↑
Thickness:	N/A	Finish:	Proof
Case of Issue:	Maroon clamshell with black beauty box, COA		

DATE	DESCRIPTION	RCM ITEM #	MINTAGE	ISSUE PRICE	FINISH	PR-69	PR-70
2018	Canada's Iconic Inukshuk: Guiding The Way	164640	5,000	114.95	Proof	115.	—

TWENTY DOLLARS, LUCKY CLOVER, 2018.

Designers and Engravers:
Obv.:	Susanna Blunt
Rev.:	Lisa Thomson Khan

Composition:	99.99% Ag		
Silver content:	31.39 g, 1.01 tr oz		
Weight:	31.39 g	**Edge:**	Reeded
Diameter:	38 mm	**Die Axis:**	↑↑
Thickness:	N/A	**Finish:**	Proof
Case of Issue:	Maroon clamshell with black beauty box, COA		

DATE	DESCRIPTION	RCM ITEM #	MINTAGE	ISSUE PRICE	FINISH	PR-69	PR-70
2018	Lucky Clover	164392	6,500	104.95	Proof	105.	—

NORSE FIGUREHEADS SERIES

TWENTY DOLLARS, NORSE FIGUREHEADS, 2018.

From about AD 800 to 1050, they were the masters of the seas whose voyages defined trade, discovery and conquest in the Viking Age, and whose seafaring abilities led them to Canada's eastern shore. Step back in time with a three-coin series that re-imagines the elaborate figureheads at the prow of legendary Viking longships, which embodied Norse craftsmanship and maritime supremacy in their time.

Common Obverse

Norse Figureheads:
Northern Fury
Des.: Patrick Bélanger

Norse Figureheads:
Viking Voyage
Des.: Neil Hamelin

Norse Figureheads:
The Dragon's Sail
Des.: Jean-Pierre Vallée

Designers:		**Engravers:**	
Obv.:	Susanna Blunt	Obv.:	Susan Taylor
Rev.:	See reverse illustrations	Rev.:	RCM Staff
Composition:	99.99% Ag,	**Silver content:**	31.39 g, 1.01 tr oz
Weight:	31.39 g	**Edge:**	Reeded
Diameter:	38 mm	**Die Axis:**	↑↑
Thickness:	N/A	**Finish:**	Proof
Case of Issue:	Maroon clamshell with a standard black beauty box, COA.		

DATE	DESCRIPTION	RCM ITEM #	MINTAGE	ISSUE PRICE	FINISH	PR-69	PR-70
2018	Norse Figureheads: Northern Fury	164708	6,000	104.95	Proof	105.	—
2018	Norse Figureheads: Viking Voyage	165352	6,000	104.95	Proof	105.	—
2018	Norse Figureheads: The Dragon's Sail	165041	6,000	104.95	Proof	105.	—

TWENTY DOLLARS, ROYAL PORTRAIT, 2018.

The Royal Canadian Mint proudly presents a picture-perfect coin that is both a birthday celebration for His Royal Highness the Prince of Wales and a touching tribute to Her Majesty as monarch and matriarch. The photograph reproduced on the reverse (©Cecil Beaton/Victoria and Albert Museum, London/Londres) was made possible by a colour application over engraved relief, which adds textural elements to an already captivating image taken in December 1948 at Buckingham Palace.

Designers and Engravers:	
Obv.:	Susanna Blunt
Rev.:	Maurice Gervais
Composition:	99.99% Ag
Silver content:	31.39 g, 1.01 tr oz
Weight:	31.39 g
Diameter:	38 mm
Thickness:	N/A
Case of Issue:	Maroon clamshell with black beauty box, COA

	Edge:	Reeded
	Die Axis:	↑↑
	Finish:	Proof

DATE	DESCRIPTION	RCM ITEM #	MINTAGE	ISSUE PRICE	FINISH	PR-69	PR-70
2018	Royal Portrait	165069	7,500	109.95	Proof	110.	—

MAJESTIC WILDLIFE SERIES

TWENTY DOLLARS, MAJESTIC WILDLIFE, 2018.

The Majestic Wildlife three-coin series will fascinate collectors with a view of Canada's most captivating wildlife.

Common Obverse

Majestic Wildlife:
Courageous Cougar
Des.: Pierre Leduc

Majestic Wildlife:
Wandering White-Tailed Deer
Des.: Maurade Baynton

Majestic Wildlife:
Mettlesome Mountain Goat
Des.: Pierre Leduc

Designers:			Engravers:	
Obv.:	Susanna Blunt		Obv.:	Susan Taylor
Rev.:	See reverse illustrations		Rev.:	RCM Staff
Composition:	99.99% Ag,			
Silver content:	31.39 g, 1.01 tr oz			
Weight:	31.39 g		Edge:	Reeded
Diameter:	38 mm		Die Axis:	↑↑
Thickness:	N/A		Finish:	Proof
Case of Issue:	Maroon clamshell with a standard black beauty box, COA.			

DATE	DESCRIPTION	RCM ITEM #	MINTAGE	ISSUE PRICE	FINISH	PR-69	PR-70
2018	Majestic Wildlife: Courageous Cougar	164726	6,000	104.95	Proof	105.	—
2018	Majestic Wildlife: Wandering White-Tailed Deer	165627	6,000	104.95	Proof	105.	—
2018	Majestic Wildlife: Mettlesome Mountain Goat	165261	6,000	104.95	Proof	105.	—

TWENTY DOLLARS, CANADA'S UNEXPLAINED PHENOMENA: THE FALCON LAKE INCIDENT, 2018.

The Falcon Lake Incident is one of Canada's most well known UFO encounters, and a fascinating mystery that is still unexplained! With an unusally shaped contour that hints at an otherworldly theme, this ovoid coin recounts the Falcon Lake Incident in vivid colour, with black-light activated features that add a preternatural glow to the unknown craft.

Designers and Engravers:
Obv.:	Susanna Blunt
Rev.:	Joel Kimmel
Composition:	99.99% Ag
Silver content:	31.82 g, 1.02 tr oz
Weight:	31.82 g
Diameter:	45 long x 22 wide mm
Thickness:	N/A
Edge:	Interrupted reeding
Die Axis:	↑↑
Finish:	Proof
Case of Issue:	Maroon clamshell with black beauty box, COA

DATE	DESCRIPTION	RCM ITEM #	MINTAGE	ISSUE PRICE	FINISH	PR-69	PR-70
2018	Canada's Unexplained Phenomena: The Falcon Lake Incident	165618	4,000	129.95	Proof	350.	—

GEOMETRIC FAUNA SERIES

TWENTY DOLLARS, GEOMETRIC FAUNA , 2018.

Each of these beloved icons of the Canadian wilderness is comprised of carefully positioned polygon shapes that are characteristic of low poly art, before merging with a more true-to-life depiction.

Common Obverse	Grey Wolves	Snowy Owls	Orcas

Designers:
		Engravers:	
Obv.:	Susanna Blunt	Obv.:	Susan Taylor
Rev.:	Claude Thivierge		

Composition:	99.99% Ag
Silver content:	31.83 g, 1.02 tr oz
Weight:	31.83 g
Diameter:	38 mm
Thickness:	N/A
Case of Issue:	Maroon clamshell with black beauty box, COA

Edge:	Reeded
Die Axis:	↑↑
Finish:	Proof

DATE	DESCRIPTION	RCM ITEM #	MINTAGE	ISSUE PRICE	FINISH	PR-69	PR-70
2018	Geometric Fauna: Grey Wolves	165437	6,000	104.95	Proof	105.	—
2018	Geometric Fauna: Snowy Owls	165470	6,000	104.95	Proof	105.	—
2018	Geometric Fauna: Orcas	165707	6,000	104.95	Proof	105.	—

FROZEN IN TIME SERIES

TWENTY DOLLARS, FROZEN IN ICE, 2018.

Frozen In Ice: a colourful window in time! Amazing Ice Age species that once roamed North America — in detailed engraving and selective colour under a frosted chunk of "ice."

Common Obverse

Woolly Mammoth

Scimitar Sabretooth Cat

Designers:		**Engravers:**	
Obv.:	Susanna Blunt	Obv.:	Susan Taylor
Rev.:	Glen Loates		
Composition:	99.99% Ag, Selective colour		
Silver content:	31.39 g, 1.01 tr oz		
Weight:	31.39 g	**Edge:**	Reeded
Diameter:	38 mm	**Die Axis:**	↑↑
Thickness:	N/A	**Finish:**	Proof
Case of Issue:	Maroon clamshell with black beauty box, COA		

DATE	DESCRIPTION	RCM ITEM #	MINTAGE	ISSUE PRICE	FINISH	PR-69	PR-70
2018	Frozen In Ice — Woolly Mammoth	164818	5,000	109.95	Proof	110.	—
2018	Frozen In Ice — Scimitar Sabretooth Cat	164948	5,000	109.95	Proof	110.	—

TWENTY DOLLARS, QUEEN ELIZABETH II's MAPLE LEAVES BROOCH, 2018.

During the Queen's most recent visit in 2010, she wore a maple leaves brooch that was originally presented to her grandmother, Queen Mary (then Duchess) during the royal tour in 1901. The Queen was inspired to wear it as an outward expression of the warmth she feels for her second home — the home of the maple leaf. This beautiful coin returns that gesture with an exquiite reproduction of the brooch she wore.

Designers and Engravers:			
Obv.:	Susanna Blunt, Susan Taylor		
Rev.:	Maurade Baynton		
Composition:	99.99% Ag, Selective colour		
	with Swarovski® pearl		
Silver content:	31.39 g, 1.01 tr oz		
Weight:	31.39 g	**Edge:**	Reeded
Diameter:	38 mm	**Die Axis:**	↑↑
Thickness:	N/A	**Finish:**	Proof
Case of Issue:	Maroon clamshell with black beauty box, COA		

DATE	DESCRIPTION	RCM ITEM #	MINTAGE	ISSUE PRICE	FINISH	PR-69	PR-70
2018	Queen Elizabeth II's Maple Leaves Brooch	166554	5,500	119.95	Proof	120.	—

TWENTY DOLLARS, A MODERN ALLEGORY: BOREALIA, 2018.

The symbolic figurehead, Borealia, is a modern take on a classic allegory, one that represents the collective spirit of Canadians in today's world: hopeful and steady in our resolve, as we rise to meet the challenges that lie ahead.

Designers and Engravers:

Obv.:	Susanna Blunt, Susan Taylor
Rev.:	Rebecca Yanovskaya
Composition:	99.99% Ag, Gold plating
Silver content:	31.39 g, 1.01 tr oz
Weight:	31.39 g **Edge:** Reeded
Diameter:	38 mm **Die Axis:** ↑↑
Thickness:	N/A **Finish:** Proof
Case of Issue:	Maroon clamshell with black beauty box, COA

DATE	DESCRIPTION	RCM ITEM #	MINTAGE	ISSUE PRICE	FINISH	PR-69	PR-70
2018	A Modern Allegory: Borealia	165933	5,000	114.95	Proof	115.	—

TWENTY DOLLARS, CAPTAIN CANUCK, 2018.

Captain Canuck personifies the spirit of Canadians by embodying self-sacrifice, determination and integrity – and all with a full dose of humility and compassion.

Designers and Engravers:

Obv.:	Susanna Blunt, Susan Taylor
Rev.:	Richard Comely
Composition:	99.99% Ag, Selective colour
Silver content:	31.56 g, 1.01 tr oz
Weight:	31.56 g
Diameter:	49.80 mm x 28.60 mm
Die Axis:	↑↑ **Edge:** Plain
Thickness:	N/A **Finish:** Proof
Case of Issue:	Maroon clamshell with graphic beauty box, COA

DATE	DESCRIPTION	RCM ITEM #	MINTAGE	ISSUE PRICE	FINISH	PR-69	PR-70
2018	Captain Canuck	164892	3,500	119.95	Proof	120.	—

TWENTY DOLLARS, THE ROYAL WEDDING OF HRH PRINCE HARRY AND MEGHAN MARKLE, 2018.

Canada's official Royal Wedding commemorative coin presents a sparkling congratulatory message on its reverse, where the portait of HRH Prince Henry (Harry) and Ms. Meghan Markle is accompanied by genuine Swarovski® crystals that represent the royal engagement ring.

Designers and Engravers:

Obv.:	Susanna Blunt, Susan Taylor
Rev.:	Joel Kimmel
Composition:	99.99% Ag, Swarovski® crystals
Silver content:	31.39 g, 1.01 tr oz
Weight:	31.39 g **Edge:** Reeded
Diameter:	38 mm **Die Axis:** ↑↑
Thickness:	N/A **Finish:** Proof
Case of Issue:	Maroon clamshell with graphic beauty box, COA

DATE	DESCRIPTION	RCM ITEM #	MINTAGE	ISSUE PRICE	FINISH	PR-69	PR-70
2018	The Royal Wedding of HRH Prince Henry and Meghan Markle	168569	15,000	104.95	Proof	105.	—

FIRST WORLD WAR ALLIED FORCES SERIES

The *First World War: Allies* series reflects on the collaborative efforst of a republic, an empire and two of her dominions — four of the many allies bound by durty and heroism throughout the war and during the Hundred Days Offensive.

TWENTY DOLLARS, FIRST WORLD WAR ALLIED FORCES, 2018.

Common Obverse	Canada	Newfoundland	France	Great Britain

Designers:
    Obv.:   Susanna Blunt
    Rev.:   Pandora Young
Composition: 99.99% Ag, Selective gold plating
Weight: 31.39 g
Diameter: 38 mm
Thickness: N/A
Case of Issue: Maroon clamshell with custom beauty box, COA.

Engravers:
    Obv.:   Susan Taylor

Silver content: 31.39 g, 1.01 tr oz
Edge: Reeded
Die Axis: ↑↑
Finish: Proof

DATE	DESCRIPTION	RCM ITEM #	MINTAGE	ISSUE PRICE	FINISH	PR-69	PR-70
2018	First World War Allied Forces: Canada	166673	5,000	114.95	Proof	115.	—
2018	First World War Allied Forces: Newfoundland	166174	5,000	114.95	Proof	115.	—
2018	First World War Allied Forces: France	166137	5,000	114.95	Proof	115.	—
2018	First World War Allied Forces: Great Britain	166722	5,000	114.95	Proof	115.	—

TWENTY DOLLARS, MAPLE TREE TUNNEL, 2018.

Designers and Engravers:
    Obv.:   Susanna Blunt, Susan Taylor
    Rev.:   Jan Poynter
Composition: 99.99% Ag, Selective colour
Silver content: 31.39 g, 1.01 tr oz
Weight: 31.39 g   Edge: Reeded
Diameter: 38 mm   Die Axis: ↑↑
Thickness: N/A   Finish: Proof
Case of Issue: Maroon clamshell with black beauty box, COA

DATE	DESCRIPTION	RCM ITEM #	MINTAGE	ISSUE PRICE	FINISH	PR-69	PR-70
2018	Maple Tree Tunnel	166662	6,000	119.95	Proof	120.	—

TWENTY DOLLARS, 150TH ANNIVERSY OF THE ROYAL ASTRONIMICAL SOCIETY OF CANADA, 2018.

Designers and Engravers:
    Obv.:   Susanna Blunt, Susan Taylor
    Rev.:   Alexandra Lefort
Composition: 99.99% Ag, Selective colour
Silver content: 31.39 g, 1.01 tr oz
Weight: 31.39 g   Edge: Reeded
Diameter: 38 mm   Die Axis: ↑↑
Thickness: N/A   Finish: Proof
Case of Issue: Maroon clamshell with black beauty box, COA

DATE	DESCRIPTION	RCM ITEM #	MINTAGE	ISSUE PRICE	FINISH	PR-69	PR-70
2018	150th Anniversary of the Royal Astronomical Society of Canada	167044	5,500	149.95	Proof	150.	—

CANADIAN MOSAICS SERIES

TWENTY DOLLARS, CANADIAN MOSAICS, 2018.

Common Obverse

Canadian Mosaics: Caribou

Canadian Mosaics: Grizzly Bear

Canadian Mosaics: Cougar

Designers:
Obv.: Susanna Blunt
Rev.: Jori van der Linde
Composition: 99.99% Ag,
Silver content: 31.39 g, 1.01 tr oz
Weight: 31.39 g
Diameter: 38 mm
Thickness: N/A
Case of Issue: Maroon clamshell with a standard black beauty box, COA.

Engravers:
Obv.: Susan Taylor

Edge: Reeded
Die Axis: ↑↑
Finish: Proof

DATE	DESCRIPTION	RCM ITEM #	MINTAGE	ISSUE PRICE	FINISH	PR-69	PR-70
2018	Canadian Mosaics: Caribou	166294	6,000	104.95	Proof	105.	—
2018	Canadian Mosaics: Grizzly Bear	166641	6,000	104.95	Proof	105.	—
2018	Canadian Mosaics: Cougar	166642	6,000	104.95	Proof	105.	—

TWENTY DOLLARS, *STAR TREK™:, DEEP SPACE NINE™*, 2018.

Designers and Engravers:
Obv.: Susanna Blunt, Susan Taylor
Rev.: RCM Staff
Composition: 99.99% Ag
Silver content: 30.75 g, 0.989 tr oz
Weight: 30.75 g **Edge:** Plain
Diameter: 36.15 mm **Die Axis:** ↑↑
Thickness: N/A **Finish:** Proof
Case of Issue: Floating frame with black beaty box, COA

DATE	DESCRIPTION	RCM ITEM #	MINTAGE	ISSUE PRICE	FINISH	PR-69	PR-70
2018	Star Trek™: Deep Space Nine™	166548	4,500	149.95	Proof	150.	—

TWENTY DOLLARS, FOUR SEASONS OF THE MAPLE LEAF, 2018.

Designers and Engravers:
Obv.: Susanna Blunt, Susan Taylor
Rev.: Margaret Best
Composition: 99.99% Ag
Silver content: 31.82 g, 1.02 tr oz
Weight: 31.82 g
Diameter: 45 long x 33 wide mm
Thickness: N/A
Edge: Interrupted reeding
Die Axis: ↑↑
Finish: Proof
Case of Issue: Maroon clamshell with black beauty box, COA

DATE	DESCRIPTION	RCM ITEM #	MINTAGE	ISSUE PRICE	FINISH	PR-69	PR-70
2018	Four Seasons Of The Maple Leaf	167307	4,000	129.95	Proof	350.	—

TWENTY DOLLARS, A NATION'S METTLE: THE DIEPPE RAID, 2018.

Designers and Engravers:
Obv.:	Susanna Blunt, Susan Taylor
Rev.:	Lori McGaw

Composition: 99.99% Ag
Silver content: 31.39 g, 1.01 tr oz
Weight: 31.39 g **Edge:** Reeded
Diameter: 38 mm **Die Axis:** ↑↑
Thickness: N/A **Finish:** Proof
Case of Issue: Maroon clamshell with black beauty box, COA

DATE	DESCRIPTION	RCM ITEM #	MINTAGE	ISSUE PRICE	FINISH	PR-69	PR-70
2018	A Nation's Mettle: The Dieppe Raid	168084	5,000	94.95	Proof	95.	—

CANADIAN HISTORICAL STAMPS SERIES

TWENTY DOLLARS, CANADIAN HISTORICAL STAMPS, 2018-2019.

Designers:
Obv.:	Susanna Blunt
Rev.:	RCM Staff

Engravers:
Obv.:	Susan Taylor

Composition: 99.99% Ag, Selective colour
Silver content: 31.86 g, 1.02 tr oz
Weight: 31.86 g **Edge:** Reeded (mimic perforations)
Diameter: 51 mm x 30 mm **Die Axis:** ↑↑
Thickness: N/A **Finish:** Proof
Case of Issue: Maroon clamshell with a standard black beauty box, COA.

Parliament Building
1927 Confederation

Arrival of Cartier –Québec 1535

Coat of Arms and Flag
Special Delivery

DATE	DESCRIPTION	RCM ITEM #	MINTAGE	ISSUE PRICE	FINISH	PR-69	PR-70
2018	Parliament Buliding 1927 Confederation	168022	5,000	139.95	Proof	140.	—
2019	Arrival of Cartier — Québec 1535	168966	5,000	139.95	Proof	140.	—
2019	Coat of Arms and Flags Special Delivery	169809	5,000	139.95	Proof	140.	—

TWENTY DOLLARS, ICONIC MAPLE LEAVES, 2018.

Designers and Engravers:
Obv.:	Susanna Blunt, Susan Taylor
Rev.:	Stan Witten

Composition: 99.99% Ag
Silver content: 26.51 g, 0.85 tr oz
Weight: 26.51 g **Edge:** Plain
Diameter: 38 mm **Die Axis:** ↑↑
Thickness: N/A **Finish:** Proof
Case of Issue: Wooden box with graphic beauty box, COA

DATE	DESCRIPTION	RCM ITEM #	MINTAGE	ISSUE PRICE	FINISH	PR-69	PR-70
2018	Iconic Maple Leaves	167235	6,000	109.95	Proof	110.	—

Note: This coin wax exclusively sold to the Mint Master's Club Members only.

TWENTY DOLLARS, PUZZLE COIN, CONNECTING CANADIAN HISTORY (1866-1916), 2018.

This new 2018 puzzle coin set tells the story of a nation's character between 1866 and 1916 — from the eve of Confederation through the five decades that followed. The set consists of 14 individual coins that piece together to tell the story of the first half century of the Dominion of Canada.

Each piece of the puzzle has a face value of $50 (central coin) and $20 (each of the jigsaw pieces). See page 379 for the $50

Designers and Engravers:

Obv.:	Susanna Blunt
Rev.:	Tony Bianco
Composition:	99.99% Ag, Selective gold plating
Silver content:	502.47 g, 16.16 tr oz
Weight:	502.47 g (complete puzzle set)
Diameter:	123.7 mm **Die Axis:** ↑↑
Finished Size:	184 mm x 184 mm **Thickness:** N/A
Edge:	Interrupted Reeding **Finish:** Proof
Case of Issue:	Wood case with black beauty box, COA

DATE	DESCRIPTION	RCM ITEM #	MINTAGE	ISSUE PRICE	FINISH	PR-69	PR-70
2018	Connecting Canadian History (1866-1916)	167787	800	1,867	Proof	2,200.	—

Note: This coin was only sold as a complete set of 14 puzzle pieces, plus a central coin.

TWENTY DOLLARS, THE SINKING OF THE *S.S. PRINCESS SOPHIA*, 2018.

Designers and Engravers:

Obv.:	Susanna Blunt, Susan Taylor
Rev.:	Yves Bérubé
Composition:	99.99% Ag
Silver content:	31.39 g, 1.01 tr oz
Weight:	31.39 g **Edge:** Reeded
Diameter:	38 mm **Die Axis:** ↑↑
Thickness:	N/A **Finish:** Proof
Case of Issue:	Maroon clamshell with black beauty box, COA

DATE	DESCRIPTION	RCM ITEM #	MINTAGE	ISSUE PRICE	FINISH	PR-69	PR-70
2018	The Sinking of the *S.S. Princess Sophia*	167535	6,000	114.95	Proof	115.	—

TWENTY DOLLARS, THE 1908 SOVEREIGN 110TH ANNIVERSARY OF THE ROYAL CANADIAN MINT, 2018.

Designers and Engravers:

Obv.:	Susanna Blunt, Susan Taylor
Rev.:	RCM Staff
Composition:	99.99% Ag
Silver content:	31.39 g, 1.01 tr oz
Weight:	31.39 g **Edge:** Reeded
Diameter:	38 mm **Die Axis:** ↑↑
Thickness:	N/A **Finish:** Proof
Case of Issue:	Maroon clamshell with black beauty box, COA

DATE	DESCRIPTION	RCM ITEM #	MINTAGE	ISSUE PRICE	FINISH	PR-69	PR-70
2018	The 1908 Sovereign 110th Ann. of RCM	170491	5,000	114.95	Proof	115.	—

TWENTY DOLLARS, CANADIAN FLAG, 2018.

Designers and Engravers:
Obv.:	Susanna Blunt, Susan Taylor
Rev.:	Tony Bianco

Composition:	99.99% Ag		
Silver content:	31.39 g, 1.01 tr oz		
Weight:	31.39 g	Edge:	Reeded
Diameter:	38 mm	Die Axis:	↑↑
Thickness:	N/A	Finish:	Proof
Case of Issue:	Maroon clamshell with black beauty box, COA		

DATE	DESCRIPTION	RCM ITEM #	MINTAGE	ISSUE PRICE	FINISH	PR-69	PR-70
2018	Canadian Flag	168122	10,000	89.95	Proof	90.	—

TWENTY DOLLARS, SPARKLE OF THE HEART, 2019.

Designers and Engravers:
Obv.:	Susanna Blunt, Susan Taylor
Rev.:	Anna Bucciarelli

Composition:	99.99% Ag		
Silver content:	20.86 g, 0.67 tr oz		
Weight:	20.86 g	Edge:	Reeded
Diameter:	36 mm	Die Axis:	↑↑
Thickness:	N/A	Finish:	Proof
Case of Issue:	Maroon clamshell with black beauty box, COA		

DATE	DESCRIPTION	RCM ITEM #	MINTAGE	ISSUE PRICE	FINISH	PR-69	PR-70
2019	Sparkle Of The Heart	173814	750	699.95	Proof	700.	—

CANADIAN FAUNA SERIES

TWENTY DOLLARS, CANADIAN FAUNA, 2019.

Common Obverse	Canadian Fauna: The Polar Bear	Canadian Fauna: The Fox	Canadian Fauna: The Sea Otter

Designers:
Obv.:	Susanna Blunt
Rev.:	W. Allen Hancock

Composition:	99.99% Ag,
Silver content:	31.39 g, 1.01 tr oz
Weight:	31.39 g
Diameter:	38 mm
Thickness:	N/A
Case of Issue:	Maroon clamshell with a standard black beauty box, COA.

Engravers:
Obv.:	Susan Taylor

Edge:	Reeded
Die Axis:	↑↑
Finish:	Proof

DATE	DESCRIPTION	RCM ITEM #	MINTAGE	ISSUE PRICE	FINISH	PR-69	PR-70
2019	Canadian Fauna: The Polar Bear	170781	4,000	99.95	Proof	100.	—
2019	Canadian Fauna: The Fox	171450	4,000	99.95	Proof	100.	—
2019	Canadian Fauna: The Sea Otter	171451	4,000	99.95	Proof	100.	—

TWENTY DOLLARS, REFLECTIONS: BALD EAGLE, 2019.

Designers and Engravers:
Obv.: Susanna Blunt, Susan Taylor
Rev.: Julius Csotonyi
Composition: 99.99% Ag
Silver content: 31.39 g, 1.01 tr oz
Weight: 31.39 g   **Edge:** Reeded
Diameter: 38 mm   **Die Axis:** ↑↑
Thickness: N/A   **Finish:** Proof
Case of Issue: Maroon clamshell with black beauty box, COA

DATE	DESCRIPTION	RCM ITEM #	MINTAGE	ISSUE PRICE	FINISH	PR-69	PR-70
2019	Reflections: Bald Eagle	168219	4,000	119.95	Proof	120.	—

TWENTY DOLLARS, MYSTICAL SNOW DAY, 2019.

Designers and Engravers:
Obv.: Susanna Blunt, Susan Taylor
Rev.: Steve Hepburn
Composition: 99.99% Ag
Silver content: 31.39 g, 1.01 tr oz
Weight: 31.39 g   **Edge:** Reeded
Diameter: 38 mm   **Die Axis:** ↑↑
Thickness: N/A   **Finish:** Proof
Case of Issue: Maroon clamshell with black beauty box, COA

DATE	DESCRIPTION	RCM ITEM #	MINTAGE	ISSUE PRICE	FINISH	PR-69	PR-70
2019	Mystical Snow Day	168550	4,000	104.95	Proof	105.	—

TWENTY DOLLARS, HOLIDAY WREATH, 2019.

Designers and Engravers:
Obv.: Susanna Blunt, Susan Taylor
Rev.: Marie-Élaine Cusson
Composition: 99.99% Ag
Silver content: 31.39 g, 1.01 tr oz
Weight: 31.39 g   **Edge:** Reeded
Diameter: 38 mm   **Die Axis:** ↑↑
Thickness: N/A   **Finish:** Proof
Case of Issue: Maroon clamshell with black beauty box, COA

DATE	DESCRIPTION	RCM ITEM #	MINTAGE	ISSUE PRICE	FINISH	PR-69	PR-70
2019	Holiday Wreath	169231	5,000	139.95	Proof	140.	—

TWENTY DOLLARS, THE VALIANT ONE: BALD EAGLE, 2019.

Designers and Engravers:
Obv.: Susanna Blunt, Susan Taylor
Rev.: W. Allan Hancock
Composition: 99.99% Ag
Silver content: 31.39 g, 1.01 tr oz
Weight: 31.39 g   **Edge:** Reeded
Diameter: 38 mm   **Die Axis:** ↑↑
Thickness: N/A   **Finish:** Reverse Proof
Case of Issue: Maroon clamshell with black beauty box, COA

DATE	DESCRIPTION	RCM ITEM #	MINTAGE	ISSUE PRICE	FINISH	PR-69	PR-70
2019	The Valiant One: Bald Ealge	172016	5,500	89.95	Reverse Proof	90.	—

TWENTY DOLLARS, THE CANADIAN FLAG, 2019.

Designers and Engravers:
Obv.:	Susanna Blunt, Susan Taylor
Rev.:	Aoifa Anctil

Composition: 99.99% Ag
Silver content: 31.39 g, 1.01 tr oz

Weight:	31.39 g	**Edge:**	Reeded
Diameter:	38 mm	**Die Axis:**	↑↑
Thickness:	N/A	**Finish:**	Proof

Case of Issue: Maroon clamshell with black beauty box, COA

DATE	DESCRIPTION	RCM ITEM #	MINTAGE	ISSUE PRICE	FINISH	PR-69	PR-70
2019	The Canadian Flag	170750	10,000	99.95	Proof	100.	—

TWENTY DOLLARS, 125TH ANNIVERSARY OF THE BIRTH OF BILLY BISHOP, 2019.

Designers and Engravers:
Obv.:	Susanna Blunt, Susan Taylor
Rev.:	RCM Staff

Composition: 99.99% Ag
Silver content: 31.39 g, 1.01 tr oz

Weight:	31.39 g	**Edge:**	Reeded
Diameter:	38 mm	**Die Axis:**	↑↑
Thickness:	N/A	**Finish:**	Proof

Case of Issue: Burgundy clamshell with black beauty box, COA

DATE	DESCRIPTION	RCM ITEM #	MINTAGE	ISSUE PRICE	FINISH	PR-69	PR-70
2019	125th Ann. Birth of Billy Bishop	170505	7,500	99.95	Proof	100.	—

TWENTY DOLLARS, NORSE GODS — THOR, 2019.

Designers and Engravers:
Obv.:	Susanna Blunt, Susan Taylor
Rev.:	Alexandra Lefort

Composition: 99.99% Ag
Silver content: 31.39 g, 1.01 tr oz

Weight:	31.39 g	**Edge:**	Reeded
Diameter:	38 mm	**Die Axis:**	↑↑
Thickness:	N/A	**Finish:**	Proof

Case of Issue: Maroon clamshell with black beauty box, COA

DATE	DESCRIPTION	RCM ITEM #	MINTAGE	ISSUE PRICE	FINISH	PR-69	PR-70
2019	Norse Gods — Thor	170566	3,500	109.95	Proof	110.	—

TWENTY DOLLARS, HATCHING HADROSAUR, 2019.

Designers and Engravers:
Obv.:	Susanna Blunt, Susan Taylor
Rev.:	RCM Staff

Composition: 99.99% Ag
Silver content: 31.82 g, 1.02 tr oz
Weight: 31.82 g
Diameter: 45 long x 33 wide mm
Thickness: N/A
Edge: Interrupted reeding
Die Axis: ↑↑
Finish: Proof
Case of Issue: Black clamshell with black beauty box, COA

DATE	DESCRIPTION	RCM ITEM #	MINTAGE	ISSUE PRICE	FINISH	PR-69	PR-70
2019	Hatching Hadrosaur	171828	4,000	139.95	Proof	140.	—

TWENTY DOLLARS, VIOLA DESMOND, 2019.

In honour of Black History Month, the Royal Canadian Mint has proudly designed a 99.99% pure silver tribute to a Canadian civil rights pioneer, Viola Desmond (1914-19165). Each commemorative coin is accompanied by a new, $10 Viola Desmond banknote recently issued by the Bank of Canada.

Designers and Engravers:

Obv.:	Susanna Blunt, Susan Taylor
Rev.:	RCM Staff
Composition:	99.99% Ag
Silver content:	31.39 g, 1.01 tr oz
Weight:	31.39 g
Diameter:	38 mm
Thickness:	N/A
Case of Issue:	Black clamshell with black beauty box, COA

			Edge:	Reeded
			Die Axis:	↑↑
			Finish:	Proof

DATE	DESCRIPTION	RCM ITEM #	MINTAGE	ISSUE PRICE	FINISH	PR-69	PR-70
2019	Viola Desmond	171542	8,000	149.95	Proof	150.	—

TWENTY DOLLARS, GIVE PEACE A CHANCE: 50TH ANNIVERSARY, 2019.

Designers and Engravers:

Obv.:	Susanna Blunt, Susan Taylor
Rev.:	Ivor Sharp
Composition:	99.99% Ag
Silver content:	31.39 g, 1.01 tr oz
Weight:	31.39 g
Diameter:	38 mm
Thickness:	N/A
Case of Issue:	Black clamshell with graphic beauty box, COA

			Edge:	Reeded
			Die Axis:	↑↑
			Finish:	Proof

DATE	DESCRIPTION	RCM ITEM #	MINTAGE	ISSUE PRICE	FINISH	PR-69	PR-70
2019	Give Peace A Chance: 50th Anniversary	171292	9,999	99.99	Proof	100.	—

TWENTY DOLLAR DERIVATIVES

DATE	DESCRIPTION	QUANTITY SOLD	ISSUE PRICE	ISSUER	FINISH	MARKET PRICE
1998	**Year of the Tiger**, Fifteen dollar coin; Souvenir stamp sheet; Presentation album	8,000	88.88	RCM, CP	PR-69	150.
1998	**Twenty Dollars** Argus and Waterbomber boxed with cardboard model	N/A	N/A	RCM	PR-69	250.
2004	**Twenty Dollars** Northern Lights twenty dollar coin mounted in a frame with a large image of the Northern Lights	N/A	399.00	RCM	PR-69	175.
2012	**Twenty Dollars**, The Queen's Diamond Jubilee, The Royal Cypher, Queen Elizabeth II and Prince Philip; 3-coin wooden collector box, within a beauty box with Diamond Jubilee Cypher	1,809	274.95	RCM	PR-69	200.
2012	**Twenty Dollars** Queen Elizabeth II and Prince Philip, Three-coin case holding UK £5, Australian 50¢, Canadian $20,	4,000	399.95	RCM	PR-69	250.
2015	**Baby Burrowing Owl Coin and Stamp Set**, Twenty dollar coin and stamped postcard	7,500	109.95	RCM/PO	PR-69	90.
2015	**Baby Puffin Coin and Stamp Set**, Twenty dollar coin and stamped postcard	7,500	109.95	RCM/PO	PR-69	90.
2015	**Baby Beaver Coin and Stamp Set**, Twenty dollar coin and stamped postcard	7,500	109.95	RCM/PO	PR-69	90.
2019	**Viola Desmond Coin and Banknote Set**, Twenty dollar coin and $10 banknote	8,000	149.95	RCM/BofC	PR-69	150.

TWENTY-FIVE DOLLARS

TWENTY-FIVE DOLLARS, VANCOUVER 2010 OLYMPIC WINTER GAMES, 2007-2009.

| 2007 Obverse | 2008 Obverse | 2009 Obverse |

ISSUES OF 2007.

Curling	Ice Hockey	Athletes' Pride	Biathlon	Alpine Skiing
Des.: Steve Hepburn	Des: Steve Hepburn	Des: Shelagh Armstrong	Des: Bonnie Ross	Des: Brian Hughes
Eng.: Stan Witten	Eng.: William Woodruff	Eng.: Christie Paquet	Eng.: Stan Witten	Eng.: Stan Witten

ISSUES OF 2008.

Snowboarding	Freestyle Skiing	Home of the 2010 Olympic	Figure Skating	Bobsleigh
Des: Steve Hepburn	Des: John Mardon	Winter Games	Des: Steve Hepburn	Des: Bonnie Ross
Eng.: Konrad Wachelko	Eng.: Christie Paquet	Des: Shelagh Armstrong	Eng.: José Osio	Eng.: Stan Witten
		Eng.: Marcos Hallam		

ISSUES OF 2009.

Speed Skating	Cross Country Skiing	Olympic Spirit	Skeleton	Ski Jumping
Des: Tony Bianco	Des: Brian Hughes	Des: Shelagh Armstrong	Des: Tony Bianco	Des: John Mardon
Eng.: William Woodruff	Eng.: William Woodruff	Eng.: Stan Witten	Eng.: Stan Witten	Eng.: Konrad Wachelko

TWENTY-FIVE DOLLARS, VANCOUVER 2010 OLYMPIC WINTER GAMES, 2007-2009 (cont.).

Designers:
Obv.:   Susanna Blunt
Rev.:   See reverse illustrations
Composition: 92.5% Ag, 7.5% Cu, Selective hologram
Silver content: 25.7 g, 0.826 tr oz
Weight: 27.78 g
Diameter: 40.0 mm
Thickness: 2.5 mm
Case of Issue: Singly: Black leatherette clam case; black flocked insert, encapsulated coin, COA, Olympic theme sleeve

Engravers:
Obv.:   Susan Taylor
Rev.:   See reverse illustrations

Edge: Reeded
Die Axis: ↑↑
Finish: Proof

Set: Black leatherette, 15-hole, square clam style case; two black flocked inserts (one with seven indentations, the other with eight); encapsulated coins; COA for each coin; Olympic theme sleeve

DATE	DESCRIPTION	RCM ITEM #	ISSUE DATE	QUANTITY SOLD	ISSUE PRICE	FINISH	PR-69	PR-70
2007	Curling	624367	Feb. 23, 2007	19,531	69.95	Proof	50.	—
2007	Ice Hockey	624327	April 14, 2007	22,512	69.95	Proof	50.	—
2007	Athletes' Pride	624347	July 11, 2007	21,886	69.95	Proof	50.	—
2007	Biathlon	324357	Sept. 12, 2007	16,003	69.95	Proof	50.	—
2007	Alpine Skiing	624337	Oct. 24, 2007	13,500	69.95	Proof	50.	—
2008	Snowboarding	624368	Feb. 20, 2008	6,377	71.95	Proof	50.	—
2008	Freestyle Skiing	624338	April 16, 2008	12,428	71.95	Proof	50.	—
2008	Home of the 2010 Olympic Winter Games	624348	July 23, 2008	12,606	71.95	Proof	50.	—
2008	Figure Skating	624358	Sept. 10, 2008	18,930	71.95	Proof	50.	—
2008	Bobsleigh	624328	Oct. 29, 2008	8,800	71.95	Proof	50.	—
2009	Speed Skating	624359	Feb. 18, 2009	27,827	71.95	Proof	50.	—
2009	Cross Country Skiing	624339	April 15, 2009	14,292	71.95	Proof	50.	—
2009	Olympic Spirit	624349	June 17, 2009	10,224	71.95	Proof	50.	—
2009	Skeleton	624329	Aug.. 5, 2009	10,582	71.95	Proof	50.	—
2009	Ski Jumping	624369	Oct. 7, 2009	11,365	71.95	Proof	50.	—
2007-2010	Set of 15 coins	N/A	—	4,764	—	Proof	700.	—

TWENTY-FIVE DOLLARS, TORONTO CITY MAP, 2011.

The reverse design of this coin depicts the City of Toronto as seen through the visor of an astronaut. These coins were struck in Switzerland.

Designers:
Obv.:   Susanna Blunt
Rev.:   Google Earth
Composition: 99.99% Ag, Selectively gold plated
Silver content: 62.41 g, 2.01 tr oz
Weight: 62.41 g
Diameter: 60.0 mm
Thickness: 2.5 mm
Case of Issue: Maroon leatherette clam style case, black flocked insert, encapsulated coin, COA

Engravers:
Obv.:   Susan Taylor
Rev.:   RCM Staff

Edge: Reeded
Die Axis: ↑↑
Finish: Proof

DATE	DESCRIPTION	RCM ITEM #	QUANTITY SOLD	ISSUE PRICE	FINISH	PR-69	PR-70
2011	Toronto City Map	115559	3,948	179.95	Proof	190.	—

TWENTY-FIVE DOLLARS, WAYNE AND WALTER GRETZKY, 2011.

The reverse design on this coin features Wayne Gretzky (the Great One) in action, with a cameo of his father Walter.

Designers and Engravers:

Obv.:	Susanna Blunt, Susan Taylor
Rev.:	Glen Green, Konrad Wachelko, José Osio
Composition:	99.99% Ag, (Hologram of jersey number 99)
Silver content:	31.39 g, 1.01 tr oz
Weight:	31.39 g
Diameter:	38.0 mm
Thickness:	3.2 mm
Case of Issue:	Maroon leatherette clam style case, black flocked insert, encapsulated coin, COA

Edge:	Reeded
Die Axis:	↑↑
Finish:	Proof

DATE	DESCRIPTION	RCM ITEM #	QUANTITY SOLD	ISSUE PRICE	FINISH	PR-69	PR-70
2011	Wayne and Walter Gretzky	114670	6,715	99.99	Proof	85.	—

O CANADA SET ONE

TWENTY-FIVE DOLLARS, O CANADA SET ONE, 2013.

These coins from the O Canada Set focus on iconic Canadian images as seen through our rich animal history. For other coins in the O Canada Set see pages 201-202 and 346, 418.

Common Obverse

Designers:

Obv.:	Susanna Blunt
Rev.:	Pierre Leduc
Composition:	99.99% Ag
Silver content:	31.1 g, 1.00 tr oz
Weight:	31.1 g
Diameter:	38.0 mm
Thickness:	3.0 mm
Case of Issue:	Singly: Maroon clam style case, black flocked insert, encapsulated coin, COA, custom coloured box
	Subscription: Brown wooden case, 5-hole black flocked insert, encapsulated coins, COA

Engravers:

Obv.:	Susan Taylor
Rev.:	See reverse illustrations

Edge:	Reeded
Die Axis:	↑↑
Finish:	Proof

The Beaver	**The Polar Bear**	**The Wolf**	**The Caribou**	**The Orca**
Engraver: José Osio	Engraver: Alex Tirabasso	Engraver: RCM Staff	Engraver: Susan Taylor	Engraver: José Osio

DATE	DESCRIPTION	RCM ITEM #	QUANTITY SOLD	ISSUE PRICE	FINISH	PR-69	PR-70
2013	The Beaver	122738	8,354	89.95	Proof	60.	—
2013	The Polar Bear	123120	8,299	89.95	Proof	60.	—
2013	The Wolf	123838	8,039	89.95	Proof	60.	—
2013	The Caribou	123185	7,580	89.95	Proof	60.	—
2013	The Orca	123935	6,342	89.95	Proof	60.	—

TWENTY-FIVE DOLLARS, GRANDMOTHER MOON MASK, 2013.

Designers and Engravers:

Obv.:	Susanna Blunt, Susan Taylor
Rev.:	Richard. Cochrane, Eric Boyer, Nicholas Martin

Composition:	99.99% Ag		
Silver content:	30.5 g, 0.98 tr oz		
Weight:	30.5 g	Edge:	Plain
Diameter:	36.2 mm	Die Axis:	↑↑
Thickness:	3.0 mm	Finish:	Proof
Case of Issue:	Maroon leatherette clam style case, black flocked insert, encapsulated coin, COA		

DATE	DESCRIPTION	RCM ITEM #	QUANTITY SOLD	ISSUE PRICE	FINISH	PR-69	PR-70
2013	Grandmother Moon Mask	124573	5,996	149.95	Proof	120.	—

TWENTY-FIVE DOLLARS, MISS CANADA: AN ALLEGORY, 2013.

Designers and Engravers:

Obv.:	Susanna Blunt, Susan Taylor
Rev.:	Laurie McGaw, RCM Staff

Composition:	99.99% Ag		
Silver content:	31.39 g, 1.01 tr oz		
Weight:	31.39 g	Edge:	Reeded
Diameter:	38.0 mm	Die Axis:	↑↑
Thickness:	3.2 mm	Finish:	Proof
Case of Issue:	Maroon leatherette clam style case, black flocked insert, encapsulated coin, COA		

DATE	DESCRIPTION	RCM ITEM #	QUANTITY SOLD	ISSUE PRICE	FINISH	PR-69	PR-70
2013	Miss Canada: An Allegory	125715	5,503	89.95	Proof	75.	—

TWENTY-FIVE DOLLARS, MATRIARCH MOON MASK, 2014.

Designers and Engravers:

Obv.:	Susanna Blunt, Susan Taylor
Rev.:	Carol Young, RCM Staff

Composition:	99.99% Ag		
Silver content:	30.76 g, 0.988 tr oz		
Weight:	30.76 g	Edge:	Reeded
Diameter:	36.15 mm	Die Axis:	↑↑
Thickness:	3.2 mm	Finish:	Proof
Case of Issue:	Maroon leatherette clam style case, black flocked insert, encapsulated coin, COA		

DATE	DESCRIPTION	RCM ITEM #	QUANTITY SOLD	ISSUE PRICE	FINISH	PR-69	PR-70
2014	Matriarch Moon Mask	130514	5,999	149.95	Proof	120.	—

TWENTY-FIVE DOLLARS, 75TH ANNIVERSARY OF THE FIRST ROYAL VISIT, 2014.

Struck in ultra-high relief, the coin celebrates King George VI and Queen Elizabeth's visit to Canada in 1939.

Designers and Engravers:

Obv.:	Susanna Blunt, Susan Taylor
Rev.:	RCM Staff

Composition:	99.99% Ag		
Silver content:	30.76 g, 0.99 tr oz		
Weight:	30.76 g	Edge:	Plain
Diameter:	36.0 mm	Die Axis:	↑↑
Thickness:	N/A	Finish:	Proof
Case of Issue:	Maroon leatherette clam style case, black flocked insert, encapsulated coin, COA, custom box		

DATE	DESCRIPTION	RCM ITEM #	QUANTITY SOLD	ISSUE PRICE	FINISH	PR-69	PR-70
2014	25th Anniversary of the First Royal Visit	130067	3,117	149.95	Proof	130.	—

O CANADA SET TWO

TWENTY-FIVE DOLLARS, O CANADA SET TWO, 2014.

Common Obverse

Designers:		Engravers:	
Obv.:	Susanna Blunt	Obv.:	Susan Taylor
Rev.:	See reverse illustrations	Rev.:	RCM Staff

Composition: 99.99% Ag
Silver content: 31.0 g, 1.0 tr oz
Weight: 31.0 g
Diameter: 38.0 mm
Thickness: 3.2 mm
Case of Issue: Singly: Maroon clam style case, black flocked insert, encapsulated coin, COA, custom coloured box
Set: Walnut display case, 5-hole black flocked insert, encapsulated coins, COA

Edge: Reeded
Die Axis: ↑↑
Finish: Proof

The Igloo	Scenic Skiing in Canada	Under the Maple Tree	Cowboy in the Canadian Rockies	The Arctic Fox and the Northern Lights
Des.: Yves Bérubé	Des.: RCM Staff	Des.: Claudio D'Angelo	Des.: Bernie Brown	Des.: Julius Csotonyi
Eng.: Konrad Wachelko	Eng.: RCM Staff	Eng.: RCM Staff	Eng.: RCM Staff	Eng.: Cecily Mok

DATE	DESCRIPTION	RCM ITEM #	QUANTITY SOLD	ISSUE PRICE	FINISH	PR-69	PR-70
2014	The Igloo	128990	6,013	89.95	Proof	75.	—
2014	Scenic Skiing in Canada		6,016	89.95	Proof	75.	—
2014	Under the Maple Tree	129015	5,972	89.95	Proof	75.	—
2014	Cowboy in the Canadian Rockies	129439	6,110	89.95	Proof	75.	—
2014	The Arctic Fox and the Northern Lights	129101	6,748	89.95	Proof	75.	—

TWENTY-FIVE DOLLARS, THE FIERCE CANADIAN LYNX, 2014.

Combining multiple finishes and ultra-high relief, this coin captures the Canada lynx, a feline native to the Boreal forests.

Designers and Engravers:
Obv.:	Susanna Blunt, Susan Taylor
Rev.:	Pierre Leduc, RCM Staff

Composition: 99.99% Ag
Silver content: 30.76 g, 0.99 tr oz
Weight: 30.76 g
Diameter: 36.15 mm
Thickness: N/A
Case of Issue: Maroon leatherette clam style case, black flocked insert, encapsulated coin, COA

Edge: Plain
Die Axis: ↑↑
Finish: Proof

DATE	DESCRIPTION	RCM ITEM #	QUANTITY SOLD	ISSUE PRICE	FINISH	PR-69	PR-70
2014	The Fierce Canadian Lynx	142158	1,519	149.95	Proof	150.	—

CHRISTMAS ORNAMENT SERIES

TWENTY-FIVE DOLLARS, CHRISTMAS ORNAMENT, 2014-2015.

Common Obverse

2014

2015

Designers:
Obv.: Susanna Blunt
Rev.: Three Degrees Creative Group Inc.
Composition: 99.99% Ag, Coloured Sheer Effect
Silver content: 30.76 g, 0.99 tr oz
Weight: 30.76 g
Diameter: 36.15 mm
Thickness: N/A
Case of Issue: Maroon leatherette clam style case, black flocked insert, encapsulated coin, COA

Engravers:
Obv.: Susan Taylor
Rev.: RCM Staff

Edge: Plain
Die Axis: ↑↑
Finish: Proof, Antique, Colour Enamel

DATE	DESCRIPTION	RCM ITEM #	QUANTITY SOLD	ISSUE PRICE	FINISH	PR-69	PR-70
2014	Christmas Ornament	130620	4,726	129.95	Proof	130.	—
2015	Christmas Ornament	147284	3,007	129.95	Proof	130.	—

SINGING MOON MASK SET

TWENTY-FIVE DOLLARS, SINGING MOON MASK SET, 2015.

Featuring three distinct finishes, all coins are struck in ultra-high relief and feature the artwork of Andy Everson of the K'omoks and Kwakwaka'wakw First Nations in British Columbia.

Common Obverse

Proof

Proof Antique

Proof Colour Enamel

Designers:
Obv.: Susanna Blunt
Rev.: Andy Everson
Composition: 99.99% Ag
Weight: 30.76 g
Diameter: 36.15 mm
Thickness: N/A
Case of Issue: Wooden case, black flocked insert, encapsulated coins, COA, black box

Engravers:
Obv.: Susan Taylor
Rev.: RCM Staff
Silver content: 30.76 g, 0.99 tr oz
Edge: Plain
Die Axis: ↑↑
Finish: Proof, Antique, Colour Enamel

DATE	DESCRIPTION	RCM ITEM #	QUANTITY SOLD	ISSUE PRICE	FINISH	PR-69	PR-70
2015	Singing Moon Mask, Proof	N/A	—	N.I.I.	Proof	120.	—
2015	Singing Moon Mask, Proof Antique	N/A	—	N.I.I.	Antique	120.	—
2015	Singing Moon Mask, Proof Colour Enamel	N/A	—	N.I.I.	Enamel	120.	—
2015	Set of 3 Coins	142296	2,974	359.95	—	325.	*

STAR CHARTS SET

TWENTY FIVE DOLLARS, STAR CHARTS SET, 2015

Based on the artwork of Western Ojibwa artist Cyril Assiniboine, these glow-in-the-dark coins, whose cases when assembled form the Big Dipper, depict the Plains Ojibwa as they hunt a great bear.

| Common Obverse | The Great Ascent | The Eternal Pursuit | The Quest | The Wounded Bear |

Designers:
Obv.: Susanna Blunt
Rev.: Cyril Assiniboine
Composition: 99.99% Ag
Weight: 31.83 g
Diameter: 40.0 mm
Thickness: N/A
Case of Issue: Maroon leatherette clam style case, black flocked insert, encapsulated coin, COA, custom case

Engravers:
Obv.: Susan Taylor
Rev.: RCM Staff
Silver content: 31.83 g, 1.02 tr oz
Edge: Reeded
Die Axis: ↑↑
Finish: Proof

DATE	DESCRIPTION	RCM ITEM #	QUANTITY SOLD	ISSUE PRICE	FINISH	PR-69	PR-70
2015	The Great Ascent	132685	6,162	104.95	Proof	90.	—
2015	The Eternal Pursuit	140555	7,294	104.95	Proof	90.	—
2015	The Quest	140548	7,445	104.95	Proof	90.	—
2015	The Wounded Bear	140563	6,919	104.95	Proof	90.	—

TWENTY-FIVE FOR TWENTY-FIVE SERIES

TWENTY-FIVE DOLLARS (½ ounce), FINE SILVER, TWENTY-FIVE FOR TWENTY-FIVE SERIES, 2015-2016.

| Common Obverse | 50th Anniversary of Canadian Flag Designer: Julius Csotonyi | Winter Fun Designer: Jesse Koreck | Woodland Elf Designer: Jesse Koreck | True North Designer: RCM Staff |

Designers:
Obv.: Susanna Blunt
Rev.: See reverse illustrations
Composition: 99.99% Ag, Coloured
Silver content: 7.96 g, 0.25 tr oz
Weight: 7.96 g
Diameter: 27.0 mm
Thickness: N/A
Case of Issue: Vinyl pouch, encapsulated coin, coloured folder

Engravers:
Obv.: Susan Taylor
Rev.: RCM Staff

Edge: Reeded
Die Axis: ↑↑
Finish: Specimen

DATE	DESCRIPTION	RCM ITEM #	QUANTITY SOLD	ISSUE PRICE	FINISH	SP-68	SP-69
2015	50th Anniversary of Canadian Flag	143041	223,373	25.00	Specimen	30.	—
2016	Winter Fun	149293	133,621	25.00	Specimen	30.	—
2016	Woodland Elf	153477	91,428	25.00	Specimen	30.	—
2016	True North	153478	118,410	25.00	Specimen	30.	—

TWENTY-FIVE DOLLARS, THE LIBRARY OF PARLIAMENT, 2016.

This coin marks the 140th anniversary of the outstandingly beautiful Library of Parliament building, which opened February 28th 1876, the only building which survived the 1916 fire that burned the rest of Parliament.

Designers and Engravers:

Obv.:	Susanna Blunt, Susan Taylor
Rev.:	RCM Staff

Composition: 99.99% Ag
Silver content: 30.75g, 0.99 tr oz

Weight:	30.75 g	**Edge:**	Reeded
Diameter:	36.07 mm	**Die Axis:**	↑↑
Thickness:	N/A	**Finish:**	Proof

Case of Issue: Maroon clamshell with black beauty box

DATE	DESCRIPTION	RCM ITEM #	QUANTITY SOLD	ISSUE PRICE	FINISH	PR-69	PR-70
2016	The Library of Parliament	149592	5,992	159.95	Proof	175.	—

TWENTY-FIVE DOLLARS, 125TH ANNIVERSARY OF THE INVENTION OF BASKETBALL, 2016.

This outstanding coloured convex-shaped coin proudly celebrates the 125th anniversary of a team sport that was invented by a Canadian and has since taken the world by storm!

Designers and Engravers:

Obv.:	Susanna Blunt, Susan Taylor
Rev.:	Glen Green

Composition: 99.99% Ag, Selective color
Silver content: 30.76 g, 0.99 tr oz

Weight:	30.75 g	**Edge:**	Reeded
Diameter:	36.07 mm	**Die Axis:**	↑↑
Thickness:	N/A	**Finish:**	Proof

Case of Issue: Maroon clamshell with black beauty box.

DATE	DESCRIPTION	RCM ITEM #	QUANTITY SOLD	ISSUE PRICE	FINISH	PR-69	PR-70
2016	125th Anniversary of the Invention of Basketball	153904	6,075	159.95	Proof	150.	—

SCULPTURAL ART OF PARLIAMENT SET

TWENTY-FIVE DOLLARS, SCULPTURAL ART OF PARLIAMENT, 2016.

In the heart of our nation's capital, the hallowed walls of Parliament are home to thousands of carved and sculpted artworks of exceptional beauty.

  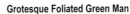 

Common Obverse	Grotesque Wild Green Man	Grotesque Foliated Green Man	Grotesque Horned Green Man

Designers:

Obv.:	Susanna Blunt
Rev.:	Phil White

Composition: 99.99% Ag
Weight: 30.75 g
Diameter: 36 mm
Thickness: N/A
Case of Issue: Maroon clamshell with black beauty box.

Engravers:

Obv.:	Susan Taylor
Rev.:	RCM Staff

Silver content: 30.75 g, 0.99 tr oz
Edge: Plain
Die Axis: ↑↑
Finish: Proof

TWENTY-FIVE DOLLARS, SCULPTURAL ART OF PARLIAMENT, 2016, PRICING PANEL.

DATE	DESCRIPTION	RCM ITEM #	QUANTITY SOLD	ISSUE PRICE	FINISH	PR-69	PR-70
2016	Grotesque Wild Green Man	151335	2,038	149.95	Proof	150.	—
2016	Grotesque Foliated Green Man	151371	1,822	149.95	Proof	150.	—
2016	Grotesque Horned Green Man	154067	1,674	149.95	Proof	150.	—

TWENTY-FIVE DOLLARS, PIEDFORT, THE COAT OF ARMS OF CANADA, 2016.

A timeless celebration of Canada, its people, its history and its heritage through this richly detailed reproduction of a distinguished national symbol.

Designers and Engravers:

Obv.:	Susanna Blunt, Susan Taylor
Rev.:	RCM Staff
Composition:	99.99% Ag
Silver content:	31.39 g, 1.01 tr oz
Weight:	31.39 g	**Edge:**	Reeded
Diameter:	34 mm	**Die Axis:**	↑↑
Thickness:	N/A	**Finish:**	Proof
Case of Issue:	Maroon clamshell with standard beauty box

DATE	DESCRIPTION	RCM ITEM #	QUANTITY SOLD	ISSUE PRICE	FINISH	PR-69	PR-70
2016	The Coat of Arms of Canada	150040	5,985	99.95	Proof	100.	—

TWENTY-FIVE DOLLARS, VIEW OF CANADA FROM SPACE, 2017.

On January 22, 1992, the NASA space shuttle *Discovery* launched from Kennedy Space Center in Cape Canaveral with a crew of seven – including neurologist Dr. Roberta Bondar, M.D., Ph.D., who holds the distinction of being Canada's first female astronaut. Proudly celebrating the 25th anniversary of Dr. Bondar's historic mission with this fine silver coin, whose convex shape provides the perfect canvas for recreating a view that is out of this world!

Designers and Engravers:

Obv.:	Susanna Blunt, Susan Taylor
Rev.:	Alexandra Lefort
Composition:	99.99% Ag
Silver content:	30.75 g, 1.01 tr oz
Weight:	30.75 g	**Edge:**	Reeded
Diameter:	36.07 mm	**Die Axis:**	↑↑
Thickness:	N/A	**Finish:**	Proof
Case of Issue:	Maroon clamshell with standard beauty box

DATE	DESCRIPTION	RCM ITEM #	QUANTITY SOLD	ISSUE PRICE	FINISH	PR-69	PR-70
2017	A View of Canada From Space	158306	4,750	159.95	Proof	160.	—

TWENTY-FIVE DOLLARS, FOOTBALL-SHAPED AND CURVED COIN, 2017.

This coin is curved (convex) to resemble an inflated football, ready for play!

Designers and Engravers:

Obv.:	Susanna Blunt, Susan Taylor
Rev.:	RCM staff
Composition:	99.99% Ag
Silver content:	31.66 g, 1.01 tr oz
Weight:	31.66 g	**Edge:**	Plain
Diameter:	48 x 30.33 mm	**Die Axis:**	↑↑
Thickness:	N/A	**Finish:**	Proof
Case of Issue:	Maroon clamshell with black beauty box

DATE	DESCRIPTION	RCM ITEM #	QUANTITY SOLD	ISSUE PRICE	FINISH	PR-69	PR-70
2017	Football-Shaped and Curved Coin	155469	5,802	161.95	Proof	150.	—

TWENTY-FIVE DOLLARS, 35TH ANNIVERSARY OF TRIVIAL PURSUIT, 2017.

Through this colourful piedfort, the 35th anniversary of a classic board game whose worldwide success has made it a household name, is proudly celebrated.

Designers and Engravers:

Obv.:	Susanna Blunt, Susan Taylor
Rev.:	RCM staff
Composition:	99.99% Ag
Silver content:	31.39 g, 1.02 tr oz
Weight:	34 g
Diameter:	36.07 mm
Thickness:	N/A
Case of Issue:	Black graphic case with graphic beauty box.

Edge:	Reeded		
Die Axis:	↑↑		
Finish:	Proof		

DATE	DESCRIPTION	RCM ITEM #	QUANTITY SOLD	ISSUE PRICE	FINISH	PR-69	PR-70
2017	35th Anniversary of Trivial Pursuit	154997	4,268	118.95	Proof	120.	—

TWENTY-FIVE DOLLARS, THE GREAT TRAIL, 2017.

Designers and Engravers:

Obv.:	S. Blunt, S. Taylor
Rev.:	Steve Hepburn
Composition:	99.99% Ag, Selective colour
Silver content:	47.35 g, 1.5 tr oz
Weight:	47.35 g
Diameter:	49.8 mm x 28.8 mm
Thickness:	N/A.
Case of Issue:	Maroon clamshell with custom beauty box, COA.

Edge:	Plain
Die Axis:	↑↑
Finish:	Proof

DATE	DESCRIPTION	RCM ITEM #	MINTAGE	ISSUE PRICE	FINISH	PR-69	PR-70
2017	The Great Trail	160949	5,500	159.95	Proof	160.	—

TWENTY-FIVE DOLLARS, THE GREAT SEAL OF CANADA, 2017.

Designers and Engravers:

Obv.:	Susanna Blunt, Susan Taylor
Rev.:	Eric Aldwinckle
Composition:	99.99% Ag, selective gold plating
Silver content:	30.76 g, 1.01 tr oz
Weight:	30.76 g
Diameter:	36 mm
Thickness:	N/A
Case of Issue:	Maroon clamshell with standard beauty box, COA

Edge:	Plain
Die Axis:	↑↑
Finish:	Proof

DATE	DESCRIPTION	RCM ITEM #	MINTAGE	ISSUE PRICE	FINISH	PR-69	PR-70
2017	The Great Seal of Canada	162362	6,000	139.95	Proof	160.	—

TWENTY-FIVE DOLLARS, 100TH ANNIVERSARY OF THE NHL, 2017.

Designers and Engravers:

Obv.:	Susanna Blunt, Susan Taylor
Rev.:	Julius Csotonyi
Composition:	99.99% Ag
Silver content:	47.35 g, 1.5 tr oz
Weight:	47.35 g
Diameter:	49.8 mm x 28.8 mm
Thickness:	N/A
Case of Issue:	Maroon clamshell with custom beauty box, COA.

Edge:	Plain
Die Axis:	↑↑
Finish:	Proof

DATE	DESCRIPTION	RCM ITEM #	MINTAGE	ISSUE PRICE	FINISH	PR-69	PR-70
2017	100th Anniversary of the NHL	163676	6,000	139.95	Proof	140.	—

TWENTY-FIVE DOLLARS, DRAGON BOAT FESTIVAL, 2017-2018.

Ultra-high relief brings the Chinese dragon to life on the reverse, which represents a stunning visual celebration of the annual Dragon Boat Festival celebrated worldwide — including several cities across Canada!

Common Obverse	2017 Dragon Boat Festival	2018 Dragon Boat Festival

Designers:
Obv.: Susanna Blunt
Rev.: Simon Ng
Composition: 99.99% Ag, Selective colour
Silver content: 30.76 g, 0.99 tr oz
Weight: 30.76 g
Diameter: 36.15 mm
Thickness: N/A
Case of Issue: Maroon clamshell with black beauty box.

Engravers:
Obv.: Susan Taylor

Edge: Plain
Die Axis: ↑↑
Finish: Proof

DATE	DESCRIPTION	RCM ITEM #	MINTAGE	ISSUE PRICE	FINISH	PR-69	PR-70
2017	Dragon Boat Festival	160575	6,000	139.95	Proof	140.	—
2018	Dragon Boat Festival	166628	6,000	149.95	Proof	150.	—

TIMELESS ICONS

TWENTY-FIVE DOLLARS, PIEDFORT, TIMELESS ICONS, 2017-2019.

The Royal Canadian Mint reflects on a nation's 150-year journey — and beyond — through the fusion of two iconic symbols that continue to inspire admiration by proudly representing all that is Canada.

2017-2018 Obverse	Beaver	Caribou	2019 Obverse	Loon

Designers:
Obv.: Susanna Blunt
Rev.: Pierre Leduc
Composition: 99.99% Ag, Selectively gold plated
Silver content: 31.39 g, 1.02 tr oz
Weight: 31.39 g
Diameter: 34 mm
Finish: Proof
Case of Issue: Maroon clamshell with standard beauty box, COA

Engravers:
Obv.: Susan Taylor
Rev.: RCM Staff

Edge: Reeded
Die Axis: ↑↑

DATE	DESCRIPTION	RCM ITEM #	MINTAGE	ISSUE PRICE	FINISH	PR-69	PR-70
2017	Timeless Icons: Beaver	158439	1,004	129.95	Proof	130.	—
2018	Timeless Icons: Caribou	163248	7,500	129.95	Proof	130.	—
2019	Timeless Icons: Loon	170039	7,000	114.95	Proof	115.	—

TWENTY-FIVE DOLLARS, CLASSIC HOLIDAY ORNAMENT, 2018.

Designers and Engravers:

Obv.:	Susanna Blunt, Susan Taylor
Rev.:	Calder Moore

Composition: 99.99% Ag
Silver content: 30.75 g, 0.99 tr oz

Weight:	30.75 g	**Edge:**	Reeded
Diameter:	36.07 mm	**Die Axis:**	↑↑
Thickness:	N/A	**Finish:**	Proof

Case of Issue: Black clamshell with black beauty box, COA.

DATE	DESCRIPTION	RCM ITEM #	MINTAGE	ISSUE PRICE	FINISH	PR-69	PR-70
2018	Classic Holiday Ornament	162721	5,500	159.95	Proof	160.	—

TWENTY-FIVE DOLLARS, 180TH ANNIVERSARY OF CANADIAN BASEBALL, 2018.

Designers and Engravers:

Obv.:	Susanna Blunt, Susan Taylor
Rev.:	Steve Hepburn

Composition: 99.99% Ag
Silver content: 30.75 g, 1.01 tr oz

Weight:	30.75 g	**Edge:**	Reeded
Diameter:	36.07 mm	**Die Axis:**	↑↑
Thickness:	N/A	**Finish:**	Proof

Case of Issue: Black clamshell with black beauty box, COA.

DATE	DESCRIPTION	RCM ITEM #	MINTAGE	ISSUE PRICE	FINISH	PR-69	PR-70
2018	180th Anniversary of Canadian Baseball	164434	5,000	169.95	Proof	170.	—

TWENTY-FIVE DOLLARS, THUNDERBIRD, 2018.

Designers and Engravers:

Obv.:	Susanna Blunt, Susan Taylor
Rev.:	Andy Everson

Composition: 99.99% Ag
Silver content: 30.76 g, 1.01 tr oz

Weight:	30.76 g	**Edge:**	Plain
Diameter:	36.15 mm	**Die Axis:**	↑↑
Thickness:	N/A	**Finish:**	Proof

Case of Issue: Standard maroon clamshell with black beauty box, COA.

DATE	DESCRIPTION	RCM ITEM #	MINTAGE	ISSUE PRICE	FINISH	PR-69	PR-70
2018	Thunderbird	165741	5,000	149.95	Proof	150.	—

TWENTY-FIVE DOLLARS, *ANCESTOR MOON* MASK, 2018.

Designers and Engravers:

Obv.:	Susanna Blunt, Susan Taylor
Rev.:	Andy Everson

Composition: 99.99% Ag, Selective colour
Silver content: 30.76 g, 1.01 tr oz

Weight:	30.76 g	**Edge:**	Plain
Diameter:	36.15 mm	**Die Axis:**	↑↑
Thickness:	N/A	**Finish:**	Proof

Case of Issue: Standard maroon clamshell with graphic beauty box, COA.

DATE	DESCRIPTION	RCM ITEM #	MINTAGE	ISSUE PRICE	FINISH	PR-69	PR-70
2018	*Ancestor Moon* Mask	165636	4,000	149.95	Proof	160.	—

Note: The *Ancestor Moon* Mask coin was exclusively sold to the Mint Master's Club Members only.

HISTORICAL CURRENCY OF CANADA:
PLAYING CARDS OF NEW FRANCE SET

TWENTY-FIVE DOLLARS, HISTORICAL CURRENCY OF CANADA: PLAYING CARDS OF NEW FRANCE, 2018.

Introduced in 1685, the playing card money of New France is one of the most interesting chapters in the story of Canadian currency but few examples survive today.

| Common Obverse | The King of Diamonds | The King of Clubs | The King of Hearts | The King of Spades |

Designers:	
Obv.:	Susanna Blunt
Rev.:	Trevor Tennant
Composition:	99.99% Ag
Weight:	47.34 g (each coin)
Diameter:	49.8 mm x 28.6 mm (each coin)
Thickness:	N/A
Case of Issue:	Maroon clamshell with graphic beauty box, COA.

Engravers:	
Obv.:	Susan Taylor
Silver content:	47.34 g, 1.5 tr oz
Edge:	Plain
Die Axis:	↑↑
Finish:	Proof

DATE	DESCRIPTION	RCM ITEM #	MINTAGE	ISSUE PRICE	FINISH	PR-69	PR-70
2018	Historical Currency of Canada: Playing Card Money of New France	169541	1,250 (set)	649.95	Proof	150.	—

TWENTY-FIVE DOLLARS, PIEDFORT, 250TH ANNIVERSARY OF TECUMSEH'S BIRTH, 2018.

Designers and Engravers:			
Obv.:	Susanna Blunt, Susan Taylor		
Rev.:	Mary McPherson		
Composition:	99.99% Ag, selective gold plating		
Silver content:	31.39 g, 1.01 tr oz		
Weight:	31.39 g	**Edge:**	Reeded
Diameter:	34 mm	**Die Axis:**	↑↑
Thickness:	N/A	**Finish:**	Proof
Case of Issue:	Maroon clamshell with standard black beauty box, COA		

DATE	DESCRIPTION	RCM ITEM #	MINTAGE	ISSUE PRICE	FINISH	PR-69	PR-70
2018	250th Anniversay of Tecumseh's Birth	166404	6,000	129.95	Proof	130.	—

HER MAJESTY QUEEN ELIZABETH II SET

TWENTY-FIVE DOLLARS, HER MAJESTY QUEEN ELIZABETH II, 2018.

Her Majesty Queen Elizabeth II is the first monarch to be crowned "Queen of Canada" and it is our first time to portray her onrepoussé-inspired coins..

| Common Obverse | The Young Princess | The New Queen | Matriarch of the Royal Family |

Designers:

Obv.:	Susanna Blunt	
Rev.:	Bonnie Ross	
Composition:	99.99% Ag	
Weight:	34.1g	
Diameter:	36.07 mm	
Thickness:	N/A	
Case of Issue:	Standard maroon clamshell with black beauty box, COA.	

Engravers:

Obv.:	Susan Taylor
Silver content:	34.1 g, 1.1 tr oz
Edge:	Reeded
Die Axis:	↑↑
Finish:	Antique

DATE	DESCRIPTION	RCM ITEM #	MINTAGE	ISSUE PRICE	FINISH	PR-69	PR-70
2018	Her Majesty Queen Elizabeth II: The Young Princess	165838	4,500	149.95	Antique	150.	—
2018	Her Majesty Queen Elizabeth II: The New Queen	167747	4,500	149.95	Antique	150.	—
2018	Her Majesty Queen Elizabeth II: Matriarch of the Royal Family	168857	4,500	149.95	Antique	150.	—

TWENTY-FIVE DOLLARS, SALMON RUN, 2018.

Designers and Engravers:

Obv.:	Susanna Blunt, Susan Taylor		
Rev.:	Emily Damstra		
Composition:	99.99% Ag		
Silver content:	47.35 g, 1.5 tr oz		
Weight:	47.35 g	**Edge:**	Plain
Diameter:	49.8 mm x 28.8 mm	**Die Axis:**	↑↑
Thickness:	N/A.	**Finish:**	Proof
Case of Issue:	Black clamshell with black beauty box, COA.		

DATE	DESCRIPTION	RCM ITEM #	MINTAGE	ISSUE PRICE	FINISH	PR-69	PR-70
2018	Salmon Run	167151	3,500	149.95	Proof	150.	—

TWENTY-FIVE DOLLARS, LEST WE FORGET, 2018.

The Royal Canadian Mint commemorates the anniversary of the Armistice with its most unusual coin yet: a poignant symbol of remembrance shaped like the steel helmets worn by Canadian combatants in the First World War.

Designers and Engravers:

Obv.:	Susanna Blunt, Susan Taylor		
Rev.:	RCM Staff		
Composition:	99.99% Ag		
Silver content:	47.6 g, 1.53 tr oz		
Weight:	47.6 g	**Edge:**	Plain
Diameter:	52.35 mm	**Die Axis:**	↑↑
Thickness:	N/A	**Finish:**	Proof
Case of Issue:	Maroon clamshell with black beauty box, COA		

DATE	DESCRIPTION	RCM ITEM #	MINTAGE	ISSUE PRICE	FINISH	PR-69	PR-70
2018	Lest We Forget	167843	6,500	199.95	Proof	200.	—

LEGENDARY LEADERS SERIES

TWENTY-FIVE DOLLARS, LEGENDARY LEADERS, 2019.

This series of rectangular coins highlights some of the Canadian members of the Hockey Hall of Fame who famously captained an Original Six NHL team.

Common Obverse

Toronto Maple Leafs®:
Doug Gilmour

Designers:		Engravers:	
Obv.:	Susanna Blunt	Obv.:	Susan Taylor
Rev.:	RCM Staff		
Composition:	99.99% Ag	Silver content:	47.35 g, 1.5 tr oz
Weight:	47.35g	Edge:	Plain
Diameter:	49.8 mm x 28.6 mm	Die Axis:	↑↑
Thickness:	N/A	Finish:	Proof
Case of Issue:	Black clamshell with graphic beauty box, COA.		

Montreal Canadiens®:
Yvan Cournoyer

New York Rangers®:
Mark Messier

Boston Bruins®:
Ray Bourque

Chicago Blackhawks®:
Denis Savard

Detroit Red Wings®:
Steve Yzerman

DATE	DESCRIPTION	RCM ITEM #	MINTAGE	ISSUE PRICE	FINISH	PR-69	PR-70
2019	*Toronto Maple Leafs®:* Doug Gilmour	166644	5,000	149.95	Proof	150.	—
2019	*Montreal Canadiens®:* Yvan Cournoyer	166645	5,000	149.95	Proof	150.	—,
2019	*New York Rangers®:* Mark Messier	166646	5,000	149.95	Proof	150.	—
2019	*Boston Bruins®:* Ray Bourque	166647	5,000	149.95	Proof	150.	—
2019	*Chicago Blackhawks®:* Denis Savard	166648	5,000	149.95	Proof	150.	—
2019	*Detroit Red Wings®:* Steve Yzerman	166649	5,000	149.95	Proof	150.	—

THIRTY DOLLARS

THIRTY DOLLARS, WELCOME FIGURE (DZUNUK'WA) TOTEM POLE, 2005.

Designers and Engravers:

Obv.:	Susanna Blunt, Susan Taylor
Rev.:	Richard Hunt, Susan Taylor

Composition: 92.5% Ag, 7.5% Cu
Silver content: 29.137 g, 0.937 tr oz

Weight:	31.50 g	**Edge:**	Reeded
Diameter:	40.0 mm	**Die Axis:**	↑↑
Thickness:	3.0 mm	**Finish:**	Proof

Case of Issue: Maroon plastic slide case, black plastic insert, encapsulated coin, COA

DATE	DESCRIPTION	QUANTITY SOLD	ISSUE PRICE	FINISH	PR-69	PR-70
2005	Welcome Figure Totem Pole	9,904	79.95	Proof	70.	—

Note: An identical design is utilized on the $300 gold coin for 2005, see page 463.

THIRTY DOLLARS, DOG SLED TEAM, 2006.

Designers and Engravers:

Obv.:	Susanna Blunt, Susan Taylor
Rev.:	Arnold Nogy, José Osio

Composition: 92.5% Ag, 7.5% Cu, Painted
Silver content: 29.137 g, 0.937 tr oz

Weight:	31.50 g	**Edge:**	Reeded
Diameter:	40.0 mm	**Die Axis:**	↑↑
Thickness:	3.0 mm	**Finish:**	Proof

Case of Issue: Maroon plastic slide case, black plastic insert, encapsulated coin, COA

DATE	DESCRIPTION	QUANTITY SOLD	ISSUE PRICE	FINISH	PR-69	PR-70
2006	Dog Sled Team	7,384	89.95	Proof	150.	—

Note: An identical design is utilized on the $250 gold coin for 2006, see page 454.

NATIONAL WAR MEMORIALS SERIES

THIRTY DOLLARS, NATIONAL WAR MEMORIALS SERIES, 2006-2007.

2006 Obverse Date on Obverse	**2006 National War Memorial** Designer: Vernon March Engraver: José Osio	**2006 Beaumont-Hamel** Newfoundland Memorial Designer: RCM Staff Engraver: Susan Taylor	**2007 Obverse** Date on Reverse	**2007 Canadian National** Vimy Memorial Designer: RCM Staff Engraver: José Osio

Designers:

Obv.:	Susanna Blunt
Rev.:	See reverse illustrations

Composition: 92.5% Ag, 7.5% Cu
Silver content: 29.137 g, 0.937 tr oz

Engravers:

Obv.:	Susan Taylor
Rev.:	See reverse illustrations

Weight:	31.50 g		
Diameter:	40.0 mm	**Edge:**	Reeded
Thickness:	3.0 mm	**Die Axis:**	↑↑
		Finish:	Proof

Case of Issue: Maroon plastic slide case, black plastic insert, encapsulated coin, COA

THIRTY DOLLARS, NATIONAL WAR MEMORIALS SERIES, 2006-2007, PRICING PANEL.

DATE	DESCRIPTION	RCM ITEM #	QUANTITY SOLD	ISSUE PRICE	FINISH	PR-69	PR-70
2006	National War Memorial	N/A	8,876	79.95	Proof	80.	—
2006	Beaumont-Hamel Newfoundland Memorial	N/A	15,325	79.95	Proof	80.	—
2007 (1917-)	Canadian National Vimy Memorial	624307	5,335	79.95	Proof	80.	—

CANADIAN ACHIEVEMENT SERIES

THIRTY DOLLARS, CANADIAN ACHIEVEMENTS, 2006-2008.

Designers and Engravers:

Obv.:	Susanna Blunt, Susan Taylor
Rev.:	See reverse illustrations
Composition:	92.5% Ag, 7.5% Cu, Decal
Silver content:	29.137 g, 0.937 tr oz
Weight:	31.50 g
Diameter:	40.0 mm
Thickness:	2.8 mm to 3.0 mm
Case of Issue:	Maroon plastic slide case, black plastic insert, encapsulated coin, COA

Edge: Reeded **Die Axis:** ↑↑ **Finish:** Proof

2006 Obverse / **5th Anniversary of Canadarm**
Designer: Cecily Mok

2006 Obverse / **Panoramic Photography in Canada, Niagara Falls**
Designer: Chris Jordson

2008 Obverse / **IMAX©**
Designer: IMAX©, RCM Staff

DATE	DESCRIPTION	RCM ITEM #	QUANTITY SOLD	ISSUE PRICE	FINISH	PR-69	PR-70
2006	5th Anniversary of Canadarm, Decal	624216	9,357	79.95	Proof	80.	—
2007	Panoramic Photography in Canada, Niagara Falls, Hologram	624217	5,702	84.95	Proof	80.	—
2008	IMAX®, Hologram	101980	3,861	84.95	Proof	80.	—

Note: For the gold coins in this series see page 464.

THIRTY DOLLARS, INTERNATIONAL YEAR OF ASTRONOMY, 2009.

Designers and Engravers:

Obv.:	Susanna Blunt, Susan Taylor
Rev.:	Colin Mayne, Stan Witten
Composition:	92.5% Ag, 7.5% Cu, Painted
Silver content:	31.22 g, 1.00 tr oz
Weight:	33.75 g
Diameter:	40.0 mm
Thickness:	2.9 mm
Case of Issue:	Maroon leatherette clam style case, black flocked insert, encapsulated coin, COA

Edge: Reeded **Die Axis:** ↑↑ **Finish:** Proof

DATE	DESCRIPTION	RCM ITEM #	QUANTITY SOLD	ISSUE PRICE	FINISH	PR-69	PR-70
2009	International Year of Astronomy	105281	7,174	89.95	Proof	90.	—

THIRTY DOLLARS, 100TH ANNIVERSARY OF THE COMPLETION OF THE GRAND TRUNK PACIFIC RAILWAY, 2014.

The same design was issued in a $250 gold coin (see page 455).

Designers and Engravers:

Obv.:	Susanna Blunt, Susan Taylor
Rev.:	Joel Kimmel, RCM Staff

Composition:	99.99% Ag		
Silver content:	56.0 g, 1.80 tr oz		
Weight:	56.0 g	**Edge:**	Reeded
Diameter:	54.0 mm	**Die Axis:**	↑↑
Thickness:	N/A	**Finish:**	Proof
Case of Issue:	Maroon leatherette clam style case, black flocked insert, encapsulated coin, COA, custom coloured box		

DATE	DESCRIPTION	RCM ITEM #	QUANTITY SOLD	ISSUE PRICE	FINISH	PR-69	PR-70
2014	100th Anniv. Grand Truck Pacific Railway	140578	500	169.95	Proof	170.	—

THIRTY DOLLARS, CANADA THROUGH THE EYES OF TIM BARNARD, 2014

Designers and Engravers:

Obv.:	Susanna Blunt, Susan Taylor
Rev.:	Tim Bernard, RCM Staff

Composition:	99.99% Ag		
Silver content:	62.7 g, 2.0 tr oz		
Weight:	62.7 g	**Edge:**	Reeded
Diameter:	54.0 mm	**Die Axis:**	↑↑
Thickness:	3.0 mm	**Finish:**	Proof
Case of Issue:	Maroon leatherette clam style case, black flocked insert, encapsulated coin, COA custom coloured box		

DATE	DESCRIPTION	RCM ITEM #	QUANTITY SOLD	ISSUE PRICE	FINISH	PR-69	PR-70
2014	Canada Through the Eyes of Tim Barnard		4,996	169.95	Proof	170.	—

THIRTY DOLLARS, 75TH ANNIVERSARY OF THE DECLARATION OF THE SECOND WORLD WAR, 1939-2014

Designers and Engravers:

Obv.:	Susanna Blunt, Susan Taylor
Rev.:	Silvia Pecota, RCM Staff

Composition:	99.99% Ag		
Silver content:	62.7 g, 2.0 tr oz		
Weight:	62.7 g	**Edge:**	Reeded
Diameter:	54.0 mm	**Die Axis:**	↑↑
Thickness:	3.0 mm	**Finish:**	Proof
Case of Issue:	Maroon leatherette clam style case, black flocked insert, encapsulated coin, COA custom coloured box		

DATE	DESCRIPTION	RCM ITEM #	QUANTITY SOLD	ISSUE PRICE	FINISH	PR-69	PR-70
2014 (1939-)	75th Anniv. Declaration of WW II	130576	4,159	169.95	Proof	170.	—

THIRTY DOLLARS, NATIONAL ABORIGINAL VETERANS MONUMENT, 2014

Designers and Engravers:

Obv.:	Susanna Blunt, Susan Taylor
Rev.:	N.L. Pinay, RCM Staff

Composition:	99.99% Ag		
Silver content:	62.7 g, 2.0 tr oz		
Weight:	62.7 g	**Edge:**	Reeded
Diameter:	54.0 mm	**Die Axis:**	↑↑
Thickness:	3.0 mm	**Finish:**	Proof
Case of Issue:	Maroon leatherette clam style case, black flocked insert, encapsulated coin, COA custom coloured box		

DATE	DESCRIPTION	RCM ITEM #	QUANTITY SOLD	ISSUE PRICE	FINISH	PR-69	PR-70
2014	National Aboriginal Veterans Monument	140432	2,026	169.95	Proof	170.	—

THIRTY DOLLARS, CANADA'S MERCHANT NAVY IN THE BATTLE OF THE ATLANTIC, 2015.

Designers and Engravers:

Obv.:	Susanna Blunt, Susan Taylor
Rev.:	Yves Bérubé
Composition:	99.99% Ag
Silver content:	62.67 g, 2.0 tr oz
Weight:	62.67 g
Diameter:	54.0 mm
Thickness:	N/A
Case of Issue:	Maroon clamshell with custom beauty box.

	Edge:	Reeded
	Die Axis:	↑↑
	Finish:	Proof

DATE	DESCRIPTION	RCM ITEM #	QUANTITY SOLD	ISSUE PRICE	FINISH	PR-69	PR-70
2015	Canada's Merchant Navy in the Battle of the Atlantic	N/A	2,460	169.95	Proof	170.	—

LOONEY TUNES™ CLASSIC SCENES SERIES

THIRTY DOLLARS, LOONEY TUNES™ CLASSIC SCENES, 2015.

Bugs. Daffy. Tweety. Sylvester. For many Canadians, the mere mention of these names evoke fond childhood memories of spending Saturday mornings in front of a television, transfixed and spellbound as these characters—and many more—outsmarted each other in situations that could only exist in our imaginations.

Common Obverse	The Rabbit of Seville	Fast and Furry-ous	Birds Anonymous

Designers:

Obv.:	Susanna Blunt
Rev.:	Warner Bros.
Composition:	99.99% Ag
Silver content:	62.67 g, 2.0 tr oz
Weight:	62.67 g
Diameter:	54.0 mm
Thickness:	3.0 mm
Case of Issue:	Maroon plastic slide case, black plastic insert, encapsulated coin, COA

Engravers:

Obv.:	Susan Taylor
Rev.:	Warner Bros.

Edge:	Reeded
Die Axis:	↑↑
Finish:	Proof

DATE	DESCRIPTION	RCM ITEM #	QUANTITY SOLD	ISSUE PRICE	FINISH	PR-69	PR-70
2015	*The Rabbit of Seville*	144791	4,995	189.95	Proof	140.	—
2015	*Fast and Furry-ous*	144825	4,877	189.95	Proof	140.	—
2015	*Birds Anonymous*	144892	4,965	189.95	Proof	140.	—

IN THE MOONLIGHT

THIRTY DOLLARS, IN THE MOONLIGHT, 2015-2016.

Common Obverse

Moonlight Fireflies
Designer: Ervin Mohan

Northern Lights in the Moonlight
Designer: Julius Csotonyl

Designers:
 Obv.: Susanna Blunt
 Rev.: See reverse illustrations
Composition: 99.99% Ag, Selective colour
Weight: 62.67 g
Diameter: 54.0 mm
Thickness: N/A
Case of Issue: Maroon clamshell with custom beauty box.

Engravers:
 Obv.: Susan Taylor

Silver content: 62.67 g, 2.0 tr oz
Edge: Reeded
Die Axis: ↑↑
Finish: Proof

DATE	DESCRIPTION	RCM ITEM #	QUANTITY SOLD	ISSUE PRICE	FINISH	PR-69	PR-70
2015	Moonlight Fireflies	145468	3,999	189.95	Proof	240.	—
2016	Northern Lights in the Moonlight	150462	3,999	189.95	Proof	400.	—

THIRTY DOLLARS, ILLUMINATED CORAL REEF, 2016.

Designers and Engravers:
 Obv.: Susanna Blunt, Susan Taylor
 Rev.: Jesse Koreck
Composition: 99.99% Ag, Selective colour
Silver content: 62.67 g, 2.0 tr oz
Weight: 62.67 g   **Edge:** Reeded
Diameter: 54.0 mm   **Die Axis:** ↑↑
Thickness: N/A   **Finish:** Proof
Case of Issue: Maroon clamshell with custom beauty box.

DATE	DESCRIPTION	RCM ITEM #	QUANTITY SOLD	ISSUE PRICE	FINISH	PR-69	PR-70
2016	Illuminated Coral Reef	154236	3,995	189.95	Proof	190.	—

THIRTY DOLLARS, POP ART: CELEBRATING THE CANADA GOOSE, 2016.

Designers and Engravers:
 Obv.: Susanna Blunt, Susan Taylor
 Rev.: Andrew Lewis
Composition: 99.99% Ag
Silver content: 62.69 g, 2.0 tr oz
Weight: 62.69 g   **Edge:** Reeded
Diameter: 50 mm   **Die Axis:** ↑↑
Thickness: N/A   **Finish:** Proof
Case of Issue: Maroon clamshell with custom beauty box.

DATE	DESCRIPTION	RCM ITEM #	QUANTITY SOLD	ISSUE PRICE	FINISH	PR-69	PR-70
2016	Pop Art: Celebrating the Canada Goose		2,332	169.95	Proof	150.	—

THIRTY DOLLARS, *BATMAN V SUPERMAN: DAWN OF JUSTICE™*, 2016.

Designers and Engravers:

Obv.:	Susanna Blunt, Susan Taylor		
Rev.:	DC Comics		
Composition:	99.99% Ag, Selective colour		
Silver content:	62.67 g, 2.0 tr oz		
Weight:	62.67 g	Edge:	Reeded
Diameter:	54 mm	Die Axis:	↑↑
Thickness:	N/A	Finish:	Proof
Case of Issue:	Premium presentation case.		

DATE	DESCRIPTION	RCM ITEM #	QUANTITY SOLD	ISSUE PRICE	FINISH	PR-69	PR-70
2016	*Batman v Superman: Dawn of Justice*	150118	6,141	189.95	Proof	175.	—

THIRTY DOLLARS, *STAR TREK™*: FIVE CAPTAINS, 2017.

The Royal Canadian Mint continues its celebration of *Star Trek™* with a unique glow-in-the-dark coin that brings together the legendary captains, who repeatedly rose to the challenges that come with boldly going "where no man has gone before."

Designers and Engravers:

Obv.:	Susanna Blunt, Susan Taylor		
Rev.:	RCM Staff		
Composition:	99.99% Ag, Selective colour		
Silver content:	62.67 g, 2.0 tr oz		
Weight:	62.67 g	Die Axis:	↑↑
Diameter:	54.0 mm	Edge:	Reeded
Thickness:	N/A	Finish:	Proof
Case of Issue:	Graphic beauty box.		

DATE	DESCRIPTION	RCM ITEM #	QUANTITY SOLD	ISSUE PRICE	FINISH	PR-69	PR-70
2017	*Star Trek™*: Five Captains	160443	5,000	194.95	Proof	200.	—

ENDANGERED ANIMAL CUTOUT SERIES

THIRTY DOLLARS, ENDANGERED ANIMAL CUTOUT, 2017.

Designers:

Obv.:	Susanna Blunt
Rev.:	Trevor Tennant
Composition:	99.99% Ag,
Weight:	52.88 g
Diameter:	54.0 mm
Thickness:	N/A
Case of Issue:	Maroon clamshell with black beauty box, COA.

Engravers:

Obv.:	Susan Taylor
Silver content:	52.88 g, 1.7 tr oz
Edge:	Reeded
Die Axis:	↑↑
Finish:	Proof

DATE	DESCRIPTION	RCM ITEM #	QUANTITY SOLD	ISSUE PRICE	FINISH	PR-69	PR-70
2017	Endangered Animal Cutout: Woodland Cairbou	156478	5,500	189.95	Proof	190.	—
2017	Endangered Animal Cutout: Whooping Crane	156480	5,500	189.95	Proof	190.	—

ANIMALS IN THE MOONLIGHT SERIES

THIRTY DOLLARS, ANIMALS IN THE MOONLIGHT, 2017.

Featuring luminescent wilderness scenes that reveal the secretive movements of the cougar, lynx, orca and owl that have facinated humanity for centuries.

Common Obverse	Cougar	Lynx	Orcas	Great Horned Owl
	Des.: Jan Poynter	Des.: Curtis Atwater	Des.: Vanessa Miller	Des.: Curtis Atwater

Designers:		Engravers:	
Obv.:	Susanna Blunt	Obv.:	Susan Taylor
Rev.:	See reverse illustrations		
Composition:	99.99% Ag, Selective colour	Thickness:	N/A
Silver content:	62.67 g, 2.0 tr oz	Edge:	Reeded
Weight:	62.67 g	Die Axis:	↑↑
Diameter:	54.0 mm	Finish:	Proof
Case of Issue:	Maroon clamshell with graphic beauty box, COA.		

DATE	DESCRIPTION	RCM ITEM #	QUANTITY SOLD	ISSUE PRICE	FINISH	PR-69	PR-70
2017	Animals in the Moonlight: Cougar	157537	4,000	189.95	Proof	175.	—
2017	Animals in the Moonlight: Lynx	158765	4,000	189.95	Proof	175.	—
2017	Animals in the Moonlight: Orcas	159917	4,000	189.95	Proof	175.	—
2017	Animals in the Moonlight: Great Horned Owl	159918	4,000	189.95	Proof	175.	—

THIRTY DOLLARS, CELEBRATING CANADA DAY, 2017.

On Canada Day, Parliament Hill is awash in a sea of red and white that is a proud expression of patriotism–especially in 2017, when Canadians came together to celebrate 150 years of Confederation.

Designers and Engravers:			
Obv.:	Susanna Blunt, Susan Taylor		
Rev.:	Jesse Koreck		
Composition:	99.99% Ag,		
Silver content:	62.67 g, 2.0 tr oz		
Weight:	62.67 g	Edge:	Reeded
Diameter:	54.0 mm	Die Axis:	↑↑
Thickness:	N/A	Finish:	Proof
Case of Issue:	Maroon clamshell with graphic beauty box, COA.		

DATE	DESCRIPTION	RCM ITEM #	QUANTITY SOLD	ISSUE PRICE	FINISH	PR-69	PR-70
2017	Celebrating Canada Day	161450	5,000	189.95	Proof	190.	—

THIRTY DOLLARS, FLORA AND FAUNA OF CANADA, 2017.

Designers and Engravers:
Obv.:	Susanna Blunt, Susan Taylor
Rev.:	Steve Hepburn
Composition:	99.99% Ag,
Silver content:	62.69 g, 2.0 tr oz

Weight:	62.69 g	Edge:	Reeded
Diameter:	50.0 mm	Die Axis:	↑↑
Thickness:	N/A	Finish:	Proof

Case of Issue:	Maroon clamshell with black beauty box.

DATE	DESCRIPTION	RCM ITEM #	QUANTITY SOLD	ISSUE PRICE	FINISH	PR-69	PR-70
2017	Flora and Fauna of Canada	160780	4,000	174.95	Proof	175.	—

PHASES OF THE MOON SET

THIRTY DOLLARS, PHASES OF THE MOON, 3-COIN SET, 2017.

This captivating 3-coin set portrays three moon phases with translucent enamel creating the shadow that defines the new and waxing gibbous moon.

Common Obverse	New Moon	Half Moon	Full Moon

Designers:
Obv.:	Susanna Blunt
Rev.:	Andy Everson
Composition:	99.99% Ag
Weight:	62.69 g
Diameter:	50.0 mm
Thickness:	N/A
Case of Issue:	Maroon clamshell with black beauty box, COA

Engravers:
Obv.:	Susan Taylor
Silver content:	62.69 g, 2.0 tr oz
Edge:	Reeded
Die Axis:	↑↑
Finish:	Proof

DATE	DESCRIPTION	RCM ITEM #	QUANTITY SOLD	ISSUE PRICE	FINISH	PR-69	PR-70
2017	Phases of the Moon 3-coin set	162272	3,000	575.95	Proof	575.	—

THIRTY DOLLARS, GOLDEN MAPLE LEAF, 2018.

An RCM first! Introducing the first fine silver coin featuring an 18Kt. gold maple leaf.

Designers and Engravers:
Obv.:	Susanna Blunt, Susan Taylor
Rev.:	Michelle Grant
Composition:	99.99% Ag,
Silver content:	62.69 g, 2.0 tr oz

Weight:	62.69 g + 1 g (18 Kt. gold maple leaf)	Edge:	Reeded
Diameter:	50.0 mm	Die Axis:	↑↑
Thickness:	N/A	Finish:	Proof

Case of Issue:	Maroon clamshell with black beauty box, COA.

DATE	DESCRIPTION	RCM ITEM #	QUANTITY SOLD	ISSUE PRICE	FINISH	PR-69	PR-70
2018	Golden Maple Leaf	162364	2,750	299.95	Proof	300.	—

GATES OF CANADA SERIES

THIRTY DOLLARS, GATES OF CANADA, 2017-2018.

To some, gates are a way to keep people out—but they can also be a beautiful invitation to enter. The intricate scrollwork on each coin of a filigree gate sets an elegant tone and catches the eye, beckoning you to look at what lies beyond!

2017 Obverse

2018 Obverse

Gate to Enchanted Garden
Des.: Tony Bainco

Halifax Public Gardens
Des.: Margaret Best

The Queen's Gate Formal Entrance to Parliament Hill
Des.: Cathy Bursey-Sabourin and Patrick Belanger

Designers:
    Obv.:   Susanna Blunt
    Rev.:   See reverse illustrations
Composition: 99.99% Ag, Selective colour
Weight: 62.69 g
Diameter: 50.0 mm
Thickness: N/A
Case of Issue: Maroon clamshell with black beauty box, COA.

Engravers:
    Obv.:   Susan Taylor

Silver content: 62.69 g, 2.0 tr oz
Edge: Reeded
Die Axis: ↑↑
Finish: Proof

DATE	DESCRIPTION	RCM ITEM #	QUANTITY SOLD	ISSUE PRICE	FINISH	PR-69	PR-70
2017	Gates of Canada: Gate to Enchanted Garden	161368	5,500	239.95	Proof	240.	—
2018	Gates of Canada: Halifax Public Gardens	163169	5,500	239.95	Proof	240.	—
2018	Gates of Canada: The Queen's Gate	164185	5,500	239.95	Proof	240.	—

ZENTANGLE® ART SERIES

THIRTY DOLLARS, ZENTANGLE® ART, 2017-2019.

Common obverse

The Great Grey Wolf

The Great Horned Owl

The Bighorn Sheep

Designers:
    Obv.:   Susanna Blunt
    Rev.:   Jori Van Der Linde
Composition: 99.99% Ag,
Weight: 62.69 g
Diameter: 50.0 mm
Thickness: N/A
Case of Issue: Maroon clamshell with black beauty box.

Engravers:
    Obv.:   Susan Taylor

Silver content: 62.69 g, 2.0 tr oz
Edge: Reeded
Die Axis: ↑↑
Finish: Proof

THIRTY DOLLARS, ZENTANGLE® ART, 2017-2019, PRICING PANEL.

DATE	DESCRIPTION	RCM ITEM #	MINTAGE	ISSUE PRICE	FINISH	PR-69	PR-70
2017	Zentangle® Art: The Great Grey Wolf	156320	4,000	174.95	Proof	175.	—
2018	Zentangle® Art: The Great Horned Owl	165667	4,000	174.95	Proof	175.	—
2019	Zentangle® Art: The Bighorn Sheep	169489	4,000	174.95	Proof	175.	—

THIRTY DOLLARS, CAPTAIN COOK AND THE HMS *RESOLUTION*, 2018.

After exploring the South Pacific and crossing the Antarctic Circle during his previous two voyages, Captain James Cook (1728-1779) came north on his third epic Pacific voyage, eventually reaching our western shores in 1778.

Designers and Engravers:
Obv.: Susanna Blunt, Susan Taylor
Rev.: Neil Hamelin
Composition: 99.99% Ag, Gold plated
Silver content: 62.69 g, 2.0 tr oz
Weight: 62.69 g **Edge:** Reeded
Diameter: 50 mm **Die Axis:** ↑↑
Thickness: N/A **Finish:** Proof
Case of Issue: Maroon clamshellf with a standard black beauty box, COA..

DATE	DESCRIPTION	RCM ITEM #	QUANTITY SOLD	ISSUE PRICE	FINISH	PR-69	PR-70
2018	Captain Cook and the HMS Resolution	166967	4,000	189.95	Proof	190.	—

ARCTIC ANIMALS AND NORTHERN LIGHTS SERIES

THIRTY DOLLARS, ARCTIC ANIMALS AND NORTHERN LIGHTS, 2018.

This must-have series showcases the Arctic's most celebrated wilderness residents with innovative, glow-in-the-dark designs that reveal how, even in the dark of night, this extreme landscape is rife with life—and magic!

Common obverse	Polar Bear	Snowy Owl

Designers:
Obv.: Susanna Blunt
Rev.: Trevor Tennant
Composition: 99.99% Ag, Selective colour
Weight: 62.69 g
Diameter: 50.0 mm
Thickness: N/A
Case of Issue: Maroon clamshell with black beauty box, COA.

Engravers:
Obv.: Susan Taylor
Silver content: 62.69 g, 2.0 tr oz
Edge: Reeded
Die Axis: ↑↑
Finish: Proof

DATE	DESCRIPTION	RCM ITEM #	QUANTITY SOLD	ISSUE PRICE	FINISH	PR-69	PR-70
2018	Arctic Animals & Northern Lights: Polar Bear	165236	4,000	189.95	Proof	190.	—
2018	Arctic Animals & Northern Lights: Snowy Owl	165963	4,000	189.95	Proof	190.	—

THIRTY DOLLARS, *THE JUSTICE LEAGUE™: THE WORLD'S GREATEST SUPER HEROES,* 2018.

The World's Greatest Super Heroes—a strike force of unprecedented power, and the A-team of the DC Universe. Through their different abilities, feats and personalities, each character symbolizes a different ideal: hope (Superman), justice (Batman), truth (Wonder Woman), optimism (The Flash), conviction (Aquaman), and adaptability (Cyborg).

Designers and Engravers:

Obv.:	Susanna Blunt, Susan Taylor		
Rev.:	Jason Fabok, Brad Anderson		
Composition:	99.99% Ag, Selective colour		
Silver content:	62.67 g, 2.0 tr oz		
Weight:	62.67 g	**Edge:**	Reeded
Diameter:	54 mm	**Die Axis:**	↑↑
Thickness:	N/A	**Finish:**	Proof
Case of Issue:	Graphic beauty box, COA..		

DATE	DESCRIPTION	RCM ITEM #	MINTAGE	ISSUE PRICE	FINISH	PR-69	PR-70
2018	*The Justice League™: The World's Greatest Super Heroes*		6,000	189.95	Proof	190.	—

100TH ANNIVERSARY OF THE CANADIAN NATIONAL INSTITUTE FOR THE BLIND SET

THIRTY DOLLARS, 100TH ANNIVERARY OF THE CNIB, 2018.

In the wake of the First World War, and the Halifax Explosion that left hundreds blind or partially sighted, seven visionaries saw beyond the tragedy and held fast to their ideal that those injured could lead productive lives, nurture their talents, and ultimately fulfill their dreams. As our first coin designed by a partially sighted artist, and the first to feature braille, this keepsake is testament to the power of the Canadian National Institute for the Blind's (CNIB) vision.

Designers and Engravers:

Obv.:	Susanna Blunt / Susan Taylor
Rev.:	Meghan Sims

	Coin	**Medallion**
Composition:	99.99% Ag	Bronze
Silver content:	62.69 g, 2.0 tr oz	
Weight:	62.69 g	77.17
Diameter:	50.0 mm	52 mm
Thickness:	N/A	
Edge:	Reeded	Plain
Die Axis:	↑↑	↑↑
Finish:	Proof	Antique
Case of Issue:	Maroon clamshell with black beauty box, COA	

DATE	DESCRIPTION	RCM ITEM #	MINTAGE	ISSUE PRICE	FINISH	PR-69	PR-70
2018	100th Anniversary CNIB Coin & Medallion set	166696	3,000	219.95	Proof / Antique	220.	—

THIRTY DOLLARS, FIREWORKS AT THE FALLS, 2018.

Designers and Engravers:

Obv.:	Susanna Blunt, Susan Taylor
Rev.:	Tony Bianco
Composition:	99.99% Ag,
Silver content:	62.69 g, 2.0 tr oz
Weight:	62.69 g
Diameter:	50.0 mm
Thickness:	N/A
Case of Issue:	Maroon clamshell with black beauty box, COA.

Edge:	Reeded
Die Axis:	↑↑
Finish:	Proof

DATE	DESCRIPTION	RCM ITEM #	MINTAGE	ISSUE PRICE	FINISH	PR-69	PR-70
2018	Fireworks at the Falls	164883	5,000	189.95	Proof	190.	—

THIRTY DOLLARS, 110TH ANNIVERSARY OF THE ROYAL CANADIAN MINT, 2018.

Designers and Engravers:

Obv.:	Susanna Blunt, Susan Taylor
Rev.:	Steve McPhee
Composition:	99.99% Ag,
Silver content:	62.69 g, 2.0 tr oz
Weight:	62.69 g
Diameter:	50.0 mm
Thickness:	N/A
Case of Issue:	Maroon clamshell with black beauty box.

Edge:	Reeded
Die Axis:	↑↑
Finish:	Proof

DATE	DESCRIPTION	RCM ITEM #	MINTAGE	ISSUE PRICE	FINISH	PR-69	PR-70
2018	110th Anniversary RCM	166165	4,000	239.95	Proof	240.	—

THIRTY DOLLARS, EVOLVING A NATION, 2018.

Designers and Engravers:

Obv.:	Susanna Blunt, Susan Taylor
Rev.:	RCM Staff
Composition:	99.99% Ag,
Silver content:	51.71 g, 1.66 tr oz
Weight:	51.71 g
Diameter:	50.0 mm
Thickness:	N/A
Case of Issue:	Custom black clamshell with beauty box.

Edge:	Reeded
Die Axis:	↑↑
Finish:	Proof

DATE	DESCRIPTION	RCM ITEM #	MINTAGE	ISSUE PRICE	FINISH	PR-69	PR-70
2018	Evolvoing A Nation	167208	4,000	179.95	Proof	180.	—

THIRTY DOLLARS, DIMENSIONAL NATURE: POLAR BEAR, 2018.

Designers and Engravers:

Obv.:	Susanna Blunt, Susan Taylor
Rev.:	Tony Bianco
Composition:	99.99% Ag,
Silver content:	62.69 g, 2.0 tr oz
Weight:	62.69 g
Diameter:	50.0 mm
Thickness:	N/A
Case of Issue:	Maroon clamshell with black beauty box, COA.

Edge:	Reeded
Die Axis:	↑↑
Finish:	Proof

DATE	DESCRIPTION	RCM ITEM #	MINTAGE	ISSUE PRICE	FINISH	PR-69	PR-70
2018	Dimensional Nature: Polar Bear	168161	3,000	199.95	Proof	200.	—

THIRTY DOLLARS, THE GREAT WHITE SHARK, 2018.

Designers and Engravers:
Obv.:	Susanna Blunt, Susan Taylor
Rev.:	Emily Damstra

Composition: 99.99% Ag,
Silver content: 62.69 g, 2.0 tr oz

Weight:	62.69 g	**Edge:**	Reeded
Diameter:	50.0 mm	**Die Axis:**	↑↑
Thickness:	N/A	**Finish:**	Proof
Case of Issue:	Maroon clamshell with black beauty box, COA.		

DATE	DESCRIPTION	RCM ITEM #	MINTAGE	ISSUE PRICE	FINISH	PR-69	PR-70
2018	The Great White Shark	166707	3,500	199.95	Proof	200.	—

CANADIAN CANOPY SERIES

THIRTY DOLLARS, CANADIAN CANOPY, 2018-2019.

Common Obverse

The Maple Leaf

The Canada Goose

Designers:
Obv.:	Susanna Blunt
Rev.:	Trevor Tennant

Composition: 99.99% Ag, Selective colour
Weight: 62.69 g
Diameter: 50.0 mm
Thickness: N/A
Case of Issue: Maroon clamshell with black beauty box, COA.

Engravers:
Obv.:	Susan Taylor

Silver content: 62.69 g, 2.0 tr oz
Edge: Reeded
Die Axis: ↑↑
Finish: Proof

DATE	DESCRIPTION	RCM ITEM #	MINTAGE	ISSUE PRICE	FINISH	PR-69	PR-70
2018	Canadian Canopy: The Maple Leaf	167699	3,500	189.95	Proof	190.	—
2019	Canadian Canopy: The Canada Goose	169981	3,500	189.95	Proof	190.	—

THIRTY DOLLARS, A HUNDRED BLESSINGS OF GOOD FURTUNE, 2019.

Designers and Engravers:
Obv.:	Susanna Blunt, Susan Taylor
Rev.:	Christopher Reid

Composition: 99.99% Ag,
Silver content: 62.69 g, 2.0 tr oz

Weight:	62.69 g	**Edge:**	Reeded
Diameter:	50.0 mm	**Die Axis:**	↑↑
Thickness:	N/A	**Finish:**	Proof
Case of Issue:	Maroon clamshell with black beauty box.		

DATE	DESCRIPTION	RCM ITEM #	MINTAGE	ISSUE PRICE	FINISH	PR-69	PR-70
2019	A Hundred Blessings of Good Fortune	168583	3,888	188.88	Proof	190.	—

THIRTY DOLLARS, FANCY DANCE, 2019.

Designers and Engravers:

Obv.:	Susanna Blunt, Susan Taylor
Rev.:	Garrison Garrow
Composition:	99.99% Ag,
Silver content:	62.69 g, 2.0 tr oz

Weight:	62.69 g	Edge:	Reeded
Diameter:	50.0 mm	Die Axis:	↑↑
Thickness:	N/A	Finish:	Proof
Case of Issue:	Maroon clamshell with black beauty box.		

DATE	DESCRIPTION	RCM ITEM #	MINTAGE	ISSUE PRICE	FINISH	PR-69	PR-70
2019	Fancy Dance	168731	3,500	189.95	Proof	190.	—

THIRTY DOLLARS, THE WILY WOLF, 2019.

Designers and Engravers:

Obv.:	Susanna Blunt, Susan Taylor
Rev.:	Emily Damstra
Composition:	99.99% Ag,
Silver content:	62.69 g, 2.0 tr oz

Weight:	62.69 g	Edge:	Reeded
Diameter:	50.0 mm	Die Axis:	↑↑
Thickness:	N/A	Finish:	Proof
Case of Issue:	Maroon clamshell with black beauty box.		

DATE	DESCRIPTION	RCM ITEM #	MINTAGE	ISSUE PRICE	FINISH	PR-69	PR-70
2019	The Wily Wolf	168462	4,000	189.95	Proof	190.	—

THIRTY DOLLARS, 60 YEARS OF PROMINENCE: THE ST. LAWRENCE SEAWAY, 2019.

Designers and Engravers:

Obv.:	Susanna Blunt, Susan Taylor
Rev.:	Claire Watson
Composition:	99.99% Ag
Silver content:	62.69 g, 2.02 tr oz

Weight:	62.69 g	Edge:	Reeded
Diameter:	52.6 mm	Die Axis:	↑↑
Thickness:	N/A	Finish:	Proof
Case of Issue:	Black clamshell with black beauty box, COA		

DATE	DESCRIPTION	RCM ITEM #	MINTAGE	ISSUE PRICE	FINISH	PR-69	PR-70
2019	60 Years Of Prominence: The St. Lawrence Seaway	170861	2,000	219.95	Proof	220.	—

PETER McKINNON PHOTO SERIES

THIRTY DOLLARS, PETER McKINNON PHOTO SERIES, 2019.

Common Obverse

Moraine Lake

Mount Rundle

Designers:		Engravers:	
Obv.:	Susanna Blunt	Obv.:	Susan Taylor
Rev.:	Peter McKinnon		
Composition:	99.99% Ag, Selective colour	Silver content:	62.69 g, 2.0 tr oz
Weight:	62.69 g	Edge:	Reeded
Diameter:	50.0 mm	Die Axis:	↑↑
Thickness:	N/A	Finish:	Proof
Case of Issue:	Black clamshell with black beauty box, COA.		

DATE	DESCRIPTION	RCM ITEM #	MINTAGE	ISSUE PRICE	FINISH	PR-69	PR-70
2019	Moraine Lake	173049	5,000	189.95	Proof	190.	—
2019	Mount Rundle	174186	5,000	189.95	Proof	190.	—

FIFTY DOLLARS

FIFTY DOLLARS, THE FOUR SEASONS, 2006.

Designers and Engravers:

Obv.:	Susanna Blunt, Susan Taylor
Rev.:	Tony Bianco, José Osio
Composition:	99.99% Ag
Silver content:	156.34 g, 5.026 tr oz
Weight:	156.36 g
Diameter:	64.8 mm
Thickness:	5.0
Case of Issue:	Black case, black flocked insert, encapsulated coin, COA

Edge: Reeded
Die Axis: ↑↑
Finish: Proof

DATE	DESCRIPTION	RCM ITEM #	QUANTITY SOLD	ISSUE PRICE	FINISH	PR-69	PR-70
2006	The Four Seasons	N/A	1,999	299.95	Proof	325.	—

FIFTY DOLLARS, 60TH WEDDING ANNIVERSARY OF QUEEN ELIZABETH AND PRINCE PHILIP, 1947-2007.

Designers and Engravers:

Obv.:	Susanna Blunt, Susan Taylor
Rev.:	Steve Hepburn, Susan Taylor
Composition:	99.99% Ag
Silver content:	156.34 g, 5.026 tr oz
Weight:	156.36 g
Diameter:	65.0 mm
Thickness:	5.0
Case of Issue:	Maroon leatherette clam style case, black flocked insert, encapsulated coin, COA

Edge: Reeded
Die Axis: ↑↑
Finish: Proof

DATE	DESCRIPTION	RCM ITEM #	QUANTITY SOLD	ISSUE PRICE	FINISH	PR-69	PR-70
2007 (1947-)	60th Wedding Anniv. Queen Elizabeth / Prince Philip	623507	1,957	299.95	Proof	300.	—

FIFTY DOLLARS, 100TH ANNIVERSARY OF THE ROYAL CANADIAN MINT, 1908-2008.

Designers and Engravers:

Obv.:	Susanna Blunt, Susan Taylor
Rev.:	Konrad Wachelko
Composition:	99.99% Ag
Silver content:	157.65 g, 5.069 tr oz
Weight:	157.67 g
Diameter:	65.0 mm
Thickness:	5.2 mm
Case of Issue:	Maroon leatherette clam style case, black flocked insert, encapsulated coin, COA

Edge: Reeded
Die Axis: ↑↑
Finish: Proof

DATE	DESCRIPTION	RCM ITEM #	QUANTITY SOLD	ISSUE PRICE	FINISH	PR-69	PR-70
2008 (1908-)	100th Anniversary of the RCM	101045	2,078	369.95	Proof	300.	—

FIFTY DOLLARS, 150TH ANNIVERSARY OF THE START OF THE CONSTRUCTION OF THE PARLIAMENT BUILDINGS, 1859-2009.

Designers and Engravers:

Obv.:	Susanna Blunt, Susan Taylor
Rev.:	Cecily Mok
Composition:	99.99% Ag
Silver content:	157.65 g, 5.069 tr oz
Weight:	157.67 g
Diameter:	65.0 mm
Thickness:	5.0 mm
Case of Issue:	Maroon leatherette clam style case, black flocked insert, encapsulated coin, COA

Edge: Reeded
Die Axis: ↑↑
Finish: Proof

DATE	DESCRIPTION	RCM ITEM #	QUANTITY SOLD	ISSUE PRICE	FINISH	PR-69	PR-70
2009 (1859-)	150th Anniv. Construction Parliament Buildings	105218	910	459.95	Proof	325.	—

FIFTY DOLLARS, 75TH ANNIVERSARY OF THE FIRST BANK NOTES ISSUED BY THE BANK OF CANADA, 1935-2010.

The reverse design on this coin is a reproduction of the allegory that appeared on the original 1935 $50 bank note, a seated woman with elements of radio broadcasting to symbolise modern inventions.

Designers and Engravers:

Obv.:	Susanna Blunt, Susan Taylor		
Rev.:	Cecily Mok		
Composition:	99.99% Ag		
Silver content:	157.65 g, 5.069 tr oz		
Weight:	157.67 g	Edge:	Reeded
Diameter:	65.3 mm	Die Axis:	↑↑
Thickness:	5.0 mm	Finish:	Proof
Case of Issue:	Maroon leatherette clam style case, black flocked insert, encapsulated coin, COA		

DATE	DESCRIPTION	RCM ITEM #	QUANTITY SOLD	ISSUE PRICE	FINISH	PR-69	PR-70
2010 (1935-)	75th Anniv. Bank of Canada Notes	109725	1,991	389.95	Proof	350.	—

FIFTY DOLLARS, VANCOUVER 2010 – LOOK OF THE GAMES, 2010.

Designers and Engravers:

Obv.:	Susanna Blunt, Susan Taylor		
Rev.:	Vancourver 2010 Design Team		
Composition:	99.99% Ag		
Silver content:	157.6 g, 5.069 tr oz		
Weight:	157.6 g	Edge:	Reeded
Diameter:	65.25 mm	Die Axis:	↑↑
Thickness:	N/A	Finish:	Proof
Case of Issue:	Maroon leatherette clam style case, black flocked insert, encapsulated coin, COA		

DATE	DESCRIPTION	RCM ITEM #	QUANTITY SOLD	ISSUE PRICE	FINISH	PR-69	PR-70
2010	Vancouver 2010 – The Look of the Games	107240	2,010	389.95	Proof	400.	—

FIFTY DOLLARS, 100TH ANNIVERSARY OF THE CALGARY STAMPEDE, 2012.

Designers and Engravers:

Obv.:	Susanna Blunt, Susan Taylor		
Rev.:	M. Grant, J. Osio		
Composition:	99.99% Ag		
Silver content:	157.65 g, 5.069 tr oz		
Weight:	157.67 g	Edge:	Reeded
Diameter:	65.3 mm	Die Axis:	↑↑
Thickness:	5.0 mm	Finish:	Proof
Case of Issue:	Maroon leatherette clam style case, black flocked insert, encapsulated coin, COA		

DATE	DESCRIPTION	RCM ITEM #	QUANTITY SOLD	ISSUE PRICE	FINISH	PR-69	PR-70
2012	100th Anniv. of the Calgary Stampede	118856	1,500	495.95	Proof	400.	—

FIFTY DOLLARS, THE BEAVER, 2013.

Designers and Engravers:

Obv.:	Susanna Blunt, Susan Taylor		
Rev.:	E. Damstra, C. Mok		
Composition:	99.99% Ag		
Silver content:	157.65 g, 5.069 tr oz		
Weight:	157.67 g	Edge:	Reeded
Diameter:	65.3 mm	Die Axis:	↑↑
Thickness:	5.0 mm	Finish:	Proof
Case of Issue:	Maroon leatherette clam style case, black flocked insert, encapsulated coin, COA		

DATE	DESCRIPTION	RCM ITEM #	QUANTITY SOLD	ISSUE PRICE	FINISH	PR-69	PR-70
2013	The Beaver	123791	1,500	519.95	Proof	400.	—

FIFTY DOLLARS, QUEEN'S CORONATION, 1953-2013.

This coin was issued to commemorate the 60th Anniversary of her Majesty Queen Elizabeth II's accession. The reverse image used for this coin is the official coronation photograph taken by Cecil Beaton, June 2nd, 1953, licensed by the Victoria & Albert Museum in London, England.

Designers and Engravers:

Obv.:	Mary Gillick, Thomas Shingles
Rev.:	See description
Composition:	99.99% Ag
Silver content:	157.65 g, 5.069 tr oz
Weight:	157.67 g
Diameter:	65.3 mm
Thickness:	5.0 mm

Edge:	Reeded
Die Axis:	↑↑
Finish:	Proof

Case of Issue: Maroon leatherette clam style case, black flocked insert, encapsulated coin, COA

DATE	DESCRIPTION	RCM ITEM #	QUANTITY SOLD	ISSUE PRICE	FINISH	PR-69	PR-70
2013 (1953-)	Queen's Coronation	125244	1,499	524.95	Proof	500.	—

FIFTY DOLLARS, *HMS SHANNON* AND *USS CHESAPEAKE*, 1813-2013.

Designers and Engravers:

Obv.:	Susanna Blunt, Susan Taylor
Rev.:	John Horton, Cecily Mok
Composition:	99.99% Ag
Silver content:	157.65 g, 5.069 tr oz
Weight:	157.67 g
Diameter:	65.0 mm
Thickness:	5.0 mm

Edge:	Reeded
Die Axis:	↑↑
Finish:	Proof

Case of Issue: Maroon leatherette clam style case, black flocked insert, encapsulated coin, COA

DATE	DESCRIPTION	RCM ITEM #	QUANTITY SOLD	ISSUE PRICE	FINISH	PR-69	PR-70
2013 (1813-)	*HMS Shannon* and *USS Chesapeake*	120796	1,490	499.85	Proof	400.	—

FIFTY DOLLARS, SWIMMING BEAVER, 2014.

Designers and Engravers:

Obv.:	Susanna Blunt, Susan Taylor
Rev.:	Emily Damstra, RCM Staff
Composition:	99.99% Ag
Silver content:	157.65 g, 5.069 tr oz
Weight:	157.67 g
Diameter:	65.3 mm
Thickness:	5.0 mm

Edge:	Reeded
Die Axis:	↑↑
Finish:	Proof

Case of Issue: Maroon leatherette clam style case, black flocked insert, encapsulated coin, COA

DATE	DESCRIPTION	RCM ITEM #	QUANTITY SOLD	ISSUE PRICE	FINISH	PR-69	PR-70
2014	Swimming Beaver	126079	1,495	519.95	Proof	450.	—

FIFTY DOLLARS, ABORIGINAL STORY: THE LEGEND OF THE SPIRIT BEAR, 2014.

Designers and Engravers:

Obv.:	Susanna Blunt, Susan Taylor
Rev.:	D. Gait, RCM Staff
Composition:	99.99% Ag
Silver content:	157.65 g, 5.069 tr oz
Weight:	157.67 g
Diameter:	65.3 mm
Thickness:	5.0 mm

Edge:	Reeded
Die Axis:	↑↑
Finish:	Proof

Case of Issue: Maroon leatherette clam style case, black flocked insert, encapsulated coin, COA

DATE	DESCRIPTION	RCM ITEM #	QUANTITY SOLD	ISSUE PRICE	FINISH	PR-69	PR-70
2014	Aboriginal Story: The Legend of the Spirit Bear	130559	700	519.95	Proof	450.	—

FIFTY DOLLARS, MAPLE LEAVES, 2014.

Designers and Engravers:

Obv.:	Susanna Blunt, Susan Taylor
Rev.:	Luc Normandin, RCM Staff

Composition:	99.99% Ag		
Silver content:	157.65 g, 5.069 tr oz		
Weight:	157.67 g	**Edge:**	Reeded
Diameter:	65.3 mm	**Die Axis:**	↑↑
Thickness:	5.0 mm	**Finish:**	Proof
Case of Issue:	Red lacquered wooden box, black flocked insert,encapsulated coin, COA		

DATE	DESCRIPTION	RCM ITEM #	QUANTITY SOLD	ISSUE PRICE	FINISH	PR-69	PR-70
2014	Maple Leaves	129499	1,505	499.95	Proof	500.	—

FIFTY FOR FIFTY SERIES

FIFTY DOLLARS, FIFTY FOR FIFTY SERIES, 2014-2016.

Common Obverse	2014 Polar Bear Designer: Emily Damstra Engraver: Alex Tirabasso	2014 Snowy Owl Designer: Trevor Tennant Engraver: RCM Staff	2015 Beaver Designer: Emily Damstra Engraver: RCM Staff	2016 Hare Designer: Emily Damstra Engraver: RCM Staff

Designers:

Obv.:	Susanna Blunt		
Rev.:	See reverse illustrations		
Composition:	99.99% Ag		
Weight:	15.87 g		
Diameter:	34.0 mm		
Thickness:	2.2 mm		
Case of Issue:	Clear vinyl pouch in a certificate booklet		

Engravers:

Obv.:	Susan Taylor		
Silver content:	15.87 g, .5 tr oz		
Edge:	Reeded		
Die Axis:	↑↑		
Finish:	Matte Proof		

DATE	DESCRIPTION	RCM ITEM #	QUANTITY SOLD	ISSUE PRICE	FINISH	PR-69	PR-70
2014	Iconic Polar Bear	129569	99,926	50.00	Matte Proof	60.	—
2014	Snowy Owl	140416	89,568	50.00	Matte Proof	60.	—
2015	Beaver	142193	78,133	50.00	Matte Proof	60.	—
2016	Hare	151087	49,545	50.00	Matte Proof	60.	—

FIFTY DOLLARS, LUSTROUS MAPLE LEAVES, 2015.

Designers and Engravers:
Obv.:	Susanna Blunt, Susan Taylor
Rev.:	Michelle Grant, RCM Staff

Composition: 99.99% Ag
Silver content: 157.65 g, 5.069 tr oz
Weight: 157.67 g   **Edge:** Reeded
Diameter: 65.3 mm   **Die Axis:** ↑↑
Thickness: 5.0 mm   **Finish:** Proof, Hologram
Case of Issue: Red lacquered wooden box, black flocked insert, encapsulated coin, COA

DATE	DESCRIPTION	RCM ITEM #	QUANTITY SOLD	ISSUE PRICE	FINISH	PR-69	PR-70
2015	Lustrous Maple Leaves	142183	2,975	519.95	Proof	550.	—

FIFTY DOLLARS, 50TH ANNIVERSARY OF THE CANADIAN FLAG, 2015.

Designers and Engravers:
Obv.:	Susanna Blunt, Susan Taylor
Rev.:	N/A

Composition: 99.99% Ag, Selective colour
Silver content: 47.34 g, 1.5 tr oz
Weight: 47.34 g   **Edge:** Reeded
Diameter: 49.8 mm x 28.8 mm   **Die Axis:** ↑↑
Thickness: N/A   **Finish:** Proof
Case of Issue: Maroon clamshell with custom beauty box.

DATE	DESCRIPTION	RCM ITEM #	QUANTITY SOLD	ISSUE PRICE	FINISH	PR-69	PR-70
2015	50th Anniv. of the Canadian Flag	143144	8,843	159.95	Proof	160.	—

FIFTY DOLLARS, 100TH ANNIVERSARY OF *IN FLANDERS FIELDS*, 2015.

Designers and Engravers:
Obv.:	Susanna Blunt, Susan Taylor
Rev.:	Tony Bianco

Composition: 99.99% Ag, Selective colour
Silver content: 157.65 g, 5.069 tr oz
Weight: 157.65 g   **Edge:** Reeded
Diameter: 65.25 mm   **Die Axis:** ↑↑
Thickness: N/A   **Finish:** Proof
Case of Issue: Maroon clamshell with custom beauty box.

DATE	DESCRIPTION	RCM ITEM #	QUANTITY SOLD	ISSUE PRICE	FINISH	PR-69	PR-70
2015	100th Anniv. of *In Flanders Fields*	145147	1,489	519.95	Proof	525.	—

FIFTY DOLLARS, MURANO MAPLE LEAF – AUTUMN RADIANCE, 2016

Designers and Engravers:
Obv.:	Susanna Blunt, Susan Taylor
Rev.:	Lisa Thomson-Khan

Composition: 99.99% Ag, Selective colour
Silver content: 157.6 g, 5.0 tr oz
Weight: 157.6 g   **Edge:** Reeded
Diameter: 65.25 mm   **Die Axis:** ↑↑
Thickness: N/A   **Finish:** Proof
Case of Issue: Red lacquered wooden case with black beauty box.

DATE	DESCRIPTION	RCM ITEM #	QUANTITY SOLD	ISSUE PRICE	FINISH	PR-69	PR-70
2016	Murano Maple Leaf – Autumn Radiance	151160	1,993	549.95	Proof	550.	—

FIFTY DOLLARS, WANDUTA: PORTRAIT OF A CHIEF, 2016

Designers and Engravers:
Obv.:   Susanna Blunt, Susan Taylor
Rev.:   Darlene Gait
Composition: 99.99% Ag, Selective colour
Silver content: 157.6 g, 5.0 tr oz
Weight: 157.6 g   **Edge:**   Reeded
Diameter: 65.25 mm   **Die Axis:**   ↑↑
Thickness: N/A.   **Finish:**   Proof
Case of Issue: Maroon clamshell with custom beauty box, COA.

DATE	DESCRIPTION	RCM ITEM #	QUANTITY SOLD	ISSUE PRICE	FINISH	PR-69	PR-70
2016	Wanduta: Portrait of a Chief	154198	1,195	519.95	Proof	525.	—

MYTHICAL REALMS OF THE HAIDA SET

FIFTY DOLLARS, MYTHICAL REALMS OF THE HAIDA SET, 2016.

Haida Gwaii is a place of astounding natural beauty; a land of ancient legends where mythical beings move about in the guise of familiar animals from our three-dimensional world. This mesmerizing new coin series portrays three of the most powerful supernatural beings from the realms of water, earth and sky.

Common Obverse	The Orca	The Eagle	The Bear

Designers:
Obv.:   Susanna Blunt
Rev.:   April White
Composition: 99.99% Ag, Selective color
Silver content: 157.6 g, 5.0 tr oz
Weight: 157.6 g
Diameter: 65.25 mm
Thickness: N/A
Case of Issue: Maroon clamshell with black beauty box.

Engravers:
Obv.:   Susan Taylor
Rev.:   April White

Edge: Reeded
Die Axis: ↑↑
Finish: Proof

DATE	DESCRIPTION	RCM ITEM #	QUANTITY SOLD	ISSUE PRICE	FINISH	PR-69	PR-70
2016	Mythical Realms of the Haida Series: The Orca	148429	792	549.95	Proof	550.	—
2016	Mythical Realms of the Haida Series: The Eagle	148416	739	549.95	Proof	550.	—
2016	Mythical Realms of the Haida Series: The Bear	149434	703	549.95	Proof	550.	—

FIFTY DOLLARS, PEACE TOWER CLOCK 90TH ANNIVERSARY, 2017.

At the stroke of noon on July 1, 1927, the Peace Tower Clock made its debut during Confederatin's Diamond Jubilee. Ninety years later, the commanding timepiece and its copper-clad apex are the pride of Canada!

Designers and Engravers:

Obv.:	Susanna Blunt, Susan Taylor
Rev.:	Calder Moore

Composition: 99.99% Ag,
Silver content: 157.6 g, 5.0 tr oz

Weight:	157.6 g	Edge:	Reeded
Diameter:	65.25 mm	Die Axis:	↑↑
Thickness:	N/A.	Finish:	Antique

Case of Issue: Maroon clamshell with black beauty box, COA.

DATE	DESCRIPTION	RCM ITEM #	MINTAGE	ISSUE PRICE	FINISH	PR-69	PR-70
2017	Peace Tower Clock 90th Anniversary	160663	1,200	579.95	Antique	600.	—

FIFTY DOLLARS, WHISPERING MAPLE LEAVES, 2017.

This 3 oz. fine silver coin captures the beauty of maple foilage swaying in a warm breeze, with the additon of reverse gold plating to mimic the golden glow of a summer day.

Designers and Engravers:

Obv.:	Susanna Blunt, Susan Taylor
Rev.:	Clader Moore

Composition: 99.99% Ag,
Silver content: 94.4 g, 3.04 tr oz

Weight:	94.4 g	Edge:	Reeded
Diameter:	55 mm	Die Axis:	↑↑
Thickness:	N/A.	Finish:	Proof

Case of Issue: Maroon clamshefll with black beauty box, COA.

DATE	DESCRIPTION	RCM ITEM #	MINTAGE	ISSUE PRICE	FINISH	PR-69	PR-70
2017	Whispering Maple Leaves	160872	3,500	299.95	Proof	300.	—

FIFTY DOLLARS, 125TH ANNIVERSARY OF THE STANLEY CUP®, 2017.

In 1892, the Governor General of Canada, Lord Stanley, donated a silver bowl for the purpose of fostering a competitive spirit between Canada's amateur hockey teams. The RCM is proud to commemorate the 125th anniversary of the Stanley Cup's origins, with a one-of-a-kind shaped coin that pays tribute to hockey's ultimate prize.

Designers and Engravers:

Obv.:	Susanna Blunt, Susan Taylor
Rev.:	RCM Staff

Composition: 99.99% Ag,
Silver content: 157.6 g, 5.07 tr oz

Weight:	99.53 g	Edge:	Reeded
Height	58 mm	Die Axis:	↑↑
Thickness:	N/A.	Finish:	Reverse Proof

Case of Issue: Rectangular black clamshell with NHL branded beauty box..

DATE	DESCRIPTION	RCM ITEM #	MINTAGE	ISSUE PRICE	FINISH	PR-69	PR-70
2017	125th Anniversary of the Stanley Cup	158058	5,000	359.95	Reverse Proof	360.	—

FIFTY DOLLARS, PUZZLE COIN, CANADA 150, 2017.

Like a puzzle, Confederation came together piece by piece, every part clicking into place over time, the end result far greater than the sum of its parts. Diverse geographies, natural wonders and resources coming together from coast to coast to coast. A multitude of traditions, languages, and skills blurring distinct cultural lines. History may have recorded the beginning of Confederation 150 years ago, but for today's citizens, Canada can begin anywhere on this nation's ever-evolving continuum. This puzzle coin is an outstanding, first-ever achievement at the Mint, and a unique portrait of Canada that will be the highlight of the most distinctive collections.

Each piece of the puzzle has a face value of $50 (central coin) and $20 (each of the jigsaw pieces). See page 337 for the $20

Designers and Engravers:
Obv.:	Susanna Blunt, Susan Taylor
Rev.:	Cathy Bursey-Sabourin

Composition: 99.99% Ag, Selective gold plating, coloured
Silver content: 502.47 g, 16.16 tr oz
Weight: 502.47 g (complete set)
Diameter: 123.7 mm   **Die Axis:** ↑↑
Finished Size: 184 mm x 184 mm   **Finish:** Proof
Thickness: N/A
Edge: Interrupted Reeding
Case of Issue: Wood case with black beauty box, COA

DATE	DESCRIPTION	RCM ITEM #	MINTAGE	ISSUE PRICE	FINISH	PR-69	PR-70
2017	Puzzle Coin, Canada 150	159701	800	1,867	Proof	2,200.	—

Note: This coin was only sold as a complete set of 14 puzzle pieces, plus a central coin.

DC COMICS ORIGINALS

FIFTY DOLLARS, *DC COMICS ORIGINALS*, 2017.

The application of gold plating throughout the reverse (except for *Superman* at the centre) gives this series a rich golden gleam – like the aged sepia tint of a page from an old book, but with much more vibrancy to highlight the engraved details!

Common Obverse	*The Brave and The Bold*	*All Star Comics*

Designers:
Obv.:	Susanna Blunt
Rev.:	DC Comics

Composition: 99.99% Ag, Reverse gold plating
Weight: 94.4 g
Diameter: 55 mm
Thickness: N/A.
Case of Issue: Maroon clamshell with graphic beauty box, COA.

Engravers:
Obv.:	Susan Taylor

Silver content: 94.4 g, 3.04 tr oz
Edge: Reeded
Die Axis: ↑↑
Finish: Proof

DATE	DESCRIPTION	RCM ITEM #	MINTAGE	ISSUE PRICE	FINISH	PR-69	PR-70
2017	*The Brave and The Bold*	161688	3,000	319.95	Proof	320.	—
2017	*All Star Comics*	161676	3,000	319.95	Proof	320.	—

FIFTY DOLLARS, MONARCH MIGRATION, 2017.

Designers and Engravers:

Obv.:	Susanna Blunt, Susan Taylor		
Rev.:	Graham Spaull		
Composition:	99.99% Ag		
Silver content:	94.4 g, 3.04 tr oz		
Weight:	94.4 g	**Edge:**	Reeded
Diameter:	55 mm	**Die Axis:**	↑↑
Thickness:	N/A.	**Finish:**	Proof
Case of Issue:	Maroon clamshell with black beauty box, COA.		

DATE	DESCRIPTION	RCM ITEM #	MINTAGE	ISSUE PRICE	FINISH	PR-69	PR-70
2017	Monarch Migration	162629	3,500	299.95	Proof	300.	—

FIFTY DOLLARS, CANADIAN ICONS, 2017.

Designers and Engravers:

Obv.:	Susanna Blunt, Susan Taylor		
Rev.:	Tami Mayrand		
Composition:	99.99% Ag		
Silver content:	157.6 g, 5.07 tr oz		
Weight:	157.6 g	**Edge:**	Reeded
Diameter:	65.25 mm	**Die Axis:**	↑↑
Thickness:	N/A.	**Finish:**	Proof
Case of Issue:	Maroon clamshell with Canada 150 themed black beauty box, COA.		

DATE	DESCRIPTION	RCM ITEM #	MINTAGE	ISSUE PRICE	FINISH	PR-69	PR-70
2017	Canadian Icons	162941	1,500	519.95	Proof	520.	—

MAPLE LEAVES IN MOTION

FIFTY DOLLARS, MAPLE LEAVES IN MOTION, 2017-2018.

2017 Maple Leaves in Motion

Designers:

Obv.:	Susanna Blunt
Rev.:	Lisa Thomson-Khan
Composition:	99.99% Ag,
Weight:	157.6 g
Diameter:	60 mm
Thickness:	N/A.
Case of Issue:	Red lacquered box with black beauty box.

2018 Maple Leaves in Motion

Engravers:

Obv.:	Susan Taylor
Silver content:	157.6 g, 5.0 tr oz
Edge:	Reeded
Die Axis:	↑↑
Finish:	Proof

DATE	DESCRIPTION	RCM ITEM #	MINTAGE	ISSUE PRICE	FINISH	PR-69	PR-70
2017	Maple Leaves in Motion	158223	2,000	579.95	Proof	580.	—
2018	Maple Leaves in Motion	165138	1,500	579.95	Antique	580.	—

FIFTY DOLLARS, HOLIDAY SPLENDOUR, 2018.

Designers and Engravers:

Obv.:	Susanna Blunt, Susan Taylor
Rev.:	Marie-Élaine Cusson

Composition: 99.99% Ag
Silver content: 157.6 g, 5.07 tr oz

Weight:	157.6 g	**Edge:**	Reeded
Diameter:	65.25 mm	**Die Axis:**	↑↑
Thickness:	N/A.	**Finish:**	Proof

Case of Issue: Maroon clamshell with Canada 150 themed black beauty box, COA.

DATE	DESCRIPTION	RCM ITEM #	MINTAGE	ISSUE PRICE	FINISH	PR-69	PR-70
2018	Holiday Spendour	162317	1,500	569.95	Proof	570.	—

FIFTY DOLLARS, POLAR BEAR SOAPSTONE SCULPTURE, 2018.

Introducing an unforgettable coin that pairs a traditional soapstone sculpture with contemporary coin-making techniques.

Designers and Engravers:

Obv.:	Susanna Blunt, Susan Taylor
Rev.:	Dave Zachary

Composition: 99.99% Ag
Silver content: 157.6 g, 5.07 tr oz

Weight:	157.6 g	**Edge:**	Reeded
Diameter:	65.25 mm	**Die Axis:**	↑↑
Thickness:	N/A.	**Finish:**	Proof

Case of Issue: Wooden circular base with black beauty box, COA.

DATE	DESCRIPTION	RCM ITEM #	MINTAGE	ISSUE PRICE	FINISH	PR-69	PR-70
2018	Polar Bear Soapstone Sculpture	160478	1,300	549.95	Proof	550.	—

THE SAN XING GODS: FU, LU, SHOU SET

FIFTY DOLLARS, THE SAN XING GODS: FU, LU, SHOU, 2018.

Common Obverse	Fu	Lu	Shou

Designers:

Obv.:	Susanna Blunt
Rev.:	Simon Ng

Composition: 99.99% Ag, Selective colour
Weight: 157.6 g (each coin)
Diameter: 65.25 mm (each coin)
Thickness: N/A.
Case of Issue: Maroon clamshell with black beauty box, COA.

Engravers:

Obv.:	Susan Taylor

Silver content: 157.6 g, 5.07 tr oz
Edge: Reeded
Die Axis: ↑↑
Finish: Proof

DATE	DESCRIPTION	RCM ITEM #	MINTAGE	ISSUE PRICE	FINISH	PR-69	PR-70
2018	The San Xing Gods: Fu, Lu, Shou 3-coin set	163291	588	1,688.88	Proof	1,700.	—

MURANO'S BEST SET

FIFTY DOLLARS, MURANO'S BEST, 2018.

| Common Obverse | Tulip and Ladybug | Purple Cone Flower & Eastern Tailed Blue Butterfly | Aster and Bumblebee |

Designers:
Obv.: Susanna Blunt
Rev.: Maurice Gervais (coins)
Giuliano Donaggio (Murano pieces)
Composition: 99.99% Ag, Selective colour
Weight: 157.6 g (each coin)
Diameter: 65.25 mm (each coin)
Thickness: N/A.
Case of Issue: Maplewood case with black beauty box, COA.

Engravers:
Obv.: Susan Taylor

Silver content: 157.6 g, 5.07 tr oz
Edge: Reeded
Die Axis: ↑↑
Finish: Proof

DATE	DESCRIPTION	RCM ITEM #	MINTAGE	ISSUE PRICE	FINISH	PR-69	PR-70
2018	Murano's Best 3-Coin Set	166490	850	1,799.95	Proof	1,800.	—

FIFTY DOLLARS, ANTIQUE CAROUSEL, 2018.

Designers and Engravers:
Obv.: Susanna Blunt, Susan Taylor
Rev.: Calder Moore
Composition: 99.99% Ag
Silver content: 188.99 g, 6.07 tr oz
Weight: 188.99 g **Edge:** Reeded
Diameter: 65 mm **Die Axis:** ↑↑
Thickness: N/A. **Finish:** Proof
Case of Issue: Wooden circular base with black box, COA.

DATE	DESCRIPTION	RCM ITEM #	MINTAGE	ISSUE PRICE	FINISH	PR-69	PR-70
2018	Antique Carousel	166265	1,000	749.95	Proof	750.	—

FIFTY DOLLARS, WHALE'S TAIL SOAPSTONE SCULPTURE, 2018.

Designers and Engravers:
Obv.: Susanna Blunt, Susan Taylor
Rev.: Dave Zachary, Cecily Mok
Composition: 99.99% Ag
Silver content: 157.6 g, 5.07 tr oz
Weight: 157.6 g **Edge:** Reeded
Diameter: 65.25 mm **Die Axis:** ↑↑
Thickness: N/A. **Finish:** Proof
Case of Issue: Wooden circular base with black beauty box, COA.

DATE	DESCRIPTION	RCM ITEM #	MINTAGE	ISSUE PRICE	FINISH	PR-69	PR-70
2018	Whale's Tail Soapstone Sculpture	167816	1,000	549.95	Proof	550.	—

FIFTY DOLLARS, PUZZLE COIN, CONNECTING CANADIAN HISTORY (1866-1916), 2018.

This new 2018 puzzle coin set tells the story of a nation's character between 1866 and 1916 — from the eve of Confederation through the five decades that followed. The set consists of 14 individual coins that piece together to tell the story of the first half century of the Dominion of Canada.

Each piece of the puzzle has a face value of $50 (central coin) and $20 (each of the jigsaw pieces). See page 379 for the $50

Designers and Engravers:
Obv.: Susanna Blunt, Susan Taylor
Rev.: Tony Bianco
Composition: 99.99% Ag, Selective gold plating, coloured
Silver content: 502.47 g, 16.16 tr oz
Weight: 502.47 g (complete set)
Diameter: 123.7 mm **Die Axis:** ↑↑
Finished Size: 184 mm x 184 mm **Finish:** Proof
Thickness: N/A
Edge: Interrupted Reeding
Case of Issue: Wood case with black beauty box, COA

DATE	DESCRIPTION	RCM ITEM #	MINTAGE	ISSUE PRICE	FINISH	PR-69	PR-70
2018	Connecting Canadian History (1866-1916)	167787	800	1,867	Proof	2,000.	—

Note: This coin was only sold as a complete set of 14 puzzle pieces, plus a central coin.

NATURE'S LIGHT SHOW SERIES

FIFTY DOLLARS, NATURE'S LIGHT SHOW, 2018.

Common Obverse	Stormy Night	Moonlit Tranquility
	Designer: Derek Wicks	Designer: Maurade Baynton

Designers:
Obv.: Susanna Blunt
Rev.: See illustrations
Composition: 99.99% Ag, Selective colour
Weight: 157.6 g
Diameter: 60 mm
Thickness: N/A.
Case of Issue: Red lacquered case with black beauty box, COA.

Engravers:
Obv.: Susan Taylor

Silver content: 157.6 g, 5.07 tr oz
Edge: Reeded
Die Axis: ↑↑
Finish: Proof

DATE	DESCRIPTION	RCM ITEM #	MINTAGE	ISSUE PRICE	FINISH	PR-69	PR-70
2018	Nature's Light Show: Stormy Night	166612	1,500	579.95	Proof	580.	—
2018	Nature's Light Show: Moonlit Tranquility	168235	1,500	579.95	Proof	580.	—

FIFTY DOLLARS, FAMOUS CANADIAN ART: EMILY CARR, 2018.

Designers and Engravers:
Obv.:	Susanna Blunt, Susan Taylor
Rev.:	Emily Carr

Composition: 99.99% Ag
Silver content: 157.69 g, 5.07 tr oz
Weight: 157.6 g   **Edge:** Reeded
Diameter: 65.25 mm   **Die Axis:** ↑↑
Thickness: N/A.   **Finish:** Proof
Case of Issue: Maroon clamshell with graphic beauty box, COA.

DATE	DESCRIPTION	RCM ITEM #	MINTAGE	ISSUE PRICE	FINISH	PR-69	PR-70
2018	Famous Canadian Art: Emily Carr	169394	1,000	529.95	Proof	530.	—

FIFTY DOLLARS, THE BUMBLE BEE AND THE BLOOM, 2019.

Designers and Engravers:
Obv.:	Susanna Blunt, Susan Taylor
Rev.:	Tony Bianco

Composition: 99.99% Ag
Silver content: 157.6 g, 5.07 tr oz
Weight: 157.6 g   **Edge:** Reeded
Diameter: 65.25 mm   **Die Axis:** ↑↑
Thickness: N/A.   **Finish:** Proof
Case of Issue: Wooden circular base with black beauty box, COA.

DATE	DESCRIPTION	RCM ITEM #	MINTAGE	ISSUE PRICE	FINISH	PR-69	PR-70
2019	The Bumble Bee And The Bloom	169571	1,200	569.95	Proof	570.	—

FIFTY DOLLARS, CELEBRATING CANADA'S ICONS, 2019.

Designers and Engravers:
Obv.:	Susanna Blunt, Susan Taylor
Rev.:	Patrick Bélanger

Composition: 99.99% Ag
Silver content: 157.6 g, 5.07 tr oz
Weight: 157.6 g   **Edge:** Reeded
Diameter: 65.25 mm   **Die Axis:** ↑↑
Thickness: N/A.   **Finish:** Proof
Case of Issue: Standard maroon clamshell with black beauty box, COA.

DATE	DESCRIPTION	RCM ITEM #	MINTAGE	ISSUE PRICE	FINISH	PR-69	PR-70
2019	Celebrating Canada's Icons	170392	1,200	559.95	Proof	560.	—

FIFTY DOLLARS, POLAR BEARS: MOTHER AND CUB, 2019.

Designers and Engravers:
Obv.:	Susanna Blunt, Susan Taylor
Rev.:	Tony Bianco

Composition: 99.99% Ag
Silver content: 157.6 g, 5.07 tr oz
Weight: 157.6 g   **Edge:** Reeded
Diameter: 68.81 mm   **Die Axis:** ↑↑
Thickness: N/A.   **Finish:** Proof
Case of Issue: Standard maroon clamshell with black beauty box, COA..

DATE	DESCRIPTION	RCM ITEM #	MINTAGE	ISSUE PRICE	FINISH	PR-69	PR-70
2019	Polar Bears: Mother And Cub	169147	1,200	579.95	Proof	580.	—

FIFTY DOLLARS, MAPLE LEAF IN MOTION, 2019.

Designers and Engravers:

Obv.:	Susanna Blunt, Susan Taylor
Rev.:	Glen Loates

Composition: 99.99% Ag
Silver content: 157.6 g, 5.07 tr oz

Weight:	157.6 g	**Edge:**	Reeded
Diameter:	65.25 mm	**Die Axis:**	↑↑
Thickness:	N/A.	**Finish:**	Proof

Case of Issue: Maroon lacquered case with black beauty box, COA..

DATE	DESCRIPTION	RCM ITEM #	MINTAGE	ISSUE PRICE	FINISH	PR-69	PR-70
2019	Maple Leaf In Motion	170554	1,000	579.95	Proof	580.	—

FIFTY DOLLARS, SYMBOLIC CANADA, 2019.

Designers and Engravers:

Obv.:	Susanna Blunt, Susan Taylor
Rev.:	Adam Young

Composition: 99.99% Ag
Silver content: 157.6 g, 5.07 tr oz

Weight:	157.6 g	**Edge:**	Reeded
Diameter:	65.25 mm	**Die Axis:**	↑↑
Thickness:	N/A.	**Finish:**	Proof

Case of Issue: Standard maroon clamshell with black beauty box, COA..

DATE	DESCRIPTION	RCM ITEM #	MINTAGE	ISSUE PRICE	FINISH	PR-69	PR-70
2019	Symbolic Canada	169965	1,250	529.95	Proof	530.	—

FIFTY DOLLARS, QUEEN VICTORIA: 200TH ANNIVERSARY OF HER BIRTH, 2019.

Designers and Engravers:

Obv.:	Susanna Blunt, Susan Taylor
Rev.:	RCM Staff

Composition: 99.99% Ag
Silver content: 157.6 g, 5.07 tr oz

Weight:	157.6 g	**Edge:**	Reeded
Diameter:	65.25 mm	**Die Axis:**	↑↑
Thickness:	N/A.	**Finish:**	Proof

Case of Issue: Black clamshell with black graphic box, COA..

DATE	DESCRIPTION	RCM ITEM #	MINTAGE	ISSUE PRICE	FINISH	PR-69	PR-70
2019	Queen Victoria: 200th Ann. of Birth	173481	1,000	529.95	Proof	530.	—

MY INNER NATURE SERIES

FIFTY DOLLARS, MY INNER NATURE, 2019.

Common Obverse

Grizzly Bear
Designer:
Caitlin Lindstrom-Milne

Arctic Fox
Designer:
Jayson Fuerstenberg

Designers:
Obv.:	Susanna Blunt
Rev.:	See illustrations
Composition:	99.99% Ag, Selective colour
Weight:	157.6 g
Diameter:	65.25 mm
Thickness:	N/A.
Case of Issue:	Black clamshell with black beauty box, COA.

Engravers:
Obv.:	Susan Taylor

Silver content:	157.6 g, 5.07 tr oz
Edge:	Reeded
Die Axis:	↑↑
Finish:	Proof

DATE	DESCRIPTION	RCM ITEM #	MINTAGE	ISSUE PRICE	FINISH	PR-69	PR-70
2019	My Inner Nature: Grizzly Bear	170947	750	569.95	Proof	570.	—
2019	My Inner Nature: Arctic Fox	170660	750	569.95	Proof	570.	—

ONE HUNDRED DOLLARS
ONE HUNDRED FOR ONE HUNDRED SERIES

ONE HUNDRED FOR ONE HUNDRED SERIES, 2013-2016.
These coins are from the $100 for $100 fine silver coin series.

Common Obverse

Bison Stampede
Des.: Cosme Saffioti
Eng.: Christie Paquet

The Grizzly
Des.: Claudio D'Angelo
Eng.: Steven Stewart

Majestic Bald Eagle
Des.: Claudio D'Angelo
Eng.: Eric Boyer

Rocky Mountain
Bighorn Sheep
Des.: Claudio D'Angelo
Eng.: RCM Staff

Musk Ox
Des.: Laurene Spino
Eng.: RCM Staff

Horse
Des.: Claudio D'Angelo
Eng.: RCM Staff

Cougar
Des.: Claudio D'Angelo
Eng.: RCM Staff

Orca
Des.: Trevor Tennant
Eng.: RCM Staff

The Nobel Elk
Des.: Glen Loates
Eng.: RCM Staff

Designers:		Engravers:	
Obv.:	Susanna Blunt	Obv.:	Susan Taylor
Rev.:	See reverse illustrations		

Composition: 99.99% Ag
Silver content: 31.6 g, 1.0 oz
Weight: 31.6 g
Diameter: 40.0 mm
Thickness: 3.0 mm

Edge: Reeded
Die Axis: ↑↑
Finish: Reverse Proof, Matte Proof

Case of Issue:
2013 Bison: Maroon leatherette clam style case, black flocked insert, encapsulated coin, COA
2013-2014: Customized paper case lined with flock, encapsulated coin, COA
2015: Graphic collector's box

DATE	DESCRIPTION	RCM ITEM #	QUANTITY SOLD	ISSUE PRICE	FINISH	PR-69	PR-70
2013	Bison Stampede, Reverse Proof	125701	49,986	100.00	Proof	120.	—
2013	The Grizzly, Matte Proof	126867	49,092	100.00	Proof	120.	—
2014	Majestic Bald Eagle, Matte Proof	129738	49,166	100.00	Proof	120.	—
2014	Rocky Mountain Bighorn Sheep, Matte Proof	130547	44,747	100.00	Proof	120.	—
2015	Musk Ox, Matte Proof	144677	43,961	100.00	Proof	120.	—
2015	Horse, Matte Proof	142779	45,151	100.00	Proof	120.	—
2016	Cougar, Matte Proof	148560	38,170	100.00	Proof	120.	—
2016	Orca, Matte Proof	151750	27,717	100.00	Proof	120.	—
2016	The Nobel Elk, Matte Proof	153127	16,377	100.00	Proof	120.	—

ONE HUNDRED DOLLARS, 100TH ANNIVERSARY OF THE DECLARATION OF FIRST WORLD WAR, 2014.

Designers and Engravers:

Obv.:	Susanna Blunt, Susan Taylor
Rev.:	Yves Bérubé, RCM Staff

Composition: 99.99% Ag
Silver content: 311.5 g, 10.0 tr oz

Weight:	311.5 g	**Edge:**	Reeded
Diameter:	76.25 mm	**Die Axis:**	↑↑
Thickness:	N/A	**Finish:**	Proof
Case of Issue:	Maple wooden case, black flocked insert, encapsulated coin, COA		

DATE	DESCRIPTION	RCM ITEM #	QUANTITY SOLD	ISSUE PRICE	FINISH	PR-69	PR-70
2014	100th Anniv. of Declaration of First World War	130518	424	899.95	Proof	900.	—

ONE HUNDRED DOLLARS, MAJESTIC MAPLE LEAVES, 2014.

Designers and Engravers:

Obv.:	Susanna Blunt, Susan Taylor
Rev.:	Pierre Leduc, RCM Staff

Composition: 99.99% Ag
Silver content: 311.5 g, 10.0 tr oz

Weight:	311.5 g	**Edge:**	Reeded
Diameter:	76.25 mm	**Die Axis:**	↑↑
Thickness:	N/A	**Finish:**	Proof
Case of Issue:	Maple wooden case black flocked insert, encapsulated coin, COA		

DATE	DESCRIPTION	RCM ITEM #	QUANTITY SOLD	ISSUE PRICE	FINISH	PR-69	PR-70
2014	Majestic Maple Leaves	131202	249	899.95	Proof	900.	—

ONE HUNDRED DOLLARS, CELEBRATING PHOTOGRAPHER YOUSUF KARSH, ALBERT EINSTEIN SPECIAL THEORY OF RELATIVITY, 2015.

Designers and Engravers:

Obv.:	Susanna Blunt, Susan Taylor
Rev.:	Original photo by Yousuf Karsh, RCM Staff

Composition: 99.99% Ag
Silver content: 311.5 g, 10.0 tr oz

Weight:	311.50 g	**Edge:**	Reeded
Diameter:	76.25 mm	**Die Axis:**	↑↑
Thickness:	N/A	**Finish:**	Proof
Case of Issue:	Maple presentation case with graphic beauty box.		

DATE	DESCRIPTION	RCM ITEM #	QUANTITY SOLD	ISSUE PRICE	FINISH	PR-69	PR-70
2015	Celebrating Cdn. Photographer Yousuf Karsh, Albert Einstein Special Theory of Relativity	147300	1,341	899.95	Proof	800.	—

ONE HUNDRED DOLLARS, 100TH ANNIVERSARY OF *IN FLANDERS FIELDS*, 2015.

Designers and Engravers:

Obv.:	Susanna Blunt, Susan Taylor
Rev.:	Tony Bianco

Composition: 99.99% Ag
Silver content: 311.5 g, 10.0 tr oz

Weight:	311.5 g	**Edge:**	Reeded
Diameter:	76.25 mm	**Die Axis:**	↑↑
Thickness:	N/A	**Finish:**	Proof
Case of Issue:	Wood case with custom beauty box.		

DATE	DESCRIPTION	RCM ITEM #	QUANTITY SOLD	ISSUE PRICE	FINISH	PR-69	PR-70
2015	100th Anniversary of *In Flanders Fields*	147042	498	899.95	Proof	900.	—

ONE HUNDRED DOLLARS, VIMY RIDGE, 2017.

Designers and Engravers:

Obv.:	Sir E. B. MacKennal
Rev.:	RCM Staff

Composition: 99.99% Ag
Silver content: 311.54 g, 10.0 tr oz
Weight: 311.54 g   **Edge:** Reeded
Diameter: 76.25 mm   **Die Axis:** ↑↑
Thickness: N/A   **Finish:** Proof
Case of Issue: Wood case with black beatuy box.

DATE	DESCRIPTION	RCM ITEM #	MINTAGE	ISSUE PRICE	FINISH	PR-69	PR-70
2017	Vimy Ridge	156489	750	999.95	Proof	1,000.	—

SCULPTURE OF MAJESTIC CANADIAN ANIMALS SERIES

ONE HUNDRED DOLLARS, SCULPTURE OF MAJESTIC CANADIAN ANIMALS, 2017.

The coin's large diameter (65 mm) provides the perfect pedestal for the silver, gold-plated animal-shaped embellishment emerging from the reverse.

Designers and Engravers:

Obv.:	Susanna Blunt, Susan Taylor
Rev.:	Karl Lansing

Composition: 99.99% Ag
Silver content: 315.71 g, 10.0 tr oz
Weight: 315.71 g   **Edge:** Reeded
Diameter: 65 mm   **Die Axis:** ↑↑
Thickness: N/A   **Finish:** Proof
Case of Issue: Wooden circular base with black box.

Common obverse   Grizzly Bear

Cougar	Elk	Bighorn Sheep	Wolf

DATE	DESCRIPTION	RCM ITEM #	QUANTITY SOLD	ISSUE PRICE	FINISH	PR-69	PR-70
2017	Grizzly Bear	156459	1,200	999.95	Proof	1,000.	—
2017	Courgar	156462	1,200	1,099.95	Proof	1,000.	—
2017	Elk	156459	1,200	1,099.95	Proof	1,000.	—
2017	Bighorn Sheep	156464	1,200	1,099.95	Proof	1,000.	—
2017	Wolf	156466	1,200	1,099.95	Proof	1,000.	—

COMMEMORATING HISTORICAL CANADIAN CONFEDERATION

ONE HUNDRED DOLLARS, COMMEMORATING HISTORICAL CANADIAN CONFEDERATION, 2017.

This low mintage 3-coin series commemorates the historical importance of Canadian Confederation.

Common Obverse	*Historia Tua Epos Est*	*Juventas et Patrius Vigor:*	*A Mari Usque Ad Mare:*
Designer and Engraver:	The 150th Anniversary of	The 1867 Confedation Medal	The Diamond Jubilee of the Con-
Susanna Blunt	Canadian Confederation	Designer: Raymond Delamarre	federation of Canada Medal
and Leonard Charles Wyon	Designer: Rebecca Yanovskaya		Designer: J.S. and A.B. Wyon

Designers		**Engravers:**	
Obv.:	See illustrations	Rev.:	See illustrations
Composition:	99.99% Ag		
Silver content:	311.535 g, 10.0 tr oz		
Weight:	311.535 g	**Edge:**	Reeded
Diameter:	76.25 mm	**Die Axis:**	↑↑
Thickness:	N/A	**Finish:**	Proof
Case of Issue:	Maroon clamshell with Canada 150 beauty box.		

DATE	DESCRIPTION	RCM ITEM #	MINTAGE	ISSUE PRICE	FINISH	PR-69	PR-70
2017	*Historia Tua Epos Est* The 150th Anniversary of Canadian Confederation	159841	1,000	899.95	Proof	900.	—
2017	*Juventas et Patrius Vigor:* The 1867 Confedation Medal	158310	1,000	899.95	Proof	900.	—
2017	*A Mari Usque Ad Mare:* The Diamond Jubilee of the Confederation of Canada Medal	159493	1,000	899.95	Proof	900.	—

ONE HUNDRED DOLLARS, DC COMICS ORIGINALS: SUPERMAN'S *SHIELD*, 2017.

Basing itself on the DC Comics style of the 1980s, this series celebrates one of the most established looks for the DC Comics pantheon of *Super Heroes* — including the *Man of Tomorrow, Superman.*

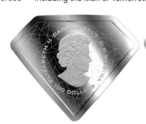 

Designers and Engravers:			
Obv.:	Susanna Blunt, Susan Taylor		
Rev.:	DC Comics		
Composition:	99.99% Ag, transparent enamel		
Silver content:	315.2 g, 10.14 tr oz		
Weight:	315.2 g	**Edge:**	Interrupted reeding
Diameter:	110 mm x 87.5 mm	**Die Axis:**	↑↑
Thickness:	N/A	**Finish:**	Proof
Case of Issue:	Basic clamshell with graphic beauty box, COA.		

DATE	DESCRIPTION	RCM ITEM #	MINTAGE	ISSUE PRICE	FINISH	PR-69	PR-70
2017	DC Comics Originals: Superman's Shield	160729	1,500	1,149.95	Proof	1,150.	—

ONE HUNDRED DOLLARS, *STAR TREK™: U.S.S. ENTERPRISE* NCC-1701, 2017.

Inspired by *Star Trek*'s spirit of innovation, the RCM pushes the boundaries of numismatic art with a remarkable feat of its own: an *Enterprise*-shaped coin!

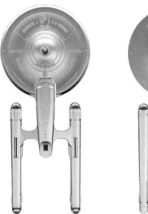

Designers and Engravers:
Obv.:	Susanna Blunt, Susan Taylor
Rev.:	RCM Staff

Composition:	99.99% Ag,
Silver content:	318.81 g, 10.25 tr oz
Weight:	318.81 g
Diameter:	113.2 long x 50.6 wide
Thickness:	N/A
Die Axis:	↑↑
Finish:	Matte Proof
Case of Issue:	Maroon clamshell with graphic beauty box, COA.

DATE	DESCRIPTION	RCM ITEM #	MINTAGE	ISSUE PRICE	FINISH	PR-69	PR-70
2017	*Star Trek™: U.S.S. Enterprise* NCC-1701	163490	1,000	1,199.95	Matte Proof	1,400.	—

ONE HUNDRED DOLLARS, THE ANGEL OF VICTORY: 100TH ANNIVERSARY OF THE FIRST WORLD WAR ARMISTICE, 2018.

Signed in 1918 "on the eleventh hour of the eleventh day of the elventh month," the Armistice of Compiègne put an end to hostilities during the First World War. This 10 oz. fine silver coin commemorates the centennial of the Armistice, to honour the thousands of men and women from Canada and Newfoundland who lost their lives in the "war to end all wars."

Designers and Engravers:
Obv.:	Susanna Blunt, Susan Taylor
Rev.:	Pandora Young

Composition:	99.99% Ag		
Silver content:	311.54 g, 10.0 tr oz		
Weight:	311.54 g	**Edge:**	Reeded
Diameter:	76.25 mm	**Die Axis:**	↑↑
Thickness:	N/A	**Finish:**	Proof
Case of Issue:	Maroon clamshell with black beatuy box, COA.		

DATE	DESCRIPTION	RCM ITEM #	MINTAGE	ISSUE PRICE	FINISH	PR-69	PR-70
2018	The Angel of Victory: 100th Anniversary of the First World War Armistice	164325	750	999.95	Proof	1,000.	—

ONE HUNDRED DOLLARS, THE BRONZE AGE OF DC COMICS, 2018.

Designers and Engravers:
Obv.:	Susanna Blunt, Susan Taylor
Rev.:	Jason Fabok and Brad Anderson

Composition:	99.99% Ag		
Silver content:	311.2 g, 10.14 tr oz		
Weight:	311.2 g	**Edge:**	Interrupted reeding
Diameter:	110 mm x 87.5 mm	**Die Axis:**	↑↑
Thickness:	N/A	**Finish:**	Proof
Case of Issue:	Basic clamshell with black beauty box, COA.		

DATE	DESCRIPTION	RCM ITEM #	MINTAGE	ISSUE PRICE	FINISH	PR-69	PR-70
2018	The Bronze Age of DC Comics	168660	750	1,049.95	Proof	1,050.	—

KEEPERS OF THE PARLIAMENT SERIES

ONE HUNDRED DOLLARS, KEEPERS OF THE PARLIAMENT, 2018.

Common Obverse	The Unicorn	The Beaver	The Soldier	The Lion

Designers
Obv.: Susanna Blunt
Rev.: Patrick Bélanger
Composition: 99.99% Ag
Silver content: 311.535 g, 10.02 tr oz
Weight: 311.535 g
Diameter: 76.25 mm
Thickness: N/A
Case of Issue: Standard maroon clamshell with black beauty box.

Engravers:
Rev.: Susan Taylor

Edge: Reeded
Die Axis: ↑↑
Finish: Proof

DATE	DESCRIPTION	RCM ITEM #	MINTAGE	ISSUE PRICE	FINISH	PR-69	PR-70
2018	Keepers of the Parliament: The Unicorn	168140	750	999.95	Proof	1,000.	—
2018	Keepers of the Parliament: The Beaver	169274	750	999.95	Proof	1,000.	—
2018	Keepers of the Parliament: The Soldier	169080	750	999.95	Proof	1,000.	—
2018	Keepers of the Parliament: The Lion	168792	750	999.95	Proof	1,000.	—

ONE HUNDRED DOLLARS, *SUPERMAN™: THE LAST SON OF KRYPTON*, 2018.

Designers and Engravers:
Obv.: Susanna Blunt, Susan Taylor
Rev.: Jason Fabok, Matthew Porter (sculptor)
Composition: 99.99% Ag
Silver content: 157.05 g, 5.05 tr oz
Weight: 157.05 g (coin); 157.60 g (statuette)
Edge: Reeded
Diameter: 65.25   **Die Axis:** ↑↑
Thickness: N/A   **Finish:** Proof
Case of Issue: Wood circular base with black beauty box, COA.

DATE	DESCRIPTION	RCM ITEM #	MINTAGE	ISSUE PRICE	FINISH	PR-69	PR-70
2018	*Superman™: The Last Son of Krypton*	166351	1,000	1,199.95	Proof	1,200.	—

ONE HUNDRED DOLLARS, PORTRAIT OF A PRINCESS, 2018.

Designers and Engravers:
Obv.: Susanna Blunt, Susan Taylor
Rev.: Original photo by Yousuf Karsh
Composition: 99.99% Ag
Silver content: 157.05 g, 5.05 tr oz
Weight: 157.05 g   **Edge:** Reeded
Diameter: 65.25   **Die Axis:** ↑↑
Thickness: N/A   **Finish:** Proof
Case of Issue: Standard maroon clamshell
with graphic beauty box, COA.

DATE	DESCRIPTION	RCM ITEM #	MINTAGE	ISSUE PRICE	FINISH	PR-69	PR-70
2018	Portrait of a Princess	167325	750	999.95	Proof	1,000.	—

NATURE'S GRANDEUR SERIES

ONE HUNDRED DOLLARS, NATURE'S GRANDEUR, 2019.

Introducing the first double-concave piedfort coins: an exquisite collectible that is twice the thickness of a typical fine silver coin and features both a concave-shaped reverse and obverse.

Common Obverse

Brown Bear

Wolves

Designers:		**Engravers:**	
Obv.:	Susanna Blunt	Obv.:	Susan Taylor
Rev.:	Denis Mayer Jr.		
Composition:	99.99% Ag	**Silver content:**	311.5 g, 10.02 tr oz
Weight:	311.5 g	**Edge:**	Reeded
Diameter:	60 mm	**Die Axis:**	↑↑
Thickness:	N/A.	**Finish:**	Proof
Case of Issue:	Standard maroon clamshell with black beauty box, COA.		

DATE	DESCRIPTION	RCM ITEM #	MINTAGE	ISSUE PRICE	FINISH	PR-69	PR-70
2019	Nature's Grandeur: Brown Bear	169973	500	999.95	Proof	1,000.	—
2019	Nature's Grandeur: Wolves	169563	500	999.95	Proof	1,000.	—

ONE HUNDRED DOLLARS, CANADIAN MAPLES, 2019.

Designers and Engravers:			
Obv.:	Susanna Blunt, Susan Taylor		
Rev.:	RCM Staff		
Composition:	99.99% Ag		
Silver content:	311.535 g, 10.02 tr oz		
Weight:	311.535 g	**Edge:**	Reeded
Diameter:	76.25	**Die Axis:**	↑↑
Thickness:	N/A	**Finish:**	Proof
Case of Issue:	Maroon clamshell with graphic beauty box, COA.		

DATE	DESCRIPTION	RCM ITEM #	MINTAGE	ISSUE PRICE	FINISH	PR-69	PR-70
2019	Canadian Maples	172275	500	999.95	Proof	1,000.	—

ONE HUNDRED TWENTY-FIVE DOLLARS

ONE HUNDRED TWENTY-FIVE DOLLARS, HOWLING WOLF, 2014

Designers and Engravers:
Obv.:	Susanna Blunt, Susan Taylor
Rev.:	Pierre Leduc, RCM Staff

Composition: 99.99% Ag
Silver content: 500.0 g, 16.07 tr oz
Weight:	500.0 g	**Edge:**	Reeded
Diameter:	85.0 mm	**Die Axis:**	↑↑
Thickness:	N/A	**Finish:**	Proof

Case of Issue: Wooden box, black flocked insert, encapsulated coin, COA

DATE	DESCRIPTION	RCM ITEM #	QUANTITY SOLD	ISSUE PRICE	FINISH	PR-69	PR-70
2014	Howling Wolf	130501	998	1,099.95	Proof	1,000.	—

ONE HUNDRED TWENTY-FIVE DOLLARS, CANADIAN HORSE, 2015

Designers and Engravers:
Obv.:	Susanna Blunt, Susan Taylor
Rev.:	Michelle Grant, RCM Staff

Composition: 99.99% Ag
Silver content: 500.0 g, 16.07 tr oz
Weight:	500.0 g	**Edge:**	Reeded
Diameter:	85.0 mm	**Die Axis:**	↑↑
Thickness:	N/A	**Finish:**	Proof

Case of Issue: Wooden box, black flocked insert, encapsulated coin, COA

DATE	DESCRIPTION	RCM ITEM #	QUANTITY SOLD	ISSUE PRICE	FINISH	PR-69	PR-70
2015	Canadian Horse	140613	504	1,099.95	Proof	1,000.	—

CONSERVATION SET

ONE HUNDRED TWENTY-FIVE DOLLARS, CONSERVATION SET, 2015.

Common Obverse	The Whooping Crane Designer: Luc Normandin	The Grey Fox Designer: Laurene Spino	The Narwhal Designer: Curtis Atwater

Designers:
Obv.:	Susanna Blunt
Rev.:	See reverse illustrations

Composition: 99.99% Ag
Weight: 500 g
Diameter: 85 mm
Thickness: N/A
Case of Issue: Maroon clamshell with black beauty box.

Engravers:
Obv.:	Susan Taylor

Silver content: 500 g, 16.075 tr oz
Edge: Reeded
Die Axis: ↑↑
Finish: Proof

DATE	DESCRIPTION	RCM ITEM #	QUANTITY SOLD	ISSUE PRICE	FINISH	PR-69	PR-70
2015	Conservation Series: The Whooping Crane	140302	395	1,099.95	Proof	1,100	—
2015	Conservation Series: The Grey Fox	147070	390	1,099.95	Proof	1,100	—
2015	Conservation Series: The Narwhal	148072	300	1,099.95	Proof	1,100	—

ONE HUNDRED TWENTY-FIVE DOLLARS, GROWLING COUGAR, 2015

Designers and Engravers:
Obv.:   Susanna Blunt, Susan Taylor
Rev.:   Pierre Leduc, RCM Staff
Composition: 99.99% Ag
Silver content: 500.0 g, 16.07 tr oz
Weight: 500.0 g   **Edge:**   Reeded
Diameter: 85.0 mm   **Die Axis:** ↑↑
Thickness: N/A   **Finish:**   Proof
Case of Issue: Wooden box, black flocked insert, encapsulated coin, COA

DATE	DESCRIPTION	RCM ITEM #	QUANTITY SOLD	ISSUE PRICE	FINISH	PR-69	PR-70
2015	Growling Cougar	142449	651	1,099.95	Proof	1,000.	—

ONE HUNDRED TWENTY-FIVE DOLLARS, ROARLING GRIZZLY, 2016.

Designers and Engravers:
Obv.:   Susanna Blunt, Susan Taylor
Rev.:   Pierre Leduc,
Composition: 99.99% Ag
Silver content: 500.0 g, 16.07 tr oz
Weight: 500.0 g   **Edge:**   Reeded
Diameter: 85.0 mm   **Die Axis:** ↑↑
Thickness: N/A   **Finish:**   Proof
Case of Issue: Wooden box with standard beauty box.

DATE	DESCRIPTION	RCM ITEM #	QUANTITY SOLD	ISSUE PRICE	FINISH	PR-69	PR-70
2016	Roaring Grizzly Bear	159581	440	1,099.95	Proof	1,100.	—

ONE HUNDRED TWENTY-FIVE DOLLARS, ELK, 2017.

Designers and Engravers:
Obv.:   Susanna Blunt, Susan Taylor
Rev.:   Pierre Leduc,
Composition: 99.99% Ag
Silver content: 500.0 g, 16.07 tr oz
Weight: 500.0 g   **Edge:**   Reeded
Diameter: 85.0 mm   **Die Axis:** ↑↑
Thickness: N/A   **Finish:**   Proof
Case of Issue: Wooden box with standard beauty box.

DATE	DESCRIPTION	RCM ITEM #	MINTAGE	ISSUE PRICE	FINISH	PR-69	PR-70
2017	Elk	157633	650	1,249.95	Proof	1,250.	—

ONE HUNDRED TWENTY-FIVE DOLLARS, THE BENEVOLENT DRAGON, 2019.

Designers and Engravers:
Obv.:   Susanna Blunt, Susan Taylor
Rev.:   Three Degrees Creative
Composition: 99.99% Ag, Selective gold plating
Silver content: 502.99 g, 16.07 tr oz
Weight: 502.99 g   **Edge:**   Reeded
Diameter: 84.85 mm   **Die Axis:** ↑↑
Thickness: N/A   **Finish:**   Proof
Case of Issue: Maroon clamshell with black beauty box, COA.

DATE	DESCRIPTION	RCM ITEM #	MINTAGE	ISSUE PRICE	FINISH	PR-69	PR-70
2019	The Benevolent Dragon	171332	588	1,288.88	Proof	1,290.	—

TWO HUNDRED DOLLARS
TWO HUNDRED FOR TWO HUNDRED SERIES

TWO HUNDRED DOLLARS, TWO HUNDRED FOR TWO HUNDRED, 2014-2016.

Common Obverse

2014
Towering Forests of Canada
Designer: Ellen Cowie

2015
Coastal Waters of Canada
Designer: Ellen Cowie

2015
Canada's Rugged Mountains
Designer: Steve Hepburn

2016
Vast Prairies
Designer: Luc Normandin

2016
Canada's Icy Arctic
Designer: Bonnie Ross

Designers:			**Engravers:**	
Obv.:	Susanna Blunt		Obv.:	Susan Taylor
Rev.:	See reverse illustrations			
Composition:	99.99% Ag			
Silver content:	62.69 g, 2.02 tr oz			
Weight:	62.69 g		**Edge:**	Reeded
Diameter:	50.0 mm		**Die Axis:**	↑↑
Thickness:	N/A		**Finish:**	Matte Proof
Case of Issue:	Paperboard case, white flocked insert, encapsulated coin, COA			

DATE	DESCRIPTION	RCM ITEM #	QUANTITY SOLD	ISSUE PRICE	FINISH	PR-69	PR-70
2014	Towering Forests of Canada	130604	19,695	200.00	Matte Proof	220.	—
2015	Coastal Waters of Canada	144675	24,760	200.00	Matte Proof	220.	—
2015	Canada's Rugged Mountains	144676	24,706	200.00	Matte Proof	220.	—
2016	Vast Prairies	151079	11,754	200.00	Matte Proof	220.	—
2016	Canada's Icy Arctic	154111	8,441	200.00	Matte Proof	220.	—

Note: Coins illustrated are smaller than actual size.

TWO HUNDRED FIFTY DOLLARS

VANCOUVER 2010 OLYMPIC WINTER GAMES SERIES, 2007-2010

These are the first coins produced in pure silver by the Royal Canadian Mint with a guaranteed weight of one kilo.

**Common Obverse
(Except for date)**

Designers:
Obv.:   Susanna Blunt
Rev.:   See reverse illustrations
Composition: 99.99% Ag
Silver content: 1,000.0 g, 32.151 tr oz
Weight: 1,000.0 g (1 kilo)
Diameter: 101.6 mm
Thickness: 12.5 mm
Case of Issue: Black display case, black flocked insert, encapsulated coin,
COA, Vancouver 2010 Olympic Winter Games theme sleeve

Engravers:
Obv.:   Susan Taylor
Rev.:   See reverse illustrations

Edge: Plain
Die Axis: ↑↑
Finish: Proof, Ultra high relief

Early Canada
Designer: Stan Witten
Engraver: Stan Witten

Towards Confederation
Designer: Susan Taylor
Engraver: Susan Taylor

The Canada of Today
Designer: Design Team of the
Vancouver Organising Committee
for the 2010 Olympic and
Paralympic Winter Games
Engraver: Konrad Wachelko

Surviving the Flood
Designer: Xwa lac tun
(Ricky Harry)
Engraver: Christie Paquet

DATE	DESCRIPTION	ISSUE DATE	RCM ITEM #	QUANTITY SOLD	ISSUE PRICE	FINISH	PR-68	PR-69
2007	Early Canada	Feb. 23, 2007	623317	2,500	1,299.95	Proof	1,500.	—
2008	Towards Confederation	Feb. 20, 2008	623318	2,500	1,599.95	Proof	1,500.	—
2009	The Canada of Today	April 15, 2009	623319	905	1,599.95	Proof	1,500.	—
2009	Surviving the Flood	Nov. 17, 2009	103705	815	1,599.95	Proof	1,500.	—

TWO HUNDRED FIFTY DOLLARS, THE EAGLE, 2010.

The eagle, an important First Nations symbol, represents power, peace and prestige. This is the first time a coin is offered in three different finishes.

Designers and Engravers:
Obv.:   Susanna Blunt, Susan Taylor
Rev.:   Xwa lac tun (Ricky Harry), Stan Witten
Composition: 99.99% Ag
Silver content: 1,000.0 g, 32.151 tr oz
Weight: 1,000.0 g (1 kilo)   **Edge:**   Plain
Diameter: 101.6 mm   **Die Axis:** ↑↑
Thickness: 12.5 mm   **Finish:**   Proof
Case of Issue: Black display case, black flocked insert,
encapsulated coin, COA, Vancouver 2010
Olympic Winter Games theme sleeve

DATE	DESCRIPTION	ISSUE DATE	RCM ITEM #	QUANTITY SOLD	ISSUE PRICE	FINISH	PR-68	PR-69
2010	The Eagle, Proof	Nov. 19, 2009	106988	349	1,649.95	Proof	1,500.	—
2010	The Eagle, Proof Enamel	Nov. 19, 2009	106989	74	1,649.95	Enamel	1,600.	—
2010	The Eagle, Proof Antique	Nov. 19, 2009	106990	349	1,649.95	Antique	1,500.	—

Note: Identical designs are utilized on the $2,500 gold coins for 2007, 2008, 2009 and 2010, see page 473.

TWO HUNDRED FIFTY DOLLARS, 125TH ANNIVERSARY OF BANFF NATIONAL PARK, 2010.

Designers and Engravers:
Obv.: Susanna Blunt, Susan Taylor
Rev.: Tony Bianco, Susan Taylor
Composition: 99.99% Ag
Silver content: 1,000.0 g, 32.151 tr oz
Weight: 1,000.0 g (1 kilo)   **Edge:** Plain
Diameter: 101.8 mm   **Die Axis:** ↑↑
Thickness: 12.5 mm   **Finish:** Proof
Case of Issue: Black display case, black flocked insert, encapsulated coin, COA

DATE	DESCRIPTION	RCM ITEM #	QUANTITY SOLD	ISSUE PRICE	FINISH	PR-69	PR-70
2010	125th Anniversary of Banff National Park	111516	525	1,904.95	Proof	1,500.	—

TWO HUNDRED FIFTY DOLLARS, 375TH ANNIVERSARY OF THE FIRST EUROPEAN OBSERVATION OF LACROSSE, 2011.

Designers and Engravers:
Obv.: Susanna Blunt, Susan Taylor
Rev.: Steve Hepburn, Christie Paquet
Composition: 99.99% Ag
Silver content: 1,000.0 g, 32.151 tr oz
Weight: 1,000.0 g (1 kilo)   **Edge:** Plain
Diameter: 101.8 mm   **Die Axis:** ↑↑
Thickness: 12.5 mm   **Finish:** Proof
Case of Issue: Black display case, black flocked insert, encapsulated coin, COA

DATE	DESCRIPTION	RCM ITEM #	QUANTITY SOLD	ISSUE PRICE	FINISH	PR-69	PR-70
2011	375th Anniv. First European Observation Lacrosse	113503	591	2,195.95	Proof	1,500.	—

TWO HUNDRED FIFTY DOLLARS, YEAR OF THE (WATER) DRAGON, 2012.

Designers and Engravers:
Obv.: Susanna Blunt, Susan Taylor
Rev.: Three Degrees Creative Group Inc., Cecily Mok
Composition: 99.99% Ag
Silver content: 1,000.0 g, 32.151 tr oz
Weight: 1,000.0 g (1 kilo)   **Edge:** Plain
Diameter: 101.8 mm   **Die Axis:** ↑↑
Thickness: 12.5 mm   **Finish:** Proof
Case of Issue: Black display case, black flocked insert, encapsulated coin, COA

DATE	DESCRIPTION	RCM ITEM #	QUANTITY SOLD	ISSUE PRICE	FINISH	PR-69	PR-70
2012	Year of the (Water) Dragon	115957	1,616	2,195.95	Proof	1,800.	—

TWO HUNDRED FIFTY DOLLARS, THE MOOSE FAMILY, ROBERT BATEMAN MOOSE COIN SERIES, 1962-2012.

Designers and Engravers:
Obv.: Susanna Blunt, Susan Taylor
Rev.: Robert Bateman, Stan Witten
Composition: 99.99% Ag
Silver content: 1,000.0 g, 32.151 tr oz
Weight: 1,000.0 g (1 kilo)   **Edge:** Reeded
Diameter: 102.1 mm   **Die Axis:** ↑↑
Thickness: 12.5 mm   **Finish:** Proof
Case of Issue: Maple wood case, black flocked insert, encapsulated coin, COA

DATE	DESCRIPTION	RCM ITEM #	QUANTITY SOLD	ISSUE PRICE	FINISH	PR-69	PR-70
2012 (1962-)	The Moose Family	121054	591	2,249.95	Proof	1,800.	—

TWO HUNDRED FIFTY DOLLARS (kilogram), GEORGE III PEACE MEDAL, 2012.

The presentation of Indian Chief Medals to the First Nations Chiefs in Canada was begun by King Louis XIV of France. This practice was continued by the Kings and Queens of England as a symbol of maintaining peaceful relations with the Indian Nations. See page 492 for the gold version of this medal.

2012 Obverse

Des.: RCM Staff's representation of the King George III Peace Medal Eng.: K. Wachelko, M. Bowen, S. Strath, S. Stewart

Designers and Engravers:
Obv..: See reverse illustration
Rev.: See reverse illustration
Composition: 99.99% Ag
Thickness: 12.5 mm
Silver content: 1,000.0 g, 32.151 tr oz
Weight: 1,000.0 g (1 kilo)   **Edge:** Reeded
Diameter: 102.1 mm   **Die Axis:** ↑↑
Finish: 2012 Proof,
2013 Proof, Selectively gold plated
Case of Issue: Maroon leatherette clam style case, black flocked insert, encapsulated coin, COA

DATE	DESCRIPTION	RCM ITEM #	QUANTITY SOLD	ISSUE PRICE	FINISH	PR-69	PR-70
2012	George III Peace Medal	119691	590	2,249.95	Proof	1,700.	—

TWO HUNDRED FIFTY DOLLARS, THE BATTLE OF QUEENSTON HEIGHTS, 2012.

This coin was issued to commemorate the first major battle in the War of 1812, which resulted in a Canadian victory.

Designers and Engravers:
Obv.: Susanna Blunt, Susan Taylor
Rev.: John David Kelly, Marcos Hallam
Composition: 99.99% Ag
Silver content: 1,000.0 g, 32.151 tr oz
Weight: 1,000.0 g (1 kilo)   **Edge:** Reeded
Diameter: 102.1 mm   **Die Axis:** ↑↑
Thickness: 12.5 mm   **Finish:** Proof
Case of Issue: Maroon clam style case, black flocked insert, encapsulated coin, COA

DATE	DESCRIPTION	RCM ITEM #	QUANTITY SOLD	ISSUE PRICE	FINISH	PR-69	PR-70
2012	The Battle of Queenston Heights	120683	225	2,249.95	Proof	1,800.	—

TWO HUNDRED FIFTY DOLLARS, YEAR OF THE DRAGON, 2012.

Designers and Engravers:
Obv.: Susanna Blunt, Susan Taylor
Rev.: Three Design Creative Group
Composition: 99.99% Ag
Silver content: 1,000.0 g, 32.151 tr oz
Weight: 1,000.0 g (1 kilo)   **Edge:** Pl,ain
Diameter: 102.6 mm   **Die Axis:** ↑↑
Thickness: 12.5 mm   **Finish:** Proof
Case of Issue: Maroon clam style case, black flocked insert, encapsulated coin, COA

DATE	DESCRIPTION	RCM ITEM #	QUANTITY SOLD	ISSUE PRICE	FINISH	PR-69	PR-70
2013	Year of the Dragon	115957	5,888	2,195.95	Proof	1,800.	—

TWO HUNDRED FIFTY DOLLARS, CANADA'S ARCTIC LANDSCAPE, 2013.

Designers and Engravers:

Obv.: Susanna Blunt, Susan Taylor
Rev.: W. David Ward, Stan Witten

Composition: 99.99% Ag
Silver content: 1,000.0 g, 32.151 tr oz
Weight: 1,000.0 g (1 kilo)   **Edge:** Reeded
Diameter: 101.8 mm   **Die Axis:** ↑↑
Thickness: 12.5 mm   **Finish:** Proof
Case of Issue: Maple wood case, black flocked insert, encapsulated coin, COA

DATE	DESCRIPTION	RCM ITEM #	QUANTITY SOLD	ISSUE PRICE	FINISH	PR-69	PR-70
2013	Canada's Arctic Landscape	123803	320	2,249.95	Proof	2,000.	—

TWO HUNDRED FIFTY DOLLARS, YEAR OF THE SNAKE, 2013.

Designers and Engravers:

Obv.: Susanna Blunt, Susan Taylor
Rev.: Three Degrees Creative Group Inc., Christie Paquet

Composition: 99.99% Ag
Silver content: 1,000.0 g, 32.151 tr oz
Weight: 1,000.0 g (1 kilo)   **Edge:** Reeded
Diameter: 102.1 mm   **Die Axis:** ↑↑
Thickness: 12.5 mm   **Finish:** Proof
Case of Issue: Silver satin-like covered case, black flocke insert, encapsulated coin, COA

DATE	DESCRIPTION	RCM ITEM #	QUANTITY SOLD	ISSUE PRICE	FINISH	PR-69	PR-70
2013	Year of the Snake	120188	359	2,249.95	Proof	2,000.	—

TWO HUNDRED FIFTY DOLLARS, 250TH ANNIVERSARY OF THE END OF THE SEVEN YEARS WAR, 2013.

The Seven Years War (1756-1763) in North America was fought between the English and French over control of the trade in this section of the world.

Designers and Engravers:

Obv.: Susanna Blunt, Susan Taylor
Rev.: Luc Normandin, Konrad Wachelko

Composition: 99.99% Ag
Silver content: 1,000.0 g, 32.151 tr oz
Weight: 1,000.0 g (1 kilo)   **Edge:** Reeded
Diameter: 102.1 mm   **Die Axis:** ↑↑
Thickness: 12.5 mm   **Finish:** Proof
Case of Issue: Maple wood box, black flocked insert, encapsulated coin, COA

DATE	DESCRIPTION	RCM ITEM #	QUANTITY SOLD	ISSUE PRICE	FINISH	PR-69	PR-70
2013	250th Anniv., End of the Seven Years War	123952	179	2,249.95	Proof	2,000.	—

TWO HUNDRED FIFTY DOLLARS, BATTLE OF CHATEAUGUAY, WAR OF 1812, 2013.

Designers and Engravers:

Obv.: Susanna Blunt, Susan Taylor
Rev.: H. Julien, J. Osio, E. Boyer

Composition: 99.99% Ag
Silver content: 1,000.0 g, 32.151 tr oz
Weight: 1,000.0 g (1 kilo)   **Edge:** Reeded
Diameter: 102.1 mm   **Die Axis:** ↑↑
Thickness: 12.5 mm   **Finish:** Proof
Case of Issue: Maple wood box, black flocked insert, encapsulated coin, COA

DATE	DESCRIPTION	RCM ITEM #	QUANTITY SOLD	ISSUE PRICE	FINISH	PR-69	PR-70
2013	Battle of Chateauguay	125168	112	2,249.95	Proof	2,000.	—

TWO HUNDRED FIFTY DOLLARS, THE CARIBOU, 2013.

Designers and Engravers:
Obv.: Susanna Blunt, Susan Taylor
Rev.: Trevor Tennant, RCM Staff
Composition: 99.99% Ag
Silver content: 1,000.0 g, 32.151 tr oz
Weight: 1,000.0 g (1 kilo) **Edge:** Reeded
Diameter: 102.1 mm **Die Axis:** ↑↑
Thickness: 12.5 mm **Finish:** Proof
Case of Issue: Maple wood box, black flocked insert, encapsulated coin, COA

DATE	DESCRIPTION	RCM ITEM #	QUANTITY SOLD	ISSUE PRICE	FINISH	PR-69	PR-70
2013	The Caribou	127070	146	2,249.95	Proof	2,000.	—

TWO HUNDRED FIFTY DOLLARS, YEAR OF THE HORSE, 2014.

Designers and Engravers:
Obv.: Susanna Blunt, Susan Taylor
Rev.: Three Degrees Creative Group Inc., RCM Staff
Composition: 99.99% Ag
Silver content: 1,000.0 g, 32.151 tr oz
Weight: 1,000.0 g (1 kilo) **Edge:** Reeded
Diameter: 102.1 mm **Die Axis:** ↑↑
Thickness: 12.5 mm **Finish:** Proof
Case of Issue: Silver satin-like covered case, black flocked insert, encapsulated coin, COA

DATE	DESCRIPTION	RCM ITEM #	QUANTITY SOLD	ISSUE PRICE	FINISH	PR-69	PR-70
2014	Year of the Horse	124637	469	2,249.95	Proof	2,250.	—

TWO HUNDRED FIFTY DOLLARS, BATTLE OF LUNDY'S LANE, 2014.

Designers and Engravers:
Obv.: Susanna Blunt, Susan Taylor
Rev.: Bonnie Ross, RCM Staff
Composition: 99.99% Ag
Silver content: 1,000.0 g, 32.151 tr oz
Weight: 1,000.0 g (1 kilo) **Edge:** Reeded
Diameter: 102.1 mm **Die Axis:** ↑↑
Thickness: N/A **Finish:** Proof
Case of Issue: Maple wood case, black flocked insert, encapsulated coin, COA

DATE	DESCRIPTION	RCM ITEM #	QUANTITY SOLD	ISSUE PRICE	FINISH	PR-69	PR-70
2014	Battle of Lundy's Lane	130543	225	2,249.95	Proof	2,250.	—

MAPLE LEAF FOREVER SERIES

TWO HUNDRED FIFTY DOLLARS, MAPLE LEAF FOREVER, 2014-2016.

2014	2015	2016
Coloured Enamel	Hologram	Natural Colour & Selective Gold Platning

Designers:
  Obv.:   Susanna Blunt
  Rev.:   See reverse illustrations
Composition: 99.99% Ag, Hologram
Silver content: 1,000.0 g, 32.151 tr oz
Weight: 1,000.0 g (1 kilo)
Diameter: 102.1 mm
Thickness: N/A
Case of Issue: Maple wood case, black flocked insert, encapsulated coin, COA

Engravers:
  Obv.:   Susan Taylor

Edge: Reeded
Die Axis: ↑↑
Finish: Proof

DATE	DESCRIPTION	RCM ITEM #	QUANTITY SOLD	ISSUE PRICE	FINISH	PR-69	PR-70
2014	Maple Leaf Forever, Coloured Enamel	134073	571	2,299.95	Proof	2,200.	—
2015	Maple Leaf Forever, Hologram	143023	500	2,299.95	Proof	2,200.	—
2016	Maple Leaf Forever, Natural Colour & Selective Gold Plating	153158	488	2,299.95	Proof	2,200.	—

IN THE EYES OF... SERIES

TWO HUNDRED FIFTY DOLLARS, IN THE EYES OF... 2014-2017.

In The Eyes Of… is a series featuring the distinctive eyes of Canada's wildlife.

Common Obverse
(except for date)

Designers and Engravers:
Obv.:	S. Blunt, S. Taylor
Rev.:	See reverse illustrations

Composition:	99.99% Ag		
Silver content:	1,000.0 g, 32.151 tr oz		
Weight:	1,000.0 g (1 kilo)	**Edge:**	Reeded
Diameter:	102.1 mm	**Die Axis:**	↑↑
Thickness:	12.5 mm	**Finish:**	Proof
Case of Issue:	Maple wood case, black flocked insert, encapsu lated coin, COA		

In The Eyes of the Snowy Owl	In The Eyes of the Cougar	In The Eyes of the Spirit Bear	In The Eyes of the Timber Wolf
Designer: A. Nogy	Designer: Glen Loates	Designer: Glen Loates	Designer: Pierre Leduc

DATE	DESCRIPTION	RCM ITEM #	QUANTITY SOLD	ISSUE PRICE	FINISH	PR-69	PR-70
2014	In The Eyes of the Snowy Owl	129422	500	2,299.95	Proof	2,200.	—
2015	In The Eyes of the Cougar	141763	500	2,299.95	Proof	2,300.	—
2016	In The Eyes of the Spirit Bear	150249	356	2,299.95	Proof	2,300.	—
2017	In The Eyes of the Timber Wolf	154122	400	2,299.95	Proof	2,300.	—

TWO HUNDRED FIFTY DOLLARS, YEAR OF THE SHEEP, 2015.

Designers and Engravers:
Obv.:	Susanna Blunt, Susan Taylor
Rev.:	Three Degrees Creative, RCM Staff

Composition:	99.99% Ag		
Silver content:	1,000.0 g, 32.151 tr oz		
Weight:	1,000.0 g (1 kilo)	**Edge:**	Reeded
Diameter:	102.1 mm	**Die Axis:**	↑↑
Thickness:	N/A	**Finish:**	Proof
Case of Issue:	Silver satin-like covered case, black flocked insert, encapsulated coin, COA, custom red sleeve		

DATE	DESCRIPTION	RCM ITEM #	QUANTITY SOLD	ISSUE PRICE	FINISH	PR-69	PR-70
2015	Year of the Sheep	130572	310	2,288.88	Proof	2,250.	—

TWO HUNDRED FIFTY DOLLARS, LOONEY TUNES™: ENSEMBLE CAST, 2015.

Designers and Engravers:

Obv.:	Susanna Blunt, Susan Taylor
Rev.:	Warner Bros.

Composition: 99.99% Ag
Silver content: 1,006.0 g, 32.151 tr oz

Weight:	1,006.0 g (1 kilo)	**Edge:**	Reeded
Diameter:	102.1 mm	**Die Axis:**	↑↑
Thickness:	N/A	**Finish:**	Proof

Case of Issue: Wooden case with custom beauty box, encapsulated coin, COA

DATE	DESCRIPTION	RCM ITEM #	QUANTITY SOLD	ISSUE PRICE	FINISH	PR-69	PR-70
2015	Looney Tunes™ Ensemble Cast	145059	342	2,350.95	Proof	2,250.	—

TWO HUNDRED FIFTY DOLLARS, YEAR OF THE MONKEY, 2016.

Designers and Engravers:

Obv.:	Susanna Blunt, Susan Taylor
Rev.:	Three Degrees Creative

Composition: 99.99% Ag
Silver content: 1,000.0 g, 32.151 tr oz

Weight:	1,000.0 g (1 kilo)	**Edge:**	Reeded
Diameter:	120 mm	**Die Axis:**	↑↑
Thickness:	N/A	**Finish:**	Proofl

Case of Issue: Silver satin-like covered case with custom red sleeve.

DATE	DESCRIPTION	RCM ITEM #	QUANTITY SOLD	ISSUE PRICE	FINISH	PR-69	PR-70
2016	Year of the Monkey	146852	199	2,288.88	Proof	2,250.	—

TWO HUNDRED FIFTY DOLLARS, ARMS OF CANADA, 2016.

Designers and Engravers:

Obv.:	Susanna Blunt, Susan Taylor
Rev.:	RCM Staff

Composition: 99.99% Ag
Silver content: 1,000.0 g, 32.151 tr oz

Weight:	1,000.0 g (1 kilo)	**Edge:**	Reeded
Diameter:	102 mm	**Die Axis:**	↑↑
Thickness:	N/A	**Finish:**	Proof

Case of Issue: Wood case and black beatuy box.

DATE	DESCRIPTION	RCM ITEM #	QUANTITY SOLD	ISSUE PRICE	FINISH	PR-69	PR-70
2016	Arms of Canada		411	2,329.95	Proof	2,500.	—

TWO HUNDRED FIFTY DOLLARS, THE CANADIAN COIN COLLECTION, 2017.

Designers and Engravers:

Obv.:	Susanna Blunt, Susan Taylor
Rev.:	RCM Staff

Composition: 99.99% Ag
Silver content: 1,000.0 g, 32.151 tr oz

Weight:	1,000.0 g (1 kilo)	**Edge:**	Reeded
Diameter:	102.1 mm	**Die Axis:**	↑↑
Thickness:	N/A	**Finish:**	Proof

Case of Issue: Wood case and black beatuy box.

DATE	DESCRIPTION	RCM ITEM #	QUANTITY SOLD	ISSUE PRICE	FINISH	PR-69	PR-70
2017	The Canadian Coin Collection	158118	220	2,499.95	Proof	2,500.	—

TWO HUNDRED FIFTY DOLLARS, YEAR OF THE ROOSTER, 2017.

Designers and Engravers:
  Obv.: Susanna Blunt, Susan Taylor
  Rev.: Three Degrees Creative
Composition: 99.99% Ag
Silver content: 1,000.0 g, 32.151 tr oz
Weight: 1,000.0 g (1 kilo)   **Edge:** Reeded
Diameter: 120 mm   **Die Axis:** ↑↑
Thickness: N/A   **Finish:** Proofl
Case of Issue: Silver satin-like covered case with custom red sleeve.

DATE	DESCRIPTION	RCM ITEM #	QUANTITY SOLD	ISSUE PRICE	FINISH	PR-69	PR-70
2017	Year of the Rooster	153810	85	2,288.88	Proof	2,300.	—

TWO HUNDRED FIFTY DOLLARS, A TRIBUTE TO THE FIRST CANADIAN GOLD COIN, 2017.

Designers and Engravers:
  Obv.: Susanna Blunt, Susan Taylor
  Rev.: W. H. J. Blackmore
Composition: 99.99% Ag
Silver content: 1,000.0 g, 32.151 tr oz
Weight: 1,000.0 g (1 kilo)   **Edge:** Reeded
Diameter: 102.1 mm   **Die Axis:** ↑↑
Thickness: N/A   **Finish:** Proof
Case of Issue: Wood case and black beauty box, COA

DATE	DESCRIPTION	RCM ITEM #	QUANTITY SOLD	ISSUE PRICE	FINISH	PR-69	PR-70
2017	A Tribute to the First Canadian Gold Coin	162556	500	2,329.95	Proof	2,350.	—

TWO HUNDRED FIFTY DOLLARS, MAPLE LEAF FOREVER (SHAPED), 2017.

Designers and Engravers:
  Obv.: Susanna Blunt, Susan Taylor
  Rev.: Lisa Thomson-Khan
Composition: 99.99% Ag
Silver content: 1,000.0 g, 32.151 tr oz
Weight: 1,000.0 g (1 kilo)   **Edge:** Plain
Diameter: 150 mm (top to bottom) **Die Axis:** ↑↑
Thickness: N/A   **Finish:** Antiqued
Case of Issue: Wood case and black beauty box, COA

DATE	DESCRIPTION	RCM ITEM #	QUANTITY SOLD	ISSUE PRICE	FINISH	PR-69	PR-70
2017	Maple Leaf Forever (shaped)	163476	700	2,499.95	Antique	2,500.	—

TWO HUNDRED FIFTY DOLLARS, A FIERCE GAZE: *TYRANNOSAURUS REX*, 2018.

Designers and Engravers:
  Obv.: Susanna Blunt, Susan Taylor
  Rev.: Julius Csotonyi
Composition: 99.99% Ag
Silver content: 1,006.0 g, 32.151 tr oz
Weight: 1,006.0 g   **Edge:** Reeded
Diameter: 102.1 mm   **Die Axis:** ↑↑
Thickness: N/A   **Finish:** Proof
Case of Issue: Wood case and black beauty box, COA

DATE	DESCRIPTION	RCM ITEM #	QUANTITY SOLD	ISSUE PRICE	FINISH	PR-69	PR-70
2018	A Fierce Gaze: *Tyrannosaurus Rex*	165461	400	2,299.95	Proof	2,300.	—

TWO HUNDRED FIFTY DOLLARS, THE VOYAGEURS, 2018.

Designers and Engravers:

Obv.:	Susanna Blunt, Susan Taylor
Rev.:	Matt Bowen

Composition: 99.99% Ag
Silver content: 1,000.0 g, 32.151 tr oz
Weight: 1,000.0 g (1 kilo)
Diameter: 161.8 mm x 100 mm
Edge: Reeded
Die Axis: ↑↑
Thickness: N/A
Finish: Antique
Case of Issue: Wood case and black beauty box, COA

DATE	DESCRIPTION	RCM ITEM #	QUANTITY SOLD	ISSUE PRICE	FINISH	PR-69	PR-70
2018	The Voyageurs	167962	400	2,499.95	Antique	2,500.	—

TWO HUNDRED FIFTY DOLLARS, MAPLE LEAF FOREVER, 2018.

Designers and Engravers:

Obv.:	Susanna Blunt, Susan Taylor
Rev.:	Stan Witten

Composition: 99.99% Ag
Silver content: 1,000.0 g, 32.151 tr oz
Weight: 1,000.0 g (1 kilo)   **Edge:** Reeded
Diameter: 102 mm   **Die Axis:** ↑↑
Thickness: N/A   **Finish:** Proofl
Case of Issue: Custom wood case, COA.

DATE	DESCRIPTION	RCM ITEM #	MINTAGE	ISSUE PRICE	FINISH	PR-69	PR-70
2018	Maple Leaf Forever	165556	500	2,499.95	Proof	2,500.	—

FIVE HUNDRED DOLLAR SILVER COINS

FIVE HUNDRED DOLLARS, THE SPIRIT OF HAIDA GWAII, 2012.

Designers and Engravers:
Obv.: Susanna Blunt, Susan Taylor
Rev.: Bill Reid, Cosme Saffioti
Composition: 99.99% Ag
Silver content: 5.000.0 g, 160.75 tr oz
Weight: 5,000.0 g, (5 kilos)
Diameter: 180.0 mm
Thickness: N/A
Edge: Reeded
Die Axis: ↑↑
Finish: Proof
Case of Issue: Canadian walnut wood case, black velvet insert,encapsulated coin, COA

DATE	DESCRIPTION	RCM ITEM #	QUANTITY SOLD	ISSUE PRICE	FINISH	PR-69	PR-70
2012	The Spirit of Haida Gwaii	116311	95	9,999.95	Proof	8,000.	—

FIVE HUNDRED DOLLARS, TSATSISNUKOMI, BC, 2013.

Designers and Engravers:
Obv.: Susanna Blunt, Susan Taylor
Rev.: Emily Carr, Christie Paquet, Stan Witten
Composition: 99.99% Ag
Silver content: 5,000.0 g, 32.160.7 tr oz
Weight: 5,000.0 g (5 kilos)
Diameter: 180.0 mm
Thickness: N/A
Edge: Reeded
Die Axis: ↑↑
Finish: Proof
Case of Issue: Canadian walnut wood case, acrylic holder, COA in booklet format

DATE	DESCRIPTION	RCM ITEM #	QUANTITY SOLD	ISSUE PRICE	FINISH	PR-69	PR-70
2013	Tsatsisnukomi, BC, 1912	127472	99	10,500.00	Proof	8,000.	—

FIVE HUNDRED DOLLARS, CANADIAN MONUMENTS: NATIONAL ABORIGINAL VETERANS MONUMENT, 2014.

Designers and Engravers:
Obv.: Susanna Blunt, Susan Taylor
Rev.: N. L. Pinay, RCM Staff
Composition: 99.99% Ag
Silver content: 5,000.0 g, 160.75 tr oz
Weight: 5,000.0 g (5 kilo)
Diameter: 180.0 mm
Thickness: N/A
Edge: Reeded
Die Axis: ↑↑
Finish: Proof
Case of Issue: Walnut wood case, acrylic box encapsulated coin, COA

DATE	DESCRIPTION	RCM ITEM #	QUANTITY SOLD	ISSUE PRICE	FINISH	PR-69	PR-70
2014	National Aboriginal Veterans Monument	130615	111	10,500.00	Proof	8,000.	—

FIVE HUNDRED DOLLARS, *THE DANCE SCREEN (THE SCREAM TOO)*, 2015.

Designers and Engravers:

Obv.:	Susanna Blunt, Susan Taylor
Rev.:	James Hart
Composition:	99.99% Ag
Silver content:	5,000.0 g, 32.160.7 tr oz
Weight:	5,000.0 g (5 kilos)
Diameter:	180.0 mm
Thickness:	N/A
Edge:	Reeded
Die Axis:	↑↑
Finish:	Proof
Case of Issue:	Canadian walnut wood case, acrylic holder, COA in booklet format

DATE	DESCRIPTION	RCM ITEM #	QUANTITY SOLD	ISSUE PRICE	FINISH	PR-69	PR-70
2015	*The Dance Screen (The Scream Too)*	148273	86	10,500.00	Proof	10,000.	—

FIVE HUNDRED DOLLARS, *CHARLES EDENSHAW: ARGILLITE CHEST*, 2016.

This five-kilogram masterpiece brings you one of the greatest works from the Pacific Northwest: the argillite chest by Charles Edenshaw (1839–1924), a renowned artist and pivotal guardian of Haida culture.

Designers and Engravers:

Obv.:	Susanna Blunt, Susan Taylor
Rev.:	RCM Engravers
Composition:	99.99% Ag
Silver content:	5,000.0 g, 160.755 tr oz
Weight:	5,000.0 g (5 kilos)
Diameter:	180 mm
Thickness:	N/A
Edge:	Reeded
Die Axis:	↑↑
Finish:	Proof
Case of Issue:	Wooden display case.

DATE	DESCRIPTION	RCM ITEM #	MINTAGE	ISSUE PRICE	FINISH	PR-69	PR-70
2016	*Charles Edenshaw: Argillite Chest*	145459	100	10,699.95	Proof	10,000.	—

FIVE HUNDRED DOLLARS, CANADA 150 FROM COAST TO COAST TO COAST, 2017.

From the soaring peaks of Western Canada to the stately lighthouses of the East Coast and the majestic wilderness of the Canadian North, some of the most iconic images of Canada are truly timeless and never cease to inspire pride.

Designers and Engravers:

Obv.:	Susanna Blunt, Susan Taylor
Rev.:	Steve Hepburn
Composition:	99.99% Ag
Silver content:	5,000.0 g, 160.755 tr oz
Weight:	5,000.0 g (5 kilos)
Diameter:	180 mm
Thickness:	N/A
Edge:	Reeded
Die Axis:	↑↑
Finish:	Proof
Case of Issue:	Wooden display case, COA.

DATE	DESCRIPTION	RCM ITEM #	MINTAGE	ISSUE PRICE	FINISH	PR-69	PR-70
2017	Canada 150 From Coast to Coast to Coast	160565	100	10,699.95	Proof	10,000.	—

SILVER SPECIAL ISSUE SETS

ARCTIC FOX FINE SILVER COIN SET, 2004.

The first fractional fine silver coins feature wildlife designs that were originally created for platinum proof coins. The Arctic Fox first appeared on the Platinum proof coins of 1993.

Designers and Engravers:
Obv.:   S. Blunt, S. Taylor
Rev.:   Claude D'Angelo
Rev.: $5 – Susan Taylor
        $4 – Sheldon Beveridge
        $3 – Ago Aarand
        $2 – Ago Aarand
Specifications: See page 568
Silver content: 1.85 tr oz
Finish: Proof, Frosted relief against a mirror background
Case of Issue: Black case, multicoloured outer sleeve

CANADA LYNX FINE SILVER COIN SET, 2005.

Designers and Engravers:
Obv.:   S. Blunt, S. Taylor
Rev.:   Michael Dumas
Rev.: $5 – Susan Taylor
        $4 – Cosme Saffioti
        $3 – Stan Witten
        $2 – Ago Aarand
Specifications: See page 568
Silver content: 1.85 tr oz
Finish: Proof, Frosted relief against a mirror background
Case of Issue: N/A

BALD EAGLE FINE SILVER COIN SET, 2015.

Designers and Engravers:
Obv.:   S. Blunt, S. Taylor
Rev.:   Michael Dumas
Rev.:   Derek C. Wicks
Specifications: See page 568
Silver content: 1.85 tr oz
Finish: Proof, Frosted relief against a mirror background
Case of Issue: Maple wood case with a graphic beauty box.

CANADA WOLF FINE SILVER COIN SET, 2016.

Designers and Engravers:
Obv.:   S. Blunt, S. Taylor
Rev.:   Pierre Leduc
Specifications: See page 568
Silver content: 1.85 tr oz
Finish: Proof, Frosted relief against a mirror background
Case of Issue: Maple wood case with graphic beauty box.

DATE	DESCRIPTION	RCM ITEM #	QUANTITY SOLD	ISSUE PRICE	FINISH	PR-69	PR-70
2004	Arctic Fox, Set of 4 coins	N/A	14,566	89.95	Proof	130.	—
2005	Canada Lynx, Set of 4 coins	N/A	7,942	89.95	Proof	150.	—
2015	Bald Eagle, Set of 4 coins	143436	7,500	199.95	Proof	200.	—
2016	Wolf, Set of 4 coins	145296	7,500	199.95	Proof	200.	—

GOLD COINS

ONE CENT GOLD COIN

ONE CENT, FAREWELL TO THE PENNY, 2012.

This coin was issued in commemoration of the last strike of the Canadian one-cent coin on May 4th, 2011.

Designers and Engravers:

Obv.:	Susanna Blunt, Susan Taylor
Rev.:	G. E. Kruger-Gray, RCM Staff

Composition: 99.99% Au
Gold content: 1.27 g, 0.04 tr oz
Weight: 1.27 g   **Edge:** Plain
Diameter: 13.9 mm   **Die Axis:** ↑↑
Thickness: 0.7 mm   **Finish:** Proof
Case of Issue: Maroon leatherette clam style case, black flock insert, encapsulated coin, COA, custom coloured box

Actual Size

DATE	DESCRIPTION	RCM ITEM #	QUANTITY SOLD	ISSUE PRICE	FINISH	PR-69	PR-70
2012	The Penny	121185	11,251	129.95	Proof	130.	—

TWENTY-FIVE CENT GOLD COINS

TWENTY-FIVE CENTS, COMMEMORATIVE GOLD COINS, 2010-2015.

Actual Size

Designers:

Obv.:	Susanna Blunt
Rev.:	See reverse illustrations

Composition: 99.99% Au
Gold content: 0.5 g, 0.016 tr oz
Weight: 0.5 g
Diameter: 11.0 mm
Case of Issue: Maroon leatherette clam style case, black flocked insert, encapsulated coin, COA

Engravers:

Rev.:	Susan Taylor
Rev.:	See reverse illustrations

Thickness: 0.5-0.6 mm
Edge: Reeded
Die Axis: ↑↑
Finish: Proof

2010	2010	2011-2015	2011	2013
Obverse with "P" Mint Mark	Caribou Des.: E. Hahn Engr.: RCM Staff	Obverse without "P" Mint Mark	Cougar Des.: E. Damstra Engr.: W. Woodruff	Hummingbird Des.: C. D'Angelo Engr.: S. Strath

2014	2014	2015	2015	2015
Rocky Mountain Bighorn Sheep Des.: E. Damstra Engr.: S. Stewart	Eastern Chipmunk Des.: Tony Bianco Engr.: S. Strath	Grizzly Bear Des.: Emily Damstra Engr.: RCM Staff	Rock Rabbit Des.: Derek Wicks Engr.: RCM Staff	Diwali: Festival of Lights Des.: Sarindar Dhaliwal Engr.: RCM Staff

TWENTY-FIVE CENTS, COMMEMORATIVE GOLD COINS, 2010-2015, PRICING TABLE.

DATE	DESCRIPTION	RCM ITEM #	QUANTITY SOLD	ISSUE PRICE	FINISH	PR-69	PR-70
2010	Caribou	111502	9,955	74.95	Proof	80.	—
2011	Cougar	115257	8,627	79.95	Proof	80.	—
2013	The Hummingbird	122598	9,993	79.95	Proof	80.	—
2014	Rocky Mountain Bighorn Sheep	120703	6,054	79.95	Proof	80.	—
2014	Eastern Chipmunk	128573	9,400	79.95	Proof	80.	—
2015	Grizzly Bear	130593	4,069	79.95	Proof	80.	—
2015	Rock Rabbit	142424	5,927	79.95	Proof	80.	—
2015	Diwali: Fesitival of Lights	147529	2,783	79.95	Proof	80.	—

TWENTY-FIVE CENT GOLD COINS PREDATOR VS. PREY SERIES

TWENTY-FIVE CENTS, GOLD COINS PREDATOR VS. PREY, 2016-2017.

Actual Size	2016 Traditional Arctic Fox Des.: Pierre Leduc	2017 Traditional Arctic Hare Des.: Pierre Leduc	2017 Inuit Arctic Fox Des.: Andrew Qappik	2017 Inuit Arctic Hare Des.: Andrew Qappik

Designers:		**Engravers:**	
Obv.:	Susanna Blunt	Rev.:	Susan Taylor
Rev.:	See reverse illustrations	Rev.:	See reverse illustrations
Composition:	99.99% Au	**Thickness:**	0.5-0.6 mm
Gold content:	0.5 g, 0.016 tr oz	**Edge:**	Reeded
Weight:	0.5 g	**Die Axis:**	↑↑
Diameter:	11.0 mm	**Finish:**	Proof
Case of Issue:	Maroon leatherette clam style case, black flocked insert, encapsulated coin, COA		

DATE	DESCRIPTION	RCM ITEM #	QUANTITY SOLD	ISSUE PRICE	FINISH	PR-69	PR-70
2016	Predator vs. Prey: Traditional Arctic Fox	149648	6,497	79.95	Proof	80.	—
2017	Predator vs. Prey: Traditional Arctic Hare	151390	6,065	79.95	Proof	80.	—
2017	Predator vs. Prey: Inuit Arctic Fox	157288	5,525	79.95	Proof	80.	—
2017	Predator vs. Prey: Inuit Arctic Hare	157289	4,444	79.95	Proof	80.	—

TWENTY-FIVE CENTS, 40TH ANNIVERSARY OF THE GML, 2019.

The year 2019 marks the 40th anniversary of the Royal Canadian Mint's iconic Gold Maple Leaf bullion coin – the standard against which other gold bullion coins are measured.

Actual Size

Designers and Engravers:			
Obv.:	Susanna Blunt, Susan Taylor		
Rev.:	Walter Ott		
Composition:	99.99% Au		
Gold content:	0.5 g, 0.016 tr oz		
Weight:	0.5 g	**Edge:**	Reeded
Diameter:	11 mm	**Die Axis:**	↑↑
Thickness:	N/A	**Finish:**	Reverse Proof
Case of Issue:	Standard maroon clamshell with black beauty box, COA.		

DATE	DESCRIPTION	RCM ITEM #	MINTAGE	ISSUE PRICE	FINISH	PR-69	PR-70
2019	40th Anniversary of the GML	168594	40,000	84.95	Reverse Proof	85.	—

FIFTY CENT GOLD COINS

FIFTY CENT (1/25 OUNCE) ISSUES, 2004-2012.

The 1/25 oz gold coin is the smallest ever produced by the Royal Canadian Mint.

Designers:		Engravers:	
Obv.:	Susanna Blunt	Obv.:	Susan Taylor
Rev.:	See reverse illustrations	Rev.:	See reverse illustrations

Composition: 99.99% Au
Gold content: 1.27 g, 0.041 tr oz
Weight: 1.27 g
Diameter: 13.9 mm
Thickness: 0.6 mm

Edge: Reeded
Die Axis: ↑↑
Finish: Proof

Actual Size

Case of Issue:
2004: Maroon leatherette case, black flocked insert, encapsulated coin, COA
2005-2006: Maroon plastic slide case, black plastic insert, encapsulated coin, COA
2007-2012: Maroon leatherette clam style case, black flocked insert, encapsulated coin, COA

Common Obverse	2004	2005	2006	2007
	Majestic Moose	Voyageur	Cowboy	Wolf
	Des. and Engr.:	Des.: E. Hahn	Des.: M. Grant	Des. and Engr.:
	José Osio	Engr.: Stan Witten	Engr.: Stan Witten	William Woodruff

2008	2009	2010	2011	2012
De Havilland	Red Maple Leaves	R.C.M.P.	Canada Geese	The Bluenose
Beaver	Des. and Engr.:	Des.: J. Griffin-Scott	Des.: E. Damstra	Des.: From the late
Des.: P. Mossman	Christie Paquet	Engr.: K. Wachelko	Engr.: K. Wachelko	Nova Scotia artist
Engr.: K. Wachelko				P. MacCready's
				watercolour
				painting
				Engr.: S. Witten

DATE	DESCRIPTION	RCM ITEM #	QUANTITY SOLD	ISSUE PRICE	FINISH	PR-69	PR-70
2004	Majestic Moose, 25th Anniv. Gold Maple Leafs	N/A	24,992	69.95	Proof	140.	—
2005	70th Anniversary of Voyageur Design	N/A	13,933	69.95	Proof	120.	—
2006	Cowboy	N/A	13,524	69.95	Proof	120.	—
2007	Wolf	620097	12,514	81.95	Proof	150.	—
2008	De Havilland Beaver	100466	13,526	85.95	Proof	120.	—
2009	Red Maple Leaves	105500	11,854	99.95	Proof	120.	—
2010	Royal Canadian Mounted Police	108185	9,594	109.95	Proof	120.	—
2011	Canada Geese	113142	7,498	109.95	Proof	120.	—
2012	The Bluenose	117117	13,524	129.95	Proof	120.	—

FIFTY CENTS, THE BOREAL FOREST, 2011.

The Boreal Forest is a vast woodland that circumvents the globe across the northern hemisphere, and 2011 was declared International Year of the Forest. These are 1/25 ounce coins.

2011   **BOREAL FOREST**

2011   **ORCA WHALE**

2011   **WOOD BISON**

2011   **PEREGRINE FALCON**

Actual Size

Designers:		Engravers:	
Obv.:	Susanna Blunt	Obv.:	Susan Taylor
Rev.:	Corrine Hunt	Rev.:	Boreal Forest / Peregrine Falcon: Marcos Hallam
Composition:	99.99% Au		Orca Whale: Cecily Mok,
Gold content:	1.27 g, 0.04 tr oz		Wood Bison: Konrad Wachelko
Weight:	1.27 g	**Edge:**	Reeded
Diameter:	13.8 to 13.9 mm	**Die Axis:**	↑↑
Thickness:	0.6 mm	**Finish:**	Proof
Case of Issue:	Maroon leatherette clam style case, black flocked insert, encapsulated coin, COA		

DATE	DESCRIPTION	RCM ITEM #	QUANTITY SOLD	ISSUE PRICE	FINISH	PR-69	PR-70
2011	Boreal Forest	116324	1,859	139.95	Proof	120.	—
2011	Orca Whale	116327	1,729	139.95	Proof	120.	—
2011	Wood Bison	116321	1,678	139.95	Proof	120.	—
2011	Peregrine Falcon	116330	1,686	139.95	Proof	120.	—

FIFTY CENTS, COMMEMORATIVE GOLD COINS, 2012-2017.

Actual Size

Designers:	
Obv.:	Susanna Blunt
Rev.:	See reverse illustrations
Composition:	99.99% Au
Gold content:	1.27 g, 0.04 tr oz
Weight:	1.27 g
Diameter:	13.9 mm
Case of Issue:	Maroon leatherette clam style case, black flocked insert, encapsulated coin, COA

Engravers:	
Obv.:	Susan Taylor
Rev.:	See reverse illustrations
Thickness:	0.5 to 0.7 mm
Edge:	Reeded
Die Axis:	↑↑
Finish:	Proof

Common Obverse

2012
150th Anniv. of the
Caribou Gold Rush
Des.: Tony Bianco
Engr.: C. Paquet

2013
Owl Shaman
Holding Goose
Des.: J. Nowkawalk
Engr.: S. Stewart

2013
Bald Eagle
Des.: Trevor Tennant
Engr.: Cecily Mok
Actual size

2013
300th Anniv. of
Louisbourg
Des.: Peter Gough
Engr.: RCM Staff

2013
Starfish
Des.: E. Damstra
Engr.: S. Strath

2014
Canada's Classic Beaver
Des. G.E. Kruger Gray
Engr. M. Bowan

2014
Osprey
Des.: RCM Staff
Engr.: K. Wachelko

2014
Seahorse
Des.: Emily Damstra
Engr.: M. Hallam

2014
Quebec/Charlottetown
Conferences
Des.: M. Bowen
Engr.: RCM Staff

2015
Owl
Des.: A. Nogy
Engr.: RCM Staff

2015
Maple Leaf
Des.: P. Leduc
Engr.: RCM Staff

2015
Sea Creatures: Lobster
Des.: Emily Damstra
Engr.: RCM Staff

2017
The Silver Maple Leaf
Des.: Margaret Best
Engr.: RCM Staff

DATE	DESCRIPTION	RCM ITEM #	QUANTITY SOLD	ISSUE PRICE	FINISH	PR-69	PR-70
2012	150th Anniv. of the Caribou Gold Rush	119111	5,988	129.95	Proof	120.	—
2013	Owl Shaman Holding Goose	121869	5,736	129.95	Proof	120.	—
2013	Bald Eagle	124254	9,712	129.95	Proof	120.	—
2013	300th Anniv. of Louisbourg	125250	3,409	129.95	Proof	120.	—
2013	Sea Creatures: Starfish	126089	4,287	129.95	Proof	120.	—
2014	Canada's Classic Beaver	128900	7,500	129.95	Proof	120.	—
2014	Osprey	129068	4,096	129.95	Proof	120.	—
2014	Sea Creatures: Seahorse	130206	3,049	129.95	Proof	120.	—
2014 (1884-)	150th Anniv. Quebec/Charlottetown Conferences	130590	4,746	129.95	Proof	130.	—
2015	Owl	141493	3,592	129.95	Proof	130.	—
2015	Maple Leaf	140602	5,102	129.95	Proof	130.	—
2015	Sea Creatures: Lobster	142775	2,994	129.95	Proof	130.	—
2017	The Silver Maple Leaf	158334	8,000	129.95	Proof	130.	—

Note: There were no fifty cent gold coins issued for 2016.

ONE DOLLAR GOLD COINS

| | **2006**
GOLD LOUIS
(1723 LOUIS D'OR MIRLITON) | **2007**
GOLD LOUIS
(1726 LOUIS D'OR AUX LUNETTES) | **2008**
GOLD LOUIS
(1720-1723 LOUIS D'OR AUX DEUX L) |

Actual Size

Actual Size

Actual Size

Designers:		**Engravers:**	
Obv.:	Susanna Blunt	Obv.:	Susan Taylor
Rev.:	RCM Staff	Rev.:	2006 Konrad Wachelko
Composition:	99.99% Au		2007-2008 Marcos Hallam
Gold content:	1.55 g, 0.05 tr oz		
Weight:	1.555 g	**Edge:**	Reeded
Diameter:	14.1 mm	**Die Axis:**	↑↑
Thickness:	0.8 mm	**Finish:**	Proof
Case of Issue:	Maroon plastic slide case, black plastic insert, encapsulated coin, COA		

DATE	DESCRIPTION	RCM ITEM #	QUANTITY SOLD	ISSUE PRICE	FINISH	PR-69	PR-70
2006	1723 Louis d'or Mirliton	N/A	5,648	102.95	Proof	100.	—
2007	1726 Louis d'or Aux Lunettes	N/A	4,023	104.95	Proof	100.	—
2008	1720 to 1723 Louis d'or aux deux L	101452	3,793	124.95	Proof	100.	—

ONE DOLLAR, 30TH ANNIVERSARY OF THE LOONIE, 2017.

To commemorate the 30th anniversary of Canada's golden-hued circulation coin, this exquisite two-coin set revisits history by featuring the now-iconic loonie alongside its original design – Canada's $1 circulation coin that never was.

Common Obverse

Loonie Designer:
Robert-Ralph Carmichael

Voyageur Designer:
Emanuel Hahn

Designers:		**Engravers:**	
Obv.:	Susanna Blunt	Obv.:	Susan Taylor
Rev.:	See reverse illustrations	Rev.:	See reverse illustrations
Composition:	99.99% Au		
Gold content:	1.55 g, 0.05 tr oz		
Weight:	31.16 g	**Edge:**	Plain
Diameter:	30 mm	**Die Axis:**	↑↑
Thickness:	N/A	**Finish:**	Proof
Case of Issue:	Wooden box with black beauty box, COA		

DATE	DESCRIPTION	RCM ITEM #	MINTAGE	ISSUE PRICE	FINISH	PR-69	PR-70
2017	2-Coin Set, 30th Anniversary of the Loonie	156041	350	5,499.95	Proof	5,500	–

FIVE DOLLAR GOLD COINS

FIVE DOLLARS, COMMEMORATIVE GOLD COINS, 2011-2014.

| Common Obverse | 2011
Norman Bethune
Des.: Harvey Chan
Engr.: José Osio | 2012
Diamond Jubilee
Des.: RCM Staff
Engr.: C. Paquet | 2014
Bald Eagle
Des.: Derek Wicks
Engr.: RCM Staff | 2014
Nanaboozhoo
Des.: C. Assiniboine
Engr.: RCM Staff |

| Actual
Size | 2014
Maple Leaves
Des.: Pierre Leduc
Engr.: RCM Staff | 2014
Cougar
Des.: Glen Loates
Engr.: RCM Staff |

Designers:	**Engravers:**
Obv.: Susanna Blunt	Obv.: Susan Taylor
Rev.: See reverse illustrations	Rev.: See reverse illustrations
Composition: 99.99% Au	
Gold content: 3.13 g, 0.10 tr oz	
Weight: 3.13 g	**Edge:** Reeded
Diameter: 16.0 mm	**Die Axis:** ↑↑
Thickness: 1.0 mm	**Finish:** Proof

Case of Issue: 2011, 2014:   Maroon leatherette clam style case, black flocked insert, encapsulated coin, COA
2012:   Wooden collector case, black flocked insert, encapsulated coin, COA, Beauty box featuring the official Diamond Jubilee Cypher

DATE	DESCRIPTION	RCM ITEM #	QUANTITY SOLD	ISSUE PRICE	FINISH	PR-69	PR-70
2011	75th Anniv. Dr. Norman Bethune's Invention of the First Mobile Blood Transfusion Vehicle	113856	1,457	319.95	Proof	230.	—
2012	The Queen's Diamond Jubilee	114605	1,538	259.95	Proof	230.	—
2014	Bald Eagle	130527	1,584	279.95	Proof	230.	—
2014	Portrait of Nanaboozhoo	132390	1,251	279.95	Proof	230.	—
2014	Overlaid Majestic Maple Leaves	132687	778	279.95	Proof	250.	—
2014	Cougar	130609	1,226	279.95	Proof	230.	—

Note: The $5 gold Overlaid Majestic Maple Leaves coin was offered as part of a five coin subscription (RCM Item # 141319) along with a $20 Silver Majestic Maple Leaves, a $20 Majestic Maple Leaves with colour, and a $20 Majestic Maple Leaves with Jade (see page 290), as well as a $5 platinum Overlaid Majestic Maple Leaves coin (see page 483).

FIVE DOLLARS, CHINESE LUNAR CALENDAR GOLD COINS, 2012-2015.

Common Obverse	2012	2013	2015	
	Year of the Dragon	Year of the Snake	Year of the Sheep	
	Des.: Three Degrees	Des.: Aries Cheung	Des.: Simon Ng	Actual Size
	Creative Group Inc.	Engr.: Stan Witten	Engr.: RCM Staff	
	Engr.: K. Wachelko			

Designers:
- Obv.: Susanna Blunt
- Rev.: See reverse illustrations

Composition: 99.99% Au
Gold content: 3.13 g, 0.10 tr oz
Weight: 3.13 g
Diameter: 16.0 mm
Thickness: 1.0 mm
Case of Issue: Maroon leatherette clam style case, black flocked insert, encapsulated coin, COA

Engravers:
- Obv.: Susan Taylor
- Rev.: See reverse illustrations

Edge: Reeded
Die Axis: ↑↑
Finish: Specimen

DATE	DESCRIPTION	RCM ITEM #	QUANTITY SOLD	ISSUE PRICE	FINISH	SP-68	SP-69
2012	Year of the Dragon	116948	8,902	229.95	Specimen	230.	—
2013	Year of the Snake	120201	3,033	229.95	Specimen	230.	—
2015	Year of the Sheep	130571	1,399	278.88	Specimen	250.	—

Note: The Year of the Horse, 2014, was not issued in a five dollar denomination.

FIVE DOLLARS (¼ ounce), DEVIL'S BRIGADE, 2013.

Canada joined forces with the United States in World War II to create the First Special Service Force.

Designers and Engravers:
- Obv.: Susanna Blunt, Susan Taylor
- Rev.: Ardell Bourgeois, RCM Staff

Composition: 99.99% Au
Gold content: 7.8 g, 0.25 tr oz
Weight: 7.8 g
Diameter: 20.0 mm
Thickness: 1.7 mm
Case of Issue: Maroon leatherette clam style case, black flock insert, encapsulated coin(s), COA

Edge: Reeded
Die Axis: ↑↑
Finish: Proof

Actual Size

DATE	DESCRIPTION	RCM ITEM #	MINTAGE	ISSUE PRICE	FINISH	PR-69	PR-70
2013	$5 (¼ oz), Devil's Brigade	126600	555	649.95	Proof	550.	—

O CANADA SET

FIVE DOLLARS, O CANADA SET, 2013-2014.

The O Canada Set focuses on iconic Canadian animals to celebrate Canadian pride. For other coins in the O Canada Set see pages 201-202 and 344.

Designers:
Obv.:	Susanna Blunt
Rev.:	2013: Pierre Leduc; 2014: RCM Staff

Composition: 99.99% Au
Weight: 3.13 g
Diameter: 16.0 mm
Thickness: 1.0 mm
Case of Issue: 2013: Maroon leatherette clam style case, black flocked insert, encapsulated coin, COA
2014: Walnut display case, black flocked insert, encapsulated coin, COA

Engravers:
Obv.:	Susan Taylor
Obv.:	2013: See reverse illustrations

Gold content: 3.13 g, 0.10 tr oz
Edge: Reeded
Die Axis: ↑↑
Finish: Proof

Actual Size

Common Obverse	2013 Beaver Engr.: S. Witten	2013 Polar Bear Engr.: E. Boyer	2013 Caribou Engr.: E. Boyer	2013 Wolf Engr.: A. Tirabasso

2013 Orca Engr.: A. Tirabasso	2014 Grizzly Bear	2014 Moose	2014 Canada Goose	2014 Bison

DATE	DESCRIPTION	RCM ITEM #	QUANTITY SOLD	ISSUE PRICE	FINISH	PR-69	PR-70
2013	Beaver	121617	3,673	279.95	Proof	230.	—
2013	Polar Bear	121727	3,634	279.95	Proof	230.	—
2013	Caribou	123919	2,248	279.95	Proof	230.	—
2013	Wolf	123633	2,582	279.95	Proof	230.	—
2013	Orca	123927	1,852	279.95	Proof	230.	—
2013	Set of 5 coins	124262	Incl. above	1,399.95	Proof	1,000.	—
2014	Grizzly Bear	129291	2,896	279.95	Proof	230.	—
2014	Moose	129170	2,471	279.95	Proof	230.	—
2014	Canada Goose	129114	2,520	279.95	Proof	230.	—
2014	Bison	129724	1,888	279.95	Proof	230.	—

FIVE DOLLARS (1/10 ounce), FIVE BLESSINGS, 2014.

Designers and Engravers:
Obv.:	Susanna Blunt, Susan Taylor
Rev.:	RCM Staff

Composition: 99.99% Au
Gold content: 3.13 g, 0.1 tr oz
Weight: 3.13 g   Edge: Reeded
Diameter: 16.0 mm   Die Axis: ↑↑
Thickness: 1.0 mm   Finish: Proof
Case of Issue: Maroon leatherette clam style case, black flock insert, encapsulated coin, COA

Actual Size

DATE	DESCRIPTION	RCM ITEM #	QUANTITY SOLD	ISSUE PRICE	FINISH	PR-69	PR-70
2014	$5 (1/10 oz), Five Blessings	133897	1,104	279.95	Proof	280.	—

Note: The design on this coin is also utilized on the $50 (1 oz) Five Blessings maple leaf coin (see page 425).

PREHISTORIC ANIMAL SERIES

FIVE DOLLARS (1/10 ounce), PREHISTORIC ANIMALS, 2014-2015.

Actual Size

2014 Woolly Mammoth
Des.: Michael Skrepnik

2015 American Scrimitar Sabre-Tooth Cat
Des.: Julius Csotonyi

Designers:
  Obv.:   Susanna Blunt
  Rev.:   See reverse illustrations
Composition: 99.99% Au
Gold content: 3.14 g, 0.1 tr oz
Weight: 3.14 g
Diameter: 16.0 mm
Case of Issue: Maroon leatherette clam style case, black flocked insert, encapsulated coin, COA, custom box

Engravers:
  Rev.:   Susan Taylor

Thickness: 1.0 mm
Edge: Reeded
Die Axis: ↑↑
Finish: Proof

DATE	DESCRIPTION	RCM ITEM #	QUANTITY SOLD	ISSUE PRICE	FINISH	PR-69	PR-70
2014	Woolly Mammoth	132486	3,001	279.95	Proof	250.	—
2015	American Scimitar Sabre-Tooth Cat	144427	1,455	279.95	Proof	250.	—

Note: The Woolly Mammoth was issued in a set of two coins (see page 481 for set), the second coin being the one ounce $20 silver (see page 289).

FIVE AND TEN DOLLAR GOLD COMMEMORATIVE COINS

FIVE AND TEN DOLLAR GOLD COMMEMORATIVES 1912-2002.

Issued to mark the 90th anniversary of Canada's first five and ten dollar gold coins in 1912, these double-dated 1912-2002 coins continue a commemorative series which began in 1998, with the issue recalling the first set of coins struck at the Ottawa Mint. Basing the overall design on the 1912 specimen coins from the Bank of Canada collection, the 1912-2002 gold coins differ only in the date and, of course, the obverse effigy.

$5 Obverse   **$5 Reverse**

$10 Obverse   **$10 Reverse**

Designers:
  Obv.:   Dora de Pédery-Hunt
  Rev.:   W. H. J. Blakemore

Engravers:
  Obv.:   Dora de Pédery-Hunt
  Rev.:   Cosme Saffioti

	$5	**$10**
Denominations:	$5	$10
Composition:	90.0% Au, 10.0 Cu	90.0% Au, 10.0% Cu
Gold content:	7.52 g, 0.242 tr oz	15.05 g, 0.484 tr oz
Weight (grams):	8.36	16.72
Diameter (mm):	21.6	26.9
Thickness (mm):	N/A	N/A
Edge:	Reeded	Reeded
Die Axis:	↑↑	↑↑
Finish:	Proof	Proof

Case of Issue: Two-coin clam style case

DATE	DESCRIPTION	RCM ITEM #	QUANTITY SOLD	ISSUE PRICE	FINISH	PR-69	PR-70
2002 (1912-)	$5	N/A	1,998	N.I.I.	Proof	450.	—
2002 (1912-)	$10	N/A	1,998	N.I.I.	Proof	850.	—
2002 (1912-)	Set of 2 coins	N/A	1,998	749.95	Proof	1,250.	*

TEN DOLLAR GOLD COINS

TEN DOLLARS (¼ ounce), THE WAR OF 1812, 1812-2012.

The reverse of this coin features a heraldic design commemorating the 250th anniversary of the war between the United States and England over the control of Canadian territories.

Actual Size

Designers and Engravers:

Obv.:	Susanna Blunt, Susan Taylor
Rev.:	Cathy Bursey-Sabourin, Konrad Wachelko
Composition:	99.99% Au
Gold content:	7.80 g, 0.25 tr oz
Weight:	7.80 g
Diameter:	20.0 mm
Thickness:	1.7 mm
Case of Issue:	Maroon leatherette clam style case, black flock insert, encapsulated coin(s), COA

Edge:	Reeded
Die Axis:	↑↑
Finish:	Proof

DATE	DESCRIPTION	RCM ITEM #	QUANTITY SOLD	ISSUE PRICE	FINISH	PR-69	PR-70
2012 (1812-)	$10 gold (¼ oz) The War of 1812	119384	1,997	569.95	Proof	550.	—

TEN DOLLARS (¼ ounce), POLAR BEAR, 2013.

Actual Size

Designers and Engravers:

Obv.:	Susanna Blunt, Susan Taylor
Rev.:	Germaine Arnaktauyak, RCM Staff
Composition:	99.99% Au
Gold content:	7.87 g, 0.25 tr oz
Weight:	7.8 g
Diameter:	20.0 mm
Thickness:	1.7 mm
Case of Issue:	See page 501

Edge:	Reeded
Die Axis:	↑↑
Finish:	Proof

DATE	DESCRIPTION	RCM ITEM #	QUANTITY SOLD	ISSUE PRICE	FINISH	PR-69	PR-70
2013	$10 Gold (¼ oz) Polar Bear	141559	4,229	N.I.I.	Proof	500.	—

TEN DOLLARS (¼ ounce), THE ARCTIC FOX, 2014.

Actual Size

Designers and Engravers:

Obv.:	Susanna Blunt, Susan Taylor
Rev.:	Maurice Gervais, RCM Staff
Composition:	99.99% Au
Gold content:	7.8 g, 0.25 tr oz
Weight:	7.8 g
Diameter:	20.0 mm
Thickness:	1.7 mm
Case of Issue:	Maroon leatherette clam style case, black flock insert, encapsulated coin, COA

Edge:	Reeded
Die Axis:	↑↑
Finish:	Proof

DATE	DESCRIPTION	RCM ITEM #	QUANTITY SOLD	ISSUE PRICE	FINISH	PR-69	PR-70
2014	$10 Gold (¼ ounce) The Arctic Fox	132492	264	649.95	Proof	700.	—

TEN DOLLARS (¼ ounce), POLAR BEAR AND CUB, 2015.

Featuring Canada's iconic polar bear and cub, the coin is struck in proof finish.

Actual Size

Designers and Engravers:

Obv.:	Susanna Blunt, Susan Taylor
Rev.:	Germaine Arnaktauyok, RCM Staff
Composition:	99.99% Au
Gold content:	7.80 g, 0.25 tr oz
Weight:	7.80 g
Diameter:	20.0 mm
Thickness:	1.7 mm
Case of Issue:	Maroon leatherette clam style case, black flock insert, encapsulated coin, COA

Edge:	Reeded
Die Axis:	↑↑
Finish:	Proof

DATE	DESCRIPTION	RCM ITEM #	QUANTITY SOLD	ISSUE PRICE	FINISH	PR-69	PR-70
2015	$10 gold (¼ oz) Polar Bear and Cub	141559	314	649.95	Proof	700.	—

TEN DOLLARS (¼ ounce), 65TH ANNIVERSARY OF THE CORONATION OF HER MAJESTY QUEEN ELIZABETH II, 2018.

Actual Size

Designers and Engravers:
Obv.: Susanna Blunt, Susan Taylor
Rev.: RCM Staff
Composition: 99.99% Au
Gold content: 7.80 g, 0.25 tr oz
Weight: 7.80 g
Diameter: 20.0 mm
Thickness: N/A
Case of Issue: Standard maroon clamshell with black beauty box, COA
Edge: Reeded
Die Axis: ↑↑
Finish: Proof

DATE	DESCRIPTION	RCM ITEM #	MINTAGE	ISSUE PRICE	FINISH	PR-69	PR-70
2018	65th Anniv. Coronation Queen Elizabeth II	169220	1,200	729.95	Proof	730.	—

TEN DOLLARS (¼ ounce), QUEEN VICTORIA: 200TH ANNIVERSARY OF HER BIRTH, 2019.

Actual Size

Designers and Engravers:
Obv.: Susanna Blunt, Susan Taylor
Rev.: RCM Staff
Composition: 99.99% Au
Gold content: 7.80 g, 0.25 tr oz
Weight: 7.80 g
Diameter: 20.0 mm
Thickness: N/A
Case of Issue: Black clamshell with black beauty box, COA
Edge: Reeded
Die Axis: ↑↑
Finish: Proof

DATE	DESCRIPTION	RCM ITEM #	MINTAGE	ISSUE PRICE	FINISH	PR-69	PR-70
2019	Queen Victoria: 200th Anniv. of Birth	172127	1,500	729.95	Proof	730.	—

TWENTY DOLLAR GOLD COINS

TWENTY DOLLARS, CENTENNIAL OF CONFEDERATION COMMEMORATIVE, 1967.

The highlight of the coins issued in 1967 to mark the centenary of Canadian Confederation was a $20 gold coin. It was issued only as part of a $40.00 specimen set (see page 519 for the set listing), but many were later removed from the sets for separate trading. The reverse design is an adaption of the Canadian coat of arms which appears on the 50-cent piece of 1960-1966. It is the only coin in the Centennial set that bears the single date 1967 instead of 1867-1967.

Designers and Engravers:

Obv.:	Arnold Machin, Myron Cook		
Rev.:	Thomas Shingles, Myron Cook		
Composition:	90.0% Au, 10.0% Cu		
Gold content:	16.443 g, 0.529 tr oz		
Weight:	18.27 g	**Edge:**	Reeded
Diameter:	27.1 mm	**Die Axis:**	↑↑
Thickness:	2.3 mm	**Finish:**	Specimen
Case of Issue:	Black leather case, black flocked insert		

DATE	DESCRIPTION	QUANTITY SOLD	ISSUE PRICE	FINISH	SP-68	SP-69
1967	Centennial of Confederation	334,288	N.I.I.	Specimen	1,000.	—

TWENTY DOLLARS (1/10 ounce), SYMBOLS OF THE NORTH, 2018.

Symbols of strength, beauty and resilience, the animals of the North are the proud emblems of our Arctic Region.

Actual Size

Designers and Engravers:

Obv.:	Susanna Blunt, Susan Taylor		
Rev.:	Andrew Qappik		
Composition:	99.99% Au		
Gold content:	3.14 g, 0.10 tr oz		
Weight:	3.14 g	**Edge:**	Reeded
Diameter:	20.0 mm	**Die Axis:**	↑↑
Thickness:	N/A	**Finish:**	Proof
Case of Issue:	Standard maroon clamshell with black beauty box, COA		

DATE	DESCRIPTION	RCM ITEM #	MINTAGE	ISSUE PRICE	FINISH	PR-69	PR-70
2018	$20 gold (1/10 oz) Symbols of the North	167012	1,500	359.95	Proof	360.	—

TWENTY-FIVE DOLLAR GOLD COINS

TWENTY-FIVE DOLLARS, MISS CANADA: AN ALLEGORY 2013.

Designers and Engravers:
Obv.:	Susanna Blunt, Susan Taylor
Rev.:	Laurie McGaw, RCM Staff

Composition:	99.99% Au		
Gold content:	7.797 g, 0.25 tr oz		
Weight:	7.797 g	**Edge:**	Reeded
Diameter:	20.0 mm	**Die Axis:**	↑↑
Thickness:	N/A	**Finish:**	Proof
Case of Issue:	Maroon leatherette clam style case, black flocked insert, encapsulated coin, COA		

DATE	DESCRIPTION	RCM ITEM #	QUANTITY SOLD	ISSUE PRICE	FINISH	PR-69	PR-70
2013	Miss Canada: An Allegory	125709	622	649.95	Proof	650.	—

UNTAMED CANADA SERIES

TWENTY-FIVE DOLLARS, UNTAMED CANADA SERIES, 2013-2014.

Common Obverse	2013 Arctic Fox	2013 Pronghorn	2014 Wolverine

Designers and Engravers:
Obv.:	Susanna Blunt, Susan Taylor
Rev.:	Tividar Bote, Steven Stewart

Composition:	99.99% Au		
Gold content:	7.797 g, 0.25 tr oz		
Weight:	7.797 g	**Edge:**	Reeded
Diameter:	20.0 mm	**Die Axis:**	↑↑
Thickness:	N/A	**Finish:**	Proof
Case of Issue:	Maroon leatherette clam style case, black flocked insert, encapsulated coin, COA		

DATE	DESCRIPTION	RCM ITEM #	QUANTITY SOLD	ISSUE PRICE	FINISH	PR-69	PR-70
2013	The Arctic Fox	123238	728	649.95	Proof	650.	—
2013	Pronghorn	123225	306	649.95	Proof	650.	—
2014	Wolverine	128921	370	649.95	Proof	650.	—

TWENTY-FIVE DOLLARS, POPE JOHN PAUL II, 2014.

Designers and Engravers:
Obv.:	Susanna Blunt, Susan Taylor
Rev.:	RCM Staff

Composition:	99.99% Au		
Gold content:	7.797 g, 0.25 tr oz		
Weight:	7.797 g	**Edge:**	Reeded
Diameter:	20.0 mm	**Die Axis:**	↑↑
Thickness:	N/A	**Finish:**	Proof
Case of Issue:	Maroon leatherette clam style case, black flocked insert, encapsulated coin, COA		

DATE	DESCRIPTION	RCM ITEM #	QUANTITY SOLD	ISSUE PRICE	FINISH	PR-69	PR-70
2014	Pope John Paul II	132612	1,500	649.95	Proof	650.	—

FIFTY DOLLAR GOLD COINS

FIFTY DOLLARS, 60TH ANNIVERSARY OF THE END OF THE SECOND WORLD WAR, 1945-2005.

World War II was a global conflict which began September 1st, 1939 when Germany invaded Poland. By September 3rd, 1939, Britain and France declared war on Germany.

There are several ending dates: VE (Victory in Europe) Day May 8th, 1945, and VJ Day (Victory in Japan) August 14th, 1945.

Designers and Engravers:

Obv.:	Susanna Blunt, Susan Taylor
Rev.:	Peter Mossman, Christie Paquet
Composition:	58.33% Au, 41.67% Ag
Gold content:	7.00 g, 0.225 tr oz
Silver content:	5.00 g, 0.161 tr oz
Weight:	12.0 g
Diameter:	27.0 mm
Thickness:	2.0 mm
Case of Issue:	Maroon plastic slide case, black plastic insert, encapsulated coin, COA

Edge:	Reeded
Die Axis:	↑↑
Finish:	Specimen

DATE	DESCRIPTION	RCM ITEM #	QUANTITY SOLD	ISSUE PRICE	FINISH	SP-68	SP-69
2005 (1945-)	60th Anniv. End of the Second World War	N/A	4,000	379.95	Specimen	500.	—

Note: While this $50 gold coin is listed as proof quality on the certificate of authenticity, the finish on the coins examined is specimen.

FIFTY DOLLARS, THE QUEEN'S DIAMOND JUBILEE, 2012.

This coin was struck for the Queen's Diamond Jubilee in 2012. It is the world's first 99.999% gold coin struck with an ultra-high relief.

Designers and Engravers:

Obv.:	Susanna Blunt, Susan Taylor
Rev.:	Laurie McGaw, Christie Paquet
Composition:	99.999% Au
Gold content:	33.17 g, 1.066 tr oz
Weight:	33.17 g
Diameter:	30.0 mm
Thickness:	2.5 to 4.5 mm
Case of Issue:	Maroon leatherette clam style case, black flocked insert, encapsulated coin, COA

Edge:	Reeded
Die Axis:	↑↑
Finish:	Proof

DATE	DESCRIPTION	RCM ITEM #	QUANTITY SOLD	ISSUE PRICE	FINISH	PR-69	PR-70
2012	The Queen's Diamond Jubilee	118416	499	2,999.95	Proof	2,200.	—

FIFTY DOLLARS, UNESCO AT HOME & ABROAD: MOUNT FUJI & THE CANADIAN ROCKIES, 2015.

The coin juxtaposes two UNESCO heritage sites, one Canadian and one non-Canadian.

Designers and Engravers:

Obv.:	Susanna Blunt, Susan Taylor
Rev.:	Trevor Tennant, RCM Staff
Composition:	99.999% Au
Gold content:	7.8 g, 0.25 oz
Weight:	7.8 g
Diameter:	20.0 mm
Thickness:	N/A
Case of Issue:	Maroon leatherette clam style case, black flocked insert, encapsulated coin, COA, custom box

Edge:	Reeded
Die Axis:	↑↑
Finish:	Proof

DATE	DESCRIPTION	RCM ITEM #	QUANTITY SOLD	ISSUE PRICE	FINISH	PR-69	PR-70
2015	Mount Fuji & the Canadian Rockies	142308	750	649.95	Proof	650.	—

VANCOUVER 2010 OLYMPIC WINTER GAMES

FIFTY DOLLARS (1 ounce), VANCOUVER 2010 WINTER OLYMPIC GAMES, 2008-2010

2008   MAPLE LEAF AND VANCOUVER 2010 OLYMPIC LOGO   2009   THUNDERBIRD

2010   HOCKEY PLAYER

Designers:	
Obv.:	Susanna Blunt,
Rev.:	2008, 2010: RCM Staff;
	2009: Xwa lac tun (R. Harry);
Composition:	99.99% Au
Gold content:	31.1 g, 1.0 tr oz
Weight:	31.1035 g, 1 oz
Diameter:	30.0 mm
Thickness:	2.9 mm
Finish:	Bullion; Bullion, Painted
Case of Issue:	Singly: Mylar pouch

Engravers:
Obv.: Susan Taylor
Rev.: 2008, 2010: S. Witten
2009: M. Hallam

Edge: Reeded
Die Axis: ↑↑

Case of Issue: Singly: Mylar pouch
Coloured Set: Maple wood box, black flocked insert, encapsulated coins, COA

DATE	DESCRIPTION	QUANTITY SOLD	ISSUE PRICE	FINISH	MS-65	MS-66
2008	$50 (1oz) Maple Leaf and 2010 Logo	49,802	BV	Bullion	1,900.	—
2008	$50 (1oz) Maple Leaf and 2010 Logo, Painted	200	2,000.	Bullion	2,250.	—
2009	$50 (1oz) Thunderbird	49,802	BV	Bullion	1,900.	—
2009	$50 (1oz) Thunderbird, Painted	200	2,000.	Bullion	2,250.	—
2010	$50 (1oz) Hockey Player	49,802	BV	Bullion	1,900.	—
2010	$50 (1oz) Hockey Player, Painted	200	2,000.	Bullion	2,250.	—
—	3 coin set, 2008, 2009, 2010, Painted	200	5,999.95	Bullion	6,500.	*

Note: The RCM Annual Reports list the Olympic gold maple leafs struck as 2008 - 75,876 oz, 2009 - 74,214 oz, and 2010 - 6 oz, totalling 150,006 units struck. Using 200 reported painted sets as struck there are 149,406 coins to be divided among the three years (49,802 per year).

FIFTY DOLLARS (1 ounce), FIVE BLESSINGS, 2014.

This coin is offered in both a bullion and proof coloured version. This design was also used on the five dollars (1/10 ounce) gold maple leaf coin (see page 416) and on the five dollar silver maple leaf coin (see page 573)

Obverse   **Reverse**   **Reverse**
Proof with Colour   Bullion

Designers:	
Obv.:	Susanna Blunt
Rev.:	RCM Staff
Composition:	99.99% Au
Gold content:	31.16 g, 1.0 tr oz
Weight:	31.16 g, 1 oz
Diameter:	30.0 mm
Thickness:	2.9 mm
Finish:	Proof Coloured, Bullion

Engravers:
Rev.: Susan Taylor
Rev.: RCM Staff

Edge: Reeded
Die Axis: ↑↑

Case of Issue: Proof: Maroon clam style case, black flocked insert, encapsulated coin, COA Bullion: Not known

DATE	DESCRIPTION	RCM ITEM #	QUANTITY SOLD	ISSUE PRICE	FINISH	SP-68	SP-69	PR-69	PR-70
2014	$50 (1oz) Five Blessings	133944	141	2,699.95	Proof, Colour	—	—	2,400.	—
2014	$50 (1oz) Five Blessings	N/A	N/A	BV	Bullion	1,900.	2,000	—	—

SEVENTY-FIVE DOLLAR GOLD COINS

SEVENTY-FIVE DOLLARS, COMMEMORATING THE VISIT OF POPE JOHN PAUL II TO CANADA, 2005.

During a 12-day tour in April 2005, Pope John Paul II visited many cities in Canada, drawing more than two million people to the Papal events. This was his third trip to Canada.

Designers and Engravers:

Obv.:	Susanna Blunt, Susan Taylor
Rev.:	Susan Taylor, Susan Taylor
Composition:	41.66% Au, 58.34 Ag
Gold content:	13.1 g, 0.421 tr oz
Silver content:	18.34 g, 0.590 tr oz

Weight:	31.44 g	**Edge:**	Reeded
Diameter:	36.1 mm	**Die Axis:**	↑↑
Thickness:	3.0 mm	**Finish:**	Proof
Case of Issue:	Maroon plastic slide case, black plastic insert, encapsulated coin, COA		

DATE	DESCRIPTION	QUANTITY SOLD	ISSUE PRICE	FINISH	PR-69	PR-70
2005	Commemorating the Visit of Pope John Paul II to Canada	1,870	544.95	Proof	750.	—

Note: In 2005 a set containing both the $10 (silver) and $75 (gold) coins was issued to commemorate the visit to Canada of Pope John Paul II. This may have been a special presentation set as only nine were issued.

VANCOUVER 2010 OLYMPIC WINTER GAMES

SEVENTY-FIVE DOLLARS, COMMEMORATING THE VANCOUVER 2010 OLYMPIC WINTER GAMES, 2007-2009.

The Vancouver 2010 Olympic Winter Games $75 gold coins were sold singly, or in three-coin sets. The three different sets offered were Canadian Wildlife, Canadian Icons, and Vancouver 2010 Winter Games.

Common Obverse (Except for date)	2007 R.C.M.P. Des.: Cecily Mok Engr.: N/A	2007 Athletes' Pride Des.: Sheila Armstrong Engr.: Christie Paquet	2007 Canada Geese Des.: Cecily Mok Engr.: N/A	2008 Four Host First Nations Des.: Kerri Burnett Engr.: Cecily Mok

2008 Home of the 2010 Olympic Winter Games Des.: Sheila Armstrong Engr.: Marcos Hallam	2008 Inukshuk Des.: Sheila Armstrong Engr.: José Osio	2009 Wolf Des.: Arnold Nogy Engr.: N/A	2009 Olympic Spirit Des.: Sheila Armstrong Engr.: N/A	2009 Moose Des.: Kerri Burnett Engr.: José Osio

Designers:

Obv.:	Susanna Blunt
Rev.:	See reverse illustrations
Composition:	58.33% Au, 41.67% Ag, Colour on reverse
Gold content:	7.0 g, 0.225 tr oz
Silver content:	5.0 g, 0.161 tr oz
Weight:	12.0 g
Diameter:	27.0 mm

Engravers:

Obv.:	Susan Taylor
Rev.:	See reverse illustrations
Thickness:	2.0 to 2.2 mm
Edge:	Reeded
Die Axis:	↑↑
Finish:	Proof

Case of Issue: Singly: Black display case, black flocked insert, encapsulated coin, COA, Vancouver 2010 Olympic Winter Games theme sleeve.
Sets: See the $75 Vancouver Winter Olympic Game Coins Sets on page 427.

COMMEMORATING THE VANCOUVER 2010 OLYMPIC WINTER GAMES, 2007-2009, PRICING TABLE.

DATE	DESCRIPTION	ISSUE DATE	RCM ITEM #	QUANTITY SOLD	ISSUE PRICE	FINISH	PR-69	PR-70
2007	Royal Canadian Mounted Police	Feb. 23, 2007	621567	6,687	389.95	Proof	500.	—
2007	Athletes' Pride	July 11, 2007	621577	4,524	389.95	Proof	500.	—
2007	Canada Geese	Oct. 24, 2007	621587	4,418	409.95	Proof	500.	—
2008	Four Host First Nations	Feb. 20, 2008	621568	4,897	409.95	Proof	500.	—
2008	Home of the Winter Games	July 23, 2008	621578	4,581	433.95	Proof	500.	—
2008	Inukshuk	Oct. 29, 2008	621588	4,907	499.95	Proof	500.	—
2009	Wolf	Feb. 18, 2009	621569	4,161	499.95	Proof	500.	—
2009	Olympic Spirit	June 17, 2009	621579	4,479	499.95	Proof	500.	—
2009	Moose	Sept. 9, 2009	621589	4,075	499.95	Proof	500.	—

SEVENTY-FIVE DOLLAR VANCOUVER WINTER OLYMPIC GAMES COIN SETS

Sets of the three $75 gold coins were offered for sale in acrylic holders. They were assembled in three themes: Canadian Wildlife, Canadian Icons, and Vancouver 2010 Olympic Winter Games.

DATE	DESCRIPTION	RCM ITEM #	QUANTITY SOLD	ISSUE PRICE	ISSUER	FINISH	MARKET VALUE
2007-2009	**Canadian Wildlife:** 2007 Canada Geese, 2009 Wolf, 2009 Moose; Acrylic holder	105926	25	1,424.95	RCM	PR-69	1,400.
2007-2008	**Canadian Icons:** 2007 R.C.M.P., 2008 Four Host First Nations, 2008 Inukshuk; Acrylic holder	105924	18	1,424.95	RCM	PR-69	1,400.
2007-2009	**Vancouver 2010 Winter Games:** 2007 Athletes' Pride, 2008 Home of the 2010 Olympic Winter Games, 2009 Olympic Spirit; Acrylic holder	105925	32	1,424.95	RCM	PR-69	1,400.

FOUR SEASONS MAPLE LEAVES SET

SEVENTY-FIVE DOLLARS, FOUR SEASONS MAPLE LEAVES SET, 2010.

Common Obverse	Spring	Summer	Fall	Winter
	Designer: A. Nogy	Designer: M. Grant	Designer: C. D'Angelo	Designer: C. Godkin
	Engraver: K. Wachelko	Engraver: S. Taylor	Engraver: M. Hallam	Engraver: K. Wachelko

Designers:
Obv.: Susanna Blunt
Rev.: See reverse illustrations
Composition: 58.33% Au, 41.67% Ag, Painted
Gold content: 7.0 g, 0.225 tr oz
Silver content: 5.0 g, 0.161 tr oz
Weight: 12.0 g
Diameter: 27.0 mm

Engravers:
Obv.: Susan Taylor
Rev.: See reverse illustrations
Thickness: 2.0 mm
Edge: Reeded
Die Axis: ↑↑
Finish: Proof

Case of Issue:
Singly: Maroon leatherette clam style case, black flocked insert, encapsulated coin, COA
Sets: Maple wood display case, 4-hole black flocked insert, encapsulated coins, serialised certificate, black sleeve

DATE	DESCRIPTION	RCM ITEM #	QUANTITY SOLD	ISSUE PRICE	FINISH	PR-69	PR-70
2010	Spring Maple Leaves	111488	130	589.95	Proof	550.	—
2010	Summer Maple Leaves	111478	136	589.95	Proof	550.	—
2010	Fall Maple Leaves	111472	162	589.95	Proof	550.	—
2010	Winter Maple Leaves	111419	136	589.95	Proof	550.	—
2010	Set of 4 Coins	111514	587	2,358.95	Proof	2,000.	—

SEVENTY-FIVE DOLLARS, 75TH ANNIVERSARY OF SUPERMAN™: THE EARLY YEARS, 2013.

The artwork of Joe Shuster, as seen on the cover of Superman™ Comic #1 published in 1939, is depicted on the reverse of this coin. Superman's™ native Kryptonian language encircles the rim spelling "75 Year of Superman".

Designers and Engravers:

Obv.:	Susanna Blunt, Susan Taylor		
Rev.:	DC Comics/Warner Brothers, RCM Staff		
Composition:	58.33% Au, 41.67% Ag		
Gold content:	7.0 g, 0.225 tr oz		
Silver content:	5.0 g, 0.161 tr oz		
Weight:	12.0 g	**Edge:**	Reeded
Diameter:	27.0 mm	**Die Axis:**	↑↑
Thickness:	3.0 mm	**Finish:**	Proof, Painted
Case of Issue:	Custom paperboard case, maroon flocked insert, encapsulated coin, COA		

DATE	DESCRIPTION	RCM ITEM #	QUANTITY SOLD	ISSUE PRICE	FINISH	PR-69	PR-70
2013	75th Anniversary of Superman™: The Early Years	125860	1,995	750.00	Proof	1,500.	—

WORLD BASEBALL CLASSIC SET

SEVENTY-FIVE DOLLARS, COMMEMORATING THE WORLD BASEBALL CLASSIC SET, 2013.

For other coins in this set see pages 370 and 438.

Common Obverse	Ball Diamond Engr.: S. Stewart	Hardball Engr.: S. Strath

Designers:		Engravers:	
Obv.:	Susanna Blunt	Obv.:	Susan Taylor
Rev.:	Steve Hepburn	Rev.:	See reverse illustrations
Composition:	99.99% Au	**Thickness:**	N/A
Gold content:	7.8 g, 0.25 tr oz	**Edge:**	Reeded
Weight:	7.8 g	**Die Axis:**	↑↑
Diameter:	20.0 mm	**Finish:**	Proof
Case of Issue:	Maroon leatherette clam style case, black flocked insert, encapsulated coin, COA		

DATE	DESCRIPTION	RCM ITEM #	QUANTITY SOLD	ISSUE PRICE	FINISH	PR-69	PR-70
2013	Ball Diamond	122380	133	899.95	Proof	600.	—
2013	Hardball	122388	121	899.95	Proof	600.	—

FIFA WOMEN'S WORLD CUP™ SET

SEVENTY-FIVE DOLLARS, FIFA WOMEN'S WORLD CUP™ SET, 2015.

For other coins in this series see page 212.

Common Obverse	The Soccer Ball Des.: T. Bianco	The Championship Game Des.: T. Bianco	The Trophy Des.: G. Green

Designers and Engravers:

Obv.:	Susanna Blunt, Susan Taylor
Rev.:	See reverse illustrations, RCM Staff
Composition:	99.99% Au
Gold content:	7.8 g, 0.25 tr oz
Weight:	7.8 g
Diameter:	20.0 mm
Edge:	Reeded
Die Axis:	↑↑
Thickness:	N/A
Finish:	Proof
Case of Issue:	Maroon leatherette clam style case, black flocked insert, encapsulated coin, COA, custom box

DATE	DESCRIPTION	RCM ITEM #	QUANTITY SOLD	ISSUE PRICE	FINISH	PR-69	PR-70
2015	The Soccer Ball	144315	1,449	699.95	Proof	650.	—
2015	The Championship Game	144004	1,523	699.95	Proof	650.	—
2015	The Trophy	144587	1,632	699.95	Proof	650.	—

ONE HUNDRED DOLLAR GOLD COINS

ONE HUNDRED DOLLARS, MONTREAL OLYMPIC COMMEMORATIVES, 1976.

As part of the series of collectors' coins struck to commemorate and help finance the XXI Olympiad, two separate $100 gold coins were issued in 1976. The reverse design for each shows an ancient Grecian athlete being crowned with laurel by the goddess Pallas Athena. The uncirculated issue is 14kt gold and has beads around the rim. The proof issue is 22k gold, slightly smaller, and lacks rim beads.

1976 Obverse
14 kt Gold

1976 Reverse
14 kt Gold

Designers and Engravers:

Obv.:	Arnold Machin, Walter Ott
Rev.:	Dora de Pédery-Hunt, Walter Ott

Composition: 58.33% Au, 41.67% Ag
Gold content: 7.78 g, 0.25 tr oz
Silver content: 5.56 g, 0.179 tr oz

Weight:	13.338 g	**Edge:**	Reeded
Diameter:	27.0 mm	**Die Axis:**	↑↑
Thickness:	2.2 mm	**Finish:**	Circulation
Case of Issue:	Plastic flip in a cardboard sleeve		

1976 Obverse
22kt Gold

1976 Reverse
22kt Gold

Designers and Engravers:

Obv.:	Arnold Machin, Walter Ott
Rev.:	Dora de Pédery-Hunt, Walter Ott

Composition: 91.67% Au, 8.33% Ag
Gold content: 15.55 g, 0.500 tr oz
Silver content: 1.14 g, 0.045 tr oz

Weight:	16.966 g	**Edge:**	Reeded
Diameter:	25.0 mm	**Die Axis:**	↑↑
Thickness:	2.2 mm	**Finish:**	Proof
Case of Issue:	Cowhide and wood case, black suede insert, COA		

DATE	DESCRIPTION	QUANTITY SOLD	ISSUE PRICE	FINISH	SP-68	SP-69	PR-68	PR-69
1976	Montreal Olympics, 14 kt	650,000	105.00	Circulation	450.	—	*	*
1976	Montreal Olympics, 22 kt	350,000	150.00	Proof	*	*	900.	—

NOTE FOR COLLECTORS

Beginning with the modern issues, gold coins were offered for sale by the Royal Canadian Mint at a small premium over face value giving investors a call on gold with a limited downside risk. Investors soon realised this and purchased large quantities of coins which resulted in high mintage figures. Currently, modern gold coins trade close to their intrinsic value. The gold coins listed here are priced at a market value of $1,750. per ounce.

ONE HUNDRED DOLLAR GOLD COINS

ONE HUNDRED DOLLAR ISSUES, 1977-1986

Designers:
  Obv.:   Arnold Machin
  Rev.:   See reverse illustrations

Engravers:
  Obv.:   RCM Staff
  Rev.:   See reverse illustrations

Composition: 91.67% Au, 8.33% Ag
Gold content: 15.55 g, 0.5 tr oz
Silver content: 1.413 g, 0.045 tr oz
Weight: 16.965 g
Diameter: 27.0 mm
Thickness: 2.2 mm

Edge: Reeded
Die Axis: ↑↑
Finish: Proof

Case of Issue: (A) 1977-1978: Black leatherette case, maroon insert, plastic coin holder, COA
                 (B) 1979-1984: Brown leatherette case, brown flocked insert, plastic coin holder, COA
                 (C) 1985-1986: Brown leatherette book type case with maple leaf emblem, beige satin interior,
                                  encapsulated coin. All enclosed in a brown plastic box

OBVERSE DESIGNS, 1977-1986

Obverse 1977	Obverse 1978, 1980-1981	Obverse 1979, 1983, 1986	Obverse 1982	Obverse 1984-1985

REVERSE DESIGNS, 1977-1986

1977	1978	1979	1980	1981
Silver Jubilee	Canadian Unity Coin	Int'l Year of Child	Arctic Territories	"O Canada"
Des.: R. Lee	Des.: R. Savage	Des.: C. Tietz	Des.: A. Marchetti	Des.: R. Savage
Engr.: W. Ott	Engr.: A. Aarand	Engr.: V. Coté	Engr.: S. Beveridge	Engr.: W. Ott

1982	1983	1984	1985	1986
Patriation of Canadian Constitution	Sir Humphrey Gilbert's Landing in Newfoundland	Jacques Cartier's Voyage of Discovery	National Parks Centenary	Int'l Year of Peace
Des.: F. Peter	Des.: J. Jaciw	Des.: C. Tietz	Des.: H. Greville	Des. and Engr.:
Engr.: W. Ott	Engr.: W. Ott	Engr.: W. Ott	Engr.: W. Ott	D. de Pédery-Hunt

ONE HUNDRED DOLLAR ISSUES, 1977-1986, PRICING TABLE.

DATE	DESCRIPTION	CASE	QUANTITY SOLD	ISSUE PRICE	FINISH	PR-68	PR-69
1977	Silver Jubilee Elizabeth II	A	180,396	140.00	Proof	900.	—
1978	Canadian Unity Coin	A	200,000	150.00	Proof	900.	—
1979	International Year of the Child	B	250,000	185.00	Proof	900.	—
1980	Arctic Territories	B	130,000	430.00	Proof	900.	—
1981	"O Canada"	B	100,950	300.00	Proof	900.	—
1982	Patriation of the Canadian Constitution	B	121,706	290.00	Proof	900.	—
1983	Sir Humphrey Gilbert's Landing in Newfoundland	B	83,128	310.00	Proof	900.	—
1984	Jacques Cartier's Voyage of Discovery	B	67,662	325.00	Proof	900.	—
1985	National Parks Centenary	C	58,520	325.00	Proof	900.	—
1986	International Year of Peace	C	76,255	325.00	Proof	900.	—

ONE HUNDRED DOLLAR ISSUES, 1987-2003

Designers:
  Obv.: See obverse illustrations
  Rev.: See reverse illustrations
Composition: 58.33% Au, 41.67% Ag
Gold content: 7.78 g, 0.25 tr oz
Weight: 13.338 g
Diameter: 27.0 mm
Thickness: 2.2 mm
Case of Issue:

Engravers:
  Obv.: See obverse illustrations
  Rev.: See reverse illustrations

Silver content: 5.56 g, 0.179 tr oz
Edge: Lettered
Die Axis: ↑↑
Finish: Proof

(A) 1987-1996: Brown leatherette book type case with maple leaf emblem, beige satin interior, encapsulated coin. All enclosed in a brown plastic box.
(B) 1997-1999: Black suede clam type case, black suede interior, encapsulated coin
(C) 2000-2003: Metal presentation case, wooden insert, COA

OBVERSE DESIGNS, 1987-2003

Obverse
1987
Des.: A. Machin
Engr.: RCM Staff

Obverse
1988-1989
Des.: A. Machin
Engr.: P. Brindley

Obverse
1990-1995
1997-2000
Des. and Engr.:
D. de Pédery-Hunt

Obverse
1996, 2002
Des. and Engr.:
D. de Pédery-Hunt

Obverse
2001
Des. and Engr.:
D. de Pédery-Hunt

Obverse
2003
Des. and Engr.:
D. de Pédery-Hunt

REVERSE DESIGNS, 1987-2003

1987
XV Olympic
Winter Games
Des.: F. Peter
Engr.: A. Aarand

1988
The Bowhead Whale
Des.: R. Carmichael
Engr.: A. Aarand

1989
Sainte-Marie
Des.: D. Craig
Engr.: A. Aarand

1990 International
Literacy Year
Des.: J. Mardon
Engr.: A. Aarand
&S. Taylor

1991
Empress of India
Des.: K. Smith
Engr.: S. Beveridge

1992
City of Montreal
350th Anniv.
Des.: S. Sherwood
Engr.: A. Aarand &
C. Saffioti

ONE HUNDRED DOLLAR ISSUES, 1987-2003 (cont.).

1993	1994	1995	1996	1997	1998
1893 The Era of the Horseless Carriage	The Home Front	275th Anniv. of Founding of Louisbourg	100th Anniv. First Major Gold Discovery in the Klondike	150th Anniv. Alexander Graham Bell's Birth	75th Anniv. Nobel Prize For Discovery of Insulin
Des.: J. Mardon	Des.: P. Clark	Des.: L. Parker	Des.: J. Mantha	Des.: D. H. Curley	Des.: R. Carmichael
Engr.: A. Aarand and W. Woodruff	Engr.: S. Taylor and A. Aarand	Engr.: S. Beveridge	Engr.: C. Saffioti	Engr.: S. Beveridge	Engr.: S. Witten

1999	2000	2001	2002	2003
Newfoundland Confederation	150th Anniv. of the Search for Northwest Passage in 1850	125th Anniv. Library of Parliament	Canada's Oil Industry	100th Anniv. Discovery Marquis Wheat
Des.: J. Gale-Vaillancourt	Des.: J. Mardon	Des.: R.R. Carmichael	Des.: J. Mardon	Des.: T. Nelson
Engr.: W. Woodruff	Engr. S. Witten	Engr.: S. Taylor and W. Woodruff	Engr.: S. Witten	Engr.: S. Witten

DATE	DESCRIPTION	CASE	QUANTITY SOLD	ISSUE PRICE	FINISH	PR-69	PR-70
1987	XV Olympic Winter Games, With edge lettering	A	145,175	255.00	Proof	450.	—.
1987	XV Olympic Winter Games, Without edge lettering	A	Included	255.00	Proof	2,500.	—
1988	Bowhead Whale (Balaena Mysticetus)	A	52,239	255.00	Proof	450.	—
1989	Sainte-Marie	A	63,881	245.00	Proof	450.	—
1990	International Literacy Year	A	49,940	245.00	Proof	450.	—
1991	Empress of India	A	33,966	245.00	Proof	450.	—
1992	City of Montreal, 350th Anniversary, 1642-1992	A	28,190	239.85	Proof	450.	—
1993	1893 The Era of the Horseless Carriage	A	25,971	239.85	Proof	450.	—
1994	The Home Front	A	17,603	249.95	Proof	450.	—
1995	275th Anniv. of the Founding of Louisbourg	A	16,916	249.95	Proof	450.	—
1996	100th Anniv. First Major Gold Discovery Klondike	A	17,973	259.95	Proof	450.	—
1997	150th Anniv. Alexander Graham Bell's Birth	B	14,030	254.95	Proof	450.	—
1998	75th Anniv. Nobel Prize Discovery of Insulin	B	11,220	254.95	Proof	450.	—
1999	50th Anniv. Newfoundland's Confederation 1949	B	10,242	254.95	Proof	450.	—
2000	150th Anniv. Search Northwest Passage in 1850	C	10,547	254.95	Proof	450.	—
2001	125th Anniv. Library of Parliament	C	8,080	260.95	Proof	450.	—
2002	Commemorating Canada's Oil Industry, Painted	C	9,994	260.95	Proof	450.	—
2003	100th Anniv. Discovery Marquis Wheat, Painted	C	9,993	277.95	Proof	450.	—

ONE HUNDRED DOLLAR ISSUES, 2004-2019

Designers:	
Obv.:	Susanna Blunt
Rev.:	See reverse illustrations
Composition:	58.33% Au, 41.67% Ag
Gold content:	7.0 g, 0.225 tr oz
Weight:	12.0 g
Diameter:	27.0 mm
Thickness:	2.2 mm

Engravers:	
Obv.:	Susan Taylor
Rev.:	See reverse illustrations
Silver content:	5.0 g, 0.16 tr oz
Edge:	Reeded
Die Axis:	↑↑
Finish:	Proof

Case of Issue: (A) 2004: Metal presentation case, wooden insert, COA
(B) 2005-2006: Maroon plastic case, black plastic insert, encapsulated coin, COA
(C) 2007-2018: Maroon leatherette clam style case, black flocked insert, encapsulated coin, COA
(D) 2014-2016 (Superman; Batman): Custom paperboard case, black insert, encapsulated coin, COA

OBVERSE DESIGNS, 2004-2019

Obverse
2004, 2006

Obverse
2005

Obverse
2007-2009

Obverse
2010-2015, 2018

Obverse
2015-2017

Obverse
2017 (Raven)

Obverse
2018 (Frog)

Obverse
2019

REVERSE DESIGNS, 2004-2019

2004
50th Ann.
St. Lawrence Seaway
Des.: J. Mardon
Engr.: J. Osio

2005
130th Ann. Supreme
Court of Canada
Des.: S. Duranceau
Engr.: J. Osio

2006
75th Game, World's
Longest Hockey
Series
Des.: T. Bianco
Engr.: K. Wachelko

2007
140th Ann. Dominion
of Canada
Des.: B. Ross
Engr.: S. Taylor

2008
200th Ann.
Descending
Fraser River
Des.: J. Mantha
Engr.: C. Paquet

2009
10th Ann.
of Nunavut
Des.: A. Qappik
Engr.: S. Taylor

2010
400th Ann. of the
Discovery of
Hudson's Bay
Des.: J. Mantha
Engr.: S. Taylor

2011
175th Ann. Canada's
First Rail Road
Des.: J. D. Kelly
Engr.: K. Wachelko

2012
150th Ann. Caribou
Gold Rush
Des.: T. Bianco
Engr.: RCM Staff

2013
100th Ann. Canadian
Arctic Expedition
Des.: B. Ross
Engr.: K. Wachelko

2014
Adventures of
Superman™ #596
Des.: DC Comics/
Warner Brothers
Engr.: RCM Staff

2014
150th Ann.
Quebec/Charlotteown
Conference
Des.: L. Normandin
Engr.: RCM Staff

ONE HUNDRED DOLLAR ISSUES, 2004-2019 (cont.).

2015	2015	2015	2016	2016	2017
200th Ann. Birth Sir John A. Macdonald Des.: G. Green Engr.: RCM Staff	Bugs Bunny and Friends Des.: Warner Bros. Engr.: RCM Staff	*Superman #4* (1940) Des.: Warner Bros. Engr.: RCM Staff	Centennial of the Parliament Builiding Fires Des.: Tony Bianco Engr.: RCM Staff	*Batman V Superman: Dawn of Justice*™ Des.: DC Comics Engr.: RCM Staff	100th Ann. of the Halifax Explosion Des.: Jamie Dssrochers Engr.: RCM Staff

2017	2018	2018	2019
Raven Brings The Light Des.: Andy Everson Engr.: RCM Staff	250th Ann. of the Birth of Techumseh Des.: Bonnie Ross Engr.: RCM Staff	Frog Reveals A Gift Des.: Andy Everson Engr.: RCM Staff	75th Ann. Normandy Campaign D-D at Juno Beach Des. & Eng. RCM Staff

DATE	DESCRIPTION	CASE	RCM ITEM #	QUANTITY SOLD	ISSUE PRICE	FINISH	PR-69	PR-70
2004	50th Ann. Commencement of St. Lawrence Seaway	A	N/A	7,454	277.95	Proof	450.	—
2005	130th Ann. Supreme Court of Canada, Painted	B	N/A	5,092	289.95	Proof	450.	—
2006	75th Game, World's Longest Hockey Series, Painted	B	N/A	5,439	329.95	Proof	450.	—
2007	140th Ann. Dominion of Canada	C	6215007	4,453	369.95	Proof	450.	—
2008	200th Ann. Descending Fraser River	C	6215008	3,089	386.95	Proof	450.	—
2009	10th Ann. of Nunavut	C	103364	2,309	509.95	Proof	450.	—
2010	400th Ann. Discovery of Hudson's Bay	C	105799	2,133	589.95	Proof	500.	—
2011	175th Ann. Canada's First Rail Road, Painted	C	111617	2,283	639.95	Proof	500.	—
2012	150th Ann. of Caribou Gold Rush, Painted	C	116955	2,488	599.95	Proof	500.	—
2013	100th Ann. Canadian Arctic Expedition	C	121656	1,937	599.95	Proof	500.	—
2014	150th Ann. Quebec / Charlottetown Conference	C	129282	1,284	599.95	Proof	500.	—
2014	The Adventures of Superman #596, Coloured	D	133893	2,000	750.95	Proof	700.	—
2015	200th Ann. Birth of Sir John A. Macdonald	C	140571	2,017	599.95	Proof	575.	—
2015	Looney Tunes: Bugs Bunny and Friends	C	144989	1,931	799.95	Proof	600.	—
2015	Superman #4 (1940)	D	146354	2,001	750.95	Proof	700.	—
2016	Centennial of the Parliament Buildings Fire	C	149317	1,463	599.95	Proof	600.	—
2016	Batman V Superman: Dawn of Justice	D	150303	3,001	749.95	Proof	700.	—
2017	100th Ann. of the Halifax Explosion	C	157388	1,500	699.95	Proof	700.	—
2017	Raven Brings The Light	C	161525	2,000	709.95	Proof	700.	—
2018	250th Ann. of the Birth of Tecumseh	C	163997	1,500	699.95	Proof	700.	—
2018	Frog Reveals A Gift	C	165020	1,500	709.95	Proof	710.	—
2019	7th Ann. Normandy Campaign D-Day at Juno Beach	C	170318	1,200	699.95	Reverse Proof	700.	—

ONE HUNDRED FIFTY DOLLAR GOLD COINS

ONE HUNDRED FIFTY DOLLARS, GOLD HOLOGRAM COINS, 2000-2011.

2000-2003 Obverse
(Except for date)
2004-2011 Obverse
(Except for date)

Designers:
2000-2003 Obv.: Dora de Pédery-Hunt
2004-2011 Obv.: Susanna Blunt
2000-2011 Rev.: Harvey Chan
Composition: 75.0% Au, 25.0% Ag, Hologram
Gold content:
 2000-2003 10.20 g, 0.328 tr oz
 2004-2011 8.88g, 0.285 tr oz
Weight: 2000-2003 13.61 g
 2004-2011 11.84 g
Thickness: 1.5 to 1.8 mm
Case of Issue: Gold satin case, taupe flocked insert, encapsulated coin, COA

Engravers:
 Obv.: Dora de Pédery-Hunt
 Obv.: Susan Taylor
 Rev.: RCM Staff

Silver Content:
 2000-2003 3.40 g, 0.109 tr oz
 2004-2011 2.96 g, 0.095 tr oz
Edge: Reeded
Die Axis: ↑↑
Finish: Proof

2000	2001	2002	2003	2004	2005
Year of the Dragon	Year of the Snake	Year of the Horse	Year of the Ram	Year of the Monkey	Year of the Rooster

2006	2007	2008	2009	2010	2011
Year of the Dog	Year of the Pig	Year of the Rat	Year of the Ox	Year of the Tiger	Year of the Rabbit

DATE	DESCRIPTION	RCM ITEM #	QUANTITY SOLD	ISSUE PRICE	FINISH	PR-69	PR-70
2000	Year of the Dragon, Hologram	N/A	8,874	388.88	Proof	650.	—
2001	Year of the Snake, Hologram	N/A	6,571	388.88	Proof	600.	—
2002	Year of the Horse, Hologram	N/A	6,843	388.88	Proof	600.	—
2003	Year of the Ram, Hologram	N/A	3,927	398.88	Proof	600.	—
2004	Year of the Monkey, Hologram	N/A	3,392	398.88	Proof	600.	—
2005	Year of the Rooster, Hologram	N/A	3,731	398.88	Proof	600.	—
2006	Year of the Dog, Hologram	N/A	2,609	448.88	Proof	600.	—
2007	Year of the Pig, Hologram	N/A	826	498.95	Proof	600.	—
2008	Year of the Rat, Hologram	N/A	582	508.95	Proof	600.	—
2009	Year of the Ox, Hologram	102311	486	638.88	Proof	600.	—
2010	Year of the Tiger, Hologram	105800	1,507	555.55	Proof	600.	—
2011	Year of the Rabbit, Hologram	110972	4,888	638.88	Proof	600.	—

Note: The mintage figures for 2007-2009 appear to be incorrect. There were no mintage figures reported in the 2010 Annual Report.

BLESSINGS SERIES

ONE HUNDRED FIFTY DOLLARS, BLESSINGS SERIES, 2009-2016.

In China blessings of wealth abound in a multitude of ancient symbols and artistic impressions, many of which are represented on these pure gold coins.

**Common
Obverse**

**2009
Blessings of
Wealth
Engr.: C. Paquet**

**2010
Blessings of
Strength
Engr.: RCM Staff**

**2011
Blessings of
Happiness
Engr.: C. Mok**

**2012
Blessings of
Good Fortune
Engr.: RCM Staff**

**2013
Blessings of Peace
Engr.: S. Strath**

**2014
Blessings of
Longevity
Engr.: C. Mok**

**2015
Blessings of
Prosperity
Engr.: RCM Staff**

**2016
Blessings of
Good Health
Engr.: RCM Staff**

Designers:		**Engravers:**	
Obv.:	Susanna Blunt	Obv.:	Susan Taylor
Rev.:	2009-2011: Harvey Chan	Rev.:	See reverse illustrations
	2012: Three Degrees Creative Group Inc.		
	2013: Aries Cheung		
	2014: Charles Vinh		
	2015: Simon Ng		
	2016: Three Degrees Creative Group Inc.		
Composition:	99.999% Au		
Gold content:	10.4 g, 0.334 tr oz		
Weight:	10.4 g	**Edge:**	Plain
Diameter:	22.5 mm	**Die Axis:**	↑↑
Thickness:	1.8 mm	**Finish:**	Proof
Case of Issue:	Maroon leatherette clam style case, black flocked insert, encapsulated coin, COA		

DATE	DESCRIPTION	RCM ITEM #	QUANTITY SOLD	ISSUE PRICE	FINISH	PR-69	PR-70
2009	Blessings of Wealth	104905	1,273	799.95	Proof	1,000.	—
2010	Blessings of Strength	110925	765	939.95	Proof	1,000.	—
2011	Blessings of Happiness	113195	880	988.88	Proof	1,000.	—
2012	Blessings of Good Fortune	119191	889	988.88	Proof	1,000.	—
2013	Blessings of Peace	123170	886	988.88	Proof	1,000.	—
2014	Blessings of Longevity	130330	887	988.88	Proof	1,000.	—
2015	Blessings of Prosperity	143257	518	988.88	Proof	1,000.	—
2016	Blessings of Good Health	152980	588	988.88	Proof	1,000.	—

CLASSIC CHINESE LUNAR SERIES

ONE HUNDRED FIFTY DOLLARS, CLASSIC CHINESE LUNAR SERIES. 2010-2019.

Identical designs are utilized on the Chinese Lunar Calendar Series $15 silver coins (2010-2021), see page 228.

Common Obverse

2010 Year of the Tiger

2011 Year of the Rabbit

2012 Year of the Dragon

2013 Year of the Snake

2014
Year of the Horse

2015
Year of the Sheep

2016
Year of the Monkey

2017
Year of the Rooster

2018
Year of the Dog

2019
Year of the Pig

Designers:
Obv.: Susanna Blunt
Rev.: Aries Cheung
Composition: 75.0% Au, 25.0% Ag
Gold content: 8.78 g, 0.282 tr oz
Weight: 11.70 g
Diameter: 28.0 mm
Thickness: 1.6 mm

Engravers:
Obv.: Susan Taylor

Silver content: 2.92 g, 0.094 tr oz
Die Axis: ↑↑
Edge: Reeded
Finish: Proof

Case of Issue: Singly: Gold satin-like covered case, black flocked insert, encapsulated coin, COA
Set: Hardwood exterior with high-gloss finish silk-screened paper. Interior has high-gloss finish in Chinese red with a silver design, wooden insert accommodates 12 coins.

DATE	DESCRIPTION	RCM ITEM #	QUANTITY SOLD	ISSUE PRICE	FINISH	PR-69	PR-70
2010	Year of the Tiger	106358	2,500	555.55	Proof	650.	—
2011	Year of the Rabbit	111154	2,500	638.88	Proof	650.	—
2012	Year of the Dragon	114068	1,430	688.88	Proof	650.	—
2013	Year of the Snake	120075	1,452	688.88	Proof	650.	—
2014	Year of the Horse	123638	2,128	688.88	Proof	700.	—
2015	Year of the Sheep	123639	602	688.88	Proof	700.	—
2016	Year of the Monkey	144594	914	688.88	Proof	700.	—
2017	Year of the Rooster	153568	2,500	688.88	Proof	700.	—
2018	Year of the Dog	161970	1,500	688.88	Proof	700.	—
2019	Year of the Pig	164808	1,500	828.88	Proof	830.	—

WORLD BASEBALL CLASSIC SET

ONE HUNDRED FIFTY DOLLARS, CELEBRATE, WORLD BASEBALL CLASSIC SET, 2013.

These coins were issued to celebrate the World Baseball Classic Tournament held March 2nd to 19th, 2013. For other coins in this set see pages 270 and 428.

Designers and Engravers:

Obv.:	Susanna Blunt, Susan Taylor		
Rev.:	Steve Hepburn, RCM Staff		
Composition:	99.99% Au		
Gold content:	15.59 g, 0.5 tr oz		
Weight:	15.59 g	**Edge:**	Reeded
Diameter:	25.0 mm	**Die Axis:**	↑↑
Thickness:	2.0 mm	**Finish:**	Proof
Case of Issue:	Maroon leatherette clam style case, black flocked insert, encapsulated coin, COA, custom sleeve		

DATE	DESCRIPTION	RCM ITEM #	QUANTITY SOLD	ISSUE PRICE	FINISH	PR-69	PR-70
2013	Celebrate, World Baseball Classic	122403	129	1,549.95	Proof	1,200.	—

ONE HUNDRED SEVENTY-FIVE DOLLAR GOLD COIN

ONE HUNDRED SEVENTY-FIVE DOLLARS, 100TH ANNIVERSARY OF THE OLYMPIC MOVEMENT, 1992-1996.

Commemorating the 100th anniversary of the Olympic movement in 1996, Canada and four other countries, Australia, France, Austria and Greece, issued three-coin sets, consisting of one gold and two silver coins. One set was issued each year beginning with Canada's in 1992. See page 230 for the Royal Canadian Mint silver issues. Only the Royal Canadian Mint issued coins are listed in the Standard Catalogue.

Designers:

Obv.:	Dora de Pédery-Hunt
Rev.:	Stewart Sherwood
Composition:	91.67% Au, 8.33% Cu
Gold content:	15.556 g, 0.5 tr oz
Weight:	16.97 g
Diameter:	28.0 mm
Thickness:	2.0 mm
Case of Issue:	Blue clam style case, black insert, encapsulated coin, COA

Engravers:

Obv.:	Dora de Pédery-Hunt
Rev.:	Ago Aarand

Edge: Lettering: Citius, altius, fortius
Die Axis: ↑↑
Finish: Proof

DATE	DESCRIPTION	QUANTITY SOLD	ISSUE PRICE	FINISH	PR-68	PR-69
1992	100th Anniversary of the Olympic Movement	22,092	429.75	Proof	900.	—

TWO HUNDRED DOLLAR GOLD COINS

TWO HUNDRED DOLLAR ISSUES, 1990-2003 (STANDARD WEIGHT)

| Common Obverse except for date 1990-1996 | Common Obverse except for date 1997-2003 | 1990 Canada's Flag Silver Jubilee Des.: S. Sherwood Engr.: A. Aarand | 1991 A National Passion Des.: S. Sherwood Engr.: S. Taylor | 1992 Niagara Falls Des.: J. Mardon Engr.: S. Taylor | 1993 R.C.M.P. Des.: S. Sherwood Engr.: S. Taylor |

| 1994 Anne of Green Gables© Des.: P. Gilman Engr.: S. Taylor | 1995 The Sugar Bush Des.: J. D. Mantha Engr.: S. Beveridge, S. Taylor | 1996 Transcontinental Landscape Des.: S. Duranceau Engr.: C. Saffioti | 1997 Haida "Raven Bringing Light to the World" Des.: R. Davidson Engr.: C. Saffioti, A. Aarand | 1998 Legend of the White Buffalo Des.: A. Janvier Engr.: C. Saffioti |

| 1999 Mikmaq Butterfly Des.: A. Syliboy Engr.: C. Saffioti | 2000 Mother and Child Des.: G. Arnaktauyok Engr.: S. Taylor | 2001 Cornelius Krieghoff Des.: C. Krieghoff Engr.: S. Taylor | 2002 Tom Thompson Des.: T. Thompson Engr.: S. Taylor | 2003 Lionel Lemoine Fitzgerald Des.: L. L. Fitzgerald Engr.: S. Taylor |

Designers:
  Obv.:   Dora de Pédery-Hunt
  Rev.:   See reverse illustrations

Engravers:
  Obv.:   Dora de Pédery-Hunt
  Rev.:   See reverse illustrations

Composition: 91.67% Au, 8.33% Ag
Gold content: 15.703 g, 0.505 tr oz
Silver content: 1.427 g, 0.046 tr oz
Weight: 17.13 g
Diameter: 29.0 mm
Thickness: 2.0 mm

Edge: Reeded
Die Axis: ↑↑
Finish: Proof

Case of Issue: (A)   1990-1996, 1999, 2002: Woven Jacquard case, black insert, encapsulated coin, COA
             (B)   1997-1998, 2000-2001, 2003: Metal trimmed case, black insert, encapsulated coin, COA

TWO HUNDRED DOLLAR ISSUES, 1990-2003 (STANDARD WEIGHT), PRICING PANEL.

DATE	DESCRIPTION	CASE	QUANTITY SOLD	ISSUE PRICE	FINISH	PR-69	PR-70
1990	Canada's Flag Silver Jubilee	A	20,980	395.00	Proof	900.	—
1991	A National Passion	A	10,215	425.00	Proof	900.	—
1992	Niagara Falls	A	9,465	389.65	Proof	900.	—
1993	Royal Canadian Mounted Police	A	10,807	389.65	Proof	900.	—
1994	Anne of Green Gables©	A	10,655	399.95	Proof	900.	—
1995	The Sugar Bush	A	9,579	399.95	Proof	900.	—
1996	Transcontinental Landscape	A	8,047	414.95	Proof	900.	—
1997	Haida "Raven Bringing Light to the World"	B	11,610	414.95	Proof	900.	—
1998	The Legend of the White Buffalo	B	7,149	414.95	Proof	900.	—
1999	Mikmaq Butterfly	A	6,510	414.95	Proof	900.	—
2000	Mother and Child	B	7,410	414.95	Proof	900.	—
2001	Cornelius Krieghoff	B	5,406	412.95	Proof	900.	—
2002	Tom Thompson	A	5,754	412.95	Proof	900.	—
2003	Lionel Lemoine Fitzgerald	B	4,118	412.95	Proof	900.	—

TWO HUNDRED DOLLAR ISSUES, 2004-2011 (REDUCED WEIGHT)

Obverse
2004-2006

Obverse
2007
With date and
RCM Logo

Obverse
2008-2009
Without date,
With RCM Logo

Obverse
2010-2011

2004
Alfred Pellan
Des.: A. Pellan
Engr.: C. Paquet

2005
Fur Trade
Des.: J. Mardon
Engr.: J. Osio

2006
Timber Trade
Des.: J. Mardon
Engr.: S. Witten

2007
Fishing Trade
Des.: J. Mardon
Engr.: S. Taylor

2008
Agriculture Trade
Des.: J. Mardon
Engr.: J. Osio

2009
Coal Mining Trade
Des.: J. Mardon
Engr.: C. Paquet

2010
First Canadian Olympic
Gold Medal on Home Soil
Des.: B. Ross
Engr.: S. Witten

2010
Petroleum and Oil Trade
Des.: J. Mardon
Engr.: RCM Staff

2011
S. S. Beaver
Des.: J. Mardon
Engr.: RCM Staff

2011
Wedding Celebration
Des.: L. McGaw
Engr.: J. Osio

2011
Wayne / Walter Gretzky
Des.: G. Green
Engr.: K. Wachelko,
J. Osio

TWO HUNDRED DOLLAR ISSUES, 2004-2011 (REDUCED WEIGHT) (continued)

Designers:
  Obv.: Susanna Blunt
  Rev.: See reverse illustrations
Composition: 91.67% Au, 8.33% Ag
Gold content: 14.667 g, 0.471 tr oz
Silver content: 1.332 g, 0.043 tr oz
Weight: 16.0 g
Diameter: 29.0 mm

Engravers:
  Obv.: Susan Taylor
  Rev.: See reverse illustrations

Thickness: 1.8 mm
Edge: Reeded
Die Axis: ↑↑
Finish: Proof

Case of Issue:
  (A) 2004: Metal trimmed case, black insert, encapsulated coin, COA
  (B) 2005: Maroon plastic slide case, black plastic insert, encapsulated coin, COA
  (C) 2006-2011: Maroon leatherette clam style case, black flocked insert, encapsulated coin, COA
  (D) 2010: Black leatherette display case, black flocked insert, encapsulated coin, COA

DATE	DESCRIPTION	CASE	RCM ITEM #	QUANTITY SOLD	ISSUE PRICE	FINISH	PR-69	PR-70
2004	Alfred Pellan	A	N/A	3,917	412.95	Proof	800.	—
2005	Fur Trade	B	N/A	3,669	489.95	Proof	800.	—
2006	Timber Trade	C	N/A	3,218	489.95	Proof	800.	—
2007	Fishing Trade	C	5210007	2,137	579.95	Proof	800.	—
2008	Agriculture Trade	C	5210008	1,951	619.95	Proof	800.	—
2009	Coal Mining Trade, Painted	C	103736	2,241	849.95	Proof	800.	—
2010	First Canadian Olympic Gold Medal on Home Soil	D	110640	2,010	989.95	Proof	900.	—
2010	Petroleum and Oil Trade, Painted	C	105798	1,732	999.95	Proof	800.	—
2011	S. S. Beaver, Painted	C	112076	1,392	1,099.95	Proof	800.	—
2011	Wedding Celebration, Duke and Duchess of Cambridge, Blue Swarovski element	C	115839	760	1,199.95	Proof	900.	—
2011	Wayne and Walter Gretzky, Laser	C	115260	471	1,299.99	Proof	900.	—

TWO HUNDRED DOLLAR ISSUES, 2012-2017 (REDUCED WEIGHT)
GREAT CANADIAN EXPLORERS, 2012-2017

Common Obverse

2012 - The Vikings
Des.: Y. Bérubé
Engr.: J. Osio

2013 - Jacques Cartier
Des.: L. McGaw
Engr.: J. Osio

2014 - Samuel de Champlain
Des.: G. Green

2015 - Henry Hudson
Des.: L. McGraw

2016 - Pierre Gaultier
De La Vérendrye
Des.: G. Green

2017 - Alexander MacKenzie
Des.: John Mantha

INTERCONNECTION SET, 2014

Common Obverse

Land - The Beaver
Des.: A. Everson

Air - The Thunderbird
Des.: A. Everson

Sea - The Orca
Des.: A. Everson

Designers:
Obv.:   Susanna Blunt
Rev.:   See reverse illustrations
Composition: 99.99% Au
Gold content: 15.43 g, 0.5 tr oz
Weight: 15.43 g
Diameter: 29.0 mm
Thickness: 1.6 mm
Case of Issue: Maroon leatherette clam style case, black flocked insert, encapsulated coin, COA

Engravers:
Obv.:   Susan Taylor
Rev.:   See reverse illustrations

Edge: Reeded
Die Axis: ↑↑
Finish: Proof

DATE	DESCRIPTION	RCM ITEM #	QUANTITY SOLD	ISSUE PRICE	FINISH	PR-69	PR-70
2012	Great Canadian Explorers: The Vikings	116887	1,749	1,199.95	Proof	1,000.	—
2013	Great Canadian Explorers: Jacques Cartier	121637	1,474	1,199.95	Proof	1,000.	—
2014	Great Canadian Explorers: Samuel de Champlain	128945	885	1,199.95	Proof	1,000.	—
2015	Great Canadian Explorers: Henry Hudson	140820	815	1,199.95	Proof	1,100.	—
2016	Great Canadian Explorers: Pierre Gaultier de la Vérendrye	148998	798	1,199.95	Proof	1,200.	—
2017	Great Canadian Expoloers: Alexander MacKenzie	156285	1,000	1,199.95	Proof	1,200.	—
2014	Interconnection: Land - The Beaver	140523	693	1,299.95	Proof	1,300.	—
2014	Interconnection: Air - The Thunderbird	140530	121	1,299.95	Proof	1,300.	—
2014	Interconnection: Sea - The Orca	140537	116	1,299.95	Proof	1,300.	—

TWO HUNDRED DOLLAR (ONE OUNCE) ISSUES, 2012-2015

**Obverse
2012, 2014**

**Obverse
2015**

Designers:
Obv.: Susanna Blunt
Rev.: See reverse illustrations
Composition: 99.99% Au
Gold content: 31.1 g, 1.0 tr oz
Weight: 31.1 g

Diameter: 30.0 mm
Thickness: N/A
Case of Issue: Maroon leatherette clam style case, black flocked insert, encapsulated coin, COA

Engravers:
Obv.: Susan Taylor
Rev.: See reverse illustrations

Edge: 2014-2015 Reeded
2014 Royal Generations: Interrupted Serrations
Die Axis: ↑↑
Finish: Proof

**2012 *The Challenge*
Robert Bateman Series
Des.: R. Bateman
Engr.: RCM Staff**

**2014 Royal Generations
Des.: C. Bursey-Sabourin
Engr.: RCM Staff**

**2014 *Zunoqua*
- Celebrating Emily Carr
Des.: E. Carr
Engr.: RCM Staff**

**2015 Largemouth Bass
Des.: C. Atwater
Engr.: RCM Staff**

DATE	DESCRIPTION	RCM ITEM #	QUANTITY SOLD	ISSUE PRICE	FINISH	PR-69	PR-70
2012	*The Challenge* R. Bateman Moose Coin Series	120898	359	2,699.95	Proof	2,500.	—
2014	Royal Generations	134356	340	2,799.95	Proof	2,600.	—
2014	*Zunoqua.* Celebrating Emily Carr	N/A	100	N.I.I.	Proof	2,800.	—
2015	North American Sportfish: Largemouth Bass	142633	300	2,699.95	Proof	2,600.	—

Note: The *Zunoqua* coin is part of the Celebrating Emily Carr three coin set. For other coins see pages 282 and 484.

TWO HUNDRED DOLLAR FIVE 9's ISSUES, (ULTRA HIGH RELIEF)

TWO HUNDRED DOLLARS, MOON MASK SERIES, 2013-2015.

**Common
Obverse**

**2013 Grandmother Moon Mask
Des.: R. Cochrane**

**2014 Matriarch Moon Mask
Des.: C. Young**

**2015 Singing Moon Mask
Des.: A. Everson**

Designers:
Obv.: Susanna Blunt
Rev.: See reverse illustrations
Composition: 99.99% Au
Weight: 33.33 g
Diameter: 30.0 mm
Thickness: N/A
Case of Issue: (A) Maroon leatherette clam style case, black flocked insert, encapsulated coin, COA
(B) Wooden clam style case, black flocked insert, encapsulated coin, COA

Engravers:
Obv.: Susan Taylor

Gold content: 33.33 g. 1.07 tr oz
Edge: Reeded
Die Axis: ↑↑
Finish: Proof

DATE	DESCRIPTION	CASE	RCM ITEM #	QUANTITY SOLD	ISSUE PRICE	FINISH	PR-69	PR-70
2013	Grandmother Moon Mask	A	124568	498	2,999.95	Proof	2,500.	—
2014	Matriarch Moon Mask	A	130515	419	2,999.95	Proof	2,300.	—
2015	Singing Moon Mask, Enamelled	B	142547	296	2,999.95	Proof	2,300.	—

TWO HUNDRED DOLLAR FIVE 9'S ISSUES, 2014-2015 (ULTRA HIGH RELIEF)

2014-2015
Obverse

2014
75th Anniv. First Royal Visit
Des.: RCM Staff

2014
Fierce Canadian Lynx
Des.: Pierre Leduc

Designers:
Obv.:	Susanna Blunt
Rev.:	See reverse illustrations

Composition: 99.999% Au
Gold content: 33.17 g, 1.07 tr oz
Weight: 33.17 g
Diameter: 30.0 mm
Thickness: N/A
Case of Issue: Maroon leatherette clam style case, black flocked insert, encapsulated coin, COA

Engravers:
Obv.:	Susan Taylor
Rev.:	See reverse illustrations

Edge: Reeded
Die Axis: ↑↑
Finish: Proof

DATE	DESCRIPTION	CASE	RCM ITEM #	QUANTITY SOLD	ISSUE PRICE	FINISH	PR-69	PR-70
2014	75th Anniversary of the First Royal Visit	A	130100	193	2,999.95	Proof	2,300.	—
2014	The Fierce Canadian Lynx	A	143863	117	2,999.95	Proof	2,300.	—

TWO HUNDRED DOLLARS (1 ounce), CANADA'S WILDLIFE SERIES, 2014.

Common Obverse

Bald Eagle Protecting Her Nest

The Bison at Home on the Plains

Designers:
Obv.:	Susanna Blunt
Rev.:	Claudio D'Angelo

Composition: 99.99% Au
Gold content: 31.16 g, 1.0 tr oz
Weight: 31.16 g, 1oz
Diameter: 30.0 mm
Thickness: 2.8 mm
Case of Issue: Maroon leatherette clam style case, black flocked insert, encapsulated coin, COA

Engravers:
Obv.:	Susan Taylor
Rev.:	RCM Staff

Edge: Reeded
Die Axis: ↑↑
Finish: Proof

DATE	DESCRIPTION	RCM ITEM #	QUANTITY SOLD	ISSUE PRICE	FINISH	PR-69	PR-70
2014	Bald Eagle Protecting Her Nest	127164	350	2,699.95	Proof	2,500.	—
2014	The Bison at Home on the Plains	130939	350	2,699.95	Proof	2,500.	—

TWO HUNDRED DOLLARS (1 ounce), THE WHITE-TAILED DEER: QUIETLY EXPLORING, 2014.

Featuring multiple finishes, this coin's design has also been used on a twenty dollar silver coin (see page 283).

Designers and Engravers:	
Obv.:	Susanna Blunt, Susan Taylor
Rev.:	Trevor Tennant, RCM Staff
Composition:	99.99% Au
Gold content:	31.16 g, 1.0 tr oz
Weight:	31.16 g, 1 oz
Diameter:	30.0 mm
Thickness:	2.8 mm
Case of Issue:	Maroon leatherette clam style case, black flock insert, encapsulated coin, COA, custom box

Edge: Reeded
Die Axis: ↑↑
Finish: Proof

DATE	DESCRIPTION	RCM ITEM #	QUANTITY SOLD	ISSUE PRICE	FINISH	PR-69	PR-70
2014	White-Tailed Deer: Quietly Exploring	130597	344	2,699.95	Proof	2,500.	—.

TWO HUNDRED DOLLARS (1 ounce), CALL OF THE WILD SERIES, 2014-2018.

Common Obverse	2014 Howling Wolf (Pr)	2015 Growling Cougar (BU)	2016 Roaring Grizzly	2017 Elk

Designers:		**Engravers:**		
Obv.:	Susanna Blunt	Obv.:	Susan Taylor	
Rev.:	Pierre Leduc	Rev.:	RCM Staff	
Composition:	99.999% Au			
Gold content:	31.16 g, 1.0 tr oz			
Weight:	31.16 g, 1 oz	**Die Axis:**	↑↑	
Diameter:	30.0 mm	**Finish:**	See below	
Thickness:	2.8 mm	**Edge:**	Interrupted serrations	
Case of Issue:	Proof: Maroon leatherette clam style case, black flocked insert, encapsulated coin, COA Bullion: Card capsule			

DATE	DESCRIPTION	RCM ITEM #	QUANTITY SOLD	ISSUE PRICE	FINISH	SP-68	SP-69	PR-69	PR-70
2014	Howling Wolf	129232	273	2,799.95	Proof	*	*	2,500.	—
2014	Howling Wolf	N/A	N/A	BV	Bullion	1,900.	—	*	*
2015	Growling Cougar	134664	250	2,799.95	Proof	—	*	2,500.	—
2015	Growling Cougar	N/A	N/A	BV	Bullion	1,900.	—	*	*
2016	Roaring Gizzly Bear	148920	246	2,799.95	Proof	*	*	2,500.	—
2016	Roaring Grizzly Bear	N/A	N/A	BV	Bullion	1,900.	—	*	*
2017	Elk	157509	400	2,799.95	Proof	*	*	2,500	—
2017	Elk	N/A	N/A	BV	Bullion	1,900.	—	*	*
2018	Golden Eagle	N/A	N/A	BV	Bullion	1,900	—	*	*

TWO HUNDRED DOLLARS, TOM THOMSON: *PINE ISLAND, GEORGIAN BAY* (1914-1916), 2015.

Designers and Engravers:

Obv.:	Susanna Blunt, Susan Taylor
Rev.:	Tom Thomson, RCM Staff

Composition: 99.99% Au
Gold content: 31.16 g. 1.0 tr oz

Weight:	31.16g	**Edge:**	Reeded
Diameter:	30.0 mm	**Die Axis:**	↑↑
Thickness:	N/A	**Finish:**	Proof

Case of Issue: Maroon leatherette clam style case, black flocked insert, encapsulated coin, COA

DATE	DESCRIPTION	RCM ITEM #	QUANTITY SOLD	ISSUE PRICE	FINISH	PR-69	PR-70
2015	Tom Thomson: *Pine Island, Georgian Bay* (1914-1916)	150557	198	2,699.95	Proof	2,500.	—

TWO HUNDRED DOLLARS, DIWALI: FESTIVAL OF LIGHTS, 2015.

Designers and Engravers:

Obv.:	Susanna Blunt, Susan Taylor
Rev.:	Sarindar Dhaliwal

Composition: 99.99% Au
Gold content: 31.16 g. 1.0 tr oz

Weight:	31.16 g	**Edge:**	Reeded
Diameter:	30.0 mm	**Die Axis:**	↑↑
Thickness:	N/A	**Finish:**	Proof

Case of Issue: Wooden box with gold foil design with graphic beauty box, encapsulated coin, COA

DATE	DESCRIPTION	RCM ITEM #	QUANTITY SOLD	ISSUE PRICE	FINISH	PR-69	PR-70
2015	Diwali: Festival of Lights	147598	275	2,699.95	Proof	2,500.	—

TWO HUNDRED DOLLARS, GRIZZLY BEAR: THE CLAN, 2015.

Designers and Engravers:

Obv.:	Susanna Blunt, Susan Taylor
Rev.:	Lauren Crawshaw

Composition: 99.99% Au
Gold content: 31.16 g. 1.0 tr oz

Weight:	31.16 g	**Edge:**	Reeded
Diameter:	30.0 mm	**Die Axis:**	↑↑
Thickness:	N/A	**Finish:**	Proof

Case of Issue: Maroon clamshell with custom beauty box, encapsulated coin, COA

DATE	DESCRIPTION	RCM ITEM #	QUANTITY SOLD	ISSUE PRICE	FINISH	PR-69	PR-70
2015	The Clan	145426	188	2,699.95	Proof	2,500.	—

TWO HUNDRED DOLLARS, DIWALI: FESTIVAL OF LIGHTS, 2016.

Designers and Engravers:

Obv.:	Susanna Blunt, Susan Taylor
Rev.:	Meera Sethil

Composition: 99.99% Au
Gold content: 31.16 g. 1.0 tr oz

Weight:	31.16 g	**Edge:**	Reeded
Diameter:	30.0 mm	**Die Axis:**	↑↑
Thickness:	N/A	**Finish:**	Proof

Case of Issue: Wooden box with gold foil design with graphic beauty box, encapsulated coin, COA

DATE	DESCRIPTION	RCM ITEM #	QUANTITY SOLD	ISSUE PRICE	FINISH	PR-69	PR-70
2016	Diwali: Festival of Lights	155449	534	2,799.95	Proof	2,500.	—

TALL SHIPS LEGACY SET

TWO HUNDRED DOLLARS, TALL SHIPS LEGACY, 2016.

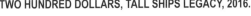

| Common Obverse | Bluenose | Marco Polo | The Amazon | HMS Discovery |

Designers
Obv.: Susanna Blunt
Rev.: Neil Hamelin
Composition: 99.99% Au
Gold content: 31.16 g, 1.0 tr oz
Weight: 31.16 g
Diameter: 30.0 mm
Thickness: N/A
Case of Issue: Maroon clamshell with black beauty box, encapsulated coin, COA.

Engravers:
Obv.: Susan Taylor
Rev.: RCM Staff

Edge: Reeded
Die Axis: ↑↑
Finish: Proof

DATE	DESCRIPTION	RCM ITEM #	QUANTITY SOLD	ISSUE PRICE	FINISH	PR-69	PR-70
2016	Tall Ships Legacy: *Bluenose*	150319	274	2,699.95	Proof	2,700.	—
2016	Tall Ships Legacy: *Marco Polo*	149203	275	2,699.95	Proof	2,700.	—
2016	Tall Ships Legacy: *The Amazon*	152962	270	2,699.95	Proof	2,700.	—
2016	Tall Ships Legacy: HMS *Discovery*	153019	244	2,699.95	Proof	2,700.	—

TWO HUNDRED DOLLARS, *STAR TREK*™: DELTA COIN, 2016.

Designers and Engravers:
Obv.: Susanna Blunt
Rev.: RCM Staff
Composition: 99.99% Au
Gold content: 16.20 g. 0.75 tr oz
Weight: 16.20 g
Diameter: 28.68 (H) X 17.50 (W)
Thickness: N/A
Case of Issue: Wood case and graphic beauty box.

Edge: Plain
Die Axis: ↑↑
Finish: Proof

DATE	DESCRIPTION	RCM ITEM #	QUANTITY SOLD	ISSUE PRICE	FINISH	PR-69	PR-70
2016	*Star Trek*™: Delta Coin	153340	1,457	1,299.95	Proof	1,500.	—

TWO HUNDRED DOLLARS, TIGER AND DRAGON YIN AND YANG, 2016.

Designers and Engravers:
Obv.: Susanna Blunt
Rev.: Charles Vinh
Composition: 99.99% Au
Gold content: 31.16 g. 1.0 tr oz
Weight: 31.16 g
Diameter: 30.0 mm
Thickness: N/A
Case of Issue: Maroon clamshell with custom beauty box, COA

Edge: Reeded
Die Axis: ↑↑
Finish: Proof

DATE	DESCRIPTION	RCM ITEM #	QUANTITY SOLD	ISSUE PRICE	FINISH	PR-69	PR-70
2016	Tiger and Dragon Yin and Yang	156944	265	2,888.88	Proof	2,900.	—

TWO HUNDRED DOLLARS, MAPLE LEAF SILHOUETTE (SHAPED), 2016.

Designers and Engravers:

Obv.:	Susanna Blunt, Susan Taylor
Rev.:	RCM Staff
Composition:	99.99% Au
Gold content:	31.25 g, 1.01 tr oz
Weight:	31.25 g
Diameter:	39.6 x 38 mm
Thickness:	N/A
Case of Issue:	Maroon clamshell with black beauty box.

Edge:	Plain			
Die Axis:	↑↑			
Finish:	Proof			

DATE	DESCRIPTION	RCM ITEM #	QUANTITY SOLD	ISSUE PRICE	FINISH	PR-69	PR-70
2016	Maple Leaf Silhouette	149830	776	2,799.95	Proof	2,800.	—

TWO HUNDRED DOLLARS, 150 YEARS OF PASSION: THE MAPLE LEAF, 2017.

Designers and Engravers:

Obv.:	Susanna Blunt, Susan Taylor
Rev.:	RCM Staff
Composition:	99.99% Au
Gold content:	31.6 g. 1.0 tr oz
Weight:	31.6 g
Diameter:	30.0 mm
Thickness:	N/A
Case of Issue:	Maroom clamshell with black beauty box, encapsulated coin, COA

Edge:	Reeded
Die Axis:	↑↑
Finish:	Proof

DATE	DESCRIPTION	RCM ITEM #	QUANTITY SOLD	ISSUE PRICE	FINISH	PR-69	PR-70
2017	150 Years of Passion: The Maple Leaf	154403	247	2,699.95	Proof	2,700.	—

TWO HUNDRED DOLLARS, FOOTBALL-SHAPED AND CURVED COIN, 2017.

Designers and Engravers:

Obv.:	Susanna Blunt
Rev.:	RCM Staff
Composition:	99.99% Au
Gold content:	31.32 g. 1.02 tr oz
Weight:	31.32 g
Diameter:	44 x 26.4 mm
Thickness:	N/A
Case of Issue:	Maroon clamshell with black beauty box, COA

Edge:	Plain
Die Axis:	↑↑
Finish:	Proof

DATE	DESCRIPTION	RCM ITEM #	QUANTITY SOLD	ISSUE PRICE	FINISH	PR-69	PR-70
2017	Football-Shaped and Curved Coin	155900	381	2,899.95	Proof	2,800.	—

TWO HUNDRED DOLLARS, WELCOME TO THE WORLD, 2017.

Designers and Engravers:

Obv.:	Susanna Blunt
Rev.:	RCM Staff
Composition:	99.99% Au
Gold content:	15.43 g. 0.5 tr oz
Weight:	15.43 g
Diameter:	29 mm
Thickness:	N/A
Case of Issue:	Premium wooden box, COA

Edge:	Reeded
Die Axis:	↑↑
Finish:	Proof

DATE	DESCRIPTION	RCM ITEM #	QUANTITY SOLD	ISSUE PRICE	FINISH	PR-69	PR-70
2017	Welcome to the World	155900	35	1,199.95	Proof	1,200	—

TWO HUNDRED DOLLARS, *FENG SHUI* GOOD LUCK CHARMS, 2017.

Rooted deep in Chinese mythology, the protective figure of Pi Yao and the auspicious Wu Lou Gourd are held in high regard by the practitioners of the *Feng Shui*, individually, they represent fortune and health; together on this 99.99% pure gold holed coin, they bring an abundance of blessings and invite positive energy to ensure prosperity, longevity and continued good fortune.

Designers and Engravers:

Obv.:	Susanna Blunt, Susan Taylor
Rev.:	Charles Vinh

Composition: 99.99% Au
Gold content: 28.25 g. 0.91 tr oz

Weight:	28.25 g	**Edge:**	Reeded
Diameter:	30.0 mm	**Die Axis:**	↑↑
Thickness:	N/A	**Finish:**	Proof

Case of Issue: Maroom clamshell with black beauty box, encapsulated coin, COA

DATE	DESCRIPTION	RCM ITEM #	MINTAGE	ISSUE PRICE	FINISH	PR-69	PR-70
2017	*Feng Shui* Good Luck Charms	160822	388	2,788.88	Proof	2,800.	—

TWO HUNDRED DOLLARS, AUTUMN FIRE (SHAPED), 2017.

A brand new technology in introduced with this coin: GRADIENCE! There's a natural radiance to the reverse, where a translucent gradient effect re-creates the smooth transition of colour seen in nature – from the deep red tips to the natural gleam of gold at the leaf's centre.

Designers and Engravers:

Obv.:	Susanna Blunt, Susan Taylor
Rev.:	RCM Staff

Composition: 99.99% Au
Gold content: 31.25 g, 1.00 tr oz
Weight: 31.25.0 g
Diameter: 39.6 mm 38 mm
Thickness: N/A
Edge: Plain
Die Axis: ↑↑
Finish: Proof
Case of Issue: Custom wooden box, COA

DATE	DESCRIPTION	RCM ITEM #	MINTAGE	ISSUE PRICE	FINISH	PR-69	PR-70
2017	Autumn Fire	161034	600	2,999.95	Proof	3,000.	—

TWO HUNDRED DOLLARS, BIGHORN SHEEP, 2018.

At home in the rangelands of the Canadian Rocky Mountains, the bighorn sheep is the embodiment of the rugged alpine wilderness it inhabits.

Designers and Engravers:

Obv.:	Susanna Blunt, Susan Taylor
Rev.:	Curtis Atwater

Composition: 99.999% Au
Gold content: 31.6g. 1.02 tr oz

Weight:	31.6 g	**Edge:**	Interrupted reeding
Diameter:	30 mm	**Die Axis:**	↑↑
Thickness:	N/A	**Finish:**	Proof

Case of Issue: Maroom clamshell with black beauty box, COA

DATE	DESCRIPTION	RCM ITEM #	MINTAGE	ISSUE PRICE	FINISH	PR-69	PR-70
2018	Bighorn Sheep	164797	400	2,899.95	Proof	2,900.	—

TWO HUNDRED DOLLARS, *ANCESTOR MOON* MASK, 2018.

As seen by Indigenous cultures in the Pacific Northwest—a gentle and caring ancestor who watches over the people, lighting the way when travellers are on the water during the night, or illuminating the beach to help people dig for clams in the dark. *Ancestor Moon* is always present, always ready to guide and protect.

Designers and Engravers:

Obv.:	Susanna Blunt, Susan Taylor		
Rev.:	Andy Everson		
Composition:	99.999% Au	**Gold content:**	31.37 g. 1.01 tr oz
Weight:	31.37 g	**Edge:**	Reeded
Diameter:	30 mm	**Die Axis:**	↑↑
Thickness:	N/A	**Finish:**	Proof
Case of Issue:	Maroom clamshell with black beauty box, COA		

DATE	DESCRIPTION	RCM ITEM #	MINTAGE	ISSUE PRICE	FINISH	PR-69	PR-70
2018	*Ancestor Moon* Mask	165226	300	2,999.95	Proof	3,000.	—

TWO HUNDRED DOLLARS, ENCHANTING MAPLE LEAVES, 2-COIN SET, 2018.

Beauty. Scarcity. Pure elegance. More than a prestigious collectible, this two-coin set is a superbly crafted ode to one of Canada's most beloved emblems, the maple leaf, whose natural beauty is unmistakable in the gleam of 99.999% pure gold—and on one coin, an added touch of platinum plating.

Common Obverse

Designers

Obv.:	Susanna Blunt
Rev.:	Nathalie Lagacé
Composition:	99.999% Au
Gold content:	31.16 g, 1.0 tr oz
Weight:	31.16 g (each coin)
Diameter:	30 mm (each coin)
Thickness:	N/A
Case of Issue:	Wood case with black beauty box, encapsulated coin, COA.

Engravers:

Obv.:	Susan Taylor
Rev.:	RCM Staff
Edge:	Interrupted reeding
Die Axis:	↑↑
Finish:	Proof

DATE	DESCRIPTION	RCM ITEM #	MINTAGE	ISSUE PRICE	FINISH	PR-69	PR-70
2018	Enchanting Maple Leaves – 2-Coin Set	165103	175	5,899.95	Proof	5,900.	—

TWO HUNDRED DOLLARS, GOOD LUCK CHARMS – FIVE BLESSINGS, 2018.

This coin features one of the most popular good luck motifs found in old Chinese houses—five bats surrounding the Chinese symbol shou (longevity) to bring five cherished blessings of health, wealth, longevity, virtue, and a peaceful natural death in old age. It's inspired by a visual pun in which the character for bat (fu) and good fortune or happiness (fu), are pronounced the same way; together they bring an abundance of blessings.

Designers and Engravers:

Obv.:	Susanna Blunt, Susan Taylor		
Rev.:	Simon Ng		
Composition:	99.99% Au		
Gold content:	28.25 g. 0.91 tr oz		
Weight:	28.25 g	**Edge:**	Reeded
Diameter:	30 mm	**Die Axis:**	↑↑
Thickness:	N/A	**Finish:**	Proof
Case of Issue:	Burgundy clamshell with black beauty box, COA		

DATE	DESCRIPTION	RCM ITEM #	MINTAGE	ISSUE PRICE	FINISH	PR-69	PR-70
2018	Good Luck Charms – Five Blessings	165565	388	2,888.88	Proof	2,900.	—

TWO HUNDRED DOLLARS, 30TH ANNIVERSARY OF THE PLATINUM MAPLE LEAF, 2018.

This extraordinary sculpted maple leaf coin shines with pride for the 30th anniverary of the Mint's Platinum Maple Leaf.

Designers and Engravers:

Obv.:	Susanna Blunt, Susan Taylor
Rev.:	RCM Staff
Composition:	99.99% Au
Gold content:	31.25 g, 1.00 tr oz
Weight:	31.25.0 g
Diameter:	39.6 mm 38 mm
Thickness:	N/A
Edge:	Plain
Die Axis:	↑↑
Finish:	Proof
Case of Issue:	Custom wooden box, COA

DATE	DESCRIPTION	RCM ITEM #	MINTAGE	ISSUE PRICE	FINISH	PR-69	PR-70
2018	30th Ann. Platinum Maple Leaf	166379	450	2,999.95	Proof	3,000.	—

TWO HUNDRED DOLLARS, ARMISTICE POPPY, 2018.

Designers and Engravers:

Obv.:	Susanna Blunt, Susan Taylor		
Rev.:	Kerri Weller		
Composition:	99.99% Au		
Gold content:	31.16 g. 1.00 tr oz		
Weight:	31.16 g	**Edge:**	Reeded
Diameter:	30.0 mm	**Die Axis:**	↑↑
Thickness:	N/A	**Finish:**	Proof
Case of Issue:	Standard maroom clamshell with black beauty box, COA		

DATE	DESCRIPTION	RCM ITEM #	MINTAGE	ISSUE PRICE	FINISH	PR-69	PR-70
2018	Armistice Poppy	167294	350	2,899.95	Proof	2,900.	—

TWO HUNDRED DOLLARS, THE 1908 SOVEREIGN 110TH ANNIVERSARY OF THE ROYAL CANADIAN MINT, 2018.

Designers and Engravers:

Obv.:	Susanna Blunt, Susan Taylor		
Rev.:	RCM Staff		
Composition:	99.99% Au	**Gold content:**	31.16 g. 1.00 tr oz
Weight:	31.16 g	**Edge:**	Interrupted reeding
Diameter:	30.0 mm	**Die Axis:**	↑↑
Thickness:	N/A	**Finish:**	Proof
Case of Issue:	Maroom clamshell with black beauty box, COA		

DATE	DESCRIPTION	RCM ITEM #	MINTAGE	ISSUE PRICE	FINISH	PR-69	PR-70
2018	The 1908 Sovereign 110th Ann. RCM	170469	500	2,899.95	Proof	2,900.	—

CANADIAN COASTAL SYMBOLS SERIES

TWO HUNDRED DOLLARS, CANADIAN COASTAL SYMBOLS, 2018-2019.

The coast is an irresistible place, that unique point where land meets sea, and animals from both realms interact in ways unseen just a short distance away.

Common Obverse	The Pacific	The Arctic

Designers
Obv.:   Susanna Blunt
Rev.:   Cathy Boursey-Sabourin
Composition: 99.999% Au
Weight: 31.16 g
Diameter: 30.0 mm
Thickness: N/A
Case of Issue: Maroon clamshell with black beauty box, COA

Engravers:
Obv.:   Susan Taylor

Gold content: 31.16 g. 1.02 tr oz
Edge: Interrupted reeding
Die Axis: ↑↑
Finish: Proof

DATE	DESCRIPTION	RCM ITEM #	MINTAGE	ISSUE PRICE	FINISH	PR-69	PR-70
2018	Canadian Coastal Symbols: The Pacific	164832	400	2,899.95	Proof	2,900.	—
2019	Canadian Coastal Symbols: The Arctic	166776	400	2,899.95	Proof	2,900.	—

EARLY CANADIAN HISTORY SERIES

TWO HUNDRED DOLLARS, EARLY CANADIAN HISTORY, 2018-2019.

Common Obverse	First Nations	Arrival of the Europeans

Designers
Obv.:   Susanna Blunt
Rev.:   Alan Daniel
Composition: 99.999% Au
Weight: 15.43 g
Diameter: 29 mm
Thickness: N/A
Case of Issue: Maroon clamshell with black beauty box, COA

Engravers:
Obv.:   Susan Taylor

Gold content: 15.43 g. 0.50 tr oz
Edge: Reeded
Die Axis: ↑↑
Finish: Proof

DATE	DESCRIPTION	RCM ITEM #	MINTAGE	ISSUE PRICE	FINISH	PR-69	PR-70
2018	Early Canadian History: First Nations	164072	1,000	1,199.95	Proof	1,200.	—
2019	Early Canadian History: Arrival of the Europeans	170054	1,000	1,199.95	Proof	1,200.	—

TWO HUNDRED DOLLARS, ATLANTIC PUFFINS, 2019.

Designers and Engravers:

Obv.:	Susanna Blunt, Susan Taylor
Rev.:	Denis Mayer Jr.r

Composition: 99.99% Au
Gold content: 31.16 g. 1.00 tr oz

Weight:	31.16 g	**Edge:**	Interrupted reeding
Diameter:	30.0 mm	**Die Axis:**	↑↑
Thickness:	N/A	**Finish:**	Proof

Case of Issue: Maroon clamshell with black beauty box, COA

DATE	DESCRIPTION	RCM ITEM #	MINTAGE	ISSUE PRICE	FINISH	PR-69	PR-70
2019	Atlantic Puffins	169408	400	2,899.95	Proof	2,900.	—

TWO HUNDRED DOLLARS, CANADIAN MOOSE, 2019.

Designers and Engravers:

Obv.:	Susanna Blunt, Susan Taylor
Rev.:	Claude Thivierge

Composition: 99.99% Au
Gold content: 31.16 g. 1.00 tr oz

Weight:	31.16 g	**Edge:**	Interrupted reeding
Diameter:	30.0 mm	**Die Axis:**	↑↑
Thickness:	N/A	**Finish:**	Proof

Case of Issue: Maroon clamshell with black beauty box, COA

DATE	DESCRIPTION	RCM ITEM #	MINTAGE	ISSUE PRICE	FINISH	PR-69	PR-70
2019	Canadian Moose	170717	400	2,899.95	Proof	2,900.	—

TWO HUNDRED DOLLARS, 100TH ANNIVERSARY OF CN, 2019.

Designers and Engravers:

Obv.:	Susanna Blunt, Susan Taylor
Rev.:	Tony Bianco

Composition: 99.99% Au
Gold content: 15.43 g. 0.5 tr oz

Weight:	15.43 g	**Edge:**	Reeded
Diameter:	29 mm	**Die Axis:**	↑↑
Thickness:	N/A	**Finish:**	Proof

Case of Issue: Maroon clamshell with black beauty box, COA

DATE	DESCRIPTION	RCM ITEM #	MINTAGE	ISSUE PRICE	FINISH	PR-69	PR-70
2019	100th Anniversary of CN	171146	1,000	1,199.95	Proof	1,200	—

TWO HUNDRED FIFTY DOLLAR GOLD COINS

TWO HUNDRED FIFTY DOLLARS, DOG SLED TEAM, 2006.

Designers and Engravers:

Obv.:	Susanna Blunt, Susan Taylor
Rev.:	Arnold Nogy, José Osio
Composition:	58.33% Au, 41.67% Ag
Gold content:	26.25 g, 0.844 tr oz
Silver content:	18.75 g, 0.603 tr oz

Weight:	45.0 g	**Edge:**	Reeded
Diameter:	40.0 mm	**Die Axis:**	↑↑
Thickness:	2.9 mm	**Finish:**	Proof
Case of Issue:	Maroon leatherette clam style case, black flocked insert, encapsulated coin, COA		

DATE	DESCRIPTION	RCM ITEM #	QUANTITY SOLD	ISSUE PRICE	FINISH	PR-69	PR-70
2006	Dog Sled Team	N/A	953	1,089.95	Proof	1,600.	—

Note: An identical design is utilized on the $30 silver coin for 2006, see page 357.

TWO HUNDRED FIFTY DOLLARS, CANADIAN CONTEMPORARY ART, 2014.

Designed by Tim Barnard, the coin's reverse features an artistic college of over fifty images depicting distinct aspects of Canadiana from flora and fauna to First Nations art. The same design was issued in a $30 dollar silver coin (see page 359).

Designers and Engravers:

Obv.:	Susanna Blunt, Susan Taylor
Rev.:	Tim Barnard, RCM Staff
Composition:	99.99% Au
Gold content:	62.34 g, 2.0 tr oz

Weight:	62.34 g	**Edge:**	Reeded
Diameter:	42.0 mm	**Die Axis:**	↑↑
Thickness:	N/A	**Finish:**	Proof
Case of Issue:	Maroon leatherette clam style case, black flocked insert, encapsulated coin, COA		

DATE	DESCRIPTION	RCM ITEM #	MINTAGE	ISSUE PRICE	FINISH	PR-69	PR-70
2014	Canadian Contemporary Art	130164	105	5,199.95	Proof	5,000.	—

TWO HUNDRED FIFTY DOLLARS, 75TH ANNIVERSARY OF THE DECLARATION OF THE SECOND WORLD WAR, 2014.

Designers and Engravers:

Obv.:	Susanna Blunt, Susan Taylor
Rev.:	Silvia Pecota, RCM Staff
Composition:	99.99% Au
Gold content:	62.34 g, 2.0 tr oz

Weight:	62.34g	**Edge:**	Reeded
Diameter:	42.0 mm	**Die Axis:**	↑↑
Thickness:	N/A	**Finish:**	Proof
Case of Issue:	Maroon leatherette clam style case, black flocked insert, encapsulated coin, COA		

DATE	DESCRIPTION	RCM ITEM #	QUANTITY SOLD	ISSUE PRICE	FINISH	PR-69	PR-70
2014	75th Anniv. Declaration of WWII	130597	100	5,199.95	Proof	5,200.	—

Note: An identical design is utilized on the $30 silver coin for 2014, see page 359.

TWO HUNDRED FIFTY DOLLARS, 100TH ANNIVERSARY OF THE COMPLETION OF THE GRAND TRUNK PACIFIC RAILWAY, 2014.

Linking Eastern Canada to the Pacific, a feat of engineering in the early 20th century, The Grand Trunk Pacific Railway is depicted crossing the Grand Trunk Bridge in Saskatoon. The same design was issued in a $30 dollar silver coin (see page 359).

Designers and Engravers:

Obv.:	Susanna Blunt, Susan Taylor
Rev.:	Joel Kimmel, RCM Staff
Composition:	99.99% Au
Gold content:	62.34 g, 2.0 tr oz
Weight:	62.34 g
Diameter:	42.0 mm
Thickness:	N/A
Case of Issue:	Maroon leatherette clam style case, black flocked insert, encapsulated coin, COA

Edge:	Reeded
Die Axis:	↑↑
Finish:	Proof

DATE	DESCRIPTION	RCM ITEM #	QUANTITY SOLD	ISSUE PRICE	FINISH	PR-69	PR-70
2014	100th Anniv. Completion of the Grand Trunk Pacific Railway	160460	338	5,199.95	Proof	5,000.	—

FLORA AND FAUNA SET

TWO HUNDRED FIFTY DOLLARS, FLORA AND FAUNA SET, 2015.

Featuring the glass work of Giuliano Donaggio, set against the artistic backdrops designed by Maurice Gervais, the set of coins was also issued in 25-cents (with the exception of the Turtle with Broadleaf Arrowhead) (see page 48) and $20 (see page 263).

Common Obverse

Designers

Obv.:	Susanna Blunt
Rev.:	Maurice Gervais, Glass: Giuliano Donaggio
Composition:	99.99% Au
Gold content:	60.08 g, 1.932 tr oz
Weight:	60.08 g
Diameter:	38.0 mm
Thickness:	N/A
Case of Issue:	Dark maple wood case, black flocked insert, encapsulated coin, COA, black outer case

Engravers:

Obv.:	Susan Taylor
Rev.:	José Osio
Edge:	Reeded
Die Axis:	↑↑
Finish:	Proof

Tulip and Ladybug	Aster and Bumblebee	Purple Cone Flower & Eastern Tailed Blue Butterfly	Water Lily and Leopard Frog	Turtle with Broadleaf Arrowhead Flower

DATE	DESCRIPTION	RCM ITEM #	QUANTITY SOLD	ISSUE PRICE	FINISH	PR-69	PR-70
2015	Tulip and Ladybug	N/A	—	N.I.I.	Proof	5,000.	—
2015	Aster and Bumblebee	N/A	—	N.I.I.	Proof	5,000.	—
2015	Purple Cone Flower and Eastern Tailed Blue Butterfly	N/A	—	N.I.I.	Proof	5,000.	—
2015	Water Lily and Leopard Frog	N/A	—	N.I.I.	Proof	5,000.	—
2015	Turtle with Broadleaf Arrowhead Flower	N/A	—	N.I.I.	Proof	5,000.	—
2015	Set of 5 coins	142146	99	15,000.	Proof	21,000.	*

MAPLE CANOPY: KALEIDOSCOPE OF COLOUR SERIES

TWO HUNDRED FIFTY DOLLARS, MAPLE CANOPY: KALEIDOSCOPE OF COLOUR, 2016-2017.

Common	2016	2017
Obverse	Kaleidoscope of Colour	Kaleidoscope of Colour

Designers
  Obv.:   Susanna Blunt
  Rev.:   Emily Damstra
Composition: 99.99% Ag
Weight: 62.34 g
Diameter: 42 mm
Thickness: N/A
Case of Issue: Maroon clamshell with beauty box, encapsulated coin, COA

Engravers:
  Obv.:   Susan Taylor

Gold content: 62.34 g, 2.00 tr oz
Edge: Reeded
Die Axis: ↑↑
Finish: Proof

DATE	DESCRIPTION	RCM ITEM #	MINTAGE	ISSUE PRICE	FINISH	PR-69	PR-70
2016	Maple Canopy: Kaleidoscope of Colour	150020	150	4,899.95	Proof	4,900.	—
2017	Maple Canopy: Kaleidoscope of Colour	157233	131	4,949.95	Proof	4,950.	—

TIARA-THEMED SERIES

TWO HUNDRED FIFTY DOLLARS, TIARA-THEMED SERIES, 2016, 2018-2019.

2016	A Celebration of Her	2018-2019	A Crown Jewel	Her Majesty
Obverse	Majesty's 90th Birthday	Common Obverse		Queen Elizabeth II's
		(Except for date)		Sapphire Tiara

Designers
  Obv.:   Susanna Blunt
  Rev.:   RCM Staff
Composition: 99.99% Ag
Weight: 60.08 g
Diameter: 38 mm
Thickness: N/A
Case of Issue: Maple wood case, black flocked insert, encapsulated coin, COA

Engravers:
  Obv.:   Susan Taylor

Gold content: 60.08, 1.93 tr oz
Edge: Reeded
Die Axis: ↑↑
Finish: Proof

DATE	DESCRIPTION	RCM ITEM #	MINTAGE	ISSUE PRICE	FINISH	PR-69	PR-70
2016	A Celebration of Her Majesty's 90th Birthday	153490	250	6,999.95	Proof	7,000.	—
2018	A Crown Jewel	164499	175	6,999.95	Proof	7,000.	—
2019	Her Majesty Queen Elizabeth II's Sapphire Tiara	171414	175	6,999.95	Proof	7,000.	—

TWO HUNDRED FIFTY DOLLARS, CELEBRATING CANADIAN BRILLIANCE, 2017.

To highlight the theme of Canadian brilliance, this coin was designed in partnership with the Canadian Intellectual Property Office, and an industrial design registered by Vancouver's Worldwide Diamond Trademarks Ltd. was selected for the diamond on this numismatic coin.

Designers and Engravers:

Obv.:	Susanna Blunt, Susan Taylor
Rev.:	Chris Reid and Rosina Li

Composition: 99.99% Au
Gold content: 60.08 g, 1.93 tr oz

Weight:	60.08 g	**Edge:**	Reeded
Diameter:	38 mm	**Die Axis:**	↑↑
Thickness:	N/A	**Finish:**	Proof

Case of Issue: Wood case with custom beauty box, COA

DATE	DESCRIPTION	RCM ITEM #	MINTAGE	ISSUE PRICE	FINISH	PR-69	PR-70
2017	Celebrating Canadian Brilliance	160460	250	6,999.95	Proof	7,000.	—

TWO HUNDRED FIFTY DOLLARS, THE MAGNIFICENT MAPLE, 2018.

The beautiful diamond on the reverse adds brilliance to an already striking design,

Designers and Engravers:

Obv.:	Susanna Blunt, Susan Taylor
Rev.:	Virginia Boulay

Composition: 99.99% Au
Gold content: 60.08 g, 1.93 tr oz

Weight:	60.08 g	**Edge:**	Reeded
Diameter:	38 mm	**Die Axis:**	↑↑
Thickness:	N/A	**Finish:**	Proof

Case of Issue: Wooden case with custom beauty box, COA

DATE	DESCRIPTION	RCM ITEM #	MINTAGE	ISSUE PRICE	FINISH	PR-69	PR-70
2018	The Magnificent Maple	165329	250	6,999.95	Proof	7,000.	—

TWO HUNDRED FIFTY DOLLARS, ETERNAL BLESSING PYSANKA, 2019.

Designers and Engravers:

Obv.:	Susanna Blunt, Susan Taylor
Rev.:	Dave Melnychuk

Composition: 99.99% Au
Silver content: 58.5 g, 1.88 tr oz
Weight: 58.5 g
Diameter: 45 mm long x 22 mm wide
Thickness: N/A
Edge: Interrupted reeding
Die Axis: ↑↑
Finish: Proof
Case of Issue: Black clamshell with black beauty box, COA

DATE	DESCRIPTION	RCM ITEM #	MINTAGE	ISSUE PRICE	FINISH	PR-69	PR-70
2019	Eternal Blessing Pysanka	171628	250	4,999.95	Proof	5,000.	—

THREE HUNDRED DOLLAR GOLD COINS

THREE HUNDRED DOLLARS, TRIPLE CAMEO PORTRAITS OF QUEEN ELIZABETH II, 2002.

This 14-karat gold coin bears triple cameo portraits of Queen Elizabeth II on the obverse: a 1953-1964 portrait by Mary Gillick, a 1965-1989 portrait by Arnold Machin, and a 1990-2003 portrait by Dora de Pédery-Hunt.

Designers:		Engravers:	
Obv.:	Dora de Pédery-Hunt	Obv.:	Stan Witten
Rev.:	Sheldon Beveridge, Cosme Saffioti	Rev.:	Cosme Saffioti
Composition:	58.33% Au, 41.67% Ag		
Gold content:	35.00 g, 1.125 tr oz		
Silver content:	25.0 g, 0.804 tr oz	Thickness:	2.5 mm
Weight:	60.0 g	Edge:	Reeded
Diameter:	50.0 mm	Die Axis:	↑↑
		Finish:	Proof / Bullion
Case of Issue:	Purple laminated wooden case, cream insert, encapsulated coin, COA, black / gold outer case		

DATE	DESCRIPTION	RCM ITEM #	QUANTITY SOLD	ISSUE PRICE	FINISH	PR-69	PR-70
2002 (1952-)	Triple Cameo Portraits	N/A	999	1,095.95	Proof	2,200.	—

THREE HUNDRED DOLLARS, GREAT SEAL OF CANADA, 2003.

The Royal Seal, or Great Seal of Canada, is the official stamp used to bring the Queen's authority to any documents produced on her behalf.

Designers:		Engravers:	
Obv.:	M. Gillick, A. Machin, D. de Pedery-Hunt, S. Blunt	Obv.:	Susan Taylor
Rev.:	RCM Staff	Rev.:	RCM Staff
Composition:	58.33% Au, 41.67% Ag		
Gold content:	35.00 g, 1.125 tr oz		
Silver content:	25.0 g, 0.804 tr oz	Thickness:	2.5 mm
Weight:	60.0 g	Edge:	Reeded
Diameter:	50.0 mm	Die Axis:	↑↑
		Finish:	Proof / Bullion
Case of Issue:	Black leatherette case, RCM plaque, black flocked insert, encapsulated coin, COA, black and gold outer case		

DATE	DESCRIPTION	RCM ITEM #	QUANTITY SOLD	ISSUE PRICE	FINISH	PR-69	PR-70
2003	Great Seal of Canada	N/A	998	1,099.95	Proof	2,200.	—

THREE HUNDRED DOLLARS, QUADRUPLE CAMEO PORTRAITS, 2004.

The four coinage portraits of Queen Elizabeth II are featured on the obverse of the $300 coin for 2004. Each is struck in 24kt gold.

Designers:		Engravers:	
Obv.:	M. Gillick, A. Machin, D. de Pedery-Hunt, S. Blunt	Obv.:	Susan Taylor
Rev.:	Christie Paquet	Rev.:	Christie Paquet
Composition:	58.33% Au, 41.67% Ag		
Gold content:	35.00 g, 1.125 tr oz		
Silver content:	25.0 g, 0.804 tr oz	Thickness:	2.5 mm
Weight:	60.0 g	Edge:	Reeded
Diameter:	50.0 mm	Die Axis:	↑↑
		Finish:	Proof / Bullion
Case of Issue:	Black leatherette case, RCM plaque, black flocked insert, encapsulated coin, COA, black and gold outer case		

DATE	DESCRIPTION	RCM ITEM #	QUANTITY SOLD	ISSUE PRICE	FINISH	PR-69	PR-70
2004	Quadruple Cameo Portraits	N/A	998	1,099.95	Proof	2,200.	—

VIGNETTES OF THE TWENTY-FIVE CENT
FRACTIONAL NOTES OF THE DOMINION OF CANADA SERIES

THREE HUNDRED DOLLARS, VIGNETTES OF THE TWENTY-FIVE CENT FRACTIONAL NOTES OF THE DOMINION OF CANADA, 2005-2007.

These coins commemorate the vignettes which appear on the Dominion of Canada twenty-five cent fractional note issues of 1870, 1900 and 1923.

| 2005-2007
Common Obverse | 2005 The 1870 Shinplaster
Vignette of Britannia
Designer: Robert-Ralph Carmichael
Engraver: José Osio | 2006 The 1900 Shinplaster
Vignette of Britannia
Designer: Christie Paquet
Engraver: Christie Paquet | 2007 The 1923 Shinplaster
Vignette of Britannia
Designer: Robert-Ralph Carmichael
Engraver: Christie Paquet |

Designers:		**Engravers:**	
Obv.:	Susanna Blunt	Obv.:	Susan Taylor
Rev.:	See reverse illustrations	Rev.:	See reverse illustrations
Composition:	58.33% Au, 41.67% Ag		
Gold content:	35.0 g, 1.125 tr oz	**Thickness:**	2.5 mm
Silver content:	25.0 g, 0.804 tr oz	**Edge:**	Reeded
Weight:	60.00 g	**Die Axis:**	↑↑
Diameter:	50.0 mm	**Finish:**	Proof / Bullion
Case of Issue:	Black leatherette case, RCM plaque, black flocked insert, encapsulated coin, COA, black and gold outer case		

DATE	DESCRIPTION	RCM ITEM #	QUANTITY SOLD	ISSUE PRICE	FINISH	PR-69	PR-70
2005	1870 Shinplaster Vignette of Britannia	N/A	994	N/A	Proof	2,200.	—
2006	1900 Shinplaster Vignette of Britannia	N/A	947	1,295.95	Proof	2,200.	—
2007	1923 Shinplaster Vignette of Britannia	621557	778	1,440.95	Proof	2,200.	—

THREE HUNDRED DOLLARS, 80TH BIRTHDAY OF QUEEN ELIZABETH II, 2006.

Designers:		**Engravers:**	
Obv.:	Susanna Blunt	Obv.:	Susan Taylor
Rev.:	Not known	Rev.:	Cecily Mok
Composition:	58.33% Au, 41.67% Ag, Enamelled		
Gold content:	35.0 g, 1.125 tr oz	**Thickness:**	2.5 mm
Silver content:	25.0 g, 0.804 tr oz	**Edge:**	Reeded
Weight:	60.0 g	**Die Axis:**	↑↑
Diameter:	50.0 mm	**Finish:**	Proof
Case of Issue:	Maroon leatherette clam style case, black flocked insert, encapsulated coin, COA		

DATE	DESCRIPTION	RCM ITEM #	QUANTITY SOLD	ISSUE PRICE	FINISH	PR-69	PR-70
2006 (1926-)	80th Birthday Elizabeth II	N/A	1,000	1,520,95	Proof	2,200.	—

CRYSTAL SNOWFLAKE SERIES

THREE HUNDRED DOLLARS, CRYSTAL SNOWFLAKE SERIES, 2006 AND 2010

Crystal Snowflake, 2006

Crystal Snowflake, 2010

Designers:		Engravers:	
Obv.:	Susanna Blunt	Obv.:	Susan Taylor
Rev.:	Konrad Wachelko	Rev.:	Konrad Wachelko
Composition:	58.33% Au, 41.67% Ag, Swarovski crystal elements		
Gold content:	35.0 g, 1.125 tr oz		
Silver content:	25.0 g, 0.804 tr oz	Thickness:	2.5 mm
Weight:	60.0 g	Edge:	Reeded
Diameter:	50.0 mm	Die Axis:	↑↑
Case of Issue:	Maroon leatherette clam style case, black flocked insert, encapsulated coin, COA	Finish:	Proof

DATE	DESCRIPTION	RCM ITEM #	QUANTITY SOLD	ISSUE PRICE	FINISH	PR-69	PR-70
2006	Crystal Snowflake	N/A	998	1,520.95	Proof	2,200.	—
2010	Crystal Snowflake	111100	305	2,295.95	Proof	2,200.	—

VANCOUVER 2010 OLYMPIC WINTER GAMES SERIES

THREE HUNDRED DOLLARS, VANCOUVER 2010 OLYMPIC WINTER GAMES SERIES, 2007-2009.

Common Obverse
(except for date)

2007 - Olympic Ideals
Engraver:
Susan Taylor, José Osio

2008 - Competition
Engraver:
Susan Taylor, Christie Paquet

2009 - Friendship
Engraver:
Susan Taylor, José Osio

Designers:		Engravers:	
Obv.:	Susanna Blunt	Obv.:	Susan Taylor
Rev.:	Laurie McGaw, David Craig	Rev.:	See reverse illustrations
Composition:	58.33% Au, 41.67% Ag		
Gold content:	35.0 g, 1.125 tr oz		
Silver content:	25.0 g, 0.804 tr oz	Thickness:	2.5 mm
Weight:	60.0 g	Edge:	Reeded
Diameter:	50.0 mm	Die Axis:	↑↑
Case of Issue:	Black leatherette case, black flocked insert, encapsulated coin, COA	Finish:	Proof

DATE	DESCRIPTION	ISSUE DATE	RCM ITEM #	QUANTITY SOLD	ISSUE PRICE	FINISH	PR-69	PR-70
2007	Olympic Ideals	Feb. 23, 2007	621597	953	1,999.95	Proof	2,200.	—
2008	Competition	Feb. 20, 2008	621598	334	1,999.95	Proof	2,200.	—
2009	Friendship	Feb. 18, 2009	621599	880	1,999.95	Proof	2,200.	—

PROVINCIAL COATS OF ARMS SERIES

THREE HUNDRED DOLLARS, PROVINCIAL COATS OF ARMS SERIES, 2008-2014.

2008-2009
Common Obverse
With RCM Logo

2009-2014
Common Obverse
Without RCM Logo

Designers:		Engravers:	
Obv.:	Susanna Blunt	Obv.:	Susan Taylor
Rev.:	Reproduction of official Coat of Arms	Rev.:	See reverse illustrations
Composition:	58.33% Au, 41.67% Ag		
Gold content:	35.0 g, 1.125 tr oz		
Silver content:	25.0 g, 0.804 tr oz	Thickness:	2.5 mm
Weight:	60.0 g	Edge:	Reeded
Diameter:	50.0 mm	Die Axis:	↑↑
Case of Issue:	Maroon leatherette clam style case, black flocked insert, encapsulated coin, COA	Finish:	Proof

2008	2008	2009	2009	2010
Newfoundland & Labrador	**Alberta**	**Yukon Territory**	**Prince Edward Island**	**British Columbia**
Eng.: Marcos Hallam	Eng.: Konrad Wachelko	Eng.: Marcos Hallam	Eng.: Marcos Hallam	Eng.: Konrad Wachelko

2010	2011	2011	2012	2012
New Brunswick	**Manitoba**	**Nova Scotia**	**Quebec**	**Nunavut**
Eng.: Marcos Hallam	Eng.: Cecily Mok	Eng.: Konrad Wachelko	Eng.: Nick Martin	Eng.: Christie Paquet

2013	2013	2014	2014
Ontario	**Northwest Territories**	**Saskatchewan**	**Canada**
Eng.: Steven Stewart	Eng.: Steven Stewart	Eng.: Samantha Strath	Eng.: Eric Boyer

THREE HUNDRED DOLLARS, PROVINCIAL COATS OF ARMS SERIES, 2008-2014, PRICING PANEL.

DATE	DESCRIPTION	RCM ITEM #	QUANTITY SOLD	ISSUE PRICE	FINISH	PR-69	PR-70
2008	Newfoundland and Labrador	621558	472	1,541.95	Proof	2,200.	—
2008	Alberta	103612	344	1,631.95	Proof	2,200.	—
2009	Yukon Territory	103879	325	1,949.95	Proof	2,200.	—
2009	Prince Edward Island	105529	236	1,949.95	Proof	2,200.	—
2010	British Columbia	107184	421	2,249.95	Proof	2,200.	—
2010	New Brunswick	110230	233	2,249.95	Proof	2,200.	—
2011	Manitoba	111558	472	2,249.95	Proof	2,200.	—
2011	Nova Scotia	115537	238	2,249.95	Proof	2,200.	—
2012	Quebec	116629	334	2,649.95	Proof	2,200.	—
2012	Nunavut	119740	189	2,649.95	Proof	2,200.	—
2013	Ontario	121672	251	2,649.95	Proof	2,200.	—
2013	Northwest Territories	123621	148	2,649.95	Proof	2,200.	—
2014	Saskatchewan	127683	172	2,649.95	Proof	2,200.	—
2014	Canada	128535	198	2,649.95	Proof	2,200.	—

MOON MASK SERIES

THREE HUNDRED DOLLARS, MOON MASK SERIES, 2008-2009.

Common Obverse	2008 Four Seasons Moon Mask	2009 Summer Moon Mask

Designers:
Obv.:   Susanna Blunt
Rev.:   Jody Broomfield
Composition: 58.33% Au, 41.67% Ag, Enamelled
Gold content: 35.0 g, 1.125 tr oz
Silver content: 25.0 g, 0.804 tr oz
Weight: 60.0 g
Diameter: 50.0 mm
Case of Issue: Maroon leatherette clam style case, black flocked insert, encapsulated coin, COA

Engravers:
Obv.:   Susan Taylor
Rev.:   Susan Taylor

Thickness: 2.5 mm
Edge: Reeded
Die Axis: ↑↑
Finish: Proof

DATE	DESCRIPTION	RCM ITEM #	QUANTITY SOLD	ISSUE PRICE	FINISH	PR-69	PR-70
2008	Four Seasons Moon Mask	6215808	544	1,559.95	Proof	2,400.	—
2009	Summer Moon Mask	102700	N/A	1,723.95	Proof	2,400.	—

THREE HUNDRED DOLLAR GOLD COIN, REDUCED SIZE

THREE HUNDRED DOLLARS, WELCOME FIGURE (DZUNUK'WA) TOTEM POLE, 2005.

Dzunuk'wa is a giant, hairy, black-bodied, big-breasted, wide-eyed female monster. She is physically strong enough to tear down large trees, spiritually powerful enough to resurrect the dead and possesses magical treasures and great wealth.

Designers:		Engravers:	
Obv.:	Susanna Blunt	Obv.:	Susan Taylor
Rev.:	Dr. Richard Hunt		
Composition:	58.33% Au, 41.67% Ag		
Gold content:	26.25 g, 0.844 tr oz		
Silver content:	18.75 g, 0.603 tr oz		
Weight:	45.0 g	**Edge:**	Reeded
Diameter:	40.0 mm	**Die Axis:**	↑↑
Thickness:	3.0 mm	**Finish:**	Proof
Case of Issue:	Maroon leatherette clam style case, black flocked insert, encapsulated coin, COA		

DATE	DESCRIPTION	RCM ITEM #	QUANTITY SOLD	ISSUE PRICE	FINISH	PR-69	PR-70
2005	Welcome Figure Totem Pole	N/A	948	1,199.95	Proof	1,600.	—

Note: An identical design is utilized on the $30 silver coin for 2005, see page 357

CANADIAN ACHIEVEMENT SERIES, REDUCED SIZE 2005-2008

THREE HUNDRED DOLLARS, 120TH ANNIVERSARY OF THE INTERNATIONAL IMPLEMENTATION OF STANDARD TIME SET, 2005.

In 1885 Sir Sandford Fleming's system of standard time was implemented, dividing the world into 24 time zones. These are the first coins in the Canadian Achievements series.

Designers:		Engravers:	
Obv.:	Susanna Blunt	Obv.:	Susan Taylor
Rev.:	Bonnie Ross	Rev.:	Stan Witten
Composition:	58.33% Au, 41.67% Ag, Colourised		
Gold content:	26.25 g, 0.844 tr oz		
Silver content:	18.75 g, 0.603 tr oz		
Weight:	45.0 g	**Edge:**	Reeded
Diameter:	40.0 mm	**Die Axis:**	↑↑
Thickness:	3.0 mm	**Finish:**	Proof
Case of Issue:	Anodized gold-coloured aluminum box with cherry wood stained side panels, encapsulated coin, COA		

Common Obverse   Pacific Time 4:00

Mountain Time 5:00   Central Time 6:00   Eastern Time 7:00   Atlantic Time 8:00   Newfoundland Time 8:30

DATE	DESCRIPTION	RCM ITEM #	QUANTITY SOLD	ISSUE PRICE	FINISH	PR-69	PR-70
2005	Pacific Time 4:00	N/A	200	999.95	Proof	1,800.	—
2005	Mountain Time 5:00	N/A	200	999.95	Proof	1,800.	—
2005	Central Time 6:00	N/A	200	999.95	Proof	1,800.	—
2005	Eastern Time 7:00	N/A	200	999.95	Proof	1,800.	—
2005	Atlantic Time 8:00	N/A	200	999.95	Proof	1,800.	—
2005	Newfoundland Time 8:30	N/A	200	999.95	Proof	1,800.	—

Note: It is reported in the 2006 Mint Report that a total of 1,199 coins were issued, however, it did not stipulate which coin was short struck.

CANADIAN ACHIEVEMENT SERIES, REDUCED SIZE (cont.).

THREE HUNDRED DOLLARS, CANADIAN ACHIEVEMENT SERIES, 2006-2008.

| 2006 Obverse | 2007-2008 Obverse | 2006 – Fifth Anniversary of Canadarm Des.: Cecily Mok, Decal | 2007 – Panoramic Photography in Canada, Niagara Falls, Hologram Des.: Chris Jordison | 2008 – IMAX© Hologram Des.: IMAX© |

Designers:
  Obv.:   Susanna Blunt
  Rev.:   See reverse illustrations
Composition: 58.33% Au, 41.67% Ag
Gold content: 26.25 g, 0.844 tr oz
Weight: 45.0 g
Diameter: 40.0 mm
Thickness: 3.0 mm
Case of Issue: Maroon leatherette clam style case, black flocked insert, encapsulated coin. COA

Engravers:
  Obv.:   Susan Taylor

Silver content: 18.75 g, 0.603 tr oz
Edge: Reeded
Die Axis: ↑↑
Finish: Proof, Decal

DATE	DESCRIPTION	RCM ITEM #	QUANTITY SOLD	ISSUE PRICE	FINISH	PR-69	PR-70
2006	5th Anniversary Canadarm, Decal	621546	581	1,089.95	Proof	1,600.	—
2007	Panoramic Photography, Niagara Falls, Hologram	N/A	551	1,111.95	Proof	1,600.	—
2008	IMAX©, Hologram	N/A	252	1,228.95	Proof	1,600.	—

THREE HUNDRED DOLLAR GOLD COIN, SMALL SIZE

THREE HUNDRED DOLLARS, THE QUEEN'S DIAMOND JUBILEE, 1952-2012.

Designers and Engravers:
  Obv.:   Susanna Blunt, Susan Taylor
  Rev.:   Laurie McGaw, Susan Taylor
Composition: 99.999% Au, Diamond
Gold content: 22.0 g, 0.707 tr oz
Weight: 22.0 g   Edge: Reeded
Diameter: 25.0 mm   Die Axis: ↑↑
Thickness: N/A   Finish: Proof
Case of Issue: Wooden collector box with the official
                 Diamond Jubilee Cypher

DATE	DESCRIPTION	RCM ITEM #	QUANTITY SOLD	ISSUE PRICE	FINISH	PR-69	PR-70
2012 (1952-)	The Queen's Diamond Jubilee	114635	684	1,999.95	Proof	1,600.	—

Note: This coin was also issued as part of a three-coin gold commemorative set. The other coins included in the set are a British £5 coin and an Australian fifty-cent piece. There were 375 sets sold to a U.S.A. distributor (APMEX).

THREE HUNDRED FIFTY DOLLAR GOLD COINS

PROVINCIAL FLORAL EMBLEM SERIES

THREE HUNDRED FIFTY DOLLARS, PROVINCIAL FLORAL EMBLEM SERIES, 1998-2011.

Begun in 1998 and issued annually, these $350 gold coins bear either a national or provincial flower. In 2004 the weight was decreased from 38.05 to 35.0 grams.

Common Obverse
1998-2003 (except for date)

Designers:	1998-2003	2004-2011	Engravers:	1998-2003	2004-2011
Obv.:	Dora de Pédery-Hunt	Susanna Blunt	Obv.:	Dora de Pédery-Hunt	SusanTaylor
Rev.:	See reverse illustrations		Rev.:	See reverse illustrations	

Composition: 99.999% Au
Gold content: 38.05 g, 1.222 tr oz   35.0 g, 1.125 tr oz
Weight: 38.05 g   35.0 g   **Edge:** Reeded
Diameter: 34.0 mm   **Die Axis:** ↑↑
Thickness: 3.2 mm   **Finish:** Proof
Case of Issue: Anodized gold-coloured aluminum box with cherry wood stained side panels, encapsulated coin, COA

Common Obverse
2004-2011 (except for date)

1998 90th Anniv. Royal Canadian Mint
Des.: Pierre Leduc
Eng.: Ago Aarand

1999 Golden Slipper Prince Edward Island
Des.: Henry Purdy
Eng.: José Osio

2000 Pacific Dogwood British Columbia
Des.: Caren Heine
Eng.: José Osio

2001 Mayflower Nova Scotia
Des.: Bonnie Ross
Eng.: Susan Taylor

2002 Wild Rose Alberta
Des.: Dr. A. K. Hellum
Eng.: William Woodruff

2003 White Trillium Ontario
Des.: Pamela Stagg
Eng.: José Osio

2004 Fireweed Yukon Territory
Des.: Catherine Ann Deer
Eng.: William Woodruff

2005 Western Red Lily Saskatchewan
Des.: Chris Jordison
Eng.: José Osio

2006 Iris Versicolor Quebec
Des.: Susan Taylor
Eng.: Susan Taylor

2007 Purple Violet New Brunswick
Des.: Sue Rose
Eng.: William Woodruff

2008 Purple Saxifrage Nunavut
Des.: Celia Godkin
Eng.: Cecily Mok

2009 Pitcher Plant Newfoundland & Labrador
Des.: Celia Godkin
Eng.: José Osio

2010 Prairie Crocus Manitoba
Des.: Celia Godkin
Eng.: N/A

2011 Mountain Avens Northwest Territories
Des.: Caren Heine
Eng.: Susan Taylor

THREE HUNDRED FIFTY DOLLARS, PROVINCIAL FLORAL SERIES, 1998-2011, PRICING PANEL.

DATE	DESCRIPTION	RCM ITEM #	QUANTITY SOLD	ISSUE PRICE	FINISH	PR-69	PR-70
1998	90th Anniversary of the RCM	N/A	1,999	999.99	Proof	2,300.	—
1999	Golden Slipper, P.E.I.	N/A	1,990	999.99	Proof	2,300.	—
2000	Pacific Dogwood, British Columbia	N/A	1,971	999.99	Proof	2,300.	—
2001	Mayflower, Nova Scotia	N/A	1,988	999.99	Proof	2,300.	—
2002	Wild Rose, Alberta	N/A	2,001	1,099.99	Proof	2,300.	—
2003	White Trillium, Ontario	N/A	1,865	1,099.99	Proof	2,300.	—
2004	Fireweed, Yukon Territory	N/A	1,836	1,099.95	Proof	2,100.	—
2005	Western Red Lily, Saskatchewan	N/A	1,634	1,295.99	Proof	2,100.	—
2006	Iris Versicolor, Quebec	N/A	1,995	1,295.95	Proof	2,100.	—
2007	Purple Violet, New Brunswick	N/A	1,392	1,520.95	Proof	2,100.	—
2008	Purple Saxifrage, Nunavut	100471	1,313	1,675.95	Proof	2,100.	—
2009	Pitcher Plant, Newfoundland & Labrador	104173	1,003	2,149.95	Proof	2,100.	—
2010	Prairie Crocus, Manitoba	108192	775	2,599.95	Proof	2,100.	—
2011	Mountain Avens, Northwest Territories	113166	1,033	2,799.95	Proof	2,100.	—

THREE HUNDRED FIFTY DOLLARS, SIR ISAAC BROCK, THE HERO OF UPPER CANADA, 2012.

Sir Isaac Brock, an English General, was killed at the first major battle of the War of 1812, at Queenston Heights.

Designers and Engravers:
Obv.:   Susanna Blunt, Susan Taylor
Rev.:   Christie Paquet
Composition: 99.999% Au
Gold content: 35.0 g, 1.125 tr oz
Weight: 35.0 g   **Edge:**   Reeded
Diameter: 34.0 mm   **Die Axis:**   ↑↑
Thickness: N/A   **Finish:**   Proof
Case of Issue: Maroon leatherette clam style case, black flocked insert, encapsulated coin, COA

DATE	DESCRIPTION	RCM ITEM #	QUANTITY SOLD	ISSUE PRICE	FINISH	PR-69	PR-70
2012	Sir Isaac Brock, The Hero of Upper Canada	120652	365	2,799.95	Proof	2,500.	—

THREE HUNDRED FIFTY DOLLARS, POLAR BEAR, ICONIC CANADIAN ANIMALS, 2013.

This is the first coin in a new series of Iconic Canadian Animals.

Designers and Engravers:
Obv.:   Susanna Blunt, Susan Taylor
Rev.:   Glen Loates, RCM Staff
Composition: 99.999% Au
Gold content: 35.0 g, 1.125 tr oz
Weight: 35.0 g   **Edge:**   Reeded
Diameter: 34.0 mm   **Die Axis:**   ↑↑
Thickness: N/A   **Finish:**   Proof
Case of Issue: Maroon leatherette clam style case, black flocked insert, encapsulated coin, COA

DATE	DESCRIPTION	RCM ITEM #	QUANTITY SOLD	ISSUE PRICE	FINISH	PR-69	PR-70
2013	Polar Bear	125879	600	2,799.95	Proof	2,500.	—

THREE HUNDRED FIFTY DOLLAR (1.125 ounce), THE MAJESTIC MOOSE, 2014.

Designers and Engravers:

Obv.:	Susanna Blunt, Susan Taylor
Rev.:	Claudio D'Angelo, RCM Staff

Composition:	99.999% Au		
Gold content:	35.0 g, 1.125 tr oz		
Weight:	35.0 g	**Edge:**	Reeded
Diameter:	34.0 mm	**Die Axis:**	↑↑
Thickness:	N/A	**Finish:**	Proof
Case of Issue:	Maroon leatherette clam style case, black flock insert, encapsulated coin, COA		

DATE	DESCRIPTION	RCM ITEM #	QUANTITY SOLD	ISSUE PRICE	FINISH	PR-69	PR-70
2014	Majestic Moose	130564	515	2,799.95	Proof	2,600.	—

THREE HUNDRED FIFTY DOLLARS, IMPOSING ALPHA WOLF, 2015.

Designers and Engravers:

Obv.:	Susanna Blunt, Susan Taylor
Rev.:	Maurade Baynton

Composition:	99.999% Au		
Gold content:	35.0 g, 1.125 tr oz		
Weight:	35.0 g	**Edge:**	Reeded
Diameter:	34.0 mm	**Die Axis:**	↑↑
Thickness:	N/A	**Finish:**	Proof
Case of Issue:	Maroon leatherette clam style case, black flocked insert, encapsulated coin, COA		

DATE	DESCRIPTION	RCM ITEM #	QUANTITY SOLD	ISSUE PRICE	FINISH	PR-69	PR-70
2015	Imposing Alpha Wolf	143696	400	2,799.95	Proof	2,800.	—

THREE HUNDRED FIFTY DOLLARS, THE BOLD BLACK BEAR, 2016.

Designers and Engravers:

Obv.:	Susanna Blunt, Susan Taylor
Rev.:	Pierre Leduc

Composition:	99.999% Au		
Gold content:	35.0 g, 1.125 tr oz		
Weight:	35.0 g	**Edge:**	Reeded
Diameter:	34.0 mm	**Die Axis:**	↑↑
Thickness:	N/A	**Finish:**	Proof
Case of Issue:	Maroon leatherette clam style case, black flocked insert, encapsulated coin, COA		

DATE	DESCRIPTION	RCM ITEM #	QUANTITY SOLD	ISSUE PRICE	FINISH	PR-69	PR-70
2016	The Bold Black Bear	148106	348	2,799.95	Proof	2,800.	—

THREE HUNDRED FIFTY DOLLAR, THE MAJESTIC ELK, 2017.

Designers and Engravers:

Obv.:	Susanna Blunt, Susan Taylor
Rev.:	Maurade Baynton

Composition:	99.999% Au		
Gold content:	35.0 g, 1.125 tr oz		
Weight:	35.0 g	**Edge:**	Reeded
Diameter:	34.0 mm	**Die Axis:**	↑↑
Thickness:	N/A	**Finish:**	Proof
Case of Issue:	Maroon leatherette clam style case, black flock insert, encapsulated coin, COA		

DATE	DESCRIPTION	RCM ITEM #	QUANTITY SOLD	ISSUE PRICE	FINISH	PR-69	PR-70
2017	$350 (1.125 oz) Majestic Elk	154989	400	2,799.95	Proof	2,800.	—

FIVE HUNDRED DOLLAR GOLD COINS

FIVE HUNDRED DOLLARS, 60TH WEDDING ANNIVERSARY OF QUEEN ELIZABETH AND PRINCE PHILIP, 1947-2007.

Designers and Engravers:

Obv.:	Susanna Blunt, Susan Taylor
Rev.:	S. Hepburn, S. Taylor
Composition:	99.99% Au
Gold content:	155.76 g, 5.01 tr oz
Weight:	155.76 g
Diameter:	60.0 mm
Thickness:	N/A
Case of Issue:	Black clam style case, black insert, encapsulated coin, COA

Edge:	Reeded
Die Axis:	↑↑
Finish:	Proof

DATE	DESCRIPTION	RCM ITEM #	QUANTITY SOLD	ISSUE PRICE	FINISH	PR-69	PR-70
2007 (1947-)	60th Wedding Anniversary Queen / Prince Philip	620507	198	5,999.95	Proof	10,000.	—

FIVE HUNDRED DOLLARS, 100TH ANNIVERSARY OF THE ROYAL CANADIAN MINT, 1908-2008.

Designers and Engravers:

Obv.:	Susanna Blunt, Susan Taylor
Rev.:	RCM Staff
Composition:	99.99% Au
Gold content:	155.76 g, 5.01 tr oz
Weight:	155.76 g
Diameter:	60.0 mm
Thickness:	N/A
Case of Issue:	Black clam style case, black insert, encapsulated coin, COA

Edge:	Reeded
Die Axis:	↑↑
Finish:	Proof

DATE	DESCRIPTION	RCM ITEM #	QUANTITY SOLD	ISSUE PRICE	FINISH	PR-69	PR-70
2008 (1908-)	100th Anniversary of the RCM	101046	248	8,159.95	Proof	10,000.	—

FIVE HUNDRED DOLLARS, 150TH ANNIVERSARY OF THE START OF CONSTRUCTION OF THE PARLIAMENT BUILDINGS, 2009.

Designers and Engravers:

Obv.:	Susanna Blunt, Susan Taylor
Rev.:	Cecily Mok
Composition:	99.99% Au
Gold content:	156.5 g, 5.03 tr oz
Weight:	156.05 g
Diameter:	60.0 mm
Thickness:	N/A
Case of Issue:	Black clam style case, black insert, encapsulated coin, COA

Edge:	Reeded
Die Axis:	↑↑
Finish:	Proof

DATE	DESCRIPTION	RCM ITEM #	QUANTITY SOLD	ISSUE PRICE	FINISH	PR-69	PR-70
2009	150th Anniv. Construction Parliament Bldgs.	105221	77	10,199.95	Proof	10,000.	—

FIVE HUNDRED DOLLARS, 75TH ANNIV. OF THE FIRST BANK NOTES ISSUED BY THE BANK OF CANADA, 1935-2010.

Designers and Engravers:

Obv.:	Susanna Blunt, Susan Taylor
Rev.:	S. Hepburn, J. Osio
Composition:	99.99% Au
Gold content:	156.5 g, 5.03 tr oz
Weight:	156.5 g
Diameter:	60.2 mm
Thickness:	N/A
Case of Issue:	Maroon leatherette clam style case, black insert, encapsulated coin, COA

Edge:	Reeded
Die Axis:	↑↑
Finish:	Proof

DATE	DESCRIPTION	RCM ITEM #	QUANTITY SOLD	ISSUE PRICE	FINISH	PR-69	PR-70
2010 (1935-)	75th Anniv. First Bank of Canada Notes	109730	191	9,495.95	Proof	10,000.	—

FIVE HUNDRED DOLLARS, 100TH ANNIVERSARY OF THE FIRST CANADIAN GOLD COINS, 1912-2012.

The first dollar denomination coins, the five and ten dollar gold coins, were struck at the Ottawa Mint in 1912.

Designers and Engravers:
Obv.:	Susanna Blunt, Susan Taylor
Rev.:	RCM Staff, W. Woodruff
Composition:	99.99% Au
Gold content:	156.5 g, 5.03 tr oz

Weight:	156.5 g	Edge:	Plain
Diameter:	60.2 mm	Die Axis:	↑↑
Thickness:	N/A	Finish:	Proof
Case of Issue:	Maroon leatherette clam style case, black insert, encapsulated coin, COA		

DATE	DESCRIPTION	RCM ITEM #	QUANTITY SOLD	ISSUE PRICE	FINISH	PR-69	PR-70
2012 (1912-)	100th Anniv. First Canadian Gold Coins	113916	115	12,274.95	Proof	12,000.	—

FIVE HUNDRED DOLLARS, 100TH ANNIVERSARY OF THE CALGARY STAMPEDE, 2012.

Designers and Engravers:
Obv.:	Susanna Blunt, Susan Taylor
Rev.:	José Osio, L. Normandin
Composition:	99.99% Au
Gold content:	156.5 g, 5.03 tr oz

Weight:	156.5 g	Edge:	Reeded
Diameter:	60.2 mm	Die Axis:	↑↑
Thickness:	N/A	Finish:	Proof
Case of Issue:	Maroon leatherette clam style case, black insert, encapsulated coin, COA		

DATE	DESCRIPTION	RCM ITEM #	QUANTITY SOLD	ISSUE PRICE	FINISH	PR-69	PR-70
2012	100th Anniv. Calgary Stampede	118849	96	11,999.95	Proof	12,000.	—

FIVE HUNDRED DOLLARS, *HMS SHANNON* AND *USS CHESAPEAKE*, 2013.

Designers and Engravers:
Obv.:	Susanna Blunt, Susan Taylor
Rev.:	J. Horton, Cecily Mok
Composition:	99.99% Au
Gold content:	156.5 g, 5.03 tr oz

Weight:	156.5 g	Edge:	Reeded
Diameter:	60.2 mm	Die Axis:	↑↑
Thickness:	N/A	Finish:	Proof
Case of Issue:	Maroon leatherette clam style case, black insert, encapsulated coin, COA		

DATE	DESCRIPTION	RCM ITEM #	QUANTITY SOLD	ISSUE PRICE	FINISH	PR-69	PR-70
2013	HMS Shannon and USS Chesapeake	120788	74	11,999.95	Proof	12,000.	—

FIVE HUNDRED DOLLARS, AN ABORIGINAL STORY, 2013.

Designers and Engravers:
Obv.:	Susanna Blunt, Susan Taylor
Rev.:	R. Weizineau, RCM Staff
Composition:	99.99% Au
Gold content:	156.5 g, 5.03 tr oz

Weight:	156.5 g	Edge:	Reeded
Diameter:	60.2 mm	Die Axis:	↑↑
Thickness:	N/A	Finish:	Proof
Case of Issue:	Maroon leatherette clam style case, black insert, encapsulated coin, COA		

DATE	DESCRIPTION	RCM ITEM #	QUANTITY SOLD	ISSUE PRICE	FINISH	PR-69	PR-70
2013	An Aboriginal Story	127152	52	11,999.95	Proof	12,000.	—

FIVE HUNDRED DOLLARS, THE LEGEND OF THE SPIRIT BEAR, AN ABORIGINAL STORY, 2014.

The reverse design on this coin is an original work by Darlene Gait, a Coast Salish First Nation's artist, recounting the legend of Spirit Bear.

Designers and Engravers:
Obv.:	Susanna Blunt, Susan Taylor
Rev.:	Darlene Gait, RCM Staff
Composition:	99.99% Au
Gold content:	156.5 g, 5.03 tr oz

Weight:	156.5 g	**Edge:**	Plain
Diameter:	60.2 mm	**Die Axis:**	↑↑
Thickness:	N/A	**Finish:**	Proof
Case of Issue:	Red lacquered wooden box, black flocked insert, encapsulated coin, COA		

DATE	DESCRIPTION	RCM ITEM #	QUANTITY SOLD	ISSUE PRICE	FINISH	PR-69	PR-70
2014	The Legend of Spirit Bear	130558	100	12,000.00	Proof	12,000.	—

MYTHICAL REALMS OF THE HAIDA SET

FIVE HUNDRED DOLLARS, MYTHICAL REALMS OF THE HAIDA, 2016.

Common Obverse	The Orca	The Eagle	The Bear

Designers:
Obv.:	Susanna Blunt
Rev.:	April White
Composition:	99.999% Au
Gold content:	156.05 g, 5.703 tr oz

Engravers:
Obv.:	Susan Taylor
Rev.:	RCM Staff

Weight:	156.05 g	**Edge:**	Reeded
Diameter:	60.15 mm	**Die Axis:**	↑↑
Thickness:	N/A	**Finish:**	Proof
Case of Issue:	Maplewood case with black beauty box, encapsulated coin, COA		

DATE	DESCRIPTION	RCM ITEM #	QUANTITY SOLD	ISSUE PRICE	FINISH	PR-69	PR-70
2016	Mythical Realms of The Haida: The Orca	148366	35	12,000	Proof	12,000.	—
2016	Mythical Realms of The Haida: The Eagle	148438	50	12,000	Proof	12,000.	—
2016	Mythical Realms of The Haida: The Bear	148596	50	12,000	Proof	12,000.	—

FIVE HUNDRED DOLLARS, PEREGRINE FALCON, 2017.

Designers and Engravers:
Obv.:	Susanna Blunt, Susan Taylor
Rev.:	Emily S. Damstra
Composition:	99.99% Au
Gold content:	156.5 g, 5.03 tr oz

Weight:	156.05 g	**Edge:**	Plain
Diameter:	60.15 mm	**Die Axis:**	↑↑
Thickness:	N/A	**Finish:**	Proof
Case of Issue:	Red lacquered with custom beauty box, COA		

DATE	DESCRIPTION	RCM ITEM #	QUANTITY SOLD	ISSUE PRICE	FINISH	PR-69	PR-70
2017	Peregrine Falcon	156623	99	12,629.95	Proof	12,500	—

FIVE HUNDRED DOLLARS, RED TAILED HAWK, 2017.

Designers and Engravers:
Obv.: Susanna Blunt, Susan Taylor
Rev.: Emily Damstra
Composition: 99.99% Au
Gold content: 156.5 g, 5.03 tr oz
Weight: 156.05 g   **Edge:** Plain
Diameter: 60.15 mm   **Die Axis:** ↑↑
Thickness: N/A   **Finish:** Proof
Case of Issue: Red lacquered case with black beauty box, COA

DATE	DESCRIPTION	RCM ITEM #	QUANTITY SOLD	ISSUE PRICE	FINISH	PR-69	PR-70
2017	Red Tailed Hawk	161856	99	12,999.95	Proof	13,000.	—

FIVE HUNDRED DOLLARS, GREAT HORNED OWL, 2018.

Designers and Engravers:
Obv.: Susanna Blunt, Susan Taylor
Rev.: Emily Damstra
Composition: 99.99% Au
Gold content: 156.5 g, 5.03 tr oz
Weight: 156.05 g   **Edge:** Plain
Diameter: 60.15 mm   **Die Axis:** ↑↑
Thickness: N/A   **Finish:** Proof
Case of Issue: Red lacquered case with black beauty box, COA

DATE	DESCRIPTION	RCM ITEM #	MINTAGE	ISSUE PRICE	FINISH	PR-69	PR-70
2018	Great Horned Owl	161865	99	12,999.95	Proof	13,000.	—

FIVE HUNDRED DOLLARS, PREDATORS OF THE WILD: THE COUGAR, 2018.

Designers and Engravers:
Obv.: Susanna Blunt, Susan Taylor
Rev.: Emily S. Damstra
Composition: 99.99% Au
Gold content: 156.5 g, 5.03 tr oz
Weight: 156.05 g   **Edge:** Plain
Diameter: 60.15 mm   **Die Axis:** ↑↑
Thickness: N/A   **Finish:** Proof
Case of Issue: Red wood lacquered case with black beauty box, COA

DATE	DESCRIPTION	RCM ITEM #	MINTAGE	ISSUE PRICE	FINISH	PR-69	PR-70
2018	Predators of the Wild: The Cougar	165031	99	12,999.95	Proof	13,000.	—

FIVE HUNDRED DOLLARS, BIRDS OF PREY: THE GOLDEN EAGLE, 2019.

Designers and Engravers:
Obv.: Susanna Blunt, Susan Taylor
Rev.: Pierre Leduc
Composition: 99.99% Au
Gold content: 156.5 g, 5.03 tr oz
Weight: 156.05 g   **Edge:** Plain
Diameter: 60.15 mm   **Die Axis:** ↑↑
Thickness: N/A   **Finish:** Proof
Case of Issue: Red wood lacquered case with black beauty box, COA

DATE	DESCRIPTION	RCM ITEM #	QUANTITY SOLD	ISSUE PRICE	FINISH	PR-69	PR-70
2019	Birds of Prey: The Golden Eagle	169472	99	12,999.95	Proof	13,000.	—

ONE THOUSAND DOLLARS

ONE THOUSAND DOLLARS, 100TH ANNIVERSARY OF THE DECLARATION OF THE FIRST WORLD WAR, 2014.

The reverse design on this coin is an original work by Yves Bérubé, to commemorate a poignant moment in history as a soldier leans against the guardrail of the *S.S. Megantic*.

Designers and Engravers:

Obv.:	Susanna Blunt, Susan Taylor
Rev.:	Yves Bérubé, Samantha Strath

Composition: 99.99% Au
Gold content: 311.5, 10.015 tr oz

Weight:	311.5 g	**Edge:**	Reeded
Diameter:	76.1 mm	**Die Axis:**	↑↑
Thickness:	N/A	**Finish:**	Proof

Case of Issue: Maple wooden case, black flocked insert, encapsulated coin, COA

DATE	DESCRIPTION	RCM ITEM #	QUANTITY SOLD	ISSUE PRICE	FINISH	PR-69	PR-70
2014	100th Anniv. of the Declaration of the First World War	130519	16	21,000	Proof	21,000.	—

ONE THOUSAND TWO HUNDRED FIFTY DOLLARS

CALL OF THE WILD SERIES, 2014-2017

2014-2015 Obverse   **2016-2017 Obverse**

Designers:

Obv.:	Susanna Blunt
Rev.:	Pierre Leduc

Composition: 99.99% Au
Gold content: 500 g, 16.08 tr oz
Weight: 500 g
Diameter: 85.36 mm

Engravers:

Obv.:	Susan Taylor
Rev.:	RCM Staff

Thickness:	N/A
Edge:	Reeded
Die Axis:	↑↑
Finish:	Proof

Case of Issue: Wooden case, black flocked insert, encapsulated coin, COA

2014 Howling Wolf   **2015 Growling Cougar**   **2016 Roaring Grizzly**   **2017 Elk**

DATE	DESCRIPTION	RCM ITEM #	QUANTITY SOLD	ISSUE PRICE	FINISH	PR-69	PR-70
2014	Howling Wolf	130500	25	32,000	Proof	32,000.	—
2015	Growling Cougar	142460	25	32,000	Proof	32,000.	—
2016	Roaring Grizzly Bear	148731	20	32,000	Proof	32,000.	—
2017	Elk	157939	25	32,000	Proof	32,000.	—

Note: The same images were utilized for the 2014-2017 $200 (1 ounce) coins (see page 445).

TWO THOUSAND FIVE HUNDRED DOLLAR GOLD COINS

VANCOUVER 2010 OLYMPIC WINTER GAMES SERIES, 2007-2010

Designers and Engravers:

Obv.:	Susanna Blunt, Susan Taylor
Rev.:	See reverse illustrations

Composition:	99.99% Au	**Thickness:**	N/A
Gold content:	1,000.0 g, 32.15 tr oz	**Edge:**	Plain
Weight:	1,000.0 g (1 kilo)	**Die Axis:**	↑↑
Diameter:	101.6 mm	**Finish:**	Proof
Case of Issue:	Black display case, encapsulated coins, COA, 2010 Olympic Winter Games theme sleeve.		

Common Obverse
(except for date)

2007 Early Canada
Des.: Stan Witten
Eng.: Stan Witten

2008 Towards Confederation
Des.: Susan Taylor
Eng.: Susan Taylor

2009 The Canada of Today
Des.: Design Team of the Vancouver
Organising Committee for the
2010 Olympic/Paralympic Games
Eng.: Konrad Wachelko

2009 Surviving the Flood
Des.: Design Team of the Vancouver
Organising Committee for the
2010 Olympic/Paralympic Games
Eng.: Christie Paquet

2010 The Eagle
Des.: Xwa lac tun (Ricky Harry)
Eng.: Stan Witten

DATE	DESCRIPTION	ISSUE DATE	RCM ITEM #	QUANTITY SOLD	ISSUE PRICE	FINISH	PR-69	PR-70
2007	Early Canada	Feb. 23, 2007	620317	20	36,000	Proof	60,000.	—.
2008	Towards Confederation	Feb. 20, 2008	620318	20	49,000	Proof	60,000.	—.
2009	The Canada of Today	Apr. 15, 2009	620319	50	54,000	Proof	60,000.	—.
2009	Surviving the Flood	Nov. 21, 2009	103703	40	49,000	Proof	60,000.	—.
2010	The Eagle	Nov. 19, 2009	106944	20	49,000	Proof	60,000.	—.

TWO THOUSAND FIVE HUNDRED DOLLARS, 125TH ANNIVERSARY OF BANFF NATIONAL PARK, 2010.

Designers and Engravers:

Obv.:	Susanna Blunt, Susan Taylor
Rev.:	Tony Bianco, Susan Taylor

Composition:	99.99% Au		
Gold content:	1000.0 g, 32.15 tr oz		
Weight:	1,000.0 g (1 kilo)	**Edge:**	Plain
Diameter:	101.6 mm	**Die Axis:**	↑↑
Thickness:	N/A	**Finish:**	Proof
Case of Issue:	Black clam style case, black insert, encapsulated coin, COA		

DATE	DESCRIPTION	RCM ITEM #	QUANTITY SOLD	ISSUE PRICE	FINISH	PR-69	PR-70
2010	125th Anniversary Banff National Park	111615	20	57,000	Proof	60,000.	—

TWO THOUSAND FIVE HUNDRED DOLLARS, 375TH ANNIVERSARY OF LACROSSE, 2011.

Designers and Engravers:

Obv.:	Susanna Blunt, Susan Taylor
Rev.:	Steve Hepburn, Christie Paquet

Composition: 99.99% Au
Gold content: 1000.0 g, 32.15 tr oz
Weight: 1,000.0 g (1 kilo)   **Edge:** Plain
Diameter: 101.6 mm   **Die Axis:** ↑↑
Thickness: N/A   **Finish:** Proof
Case of Issue: Black clam style case, black insert, encapsulated coin, COA

DATE	DESCRIPTION	RCM ITEM #	QUANTITY SOLD	ISSUE PRICE	FINISH	PR-69	PR-70
2011	375th Anniversary of Lacrosse	113507	29	69,000	Proof	70,000.	—

TWO THOUSAND FIVE HUNDRED DOLLARS, THE CHALLENGE, ROBERT BATEMAN MOOSE COIN, 2012.

The coin was issued to commemorate the 50th anniversary of the Canadian Wildlife Federation. For other coins in the Robert Bateman Moose series, see pages 269, 398 and 443.

Designers and Engravers:

Obv.:	Susanna Blunt, Susan Taylor
Rev.:	Robert Bateman, Stan Witten

Composition: 99.99% Au
Gold content: 1000.0 g, 32.15 tr oz
Weight: 1,000.0 g (1 kilo)   **Die Axis:** ↑↑
Diameter: 101.6 mm   **Edge:** Plain
Thickness: N/A   **Finish:** Proof
Case of Issue: Maple wood box lacquered in walnut coloured finish, black flocked insert, encapsulated coin, COA

DATE	DESCRIPTION	RCM ITEM #	QUANTITY SOLD	ISSUE PRICE	FINISH	PR-69	PR-70
2012 (1962-)	The Challenge, Robert Bateman	121060	12	69,000	Proof	70,000.	—.

TWO THOUSAND FIVE HUNDRED DOLLARS, THE BATTLE OF QUEENSTON HEIGHTS, 2012.

Designers and Engravers:

Obv.:	Susanna Blunt, Susan Taylor
Rev.:	John David Kelly, Marcus Hallam

Composition: 99.99% Au
Gold content: 1000.0 g, 32.15 tr oz
Weight: 1000.0 g (1 kilo)   **Edge:** Reeded
Diameter: 102.1 mm   **Die Axis:** ↑↑
Thickness: N/A   **Finish:** Proof
Case of Issue: Maroon clam style case, black flocked insert, encapsulated coin, COA

DATE	DESCRIPTION	RCM ITEM #	QUANTITY SOLD	ISSUE PRICE	FINISH	PR-69	PR-70
2012	Battle of Queenston Heights	120689	19	69,000	Proof	70,000.	—.

TWO THOUSAND FIVE HUNDRED DOLLARS, KING GEORGE III PEACE MEDAL, THE WAR OF 1812, 2012.

Designers and Engravers:

Obv.:	Susanna Blunt, Susan Taylor
Rev.:	See illustrations

Composition: 99.99% Au
Gold content: 1000.0 g, 32.15 tr oz
Weight: 1000.0 g (1 kilo)   **Edge:** Reeded
Diameter: 101.6 mm   **Die Axis:** ↑↑
Thickness: N/A   **Finish:** Proof
Case of Issue: Maroon clam style case, black flocked insert, encapsulated coin, COA

Reverse Des.: RCM engravers' representation of the King George III Peace Medal
Reverse Engr.: Konrad Wachelko, Matt Bowen Samantha Strath, Steven Stewart

DATE	DESCRIPTION	RCM ITEM #	QUANTITY SOLD	ISSUE PRICE	FINISH	PR-69	PR-70
2012	King George III Peace Medal	119698	20	69,000	Proof	70,000.	—

CLASSIC CHINESE ZODIAC SERIES

TWO THOUSAND FIVE HUNDRED DOLLARS, CLASSIC CHINESE ZODIAC, 2012-2015.

Common Obverse
(Except for date)

2012 Year of the
(Water) Dragon
Des.: Three Degrees Creative
Group Inc.
Eng.: Cecily Mok

Designers and Engravers:
Obv.:	Susanna Blunt, Susan Taylor
Rev.:	See reverse illustrations

Composition:	99.99% Au		
Gold content:	1000.0 g, 32.15 tr oz		
Weight:	1,000.0 g (1 kilo)	**Edge:**	Plain
Diameter:	101.6 mm	**Die Axis:**	↑↑
Thickness:	N/A	**Finish:**	Proof
Case of Issue:	Black clam style case, black insert, encapsulated coin, COA		

2012 Year of the (Classic) Dragon
Des.: Aries Cheung
Eng.: Stan Witten

2013 Year of the Snake
Des.: Three Degrees Creative
Group Inc.
Eng.: RCM Staff

2014 Year of the Horse
Des.: Three Degrees Creative
Group Inc.
Eng.: Stan Witten

2015 Year of the Sheep
Des.: Three Degrees Creative
Group Inc.
Eng.: RCM Staff

DATE	DESCRIPTION	RCM ITEM #	QUANTITY SOLD	ISSUE PRICE	FINISH	PR-69	PR-70
2012	Year of the (Water) Dragon	116723	37	69,000	Proof	70,000.	—
2012	Year of the (Classic) Dragon	N/A	37	69,000	Proof	70,000.	—.
2013	Year of the Snake	120196	37	69,000	Proof	70,000.	—
2014	Year of the Horse	124645	5	69,000	Proof	70,000.	—
2015	Year of the Sheep	130573	11	69.000	Proof	70,000.	—

TWO THOUSAND FIVE HUNDRED DOLLARS, 250TH ANNIVERSARY OF THE END OF THE SEVEN YEARS WAR, 2013.

Designers and Engravers:
Obv.:	Susanna Blunt, Susan Taylor
Rev.:	L. Normandin, RCM Staff

Composition:	99.99% Au		
Gold content:	1000.0 g, 32.15 tr oz		
Weight:	1000.0 g (1 kilo)	**Edge:**	Reeded
Diameter:	102.1 mm	**Die Axis:**	↑↑
Thickness:	N/A	**Finish:**	Proof
Case of Issue:	Maple wood case, black flocked insert, encapsulated coin, COA		

DATE	DESCRIPTION	RCM ITEM #	QUANTITY SOLD	ISSUE PRICE	FINISH	PR-69	PR-70
2013	250th Ann. End of the Seven Years War	123948	12	69,000	Proof	70,000.	—

TWO THOUSAND FIVE HUNDRED DOLLARS, CANADA'S ARCTIC LANDSCAPE, 2013.

Designers and Engravers:

Obv.:	Susanna Blunt, Susan Taylor
Rev.:	W. David Ward, S. Witten

Composition: 99.99% Au
Gold content: 1000.0 g, 32.15 tr oz
Weight: 1000.0 g (1 kilo)   **Edge:** Reeded
Diameter: 102.1 mm   **Die Axis:** ↑↑
Thickness: N/A   **Finish:** Proof
Case of Issue: Maple wood case, black flocked insert, encapsulated coin, COA

DATE	DESCRIPTION	RCM ITEM #	QUANTITY SOLD	ISSUE PRICE	FINISH	PR-69	PR-70
2013	Canada's Arctic Landscape	123807	13	69,000	Proof	70,000.	—

TWO THOUSAND FIVE HUNDRED DOLLARS, 1813 BATTLE OF CRYSLER'S FARM AND BATTLE OF CHATEAUGUAY, 2013.

Designers and Engravers:

Obv.:	Susanna Blunt, Susan Taylor
Rev.:	A. Sherriff-Scott, H. Julie, E. Boyer

Composition: 99.99% Au
Gold content: 1000.0 g, 32.15 tr oz
Weight: 1000.0 g (1 kilo)   **Edge:** Reeded
Diameter: 102.1 mm   **Die Axis:** ↑↑
Thickness: N/A   **Finish:** Proof
Case of Issue: Maple wood case, black flocked insert, encapsulated coin, COA

DATE	DESCRIPTION	RCM ITEM #	QUANTITY SOLD	ISSUE PRICE	FINISH	PR-69	PR-70
2013	1813 Battle of Crysler's Farm and Battle of Chateauguay	125377	10	69,000	Proof	70,000.	—

TWO THOUSAND FIVE HUNDRED DOLLARS, THE CARIBOU, 2013.

Designers and Engravers:

Obv.:	Susanna Blunt, Susan Taylor
Rev.:	T. Tennant, RCM Staff

Composition: 99.99% Au
Gold content: 1000.0 g, 32.15 tr oz
Weight: 1,000.0 g (1 kilo)   **Edge:** Reeded
Diameter: 101.6 mm   **Die Axis:** ↑↑
Thickness: N/A   **Finish:** Proof
Case of Issue: Maple wood case, black insert, encapsulated coin, COA

DATE	DESCRIPTION	RCM ITEM #	QUANTITY SOLD	ISSUE PRICE	FINISH	PR-69	PR-70
2013	The Caribou	127079	8	69,000	Proof	70,000.	—

TWO THOUSAND FIVE HUNDRED DOLLARS, BATTLE OF LUNDY'S LANE, 2014.

Designers and Engravers:

Obv.:	Susanna Blunt, Susan Taylor
Rev.:	Bonnie Ross, RCM Staff

Composition: 99.99% Au
Gold content: 1000.0 g, 32.15 tr oz
Weight: 1,000.0 g (1 kilo)   **Edge:** Reeded
Diameter: 101.6 mm   **Die Axis:** ↑↑
Thickness: N/A   **Finish:** Proof
Case of Issue: Maple wood case, black insert, encapsulated coin, COA

DATE	DESCRIPTION	RCM ITEM #	QUANTITY SOLD	ISSUE PRICE	FINISH	PR-69	PR-70
2014	Battle of Lundy's Lane	130542	10	69,000	Proof	70,000.	—

IN THE EYES OF... SERIES

TWO THOUSAND FIVE HUNDRED DOLLARS, IN THE EYES OF..., 2014-2017.

**Common Obverse
(Except for date)**

Designers and Engravers:
Obv.:	Susanna Blunt, Susan Taylor
Rev.:	See reverse illustrations

Composition: 99.99% Au
Gold content: 1000.0 g, 32.15 tr oz
Weight: 1,000.0 g (1 kilo)   **Edge:** Reeded
Diameter: 101.6 mm   **Die Axis:** ↑↑
Thickness: N/A   **Finish:** Proof
Case of Issue: Maple wood case, black insert, encapsulated coin, COA

In The Eyes of the Snowy Owl
Des.: Arnold Nogy

In The Eyes of the Cougar
Des.: Glen Loates

In The Eyes of the Spirit Bear
Des.: Glen Loates

In The Eyes of the Timber Wolf
Des.: Pierre Leduc

DATE	DESCRIPTION	RCM ITEM #	QUANTITY SOLD	ISSUE PRICE	FINISH	PR-69	PR-70
2014	In the Eyes of the Snowy Owl	129414	10	69,000	Proof	70,000.	—
2015	In the Eyes of the Cougar	141783	10	69,000	Proof	70,000.	—
2016	In the Eyes of the Spirit Bear	150256	10	69,000	Proof	70,000.	—
2017	In the Eyes of the Timber Wolf	154137	10	69,000	Proof	70,000.	—

TWO THOUSAND FIVE HUNDRED DOLLARS, LOONEY TUNES™: ENSEMBLE CAST, 2015.

Designers and Engravers:
Obv.:	Susanna Blunt, Susan Taylor
Rev.:	Warner Bros.

Composition: 99.99% Au
Gold content: 1006.1 g, 32.15 tr oz
Weight: 1,006.1 g (1 kilo)   **Edge:** Reeded
Diameter: 101.6 mm   **Die Axis:** ↑↑
Thickness: N/A   **Finish:** Proof
Case of Issue: Maple wood case, black insert, encapsulated coin, COA

DATE	DESCRIPTION	RCM ITEM #	QUANTITY SOLD	ISSUE PRICE	FINISH	PR-69	PR-70
2015	Looney Tunes™: Ensemble Cast	145004	10	69,000	Proof	70,000.	—

TWO THOUSAND FIVE HUNDRED DOLLARS, MAPLE LEAF FOREVER, 2015-2016.

Common Obverse (Except for date)	2015 Maple Leaf Forever Designer: Celia Godkin	2016 Maple Leaf Forever Designer: Julia Csotonyi

Designers:
Obv.: Susanna Blunt
Rev.: See reverse illustrations
Composition: 99.99% Au
Gold content: 1000.0 g, 32.15 tr oz
Weight: 1,000.0 g (1 kilo)
Diameter: 101.6 mm
Thickness: N/A
Case of Issue: Maple wood case, black insert, encapsulated coin, COA

Engravers:
Obv.: Susan Taylor

Edge: Reeded
Die Axis: ↑↑
Finish: Proof

DATE	DESCRIPTION	RCM ITEM #	QUANTITY SOLD	ISSUE PRICE	FINISH	PR-69	PR-70
2015	Maple Leaf Forever	142884	10	69,000	Proof	70,000.	—
2016	Maple Leaf Forever	153309	10	69,000	Proof	70,000.	—

TWO THOUSAND FIVE HUNDRED DOLLARS, THE ARMS OF CANADA, 2016.

Designers and Engravers:
Obv.: Susanna Blunt, Susan Taylor
Rev.: RCM Staff
Composition: 99.99% Au
Gold content: 1000.0 g, 32.15 tr oz
Weight: 1,000.0 g (1 kilo)
Diameter: 101.6 mm
Thickness: N/A
Case of Issue: Maple wood case, black insert, encapsulated coin, COA

Edge: Reeded
Die Axis: ↑↑
Finish: Proof

DATE	DESCRIPTION	RCM ITEM #	QUANTITY SOLD	ISSUE PRICE	FINISH	PR-69	PR-70
2016	The Arms of Canada	154145	9	69,000	Proof	70,000	—

LUNAR LOTUS SERIES

TWO THOUSAND FIVE HUNDRED DOLLARS, LUNAR LOTUS, 2016-2019.

**Common Obverse
(Except for date)**

Designers and Engravers:

Obv.:	Susanna Blunt, Susan Taylor
Rev.:	Three Degrees Creative Group

Composition: 99.99% Au
Gold content: 1000.0 g, 32.15 tr oz
Weight: 1,000.0 g (1 kilo)   **Edge:** Reeded
Diameter: 120 mm   **Die Axis:** ↑↑
Thickness: N/A   **Finish:** Proof
Case of Issue: Gold satin-like covered case with custom red sleeve, COA

2016 Year of the Monkey   2017 Year of the Rooster   2018 Year of the Dog   2019 Year of the Pig

DATE	DESCRIPTION	RCM ITEM #	MINTAGE	ISSUE PRICE	FINISH	PR-69	PR-70
2016	Year of the Monkey	147011	10	69,000	Proof	70,000.	—
2017	Year of the Rooster	153802	10	69,000	Proof	70,000.	—
2018	Year of the Dog	160862	10	75,000	Proof	75,000.	—
2019	Year of the Pig	165306	10	75,000	Proof	75,000.	—

TWO THOUSAND FIVE HUNDRED DOLLARS, A TRIBUTE TO THE FIRST CANADIAN GOLD COIN, 2017.

Designers and Engravers:

Obv.:	Susanna Blunt, Susan Taylor
Rev.:	W. H. J. Blackmore

Composition: 99.99% Au
Gold content: 1000.0 g, 32.15 tr oz
Weight: 1,000.0 g (1 kilo)   **Edge:** Reeded
Diameter: 101.6 mm   **Die Axis:** ↑↑
Thickness: N/A   **Finish:** Proof
Case of Issue: Wood case, and black beauty box, COA

DATE	DESCRIPTION	RCM ITEM #	MINTAGE	ISSUE PRICE	FINISH	PR-69	PR-70
2017	A Tribute to the First Canadian Gold Coin	162566	20	75,000	Proof	75,000.	—

TWO THOUSAND FIVE HUNDRED DOLLARS, SUGAR MAPLE MAJESTY, 2018.

Designers and Engravers:
Obv.:	Susanna Blunt, Susan Taylor
Rev.:	Maurade Baynton

Composition: 99.99% Au
Gold content: 1000.0 g, 32.35 tr oz
Weight: 1,006.1 g (1 kilo)
Diameter: 101.6 mm
Thickness: N/A
Edge: Reeded
Die Axis: ↑↑
Finish: Proof
Case of Issue: Premium wood case with black beauty box, COA

DATE	DESCRIPTION	RCM ITEM #	MINTAGE	ISSUE PRICE	FINISH	PR-69	PR-70
2018	Sugar Maple Majesty	164094	10	75,000.	Proof	75,000.	—

TWO THOUSAND FIVE HUNDRED DOLLARS, GREAT SEAL OF THE PROVINCE OF CANADA (1841-1867), 2019.

Designers and Engravers:
Obv.:	Susanna Blunt, Susan Taylor
Rev.:	RCM Staff

Composition: 99.99% Au
Gold content: 1000.0 g, 32.35 tr oz
Weight: 1,006.1 g (1 kilo)
Diameter: 101.6 mm
Thickness: N/A
Edge: Reeded
Die Axis: ↑↑
Finish: Proof
Case of Issue: Premium wood case with black beauty box, COA

DATE	DESCRIPTION	RCM ITEM #	MINTAGE	ISSUE PRICE	FINISH	PR-69	PR-70
2019	Great Seal of the Province of Canada	170375	15	75,000	Proof	75,000.	—

ONE HUNDRED THOUSAND DOLLAR GOLD COIN

ONE HUNDRED THOUSAND DOLLARS, THE SPIRIT OF HAIDA GWAII, 2011

The Spirit of Haida Gwaii is the world's first 10,000 kilogram gold coin of 99.999% purity. The design features Bill Reid's monumental sculpture which was commissioned for the courtyard of the new Canadian Embassy which was being built in Washington. The Spirit of Haida Gwaii was completed and installed in 1992, subtitled The Black Canoe. The bronze casting was given a glossy black patina to give the appearance of argillite. The sculpture is 6.05 m long, 3.9 m high, 3.35 m wide and weighs 4.9 kg. A duplicate sculpture was commissioned by the Vancouver International Airport, with a green patina, in recognition of the dark green jade found in British Columbia. The Jade Canoe was completed in 1994.

Designers:
Obv.:	Susanna Blunt
Rev.:	Bill Reid

Engravers:
Obv.:	Susan Taylor
Rev.:	Cosme Saffioti

Composition: 99.999% Au
Gold content: 10,000.0 g, 321.50 tr oz
Weight: 10,000.0 g (10 kilos)
Diameter: 180.0 mm
Thickness: N/A
Edge: Reeded
Die Axis: ↑↑
Finish: Proof
Case of Issue: Walnut wood case, certificate in book format

DATE	DESCRIPTION	RCM ITEM #	MINTAGE	ISSUE PRICE	FINISH	PR-69	PR-70
2011	The Spirit of Haida Gwaii, 321.50 tr oz	N/A	2	BV	Proof	Market Value	—

Note:
1. An identical design is utilized on the $500 silver coin for 2012, see page 407.
2. Coin illustrated smaller than actual size.
3. Price is subject to the price of gold plus a premium on the day of purchase or sale.

GOLD AND SILVER SETS

TEN DOLLAR GOLD AND EIGHT DOLLAR SILVER POLAR BEAR SET, 2013.

  **Ten Dollars Gold**  **Eight Dollars Silver**

Designers:
Obv.: Susanna Blunt
Rev.: Germaine Arnaktauyok

$10 Gold
Composition: 99.99% Au
Gold content: 7.97 g, 0.25 tr oz
Weight: 7.97 g
Diameter: 20.0 mm
Thickness: 1.7 mm
Edge: Reeded
Die Axis: ↑↑
Finish: Proof
Case of Issue: Maple wood box, black flock insert, encapsulated coins, COA

Engravers:
Rev.: Susan Taylor
Rev.: RCM Staff

$8 Silver
Composition: 99.99% Ag
Silver content: 46.65 g, 1.5 tr oz
Weight: 46.65 g
Diameter: 38.0 mm
Thickness: 4.5 mm
Edge: Reeded
Die Axis: ↑↑
Finish: Proof

DATE	DESCRIPTION	RCM ITEM #	QUANTITY SOLD	ISSUE PRICE	FINISH	PR-69	PR-70
2013	$10 Gold & $8 Silver, Polar Bear Set	129880	4,832	774.95	Proof	650.	—

FIVE DOLLAR GOLD AND TWENTY DOLLAR SILVER WOOLLY MAMMOTH, 2014.

 Five Dollars Gold  **Twenty Dollars Silver**

Designers:
Obv.: Susanna Blunt
Rev.: Michael Skrepnick

$5 Gold
Composition: 99.99% Au
Gold content: 3.14 g, 0.10 tr oz
Weight: 3.14 g
Diameter: 16.0 mm
Thickness: N/A
Edge: Reeded
Die Axis: ↑↑
Finish: Proof
Case of Issue: Maroon leatherette clam style case, black flocked insert, encapsulated coin(s), COA

Engravers:
Obv.: Susan Taylor
Rev.: RCM Staff

$20 Silver
Composition: 99.99% Ag
Silver content: 31.39 g, 1.01 tr oz
Weight: 31.39 g
Diameter: 38.0 mm
Thickness: N/A
Edge: Reeded
Die Axis: ↑↑
Finish: Proof

DATE	DESCRIPTION	RCM ITEM #	QUANTITY SOLD	ISSUE PRICE	FINISH	PR-69	PR-70
2014	$5 Gold & $20 Silver, Woolly Mammoth Set	141852	3,000	369.95	Proof	280.	—

PALLADIUM COINS

FIFTY DOLLAR PALLADIUM COINS

FIFTY DOLLARS, BIG AND LITTLE BEAR CONSTELLATIONS, 2006.

Each coin has been crafted with a special laser effect to illustrate the position of Big Bear and Little Bear constellations above a conceptual Canadian forest, as they would appear when viewed from the nation's capital during each of the four seasons.

Common Obverse

Designers and Engravers:

Obv.:	Susanna Blunt, Susan Taylor
Rev.:	Colin Mayne, José Osio
Composition:	99.95% Pd, Laser effect
Palladium content:	31.144 g, 1.0 tr oz
Weight:	31.16 g
Diameter:	34.0 mm
Thickness:	3.5 mm
Edge:	Reeded
Die Axis:	↑↑
Finish:	Specimen
Case of Issue:	Maroon clam style case; black flocked insert, encapsulated coin, COA

| Spring | Summer | Autumn | Winter |

DATE	DESCRIPTION	RCM ITEM #	QUANTITY SOLD	ISSUE PRICE	FINISH	SP-68	SP-69
2006	Spring	N/A	300	849.95	Specimen	1,700.	—
2006	Summer	N/A	300	849.95	Specimen	1,700.	—
2006	Autumn	N/A	300	849.95	Specimen	1,700.	—
2006	Winter	N/A	300	849.95	Specimen	1,700.	—

PLATINUM COINS

FIVE DOLLAR PLATINUM COINS

FIVE DOLLARS, COMMEMORATIVE PLATINUM COINS, 2014.

Actual Size

Common Obverse

Portrait Nanaboozhoo
Des.: C. Assiniboine

Bald Eagle
Des.: D. Wicks

**Overlaid Majestic
Maple Leaves
Des.: P. Leduc**

**Cougar
Des.: G. Loates**

Designers:		Engravers:	
Obv.:	Susanna Blunt	Obv.:	Susan Taylor
Rev.:	See reverse illustrations	Rev.:	RCM Staff
Composition:	99.95% Pt		
Gold content:	3.13 g, 0.10 tr oz		
Weight:	3.13 g	**Edge:**	Reeded
Diameter:	16.0 mm	**Die Axis:**	↑↑
Thickness:	N/A	**Finish:**	Proof
Case of Issue:	Maroon leatherette clam style case, black flocked insert, encapsulated coin, COA		

DATE	DESCRIPTION	RCM ITEM #	QUANTITY SOLD	ISSUE PRICE	FINISH	PR-69	PR-70
2014	Portrait of Nanaboozhoo	132393	2,400	299.95	Proof	260.	—
2014	Bald Eagle	132668	1,638	299.95	Proof	260.	—
2014	Overlaid Majestic Maple Leaves	132688	1090	299.95	Proof	260.	—
2014	Cougar	130610	687	299.95	Proof	275.	—

Note: 1.   The $5 platinum Overlaid Majestic Maple Leaves coin was offered as part of a five coin subscription along with a $20 Silver Majestic Maple Leaves, a $20 Majestic Maple Leaves with colour, and a $20 Majestic Maple Leaves with Jade (see page 290), as well as a $5 gold Overlaid Majestic Maple Leaves coin (see page 416).

   2.   The Bald Eagle was also offered as part of a subscription series which included three twenty dollar coins (see page 272), and a five dollar gold coin (see page 416).

THREE HUNDRED DOLLAR PLATINUM COINS

THREE HUNDRED DOLLARS, COMMEMORATIVE PLATINUM COINS, 2007-2016.

2007-2008	2009-2015	2012, 2014	2013	2015 Common Obverse
Obverse With RCM Logo	Obv. Without RCM Logo	Common Obverse	Common Obverse	Des.: Susanna Blunt
				Engr.: Susan Taylor

2007	2008	2009	2010	2011
Woolly Mammoth	Scimitar Cat	Steppe Bison	Ground Sloth	Cougar
Des.: RCM Staff	Des.: RCM Staff	Des. RCM Staff	Des.: Jerri Burnett	Des.: William Woodruff
Engr.: José Osio	Engr.: Christie Paquet	Engr.: José Osio	Engr.: Stan Witten	Engr.: RCM Staff
	Obv. Without RCM Logo			

2012	2013	2013 Rocky Mountain	2013 HMS Shannon and	2014
The Bull Moose	The Bald Eagle	Bighorn Sheep	USS Chesapeake	Challenge for Power
Des.: Robert Bateman	Des.: Claudio D'Angelo	Des.: Emily Damstra	Des.: Luc Normandin	Des.: Claudio D'Angelo
Engr.: Cecily Mok	Engr.: Konrad Wachelko	Engr.: Steven Stewart	Engr.: Cecily Mok	Engr.: RCM Staff

2014 Emily Carr	2015	2015	2015	2016
A Skidegate Beaver Pole	Grizzly Bear	Rainbow Trout	White-Tailed Deer	Grizzly Bear: The Struggle
Des.: Emily Carr	Des.: Emily Damstra	Des.: C. Atwater	Des.: D. McCaffrey	Des.: Lauren Crawshaw
Engr.: RCM Staff	Engr.: RCM Staff	Engr.: RCM Staff	Engr.: RCM Staff	Engr.: RCM Staff

THREE HUNDRED DOLLARS, COMMEMORATIVE PLATINUM COINS, 2007-2016 (cont.).

Designers:
  Obv.: Susanna Blunt
  Rev.: See reverse illustrations
Composition: 99.95% Pt
Platinum content: 31.15 g, 1.00 tr oz
Weight: 31.15 g
Diameter: 30.0 mm
Thickness: 2.5 mm
Case of Issue: Maroon leatherette clam style case, black flocked insert, encapsulated coin, COA

Engravers:
  Obv.: Susan Taylor
  Rev.: See reverse illustrations

Edge: Reeded
Die Axis: ↑↑
Finish: Proof

DATE	DESCRIPTION	RCM ITEM #	QUANTITY SOLD	ISSUE PRICE	FINISH	PR-69	PR-70
2007	Woolly Mammoth	N/A	287	2,999.95	Proof	2,500.	—
2008	Scimitar Cat	101580	200	3,419.95	Proof	2,500.	—
2009	Steppe Bison	105866	197	2,999.95	Proof	2,500.	—
2010	Ground Sloth	110317	189	2,999.95	Proof	2,500.	—
2011	Cougar	115941	183	2,999.95	Proof	2,500.	—
2012	The Bull Moose	120904	250	2,999.95	Proof	2,500.	—
2013	Rocky Mountain Bighorn Sheep	123627	188	2,999.95	Proof	2,500.	—
2013	The Bald Eagle	123472	199	2,999.95	Proof	2,500.	—
2013	HMS Shannon and USS Chesapeake	123722	231	2,999.95	Proof	2,500.	—
2014	Bison: Challenge for Power	126398	24	2,999.95	Proof	2,500.	—
2014	Emily Carr: *A Skidegate Beaver Pole*	N/A	250	N.I.I.	Proof	2,500.	—
2015	Grizzly Bear	130594	138	2,999.95	Proof	2,500.	—
2015	The White-Tailed Deer	130636	187	2,999.95	Proof	2,500.	—
2015	Rainbow Trout: North American Sportfish	143924	200	2,999.95	Proof	2,500.	—
2016	Grizzly Bear: The Struggle	145432	150	2,999.95	Proof	3,000.	—

SPECIAL RCM WRAPPED ROLLS OF COINS

Specialty Rolls are generated by the Royal Canadian Mint printing a specially designed wrapper for a standard roll of a denomination.

DATE	DENOMINATION	DESCRIPTION	RCM ITEM #	QUANTITY SOLD	PRICE
2004P	One Cent	Standard, CPS, Roll of 50	N/A	N/A	8.
2004	One Cent	Standard, CPZ, Roll of 50	N/A	N/A	10.
2005	One Cent	Standard, CPZ, Roll of 50	N/A	N/A	10.
2005P	One Cent	Standard, CPS, Roll of 50	N/A	N/A	15.
2012	One Cent	Farewell to the Penny, Roll of 50	121588	20,000	80.
2005P	Five Cents	Standard, Roll of 40	N/A	N/A	8.
2005P	Five Cents	V-E Day, Roll of 40	N/A	N/A	10.
2005P	Ten Cents	Standard, Roll of 50	N/A	N/A	10.
2004P	Twenty-Five Cents	Poppy, Roll of 40	N/A	N/A	25.
2005P	Twenty-Five Cents	Standard, Roll of 40	N/A	N/A	18.
2005P	Twenty-Five Cents	Alberta, Roll of 40	N/A	N/A	20.
2005P	Twenty-Five Cents	Saskatchewan, Roll of 40	N/A	N/A	20.
2005P	Twenty-Five Cents	Veteran, Roll of 40	N/A	N/A	20.
2006P	Twenty-Five Cents	Breast Cancer, Roll of 40	N/A	102	25.
2006P	Twenty-Five Cents	Standard, Roll of 40	N/A	N/A	18.
2006P	Twenty-Five Cents	Bravery, Roll of 40	N/A	205	20.
2007	Twenty-Five Cents	Curling, Roll of 40	9943107	10,000	18.
2007	Twenty-Five Cents	Ice Hockey, Roll of 40	9943117	10,000	18.
2007	Twenty-Five Cents	Biathlon, Roll of 40	9943137	10,000	18.
2007	Twenty-Five Cents	Alpine Skiing, Roll of 40	9943147	10,000	18.
2007	Twenty-Five Cents	Wheelchair Curling, Roll of 40	9943127	10,000	18.
2008	Twenty-Five Cents	Snowboarding, Roll of 40	9943108	10,000	18.
2008	Twenty-Five Cents	Freestyle Skiing, Roll of 40	9943118	10,000	18.
2008	Twenty-Five Cents	Figure Skating, Roll of 40	9943128	10,000	18.
2008	Twenty-Five Cents	Bobsleigh, Roll of 40	9943138	10,000	18.
2009	Twenty-Five Cents	Speedskating, Roll of 40	9943109	10,000	18.
2009	Twenty-Five Cents	Cross Country Skiing, Roll of 40	9943119	10,000	18.
2009	Twenty-Five Cents	Ice Sledge Hockey, Roll of 40	9943129	10,000	18.
2017	Twenty-Five Cents	125th Anniversary of the Stanley Cup	155955	50,000	20.
2005P	Fifty Cents	Roll of 25	N/A	8,000	35.
2006P	Fifty Cents	Roll of 25	N/A	3,920	50.
2007	Fifty Cents	Roll of 25	N/A	4,462	40.
2008	Fifty Cents	Roll of 25	N/A	6,000	35.
2009	Fifty Cents	Roll of 25	104108	6,000	45.
2010	Fifty Cents	Roll of 25	109710	6,000	45.
2011	Fifty Cents	Roll of 25	112208	6,880	45.
2012	Fifty Cents	Roll of 25	116547	9,960	45.
2013	Fifty Cents	Roll of 25	121760	15,000	30.
2014	Fifty Cents	Roll of 25	127965	20,000	25.
2015	Fifty Cents	Roll of 25	135180	25,000	25.
2016	Fifty Cents	Roll of 25	147982	24,829	25.
2017	Fifty Cents	Coat of Arms of Canada	157747	35,000	25.
2017	Fifty Cents	Canada 150 Official Logo	157747	35,000	25.
2018	Fifty Cents	Roll of 25	163763	30,000	25.
2019	Fifty Cents	Roll of 25	168248	30,000	25.

SPECIAL RCM WRAPPED ROLLS OF COINS (cont.)

2017
Special Wrap Roll
My Canada,
My Inspiration

2018
Special Wrap Roll
First Strikes
in 2018

DATE	DENOMINATION	DESCRIPTION	RCM ITEM #	QUANTITY SOLD	PRICE
2004	One Dollar	Olympic Flame, Roll of 25	N/A	N/A	40.
2005	One Dollar	Loon, Roll of 25	N/A	N/A	40.
2005	One Dollar	Terry Fox, Roll of 25	N/A	N/A	50.
2008	One Dollar	Loon Dance, Roll of 25	9943148	10,000	40.
2009	One Dollar	Montreal Canadiens, Roll of 25	105300	10,000	50.
2010	One Dollar	Inukshuk, Roll of 25	99431010	10,000	40.
2016	One Dollar	Lucky Loonie, Roll of 25	154463	52,000	40.
2017	One Dollar	100th Ann. of the Toronto Maple Leafs	165453	50,000	50.
2019	One Dollar	Equality	168168	15,000	55.
1996	Two Dollars	Polar Bear, Roll of 25	N/A	N/A	100.
2004	Two Dollars	Polar Bear, Roll of 25	N/A	N/A	70.
2005	Two Dollars	Polar Bear, Roll of 25	N/A	N/A	80.
2006	Two Dollars	Double Date, Roll of 25	N/A	356	100.
2006	Two Dollars	Churchill, Roll of 25	N/A	N/A	70.
2008	Two Dollars	Quebec City, Roll of 25	N/A	N/A	80.
2011	Two Dollars	Polar Bear, Roll of 25	N/A	N/A	80.
2017	Two Dollars	The Battle of Vimy Ridge	165436	10,000	80.
2018	Two Dollars	Armistice	167480	10,000	80.
2019	Two Dollars	D-Day (non-coloured)	174707	5,000	80.
2019	Two Dollars	D-Day (coloured)	172968	15,000	80.
2017	Special Wrap Roll Collection (5¢, 10¢, 25¢ x2, $1, $2 x2)	My Canada, My Inspiration	157556	10,000	185.
2017	Special Wrap Roll Collection (5¢, 10¢, 25¢, $1, $2)	Classic Canadian	156025	10,000	185.
2018	Special Wrap Collection First Strikes in 2018	Classic Canadian	167062	5,000	185.
2019	Special Wrap Roll Collection First Strikes in 2019	Classic Canadian	170353	5,000	130.

FIRST AND LAST DAY OF ISSUE CARDS

DATE	DENOMINATION	DESCRIPTION	QUANTITY SOLD	PRICE
2005P	One Cent	Standard, CPS, First Day	1,919	10.
2006P / 2006	One Cent	Standard, CPS, Last Day / First Day	750	20.
2005P	Five Cents	Standard, First Day	1,951	10.
2006P / 2006	Five Cents	Standard, Last Day / First Day	739	10.
2006P	Five Cents	Victory, First Day	11,192	8.
2005P	Ten Cents	Standard, First Day	1,961	8.
2006P / 2006	Ten Cents	Standard, Last Day / First Day	742	10.
2004P	Twenty-Five Cents	Poppy, Coloured	N/A	12.
2005P	Twenty-Five Cents	Standard, First Day	5,000	8.
2005P	Twenty-Five Cents	Alberta, First Day	9,108	8.
2005P	Twenty-Five Cents	Saskatchewan, First Day	6,980	8.
2005P	Twenty-Five Cents	Veteran, First Day	8,361	8.
2006P / 2006	Twenty-Five Cents	Standard, Last Day / First Day	742	8.
2006P	Twenty-Five Cents	Breast Cancer, First Day	7,348	8.
2006	Twenty-Five Cents	Bravery, First Day	4,906	8.
2007	Twenty-Five Cents	Curling, First Day	10,000	5.
2007	Twenty-Five Cents	Ice Hockey, First Day	10,000	5.
2007	Twenty-Five Cents	Biathlon, First Day	10,000	5.
2007	Twenty-Five Cents	Alpine Skiing, First Day	10,000	5.
2007	Twenty-Five Cents	Wheelchair Curling, First Day	10,000	5.
2008	Twenty-Five Cents	Snowboarding, First Day	10,000	5.
2008	Twenty-Five Cents	Freestyle Skiing, First Day	10,000	5.
2008	Twenty-Five Cents	Figure Skating, First Day	10,000	5.
2008	Twenty-Five Cents	Bobsleigh, First Day	10,000	5.
2009	Twenty-Five Cents	Speed Skating, First Day	10,000	5.
2009	Twenty-Five Cents	Cross Country Skiing, First Day	10,000	5.
2009	Twenty-Five Cents	Ice Sledge Hockey, First Day	10,000	5.
2005P	Fifty Cents	Standard, First Day	2,445	12.
2006P / 2006	Fifty Cents	Standard, Last Day / First Day	1,065	15.
2004	One Dollar	Standard, First Day	34,488	5.
2005	One Dollar	Standard, First Day	2,048 1	5.
2005	One Dollar	Terry Fox, First Day	19,933	10.
2006	One Dollar	Standard, Last Day / First Day	935	15.
2006	One Dollar	Loon Settling, First Day	7,481	15.
2008	One Dollar	Loon Dance, First Day	10,000	15.
2010	One Dollar	Lucky Loonie, First Day	4,252	12.
2005	Two Dollars	Standard, First Day	2,501	12.
2006	Two Dollars	Standard, Last Day / First Day	1,971	12.
2006	Two Dollars	10th Anniversary, First Day	1,971	12.

BOOKMARKS

Snowboarding
Bookmark and
Lapel Pin

Ice Hockey
Bookmark and
Lapel Pin

DATE	DENOMINATION	DESCRIPTION	QUANTITY SOLD	PRICE
2004P	Twenty-Five Cents	Poppy, Coloured	29,951	25.
2005P	Twenty-Five Cents	Poppy, Coloured	N/A	25.
2006P	Twenty-Five Cents	Breast Cancer	40,911	25.
2007	Twenty-Five Cents	Curling	N/A	8.
2007	Twenty-Five Cents	Ice Hockey	N/A	8.
2007	Twenty-Five Cents	Biathlon	N/A	8.
2007	Twenty-Five Cents	Alpine Skiing	N/A	8.
2007	Twenty-Five Cents	Wheelchair Curling	N/A	8.
2008	Twenty-Five Cents	Snowboarding	N/A	8.
2008	Twenty-Five Cents	Freestyle Skiing	N/A	8.
2008	Twenty-Five Cents	Figure Skating	N/A	8.
2008	Twenty-Five Cents	Bobsleigh	N/A	8.
2008	Twenty-Five Cents	Armistice	N/A	15.
2009	Twenty-Five Cents	Speed Skating	N/A	8.
2009	Twenty-Five Cents	Cross Country Skiing	N/A	8.
2009	Twenty-Five Cents	Ice Sledge Hockey	N/A	8.

COLLECTOR CARDS FOR CIRCULATION COINAGE, 2004-2018

2004 "Lest We Forget" The Poppy Coin Collector Card

DATE	DESCRIPTION	RCM ITEM #	QUANTITY SOLD	ISSUE PRICE	FINISH	MS-65
2004	**Lucky Loonie Coin Collector Card** to hold Standard 5 coins, Lucky Loonie $1	N/A	N/A	Free	Empty	5.
2004	**"Lest We Forget" Poppy Coin Collector Card** to hold Standard 5 coins, Poppy 25¢		21,738	Free	Empty	5.
2004	**400th Anniversary First French Settlement Collector Card** to hold Standard 5 coins, Île Sainte-Croix 25¢		N/A	Free	Empty	5.
2005	**Alberta Centennial Collector Card** to hold Standard 5 coins, Alberta 25¢		N/A	Free	Empty	5.
2005	**Saskatchewan Centennial Collector Card** to hold Standard 5 coins, Saskatchewan 25¢		N/A	Free	Empty	5.
2005	**"Canada Celebrates Peace" Victory Anniversary Collector Card** to hold Standard 5 coins, 1945-2005 Victory 5¢		N/A	Free	Empty	5.
2005	**Year of the Veteran Collector Card** to hold Standard 5 coins, Veteran 25¢		N/A	Free	Empty	5.
2005	**Terry Fox Coin Collector Card** to hold Standard 5 coins, Terry Fox $1		N/A	Free	Empty	5.
2005	**Creating a Future Without Breast Cancer 25-Cent Collector Card** to hold Standard 5 coins, Breast Cancer 25¢		N/A	Free	Empty	5.
2006	**Lucky Loonie Collector Card** to hold Standard 5 coins, 2006 Lucky Loonie $1		N/A	Free	Empty	5.
2006	**10th Anniversary Toonie Collector Card** to hold Standard 5 coins, Churchill $2		N/A	Free	Empty	5.
2006	**Medal of Bravery Collector Card** to hold Standard 5 coins, Medal of Bravery 25¢		N/A	Free	Empty	5.
2006	**Creating a Future without Breast Cancer Coin Collector Card** to hold Standard 5 coins, Breast Cancer 25¢		N/A	Free	Empty	5.
2007-2010	**Vancouver Landscape** display card holding 10 Olympic and 2 Paralympic 25¢ coins; $1 Loon Dance, $1 Inukshuk		48,198	29.95	Uncirculed	15.
2007-2010	**Vancouver City** display card holding 10 Olympic and 2 Paralympic 25¢ coins; $1 Loon Dance, $1 Inukshuk		47,691	29.95	Uncirculated	15.
2007-2010	**Vancouver Skier** display card holding 10 Olympic and 2 Paralympic 25¢ coins; $1 Loon Dance, $1 Lucky Loonie		46,361	29.95	Uncirculated	15.
2007-2010	**Inukshuk** display card holding 10 Olympic and 2 Paralympic 25¢ coins; $1 Loon Dance, $1 Inukshuk		111,283	29.95	Uncirculated	15.
2010	**Canoe Coin Collector Card** holds Standard six coins (1¢–$2)		1,466	19.95	Uncirculated	15.
2010	**Maple Leaves Coin Collector Card** holds Standard six coins (1¢–$2)		2,734	19.95	Uncirculated	15.
2010	**Polar Bear Coin Collector Card** holds Standard six coins (1¢–$2)		2,127	19.95	Uncirculated	15.

COLLECTOR CARDS FOR CIRCULATION COINAGE, 2004-2018 (cont.).

2017 Canada 150
Collector Card

DATE	DESCRIPTION	RCM ITEM #	QUANTITY SOLD	ISSUE PRICE	FINISH	MS-65
2010	**RCMP Coin Collector Card** holds Standard six coins (1¢ – $2)		13,036	19.95	Uncirculated	15.
2010	**11-sided Red Maple Vancouver 2010 Olympic Winter Games Display Card** to hold 10 Olympic and 2 Paralympic 25¢ coins; 2008 Loon Dance $1; and 2010 Inukshuk $1		104,400	4.95	Empty	5.
2010	**11-sided Red Maple Vancouver 2010 Olympic Winter Games Display Card** holding 10 Olympic and 2 Paralympic 25¢; 2008 Loon Dance $1; 2010 Inukshuk $1		164,295	29.95	Uncirculated	20.
2010	**Vancouver 2010 Olympic Winter Games Collector Card**, to hold 10 Olympic/2 Paralympic 25¢; 2008 Loon Dance $1; 2010 Inukshuk $1		N/A	Free	Empty	5.
2010	**Remembrance Day Collector Card** contains the 2010 25¢ Remembrance Day coin, two die-cut holes to hold the 2004 and 2008 25¢ Poppy coins; Postage paid postcard		21,738	9.95	Uncirculated	10.
2011	**Our Legendary Nature Collector Card** to hold 8 coins, 2011 $2 Boreal Forest, $1 Parks Canada, 2011 25¢ coloured and plain Peregrine Falcon, Orca Whale and Wood Bison		N/A	Free	Empty	5.
2011	**CN Tower Coin Collector Card** holds Standard six coins (1¢–$2)		6,064	19.95	Uncirculated	15.
2011	**Vancouver Coin Collector Card** holds Standard six coins (1¢–$2)		3,784	19.95	Uncirculated	15.
2012	**The War of 1812 Collector Card** to hold 9 coins, 2012 $1 HMS Shannon, 2012 25¢ coloured and plain Brock, Tecumseh, de Salaberry and Secord		N/A	Free	Empty	5.
2013	**Heart of the Arctic Collector Card** to hold four 25¢ coins, two Canadian Arctic Expedition Centennial and two Arctic Symbols		N/A	Free	Empty	5.
2013	**$20 For $20 Collector Card** to hold four 2013 $20 For $20 coins		N/A	1.00.	Empty	5.
2014	**"Wait For Me, Daddy" Collector Card** to hold one $2 "Wait For Me, Daddy" coin		N/A	Free	Empty	5.
2015	**Sir John A. Macdonald Collector Card** to hold one $2 coin issued in his honour		N/A	Free	Empty	5.
2015	**Flag 50th Anniversary Collector Card** to hold one of each 25¢ coloured and non-coloured		N/A	Free	Empty	5.
2017	**My Canada, My Inspiration Collector Card** to hold 5 coins, glow-in-the-dark $2, $1, coloured 25¢, 10¢, 5¢		N/A	19.95	Uncirculated	20.
2017	**Canada 150 Circulation Collection** to hold 7 coins, glow-in-the-dark $2, $2 plain, $1, coloured 25¢, 25¢ plain, 10¢, 5¢		N/A	34.95	Uncirculated	35.
2017	**My Canada, My Inspiration Collector Card** to hold all Canada 150 coins.		N/A	Free	Empty	5
2018	**Armistice Collector Card** to hold 6 coins: $2 with engraved poppy, $2 with engraved colour poppy, $1, 25¢, 10¢, 5¢		WSL	21.95	Uncirculated	22.

PROOF-LIKE SETS 1954-1967

SIX COIN SILVER PROOF-LIKE SETS, 1954-1960

The year 1953 saw the first use of the white cardboard six-coin holder that in 1954 became the package for public sale of sets. The holder with the coins included was wrapped in cellophane. The finish on the coins offered acquired the name Proof-like.

Prior to public sale of the 1954 Proof-like set, W. C. Ronson, the Mint Master at the time (1947-1953), ordered specially struck coins as samples, or gifts. It is during the 1947-1953 period that you find a broad sample of coins of various finishes. Please see Canadian Coins, Volume One.

1954-1959

1960

In 1960 the white cardboard holders appeared with a Royal Canadian Mint domicile. Four varieties of stamps exist. A sealed wooden box containing 250 Proof-like sets was available directly from the Mint in 1960.

ROYAL CANADIAN MINT
320 SUSSEX DRIVE
OTTAWA 2, ONTARIO.

Stamp One

ROYAL CANADIAN MINT
OTTAWA   CANADA

Stamp Two

ROYAL CANADIAN MINT
OTTAWA   CANADA

Stamp Three

ROYAL CANADIAN MINT
320 SUSSEX DRIVE
OTTAWA 2, ONTARIO.

Stamp Four

DATE	QUANTITY SOLD	ISSUE PRICE	FINISH	PL-65
1954 NSF	3,000	2.50	Proof-like	2,600.
1954 SF	Included	2.50	Proof-like	850.
1955	6,300	2.50	Proof-like	500.
1955 ARN	Included	2.50	Proof-like	675.
1956	6,500	2.50	Proof-like	275.
1957	11,862	2.50	Proof-like	200.
1957 1WL	Included	2.50	Proof-like	275.
1958	18,259	2.50	Proof-like	175.
1959	31,577	3.00	Proof-like	90.
1960	64,097	3.00	Proof-like	70.

NOTES ON 1954 TO 1960 PROOF-LIKE SETS

1. The 1954 No Shoulder Fold designation applies only to the one cent coin; the balance of the coins (5) are of the Shoulder Fold variety.
2. Proof-like-65 prices are for sets in their original packaging.
3. The single denomination proof-like coins have now been incorporated into the pricing tables in the circulating coinage section of *Volume One*.
4 Prices are for sets that have nice full red pennies. Sets that have toned or impaired pennies should be discounted.

SIX COIN SILVER PROOF-LIKE SETS, 1961-1967

In 1961 a new system of packaging sets was introduced. The six coins were heat sealed between two layers of pliofilm which was embossed with the words ROYAL CANADIAN MINT. The set was then inserted in an envelope along with an explanatory card.

1961-1967

DATE	QUANTITY SOLD	ISSUE PRICE	FINISH	PL-65
1961	98,373	3.00	Proof-like (PL)	55.
1962	200,950	3.00	Proof-like (PL)	40.
1963	673,006	3.00	Proof-like (PL)	30.
1964	1,653,162	3.00	Proof-like (PL)	30.
1965 Type 1 $1	2,904,352	4.00	Proof-like (PL)	30.
1965 Type 2 $1	Included	4.00	Proof-like (PL)	30.
1965 Type 3 1¢	Included	4.00	Proof-like (PL)	100.
1966 LB	672,514	4.00	Proof-like (PL)	30.
1967 5¢ ↑↑	963,714	4.00	Proof-like (PL)	35.
1967 5¢ ↑↓	Included	4.00	Proof-like (PL)	500.

NOTES ON 1961 TO 1967 PROOF-LIKE SETS

1. The 1961 set, which of course was the first set packaged in the pliofilm, did not come without problems. The one cent coin was prone to discolouring, making a brilliant, red PL-65 cent a scarcity.
2. Only Types One, Small Bead, Pointed 5 and Type 2, Small Bead, Blunt 5, 1965 silver dollars were used in the assembly of proof-like sets for that year.
3. The following variety combinations will be found in the 1965 proof-like sets.
   A. Type 1 dollar with Type 1 cent
   B. Type 1 dollar with Type 3 cent
   C. Type 2 dollar with Type 1 cent
   D. Type 2 dollar with Type 3 cent
4. Since they were not officially released, no 1966 small bead dollars were issued in proof-like sets.
5. A very limited number of 1967 Proof-like sets contain a striking variety: a coinage (↑↓) five cent coin.

BRILLIANT UNCIRCULATED and UNCIRCULATED SETS, 1968-2006

SIX COIN NICKEL BRILLIANT UNCIRCULATED SETS, 1968-1987

This is a continuation of the silver proof-like sets previously offered, except that the 10 cents through one-dollar coins were now nickel in composition. Naturally, the one cent and five cents remained the same, and the pliofilm packaging continued. The outer envelope was white with blue printing. The finish on the coins in the sets is brilliant uncirculated (MS-65-NC): brilliant relief on brilliant background.

The qualities of the coins in the sets were mixed but by 1977 the quality began to improve, probably as a result of the purchase of numismatic presses in 1972 to produce Canada's first officially recognised proof coins for the Montreal Olympic sets. The finish on the coins in the sets was now advertised by the Royal Canadian Mint as brilliant relief against a brilliant background. In 1980 the Mint's marketing department began a restructuring of the selection of sets and coins offered to collectors with the result the Mint Set was officially called "The Brilliant Uncirculated Set.". This set featured one coin of each denomination issued for circulation in Canada. The quality improvement which began in 1977 continued with the 1981 introduction of a confirmed finish on the pliofilm set of "brilliant relief on brilliant background."

In 1985 the Mint experimented with a clear hard plastic package to replace the soft pliofilm package used in previous years. As it did not prove to be practical, the experimental package was not adopted. The last year the nickel voyageur dollar was used in the brilliant uncirculated sets was 1987.

Pliofilm packaging, 1968-1987

1973 TWENTY-FIVE CENT VARIETIES IN SETS

1973 Large Bust
Beads near rim

1973 Small Bust
Beads far from rim

1974 NICKEL DOLLAR VARIETIES IN SETS

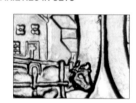

1974 Double Yoke
Doubled Die, Variety 1

1974 Double Yoke
Doubled Die, Variety 3

1968 NICKEL DOLLAR VARIETIES IN SETS

Normal Island Small Island

Small Island (S Is)

No Island (N Is) 1968

Double Waterlines
Doubled Die (DD)

DATE	QUANTITY SOLD	ISSUE PRICE	FINISH	PL-65 NC
1968	521,641	4.00	PL	5.
1968 S. Is.	Included	4.00	PL	60.
1968 No Is.	Included	4.00	PL	15.
1968 DD	Included	4.00	PL	40.
1969	326,203	4.00	PL	5.
1970	349,120	4.00	PL	7.
1971	253,311	4.00	PL	7.
1972	224,275	4.00	PL	7.
1973 L.B.	243,695	4.00	PL	350.
1973 S.B.	Included	4.00	PL	7.
1974	213,589	5.00	PL	7.
1974 Var. 1	Included	5.00	PL	900.
1974 Var. 3	Included	5.00	PL	1,100.

1975 NICKEL DOLLAR VARIETIES IN SETS

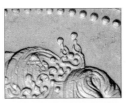

1975 Attached Jewels (AJ)

1975 Detached Jewels (DJ)

1978 FIFTY CENT VARIETIES IN SETS

1978 Reverse
Square Jewels (SJ)

1978 Reverse
Round Jewels (RJ)

1976 NICKEL DOLLAR VARIETIES IN SETS

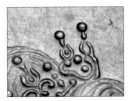

1976 Attached Jewels (AJ)

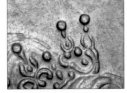

1976 Detached Jewels (DJ)

1977 NICKEL DOLLAR VARIETIES IN SETS

1977 Attached Jewels (AJ)

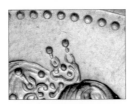

1977 Detached Jewels (DJ)

1977 Full Water Lines

1977 Short Water Lines

DATE	QUANTITY SOLD	ISSUE PRICE	FINISH	PL-65 NC
1975 AJ, FWL	197,372	5.00	PL	10.
1975 DJ, FWL	Included	5.00	PL	10.
1976 AJ, FWL	171,737	5.15	PL	40.
1976 DJ, FWL	Included	5.15	PL	8.
1977 AJ, SWL	225,307	5.15	PL	15.
1977 DJ, FWL	Included	5.15	PL	7.
1977 DJ, SWL	Included	5.15	PL	15.
1978 SJ	260,000	5.25	PL	7.
1978 RJ	Included	5.25	PL	25.
1979	187,624	6.25	PL	8.
1980	169,390	8.00	PL	7.
1981	186,250	5.00	PL	8.
1982	203,287	5.00	PL	7.
1983	190,838	5.00	PL	9.
1984	181,415	5.00	PL	9.
1985 Pliofilm	173,924	6.95	PL	10.
1985 Experimental	Included	N/A	PL	50.
1986	167,338	6.95	PL	9.
1987	212,136	6.95	PL	9.

Note: Currently no examples of the 1977 Attached Jewel obverse and Full Water Line reverse nickel dollar have been found.

SIX COIN NICKEL BRILLIANT UNCIRCULATED SETS, 1988-1996

In 1987 the nickel Voyageur dollar was retired and in 1988 the bronze Loon dollar was introduced into the Brilliant Uncirculated Set. The finish on the coins in these sets was brilliant relief on a brilliant background.

In 1989 the pliofilm heat-sealing dies were modified. The embossed words ROYAL CANADIAN MINT were removed from the dies and replaced with the Circle M logo.

In 1996 the finish on the coins was changed to brilliant relief against a parallel lined background. This finish was first developed for the bullion maple leaf program, and used in 1981 on the Specimen sets issued by the Mint for that year.

DATE	QUANTITY SOLD	ISSUE PRICE	FINISH	MS-65 NBU
1988 RCM Logo	182,048	6.95	PL	10.
1988 Mint Logo	Included	6.95	PL	15.
1989	158,636	7.70	PL	10.
1990	170,791	7.70	PL	10.
1990 CNA	Included	7.70	PL	60.
1991	147,814	8.50	PL	28.
1992	217,597	9.50	PL	15.
1993	171,680	9.50	PL	9.
1993 CNA	Included	9.50	PL	60.
1994	141,676	9.75	PL	9.
1995	143,892	9.75	PL	9.
1996	120,217	11.95	Specimen	30.

NOTES FOR COLLECTORS

1. The 1990 and 1993 Canadan Numismatic Association sets are packaged in commemorative envelopes.
2. The 1996 Specimen set contains the 5¢ Near Six 6 variety, see Canadian Coins, Volume One, for details.

SEVEN COIN NICKEL BRILLIANT UNCIRCULATED SETS WITH SPECIMEN FINISH, 1997

In 1997 the two-dollar Polar Bear coin was added to the set. In mid-1997 the Royal Canadian Mint transferred production of the Brilliant Uncirculated Sets to the Winnipeg mint. The Ottawa and Winnipeg issues of 1997 can be distinguished by the method of packaging, and by the finish on the two dollar coins. Those produced in Ottawa have a brilliant, or shiny, polar bear, whereas on coins produced at Winnipeg, the bear has a frosted appearance. They coins are indicated by (O) for Ottawa and (W) for Winnipeg in the listings. No mint marks appear on 1997-dated coins. The finishes on both sets (1997) are technically equal, being Brilliant Relief on Parallel Lined background.

1997 Ottawa Brilliant Uncirculated Set with Specimen Finish
The $1.00 Loon is at top right
with the $2.00 (shiny) Polar Bear at top centre

1997 Winnipeg Brilliant Uncirculated Set with Specimen Finish
The $1.00 Loon is at top left
with the $2.00 (frosted) Polar Bear at top centre

DATE	DESCRIPTION	QUANTITY SOLD	ISSUE PRICE	FINISH	SP-65
1997 (O)	Loon/Polar Bear	174,692	13.95	Specimen	30.
1997 (W)	Loon/Polar Bear	Included	13.95	Proof-Like	15.

SEVEN COIN NICKEL BRILLIANT UNCIRCULATED SETS, 1998-2000

In 1998 the finish on the coins returned to a brilliant relief with a brilliant background, and this was continued until 2000. To distinguish the sets produced at the Winnipeg mint in 1998, a "W" was added to all coins from the one cent through to the two-dollar coin. This is the first time the Canadian mint placed a mint mark on Canadian coins. When the set production was moved back to Ottawa, in mid-1998, the coins were struck without a mint mark. In 2000, the mint mark appeared again as set production was moved back to the Winnipeg mint. The packaging of the sets in transparent plastic film was continued, and 2000 was the last year of issue for sets containing pure nickel coinage. The Winnipeg mint mark 'W' is found on the obverse, to the lower left of the portrait.

"W" Mint Mark

DATE	DESCRIPTION	QUANTITY SOLD	ISSUE PRICE	FINISH	MS-65 NC
1998	Loon/Polar Bear	145,439	13.95	PL	30.
1998 W	Loon/Polar Bear	Included	13.95	PL	30.
1999	Loon/Polar Bear	117,318	13.95	PL	15.
1999	Loon/Nunavut	74,821	13.95	PL	18.
1999	Loon/Nun. Mule	Included	13.95	PL	275.
2000	Loon/Knowledge	186,985	15.95	PL	15.
2000 W	Loon/Polar Bear	Included	15.95	PL	15.

Note: See page 138 for the listing and explanation of the 1999 Nunavut Mule.

FIVE COIN MULTI-PLY PLATED STEEL TEST SET FOR 1999

This set is a Royal Canadian Mint test token set (TTS-3); see *Canadian Coins, Numismatic Issues, Volume One* for a complete listing.

SEVEN COIN MULTI-PLY PLATED STEEL BRILLIANT UNCIRCULATED SETS, "P" COMPOSITION MARK, 2001-2006

The first issue of the new multi-ply plated steel Brilliant Uncirculated Sets was in 2001. Five coins, one cent through fifty cents, carried the new composition mark "P". The $1.00 and $2.00 coins did not; they were struck on the standard planchets for those denominations. The finish on the multi-ply plated steel coins is brilliant relief on a brilliant background, continuing from the 2000 nickel sets.

In 2002, to commemorate the Golden Jubilee of Queen Elizabeth II, the Mint issued double dated (1952-2002) plated steel coinage for circulation. These coins were used in the collectors' sets, and are identical to those of the previous year except for the double dates. Special Edition Jubilee Sets are found on page 518.

Mid-year 2003 the tiara portrait of Elizabeth II, which had been used since 1990, was replaced with the new uncrowned portrait by Susanna Blunt. The first set with this portrait was issued in 2004.

DATE	DESCRIPTION	QUANTITY SOLD	ISSUE PRICE	FINISH	MS-65 NC
2001P	Loon/Polar Bear mintage on COA	115,897	15.95	PL	22.
2001P	Loon/Polar Bear mintage on COA	Included	15.95	PL	12.
2002P (1952-)	Loon/Polar Bear	100,467	15.95	PL	12.
2003P	Loon/Polar Bear	94,126	15.95	PL	30.
2004P	Loon/Polar Bear	96,847	15.95	PL	22.
2005P	Loon/Polar Bear	114,650	15.95	PL	15.
2005P	Loon/Polar Bear with Non-Magnetic Cent	Incl. Above	15.95	PL	1,200.
2006P (1996-)	Loon/Polar Bear	93,361	15.95	PL	18.

Note: The 2006 Brilliant Uncirculated set contains the 10th anniversary two dollar coin, double dated 1996-2006.

SPECIAL EDITION BRILLIANT UNCIRCULATED SETS, 2002-2010

QUEEN ELIZABETH II, DIADEMED PORTRAIT, GOLDEN JUBILEE, 1952-2002

The Special Edition Brilliant Uncirculated Set of 1952-2002 contains the Golden Jubilee 50-cent piece, and the 1952-2002 Canada Day 25-cent coin. The remaining coins in the set are the regular double-dated Jubilee 1952-2002P issue.

Golden Jubilee, 1952-2002

DATE	DESCRIPTION	QUANTITY SOLD	ISSUE PRICE	FINISH	MS-65 NC
2002P (1952-)	Diademed Portrait Obverse (Special Edition)	49,869	15.95	BU	12.

QUEEN ELIZABETH II, MATURE PORTRAIT, 2003

In mid-year 2003, the "Diademed Portrait" of Queen Elizabeth, by Dora de Pédery-Hunt, was replaced by a more mature portrait by Susanna Blunt. The Special Edition Brilliant Uncirculated Set of 2003 contains the seven circulating denominations, with the new effigy of Queen Elizabeth II. This set was struck at the Winnipeg Mint, and naturally carries the mint mark W (WP). The lower denominations, one cent to fifty cents, also carry the composition mark "P."

Mint and
Composition Mark

Mature Portrait Obverses

DATE	DESCRIPTION	QUANTITY SOLD	ISSUE PRICE	FINISH	MS-65 NC
2003WP	Mature Portrait Obverse	71,142	15.95	BU	25.

CENTENARIES OF ALBERTA AND SASKATCHEWAN, 2005

This Special Edition Brilliant Uncirculated Set was issued to commemorate the centenaries of both Alberta and Saskatchewan. The set contains two commemorative twenty-five-cent coins, one depicting an oil derrick (Alberta), the other the Western Meadowlark (Saskatchewan). The remaining coins in the set are the regular 2005P issue.

Alberta Centenary
25¢ Coin

Saskatchewan
Centenary
25¢ Coin

Alberta and Saskatchewan 100th Anniversary Set

DATE	DESCRIPTION	QUANTITY SOLD	ISSUE PRICE	FINISH	MS-65 NC
2005P	Centenaries of Alberta and Saskatchewan	N/A	15.95	BU	12.

10TH ANNIVERSARY OF THE TWO DOLLAR COIN, RCM LOGO, 2006

This 2006 Special Edition Brilliant Uncirculated Set contains the "Churchill" two dollar coin. The unique Royal Canadian Mint logo that was introduced to Canadian circulating coins in 2006 is featured on the obverse of all coins in this set.

Churchill
Two Dollar Coin

10th Anniversary of the Two Dollar Coin

DATE	DESCRIPTION	QUANTITY SOLD	ISSUE PRICE	FINISH	MS-65 NC
2006	10th Anniversary; Churchill two dollar coin	31,636	19.95	BU	25.

SEVEN COIN MULTI-PLY PLATED STEEL BRILLIANT UNCIRCULATED SETS, MAPLE LEAF LOGO, 2007-2010

Two thousand and seven saw the first coins to carrying the new Royal Canadian Mint logo (Circle M) in brilliant uncirculated sets. The composition mark "P" was now removed.

Also, in 2007 two different pairs of dies were used to strike the ten cent pieces. One pair has an obverse die carrying a small, far logo, with the reverse die having a curved 7. The other pair has an obverse die carrying a large, near logo, with the reverse die having a straight 7.

In 2009 brilliant uncirculated sets were assembled in two locations, the Mint in Ottawa, and an outside contractor. The sets assembled at the Mint have the Circle M logo embossed into the pliofilm packaging, while those assembled by the contractor do not.

Ten Cents 2007
Obverse:
Small, Far, RCM Logo

Ten Cents 2007
Reverse:
Curved 7

Ten Cents 2007
Obverse:
Large, Near, RCM Logo

Ten Cents 2007
Reverse:
Straight 7

DATE	DESCRIPTION	RCM ITEM #	QUANTITY SOLD	ISSUE PRICE	FINISH	MS-65 NC
2007	Standard 7 coins, 10 Cents Small RCM Logo / Curved	N/A	7 45,733	21.95	BU	28.
2007	Standard 7 coins, 10 Cents Large RCM Logo / Straight 7	N/A	Incl. above	21.95	BU	150.
2008	Standard 7 coins	N/A	42,833	21.95	BU	25.
2009	Standard 7 coins, with RCM logo embossed into pliofilm	103600	37,980	22.95	BU	28.
2009	Standard 7 coins, without RCM logo embossed into pliofilm	103600	Incl. above	22.95	BU	28.
2009	Standard 7 coins, without RCM logo; World Money Fair, Berlin, Germany	N/A	1,000	50.00	BU	75.
2010	Standard 7 coins	105796	43,074	23.95	BU	40.

SEVEN COIN MULTI-PLY PLATED STEEL UNCIRCULATED SETS, MAPLE LEAF LOGO, 2011-2012

Beginning in 2011, the finish on the coins was lowered to circulation. The brilliant uncirculated (MS-65-NC) finish found on the coins in sets since 1968 was discontinued.

DATE	DESCRIPTION	RCM ITEM #	QUANTITY SOLD	ISSUE PRICE	FINISH	MS-65 NC
2011	Standard 7 coins	111305	37,881	23.95	Uncirculated	25.
2012	Standard 7 coins	116915	75,083	23.95	Uncirculated	40.

NOTES FOR COLLECTORS

1. In the description column of the pricing table the use of the word "standard" refers to the everyday denominations in use for daily transactions.
2. While the 2007 ten-cent coin with the Large, Near RCM Logo obverse and the Straight 7 Reverse is a relatively common coin, the rarity factor changes when it is struck with a Brilliant Uncirculated finish, and is packaged in a Brilliant Uncirculated set.
3. The 2009 Brilliant Uncirculated sets sold at the World Money Fair in Berlin, Germany, included a certificate of authenticity for the Fair. The set was issued in a limited edition of 1,000.

VANCOUVER 2010 WINTER OLYMPIC GAMES, 2007-2008

Over the four years, 2007-2010, all Vancouver 2010 twenty-five cent coins, and the two bronze one dollar coins, were incorporated into Special Edition Brilliant Uncirculated Sets.

2007 Vancouver 2010 Olympic Winter Games

2008 Vancouver 2010 Olympic Winter Games

2007 Obverse	**2007 Reverse**
Paralympic Logo	**Wheelchair Curling**

Standard 25¢ Wheelchair Curling

2007 Obverse	**2007 Reverse**
Vancouver Logo	**Wheelchair Curling**

25¢ Wheelchair Curling Mule

The Vancouver Olympic obverse was paired with the Paralympic Wheelchair Curling reverse to form a mule which is found only in the 2007 Vancouver Olympic Winter Games Special Edition Set.

Note For Collectors

The 2007 Special Edition Brilliant Uncirculated Set contains the 10-cent variety: Small, Far Logo Obverse / Curved 7 Reverse

DATE	DESCRIPTION	RCM ITEM #	QUANTITY SOLD	ISSUE PRICE	FINISH	MS-65 NC
2007	Standard 5 coins 1¢, 5¢, 10¢, 50¢ and $2; 5 x 25¢ Alpine Skiing, Biathlon, Curling, Ice Hockey, Wheelchair Curling, $1 Loon Dance; (11 coins)	6260217	28,852	23.95	BU	20.
2007	As above, but with the Mule 25¢ Vancouver Logo Obverse paired with the Wheelchair Curling Reverse	N/A	Included	23.95	BU	600.
2008	Standard 5 coins 1¢, 5¢, 10¢, 50¢ and $2; 4 x 25¢ Bobsleigh, Figure Skating, Freestyle Skiing, Snow Boarding; $1 Loon Dance; (10 coins)	6260218	16,471	23.95	BU	22.

VANCOUVER 2010 OLYMPIC WINTER GAMES, 2009-2010

The Golden Moments Set commemorates the Olympic gold medals won by the Men's and Women's Hockey Teams in 2002, and Cindy Klassen's gold medal of 2006. These quarters have the partial maple leaf painted red.

2009 Vancouver 2010 Olympic Winter Games

2010 Golden Moments Special Edition Set

DATE	DESCRIPTION	RCM ITEM #	QUANTITY SOLD	ISSUE PRICE	FINISH	MS-65 NC
2009	Standard 5 coins 1¢, 5¢, 10¢, 50¢ and $2; 3 x 25¢ Cross Country Skiing, Ice Sledge Hockey, Speed Skating, $1 Loon Dance; (9 coins)	6260219	11,313	23.95	BU	22.
2010	Standard 5 coins 1¢, 5¢, 10¢, 50¢ and $2; 3 x 25¢ Painted Men's Ice Hockey 2002, Painted Women's Ice Hockey 2002, Painted Speed Skating, Cindy Klassen; $1 Inukshuk; (9 coins)	6260210	21,432	27.95	BU	35.

SPECIAL EDITION UNCIRCULATED SETS, 2010-2019

SPECIAL EDITION UNCIRCULATED SET, 2010

This set of 8 coins features the standard 1¢, 5¢, 10¢, 50¢ and $2 coins, but also includes the 2010 25¢ Remembrance Day Poppy coin, and two one-dollar coins which commemorate the 100th Anniversary of the Royal Canadian Navy, and the Saskatchewan Roughriders Centennial. The finish on all coins is circulation. The set is shrink wrapped in clear plastic.

25¢ Remembrance Day Poppies

$1 Royal Canadian Navy

$1 Saskatchewan Roughriders

DATE	DESCRIPTION	QUANTITY SOLD	ISSUE PRICE	FINISH	MS-65 NC
2010	8-coin set, $2 with 16 serrations	19,233	25.95	Circulation	30.
2010	8-coin set, $2 with 14 serrations	Incl above	25.95	Circulation	75.

SPECIAL EDITION UNCIRCULATED SETS, 2011-2012

The 2011 8-coin set features the following coins: $2 Boreal Forest, $1 Parks Canada, 25¢ Wood Bison, coloured and uncoloured; 25¢ Orca Whale, coloured and uncoloured; 25¢ Peregrine Falcon, coloured and uncoloured. It was issued in a keepsake envelope with a serial certificate of authorization. The finish on all coins is circulation.

The 2012 set includes the $1 Grey Cup and $1 Lucky Loonie.

2011 Parks Canada
with $1 Parks Canada & $2 Boreal Forest

2012 Special Edition Uncirculated Set
with $1 Grey Cup and $1 Lucky Loonie

DATE	DESCRIPTION	RCM ITEM #	QUANTITY SOLD	ISSUE PRICE	FINISH	MS-65 NC
2011	Special Edition Uncirculated Set (8 coins)	116344	19,233	23.95	Circulation	30.
2011	Parks Canada $1 (5 coin pack)	116333	N/A	5.00	Uncirculated	10.
2011	Legendary Nature $2 (5 coin pack)	116341	N/A	10.00	Uncirculated	15.
2012	Special Edition Uncirculated Set (4 coins)	120640	14,987	19.95	Circulation	25.

SPECIAL EDITION UNCIRCULATED SETS, 2012-2013

THE WAR OF 1812

Obverse	Tecumseh	Sir Isaac Brock	Charles-Michel de Salaberry	Laura Secord

The 2012-2013 5-coin Gift Sets features the following coins: $2 H.M.S. Shannon, 25¢ Laura Secord, coloured and uncoloured, 25¢ Charles-Michel de Salaberry, coloured and uncoloured, all enclosed in a maroon folder.

DATE	DESCRIPTION	RCM ITEM #	QUANTITY SOLD	ISSUE PRICE	FINISH	MS-65 NC
2012-2013	The War of 1812 (5 coins) Gift set	122510	14,831	19.95	Circulation	18.
2012-2013	The War of 1812 (9 coins)	122602	14,941	26.95	Circulation	28.
2012	The War of 1812 $2 (5 coin pack)	119329	N/A	10.00	Uncirculated	15.
2012	Sir Isaac Brock 25¢ (10 coin pack)	119907	N/A	2.50	Uncirculated	10.
2012	Techumseh 25¢ (10 coin pack)	119680	N/A	2.50	Uncirculated	6.
2013	de Salaberr 25¢ (10 coin pack)	122054	N/A	2.50	Uncirculated	6.
2013	Laura Secord 25¢ (10 coin pack)	120237	N/A	2.50	Uncirculated	6.

SPECIAL EDITION UNCIRCULATED SETS, 2013-2014

The 2013-2014 Special Edition Uncirculated set of 4 coins features the following coins: $2 Wait For Me Daddy, $1 Lucky Loonie, 25¢ Arctic Expedition - Life in the North, and 25¢ Arctic Expedition - Exploration all enclosed in a presentation folder.

DATE	DESCRIPTION	RCM ITEM #	QUANTITY SOLD	ISSUE PRICE	FINISH	MS-65 NC
2013-2014	Special Edition Uncirculated Set (4 coins)	132485	12,105	25.95	Circulation	25.
2014	Wait For Me, Daddy $2 (5 coin pack)	120237	N/A	10.00	Uncirculated	15.

SPECIAL EDITION UNCIRCULATED SETS, 2015-2017

The 2015 Special Edition Uncirculagted set of 6 coins features the following coins: $2 200th Anniversary of the Birth of Sir John A. Macdonald, $2 100th Anniversary of *In Flanders Fields*, 25¢ 50th Anniversary of the Canadian Flag, and 25¢ Poppy, all enclosed in a presentation folder.

The 2017 Special Edition Uncirculated set features the unique coins issued exclusively for 2017 that were designed by Canadians, for Canadians, and were selected through popular vote in the *MY CANADA, MY INSPIRATION* contest as well as the 50-cent piece which illustrates the Heritage Canada — Canada 150 logo.

DATE	DESCRIPTION	RCM ITEM #	QUANTITY SOLD	ISSUE PRICE	FINISH	MS-65 NC
2015	Special Edition Uncirculated Set (6 coins)	146439	12,450	25.95	Uncirculated	30.
2015	Canada Flag 25¢ (10 coin pack)	143484	N/A	2.50	Uncirculated	15.
2015	Sir John A. Macdonald $2 (5 coin pack)	143452	N/A	10.00	Uncirculated	15.
2016	Women's Right to Vote $1 (5 coin pack)	148545	N/A	5.00	Uncirculated	10.
2017	Special Edition Uncirculated Set (8 coins)	157734	8,017	26.95	Uncirculated	30.
2017	Stanley Cup 25¢ (10 coin pack)	158353	N/A	2.50	Uncirculated	5.
2017	Vimy Ridge $2 (5 coin pack)	158852	N/A	10.00	Uncirculated	15.

SIX COIN MULTI-PLY PLATED STEEL UNCIRCULATED SETS, MAPLE LEAF LOGO, 2013-2019

With production of the penny ending May 4th, 2012, the uncirculated sets for 2013 do not contain a one cent coin. The six coins contained in the set are: 5¢, 10¢, 25¢, 50¢, $1 and $2.

DATE	DESCRIPTION	RCM ITEM #	QUANTITY SOLD	ISSUE PRICE	FINISH	MS-65 NC
2013	Standard 6 coins	121284	61,702	24.95	Uncirculated	25.
2014	Standard 6 coins	128688	52,946	24.95	Uncirculated	25.
2015	Standard 6 coins	133254	51,902	24.95	Uncirculated	25.
2016	Standard 6 coins	148390	10,225	24.95	Uncirculated	25.
2016	Standard 6 coins $1 dated 2015	148390	Incl. above	24.95	Uncirculated	120.
2017	Standard 6 coins	156014	75,000	24.95	Uncirculated	25.
2018	Standard 6 coins	164002	75,000	26.95	Uncirculated	27.
2019	Standard 6 coins	168491	75,000	26.95	Uncirculated	27.

TEST TOKEN SETS

DATE	DESCRIPTION	RCM ITEM #	QUANTITY SOLD	ISSUE PRICE	FINISH	MS-65 NC
1999P	Test Token Set (6 coins)	N/A	20,000	99.95	Uncirculated	75.
2004	Test Token Set (7 coins)	N/A	9,534	49.95	Uncirculated	75.
2006	Test Token Set (7 cons)	N/A	10,061	49.95	Uncirculated	90.
2011-2012	Test Token Set (6 coins)	118258	25,000	29.95	Uncirculated	30.
2018	Test Token Set (6 coins)	170774	10,000	49.95	Uncirculated	60.

MISCELLANEOUS GIFT SETS, 1983-2019

MISCELLANEOUS GIFT SETS, 1983, 1998, 2001, 2006-2007, 2018-2019.
The miscellaneous gift sets issued between 1983 and 2001 have a brilliant uncirculated finish, while sets from 2006 forward have a circulation finish. The 2019 set has a Specimen finish.

2007 Calendar Coin Set

2018 From Far and Wide

DATE	DESCRIPTION	RCM ITEM #	QUANTITY SOLD	ISSUE PRICE	ISSUER	FINISH	MARKET VALUE
1983	British Royal Mint, (6 coins)	N/A	N/A	N/A	RCM,BRM	BU	100.
1998	Canadian Imperial Bank of Commerce,"Oh! Canada!" Set; (7 coins)	N/A	N/A	21.95	RCM	BU	30.
2001P	Canada 2001 Set, (7 coins); Medallion	N/A	N/A	N/A	RCM	BU	15.
2001P	"OH! CANADA!", Banff, (7 coins)	N/A	500	22.95	RCM	BU	25.
2001P	"OH! CANADA!", Calgary, (7 coins)	N/A	500	22.95	RCM	BU	25.
2001P	"OH! CANADA!", Halifax, (7 coins)	N/A	500	22.95	RCM	BU	25.
2001P	"OH! CANADA!", Montreal, (7 coins)	N/A	500	22.95	RCM	BU	25.
2001P	"OH! CANADA!", Niagara Falls, (7 coins)	N/A	500	22.95	RCM	BU	25.
2001P	"OH! CANADA!", Quebec City, (7 coins)	N/A	500	22.95	RCM	BU	25.
2001P	"OH! CANADA!", R.C.M., (7 coins)	N/A	500	22.95	RCM	BU	25.
2001P	"OH! CANADA!", St. John's, (7 coins)	N/A	500	22.95	RCM	BU	25.
2001P	"OH! CANADA!", Vancouver, (7 coins)	N/A	500	22.95	RCM	BU	25.
2001P	"OH! CANADA!", Whistler, (7 coins)	N/A	500	22.95	RCM	BU	25.
2006P	QUEBEC WINTER CARNIVAL; (7 coins), incl. Colourised 25¢ "Bonhomme"; Festive folder	N/A	8,200	19.95	RCM	Circulation	25.
2007	Calendar Coin Set, (7 coins)	N/A	5,264	29.95	RCM	Circulation	25.
2018	From Far and Wide (6 coins), incl. Glow-In-The-Dark 50¢	170281	W.S.L.	29.95	RCM	Specimen	30.
2019	D-Day Commemorative Keepsake (6 coins), incl. Selectively coloured $2	174205	100,000	21.95	RCM	Circulation	22.

Note: 1. For the coloured design of the Quebec Winter Carnival twenty-five cent coin, see page 29.
2. The 2007 Calendar Coin Set contains the Large, Near Logo obverse / Straight 7 reverse.
3. The 2019 D-Day Commemorative Collector Keepsake set includes two versions of the special-themed $2 coins – engraved-only and selectively coloured.

GRADUATION / CONGRATULATIONS GIFT SETS, 2004-2008

MULTI-PLY PLATED STEEL BRILLIANT UNCIRCULATED SETS, 2004-2005.

The gift set in 2004 was directed at the school or college graduation market. By 2006 the scope was broadened to a Congratulations Gift Set. The Graduation Sets have a brilliant uncirculated finish, while the Congratulations Gift Sets have a circulation finish.

MULTI-PLY PLATED STEEL UNCIRCULATED SETS, 2006-2008.

Beginning in 2006, the finish on the coins in these sets was changed to circulation. The circulation sets were struck and assembled at the Winnipeg Mint, however, they do not carry the "W" mint mark.

The ten cent coins contained in the 2007 Congratulations Gift Sets are the Large, Near Logo obverse / Straight 7 reverse variety.

These sets were discontinued in 2009 and replaced by the Coins With Cards Series, see page 34-35.

2005 Graduation Gift Set

2008 Congratulations Gift Set

DATE	DESCRIPTION	RCM ITEM #	QUANTITY SOLD	ISSUE PRICE	FINISH	MS-65 NC
2004P	Graduation Set, (7 coins), Folder	N/A	22,094	19.95	BU	15.
2005P	Graduation Set, (7 coins), Folder	N/A	12,411	19.95	BU	15.
2006P	Congratulations Set, (7 coins), Folder	N/A	9,428	19.95	Uncirculated	15.
2007	Congratulations Set, (7 coins); incl. coloured 25¢ Fireworks; Folder	N/A	9,671	19.95	Uncirculated	40.
2008	Congratulations Set, (7 coins), incl. coloured 25¢ Trophy; Folder	100521	6,821	19.95	Uncirculated	50.

Note: For the coloured designs of the twenty-five cent coins contained in the sets of 2007-2008, see page 31-32.

NHL TEAM GIFT SETS, UNCIRCULATED, 2006-2009

MULTI-PLY PLATED STEEL, UNCIRCULATED SETS, 2006-2009.

These sets were introduced for the 2005-2006 hockey season with only three Canadian NHL teams being represented: Montreal Canadiens, Ottawa Senators and the Toronto Maple Leafs. Each set contained the standard six coins, 1¢, 5¢, 10¢, 50¢, $1 and $2, with the twenty-five-cent Caribou design being replaced by a coloured NHL team logo. For the 2006-2007 Season, all six Canadian NHL teams were represented.

In the Fall of 2008 the sets issued for the 2008-2009 season had the twenty-five-cent Caribou design as one of the standard six coins, but the loon design on the one dollar coin was replaced by a coloured team jersey logo.

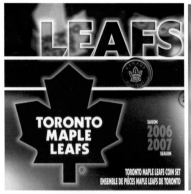
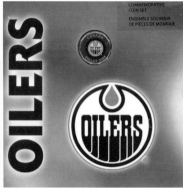

2006-2007 Season	2007-2008 Season	2008-2009 Season
Toronto Maple Leafs	Edmonton Oilers	Calgary Flames

DATE	DESCRIPTION	RCM ITEM #	QUANTITY SOLD	ISSUE PRICE	FINISH	MS-65 NC
2006P	Montreal Canadiens, Standard 6 coin set; Coloured 25¢	N/A	11,765	24.95	Uncirculated	25.
2006P	Ottawa Senators; Standard 6 coin set; Coloured 25¢	N/A	Included	24.95	Uncirculated	25.
2006P	Toronto Maple Leafs; Standard 6 coin set; Coloured 25¢	N/A	Included	24.95	Uncirculated	25.
2007	Calgary Flames; Standard 6 coins; Coloured 25¢	N/A	1.082	24.95	Uncirculated	25.
2007	Edmonton Oilers; Standard 6 coins; Coloured 25¢	N/A	2,214	24.95	Uncirculated	25.
2007	Montreal Canadiens; Standard 6 coins; Coloured 25¢	N/A	4,091	24.95	Uncirculated	30.
2007	Ottawa Senators; Standard 6 coin set; Coloured 25¢	N/A	2,474	24.95	Uncirculated	25.
2007	Toronto Maple Leafs; Standard 6 coin set; Coloured 25¢	N/A	5,365	24.95	Uncirculated	25.
2007	Vancouver Canucks; Standard 6 coin set; Coloured 25¢	N/A	1,526	24.95	Uncirculated	25.
2008	Calgary Flames; Standard 6 coins; Coloured $1	102661	N/A	24.95	Uncirculated	20.
2008	Edmonton Oilers; Standard 6 coins; Coloured $1	102662	1,584	24.95	Uncirculated	20.
2008	Montreal Canadiens; Standard 6 coins; Coloured $1	102531	2,659	24.95	Uncirculated	50.
2008	Ottawa Senators; Standard 6 coin set; Coloured $1	102659	1,633	24.95	Uncirculated	20.
2008	Toronto Maple Leafs; Standard 6 coin set; Coloured $1	102533	N/A	24.95	Uncirculated	20.
2008	Vancouver Canucks; Standard 6 coin set; Coloured $1	102651	1,302	24.95	Uncirculated	20.
2009	Calgary Flames; Standard 6 coins; Coloured $1	102534	382	24.95	Uncirculated	25.
2009	Edmonton Oilers; Standard 6 coins; Coloured $1	102535	472	24.95	Uncirculated	25.
2009	Montreal Canadiens; Standard 6 coins; Coloured $1	102531	4,857	24.95	Uncirculated	40.
2009	Ottawa Senators; Standard 6 coin set; Coloured $1	102659	387	24.95	Uncirculated	25.
2009	Toronto Maple Leafs; Standard 6 coin set; Coloured $1	102533	1,328	24.95	Uncirculated	30.
2009	Vancouver Canucks; Standard 6 coin set; Coloured $1	102536	794	24.95	Uncirculated	25.

NOTES

1. For the coloured designs of the twenty-five cent coins used in the NHL Team Gift Sets see page 30-31.
2. For the coloured designs of the one dollar coins used in the NHL Team Gift Sets see pages 126-128.
3. No "Quantity Sold" number was listed in the 2008 Royal Canadian Mint Report for the 2008 issue of NHL Team Gift Sets. There is a partial listing in 2009.
4. The 2007 NHL Team Gift Sets contain the Large, Near Logo obverse / Straight 7 reverse variety ten cent coin.

OH! CANADA! GIFT SETS, 1994-2019

BRILLIANT UNCIRCULATED SETS, 1994-2000

First issued in 1994, this set included the bronze dollar plus the other five denominations for that year. In 1997 this set was expanded to include the two-dollar polar bear coin. In 1998 the packaging of the Oh! Canada! Gift Sets changed from card displays to clear plastic display units. The coins in the Oh Canada! set are identical in finish to those of the corresponding year of the Brilliant Uncirculated Set.

MULTI-PLY PLATED STEEL BRILLIANT UNCIRCULATED SETS, 2001-2005.

In 2001, the five subsidiary coins in the Oh! Canada! Set were replaced by the five multi-ply plated steel coins.

In the 2002 set all coins bear the double dates 1952-2002 to commemorate the 50th anniversary of Her Majesty Queen Elizabeth II's accession to the throne.

Beginning in 2004 the coins carried the new Susanna Blunt effigy of Queen Elizabeth II. The coins in the "Oh Canada!" set were identical in finish to coins of the Brilliant Uncirculated Set of that year.

MULTI-PLY PLATED STEEL UNCIRCULATED SETS, 2006-2019.

In 2006 the finish on all coins contained in these sets was changed to circulation. This was also the last year the composition mark "P" would be seen on coins in the sets.

Starting in 2007 several changes were made to the Oh Canada! Set. All coins now carried the Royal Canadian Mint logo on the obverse, and the Caribou design on the twenty-five-cent coin was replaced by a coloured design. For the coloured designs of the twenty-five cent coins of 2007-2010, see pages 31-32.

The 2011 Oh Canada! Set saw the return of the struck twenty-five cent piece. The reverse design is a single maple leaf.

The Oh Canada! Gift Set for 2012 contains the standard coins, 1¢, 5¢, 10¢, $1, $2, and a 25¢ coin with a struck multiple maple leaf design. The fifty-cent coin is not included in the set.

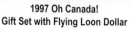

1997 Oh Canada!
Gift Set with Flying Loon Dollar

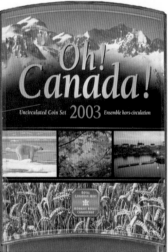

2003 Oh! Canada!

2019 Ô Canada

OH! CANADA! GIFT SETS, 1994-2019, PRICING PANEL.

DATE	DESCRIPTION	RCM ITEM #	QUANTITY SOLD	ISSUE PRICE	FINISH	MS-65 NC
1994	Oh Canada! (6 coins), Folder	N/A	18,794	16.95	BU	12.
1995	Oh Canada! (6 coins), incl. Peacekeeping dollar, Folder	N/A	50,927	16.95	BU	12.
1996	Oh Canada! (6 coins), Folder	N/A	31,083	16.95	BU	20.
1997	OhCanada! (7 coins), incl. Flying Loon dollar, Folder	N/A	84,124	21.95	Specimen	30.
1998	Oh! Canada! (7 coins), Folder	N/A	42,710	21.95	BU	25.
1998W	Oh! Canada! Winnipeg Mint (7 coins), Folder	N/A	24,792	21.95	BU	25.
1999	Oh! Canada, (7 coins), Folder	N/A	82,754	21.95	BU	18.
2000	Oh! Canada! (7 coins), Folder	N/A	107,884	21.95	BU	15.
2000W	Oh! Canada! (7 coins), Folder	N/A	Included	21.95	BU	15.
2001P	Oh! Camada! (7 coins), Display case	N/A	66,726	22.95	BU	18.
2002P (1952-)	Oh! Canada! (7 coins), Double Date, Display case	N/A	61,484	22.95	BU	15.
2003P	Oh! Canada! (7 coins), Display case	N/A	51,146	23.95	BU	25.
2004P	Oh! Canada! (7 coins), Folder	N/A	53,111	23.95	BU	18.
2005P	Oh! Canada! (7 coins), Folder	N/A	40,890	19.95	BU	15.
2006P	Oh! Canadda! (7 coins), Folder	N/A	28,213	19.95	Uncirculated	20.
2007	Oh! Canada! (7 coins), incl. coloured 25¢ Maple Leaf; Folder	N/A	24,096	19.95	Uncirculated	30.
2008	Oh! Canada! (7 coins), incl. coloured 25¢ Canadian Flag; Folder	6260508	30,567	19.95	Uncirculated	25.
2009	Oh! Canada! (7 coins), incl. coloured 25¢ Four Maple Leaves; Folder	103353	14,451	19.95	Uncirculated	30.
2010	Oh! Canada! (7 coins), incl. coloured 25¢ Three Maple Leaves; Folder	105802	19,769	19.95	Uncirculated	25.
2011	O Canada (7 coins), incl. 25¢ Single maple leaf design, Folder	111599	22,475	19.95	Uncirculated	20.
2012	O Canada (6 coins), incl. 25¢ Multiple maple leaf design, Folder	117367	31,464	19.95	Uncirculated	20.
2013	O Canada (5 coins), incl. 25¢ Maple Leaf, Folder	121966	26,068	19.95	Uncirculated	20.
2014	O Canada (5 coins), incl. $1 Maple Leaf, Folder	128260	32,289	19.95	Uncirculated	20.
2015	Ô Canada (5 coins), incl. $1 Large Maple Leaf, Folder	133222	23,705	19.95	Uncirculated	20.
2016	Ô Canada (5 coins), incl. $1 Large Maple Leaf, Folder	148977	40,169	19.95	Uncirculated	20.
2017	Ô Canada (5 coins), incl. $1 Large Maple Leaf, Folder	156969	20,652	21.95	Uncirculated	22.
2018	Ô Canada (5 coins), incl. $1 Maple Leaves & Keys	164007	W.S.L.	21.95	Uncirculated	22.
2019	Ô Canada (5 coins), incl. $1 Three Maple Leaves	171469	W.S.L.	21.95	Uncirculated	22.

Note: The ten-cent coins contained in the 2007 Oh! Canada! sets are the Large, Near Logo obverse / Straight 7 reverse variety.

Note: For the designs of the twenty-five cent coins contained in the sets of 2007-2013 see pages 31-34, the 2014-2019 dollar coins can be found on pages 132-133.

BABY GIFT SETS, 1995-2019

NICKEL BRILLIANT UNCIRCULATED SETS, 1995-2000.

First issued in 1995, the brilliant uncirculated set of coins was specially packaged for the gift market using the six coins from the brilliant uncirculated set of that year. In 1997 this set was expanded to include the two-dollar polar bear coin.

In 1998 the name changed from Bundle of Joy to Tiny Treasures Brilliant Uncirculated Sets. In that same year the packaging of the sets of Tiny Treasures changed from card displays to clear plastic display units. The movement of set production to Winnipeg and back to Ottawa that occurred in 1998 also affected the Oh! Canada! and Tiny Treasures sets.

In 2000, production of the sets occurred in both the Ottawa and Winnipeg mints.

The finish on the coins in these sets (1995-2005) is brilliant relief on brilliant background, brilliant uncirculated (MS-65-NC). The finish was downgraded in 2006 to uncirculated. See pages xvi-xvii for an outline on finishes.

MULTI-PLY PLATED STEEL BRILLIANT UNCIRCULATED SETS, 2001-2005.

As with the Brilliant Uncirculated sets of 2001, the nickel coinage of the previous year was replaced with the new patented multi-ply plated steel coins. In the 2002 set all coins bear the double dates 1952-2002 to commemorate the 50th anniversary of Her Majesty Queen Elizabeth II's accession to the throne. Two thousand and three was the last year of issue for the Tiny Treasures sets. The finish on the coins in these sets is brilliant uncirculated (MS-65-NC).

With the revamping of the Gift Sets in 2004, a name change took place, Tiny Treasures became Baby Gift Sets. The finish on the coins remained the same as the previous sets.

MULTI-PLY PLATED STEEL UNCIRCULATED SETS, 2006-2019.

Beginning in 2006, the finish on the coins in these sets was changed to circulation. The uncirculated sets were struck and assembled at the Winnipeg Mint, however, they do not carry the "W" mint mark.

In 2007 the Caribou design on the twenty-five-cent coin was replaced with a coloured design.

In 2011 the coloured designs used on the reverse of the twenty-five cent pieces were discontinued. The $1 coin now carries a new yearly struck design.

1997 Bundle of Joy Set

2002 Tiny Treasures Set

Born In 2019

BABY GIFT SETS, 1995-2019, PRICING PANEL.

DATE	DESCRIPTION	RCM ITEM #	QUANTITY SOLD	ISSUE PRICE	FINISH	MS-65 NC
1995	Bundle of Joy (6 coins), Folder	N/A	36,443	19.95	BU	30.
1996	Bundle of Joy (6 coins), Folder	N/A	56,618	19.95	BU	20.
1997	Bundle of Joy (7 coins), Folder	N/A	55,199	21.95	BU	25.
1998	Bundle of Joy (7 coins), Display case	N/A	46,139	21.95	BU	24.
1998W	Bundle of Joy, Winnipeg Mint, (7 coins), Display case	N/A	12,625	21.95	BU	24.
1999	Bundle of Joy (7 coins), Display case	N/A	67,694	21.95	BU	20.
2000	Bundle of Joy (7 coins), Display case	N/A	82,964	21.95	BU	20.
2000W	Bundle of Joy, Winnipeg Mint, (7 coins), Display case	N/A	Included	21.95	BU	20.
2001P	Tiny Treasures (7 coins), Display case	N/A	52,085	22.95	BU	25.
2002P (1952-)	Tiny Treasures (7 coins), Display case	N/A	51,491	22.95	BU	20.
2003P	Tiny Treasures (7 coins), Display case	N/A	43,197	22.95	BU	25.
2004P	Baby Gift Set (7 coins), Folder	N/A	53,726	19.95	BU	45.
2005P	Baby Gift Set (7 coins), Folder	N/A	42,245	19.95	BU	50.
2006P	Baby Gift Set (7 coins), Folder	N/A	33,786	19.95	Uncirculated	30.
2007	Baby Gift Set (7 coins), incl. coloured 25¢ Rattle; Folder	N/A	30,090	19.95	Uncirculated	140.
2008	Baby Gift Set (7 coins), incl. coloured 25¢ Teddy Bear; Folder	N/A	29,819	19.95	Uncirculated	120.
2009	Baby Gift Set (7 coins), incl. coloured 25¢ Teddy Bear & Blanket; Folder	N/A	25,182	19.95	Uncirculated	120.
2010	Baby Gift Set (7 coins), incl. coloured 25¢ Baby Carriage; Folder	N/A	27,048	19.95	Uncirculated	50.
2011	Born In... (7 coins), incl. 25¢ Baby's Feet, Folder	111600	38,576	19.95	Uncirculated	110.
2012	Born In... (6 coins), incl. 25¢ Mobiles, Folder	117638	43,920	19.95	Uncirculated	25.
2013	Born In... (5 coins), incl. 25¢ Baby's Feet, Folder	121967	53,708	19.95	Uncirculated	35.
2014	Born In... (5 coins), incl. $1 Stork, Folder	128286	54,122	19.95	Uncirculated	35.
2015	Born In... (5 coins), incl. $1 Teddy Bear, Folder	133223	50,279	19.95	Uncirculated	25.
2016	Born In... (5 coins), incl. $1 "ABC" Building Blocks	148982	47,733	19.95	Uncirculated	20.
2017	Born In... (5 coins), incl. $1 Rocking Horse, Folder	153970	20,189	21.95	Uncirculated	25.
2018	Born In... (5 coins), incl. $1 Crib and Teddy Bears	164003	W.S.L.	21.95	Uncirculated	22.
2019	Born In... (5 coins), incl. $1 Baby Shoes	170583	W.S.L.	21.95	Uncirculated	22.

Note: For the designs of the twenty-five cent coins contained in the sets of 2007-2013 see pages 31-34.
For the design of the one dollar coin contained in the 2014-2019 set see pages 132-133.

HOLIDAY GIFT SETS, 2004-2018

MULTI-PLY PLATED STEEL, BRILLIANT UNCIRCULATED SETS, 2004-2005.

In 2004 the Royal Canadian Mint introduced a new Holiday Gift Set to their product line. This set was issued in a colourful Season's Greetings folder and included a coloured twenty-five-cent coin in place of the standard Caribou design. The finish on all coins is Brilliant Uncirculated.

MULTI-PLY PLATED STEEL, UNCIRCULATED SETS 2006-2018.

In 2006 the finish on all coins contained in these sets was downgraded to circulation.
The ten cent coin contained in the 2007 Holiday Gift Set is the Large, Near Logo obverse / Straight 7 reverse variety.

| **2006 Holiday Carols** | **2006 Happy Holidays** | **2018 Peace and Joy** |

DATE	DESCRIPTION	RCM ITEM #	QUANTITY SOLD	ISSUE PRICE	FINISH	MS-65 NC
2004P	Happy Holidays (7 coins), incl. coloured 25¢ Santa Claus; Folder	N/A	62,777	19.95	BU	25.
2005P	Season's Greetings (7 coins), incl. coloured 25¢ Christmas Stocking; Folder	N/A	72,831	19.95	BU	18.
2006P	Ho! Ho! Ho! (7 coins), incl. coloured 25¢ Santa in Sleigh Reindeer; Folder	N/A	99,258	19.95	Uncirculated	15.
2006P	Holiday Carols CD, incl. coloured Sterling Silver $1 Snowflake	N/A	N/A	39.95	Uncirculated	40.
2007	Happy Holidays (7 coins), incl.coloured 25¢ Christmas Tree; Folder	N/A	66,267	19.95	Uncirculated	20.
2008	Happy Holidays (7 coins), incl.coloured 25¢ Santa, Folder	100525	42,344	19.95	Uncirculated	20.
2009	Happy Holidays (7 coins), incl. coloured 25¢ Santa Ornaments; Folder	103359	32,967	19.95	Uncirculated	25.
2010	Happy Holidays (7 coins), incl.coloured 25¢ Santa, Christmas Tree; Folder	107021	10,870	19.95	Uncirculated	25.
2011	Peace and Joy (7 coins), incl. 25¢ Snowflake, Folder	111603	41,666	19.95	Uncirculated	20.
2012	Happy Holidays (6 coins), incl. 25¢ Christmas Tree Ornaments, Folder	117371	26,404	19.95	Uncirculated	20.
2013	Happy Holidays (5 coins), incl. 25¢ Wreath, Folder	121970	26,491	19.95	Uncirculated	20.
2014	Peace and Joy (5 coins), incl. $1 Reindeer	128274	31,951	19.95	Uncirculated	20.
2015	Peace and Joy (5 coins), incl. $1 Snowflake, Folder	141476	32,994	19.95	Uncirculated	20
2016	Peace and Joy (5 coins), incl. $1 Holly Leaves & Pine Cone, Folder	149270	23,696	21.95	Uncirculated	22.
2017	Peace and Joy (5 coins), incl. $1 Ornaments & Holly Leaves, Folder	153971	W.S.L.	21.95	Uncirculated	22.
2018	Peace and Joy (5 coins), incl. $1 Holly & Candy Canes, Folder	164005	W.S.L.	21.95	Uncirculated	22.

Note: For the designs of the twenty-five cent coins contained in the sets of 2004-2013 see pages 27, and 33-34, for the 2014-2018 dollar coins, see pages 132-133.

WEDDING GIFT SETS, 2004-2019

MULTI-PLY PLATED STEEL UNCIRCULATED SETS, 2004-2006.

The Gift Set line was expanded in 2004 to include a Wedding set, which included the seven standard circulating denominations housed in a colourful wedding folder. The finish on these sets is circulation.

MULTI-PLY PLATED STEEL UNCIRCULATED SETS, 2007-2019.

In 2007 the standard twenty-five-cent Caribou design was replaced with a coloured design which changed each year. The finish on this set is uncirculated. The ten-cent coin contained in the 2007 Wedding Gift Set is the Large, Near Logo obverse / Straight 7 reverse variety.

The Wedding Gift Set was not issued in 2009, it was replaced by the Coins With Cards series (see page 34-35), however it was reintroduced in 2010.

| 2008 Wedding Gift Set | 2017 Wedding Gift Set | 2018 Wedding Gift Set |

DATE	DESCRIPTION	RCM ITEM #	QUANTITY SOLD	ISSUE PRICE	FINISH	MS-65 NC
2004P	Wedding Gift Set (7 coin), Folder	N/A	18,660	19.95	Uncirculated	15.
2005P	Wedding Gift Set (7 coin), Folder	N/A	11,597	19.95	Uncirculated	15.
2006P	Wedding Gift Set (7 coin), Folder	N/A	8,012	19.95	Uncirculated	20.
2007	Wedding Gift Set (7 coin), incl. coloured 25¢ Bouquet; Folder	N/A	10,687	19.95	Uncirculated	25.
2008	Wedding Gift Set (7 coin), incl. coloured 25¢ Wedding Cake; Folder	6260808	7,407	19.95	Uncirculated	50.
2010	Wedding Gift Set (7 coin), incl. coloured 25¢ Heart and Roses; Folder	107023	8,194	19.95	Uncirculated	20.
2011	Married In... (7 coin), incl. 25¢ Wedding Rings, Folder	111602	20,461	19.95	Uncirculated	20.
2012	On Your Wedding Day (6 coins), incl. 25¢ Wedding Rings/Heart Folder	117369	24,325	19.95	Uncirculated	20.
2013	Married In... (5 coins) incl. 25¢ Wedding Rings, Folder	121969	20,317	19.95	Uncirculated	20.
2014	Married In... (5 coins) incl. $1 Two Turtle Doves, Folder	128267	35,742	19.95	Uncirculated	20.
2015	Married In... (5 coins) incl. $1 Two Swans, Folder	133221	23,927	19.95	Uncirculated	20.
2016	Married In... (5 coins) incl. $1 Wedding Bells, Folder	148987	23,788	19.95	Uncirculated	20.
2017	Married In... (5 coins) incl. $1 Rose, Wedding Rings, Hearts, Folder	153968	14,145	21.95	Uncirculated	20.
2018	Married In... (5 coins) incl. $1 Doves & Wedding Rings, Folder	164004	W.S.L.	21.95	Uncirculated	22.
2019	Married In... (5 coins) incl. $1 Wedding Cake, Folder	170928	W.S.L.	21.95	Uncirculated	22.

Note: For the designs of the twenty-five cent coins contained in the sets of 2007-2013 see pages 31-34.
For the design on the one dollar coin contained in the 2014-2019 set see pages 132-133.

BIRTHDAY GIFT SETS, 2005-2019

MULTI-PLY PLATED STEEL BRILLIANT UNCIRCULATED SETS, 2005.

The Birthday Gift Set was first introduced in 2005. The finish on these seven-coin sets is brilliant uncirculated. The ten cent coins contained in the 2007 Birthday Gift Sets are the Large, Near Logo obverse / Straight 7 reverse variety.

MULTI-PLY PLATED STEEL UNCIRCULATED SETS, 2006-2008, 2011-2019.

Beginning in 2006, the finish on the coins contained in the Birthday Gift Sets was uncirculated. The uncirculated sets were struck and assembled at the Winnipeg Mint, however, they do not carry the "W" mint mark.

In 2007 the Caribou design on the twenty-five-cent coin was replaced with a coloured design. The ten cent coins contained in the 2007 Birthday Gift Sets are the Large, Near Logo obverse / Straight 7 reverse variety.

For 2008 the set carried the name "Commemorative Coin Set."

The Birthday Gift Set was discontinued in 2009 and replaced by the Coins With Cards series, see page 31-34.

The Birthday Gift Set was reintroduced in 2011. Coins contained in the sets are:

2008 Birthday Gift Set

2017 Happy Birthday Gift Set

2018 Happy Birthday Gift Set

DATE	DESCRIPTION	RCM ITEM #	QUANTITY SOLD	ISSUE PRICE	FINISH	MS-65 NC
2005P	Birthday Gift Set (7 coins), Folder	N/A	20,227	19.95	BU	15.
2006P	Birthday Gift Set (7 coins), Folder	N/A	11,984	19.95	Uncirculated	20.
2007	Birthday Gift Set (7 coins), incl. coloured 25¢ Balloons; Folder	N/A	13,423	19.95	Uncirculated	25.
2008	Birthday Gift Set (7 coins), incl. coloured 25¢ Party Hat; Folder	100514	11,376	19.95	Uncirculated	40.
2011	Happy Birthday (7 coins), incl. 25¢ Four Balloons, Folder	111601	21,173	19.95	Uncirculated	20.
2012	Happy Birthday (6 coins), incl. 25¢ Ice Cream Cone, Folder	117370	24,659	19.95	Uncirculated	20.
2013	Happy Birthday (5 coins), incl. 25¢ Slice of Birthday Cake, Folder	121968	22,678	19.95	Uncirculated	20.
2014	Happy Birthday (5 coins), incl. $1 Gift Box and Balloons, Folder	128280	44,539	19.95	Uncirculated	18.
2015	Happy Birthday (5 coins), incl. $1 3 Balloons, Folder	133220	24,781	19.95	Uncirculated	20.
2016	Happy Birthday (5 coins), incl. $1 Cupcake, Party Hat, Present	148972	25,648	19.95	Uncirculated	20.
2017	Happy Birthday (5 coins), incl. $1 Birthday Presents, Folder	153967	14,149	21.95	Uncirculated	22.
2018	Happy Birthday (5 coins), incl. $1 Birthday Cake	164006	W.S.L.	21.95	Uncirculated	22.
2019	Happy Birthday (5 coins), incl. $1 Balloons & Party Hat	170906	W.S.L.	21.95	Uncirculated	22.

Note: For the designs of the twenty-five cent coins contained in the sets of 2007-2013 see pages 31-34.

For the design of the one dollar coin contained in the 2014-2019 set see pages 132-133.

VANCOUVER 2010 WINTER OLYMPIC AND PARALYMPIC GAMES COIN AND STAMP SETS, 2010

These sets were issued in conjunction with Canada Post in three versions: gold, silver and bronze.

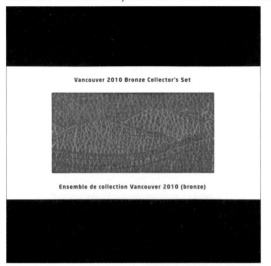

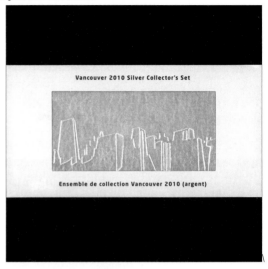

Bronze Collector Set   Silver Collector Set

DATE	DESCRIPTION	RCM ITEM #	QUANTITY SOLD	ISSUE PRICE	FINISH	MS-65 NC
2010	**Vancouver 2010 Emblems and Mascots Set, Bronze Collector Set**, Three 50¢ Mascot coins, Vancouver 2010 Souvenir Sheet of five Mascot theme stamps, 2 bronze lapel pins	106155	16,000	49.95	Uncirculated	60.
2010	**Vancouver 2010 Winter Games Sports Set, Silver Collector Set**, Five painted 25¢ coins, Bobsleigh, Curling, Free Style Skiing, Ice Sledge Hockey, Snowboarding; Vancouver 2010 Souvenir Sheet of five Olympic theme stamps; 2 silver lapel pins	105156	16,000	49.95	Uncirculated	60.
2010	**Vancouver 2010 Logo Set, Gold Collector Set**, Bronze Inukshuk dollar, Nickel painted Inukshuk dollar, 50¢ Inukshuk lenticular coin; Vancouver 2010 Souvenir Sheet of two stamps (Whistler and Vancouver) 2 gold plated pins.	106980	11,991	49.95	Uncirculated	60.

COMMEMORATIVE CANADIAN COIN, TOKEN, OR MEDAL SETS, 2010-2013

COMMEMORATIVE CANADIAN COIN AND TOKEN SETS, 2010-2011.

These sets contain six coins: 1¢, 10¢, 25¢, 50¢, $1.00, $2.00, plus a copper token commemorating the Fair or Exposition where the set was introduced.

DATE	DESCRIPTION	QUANTITY SOLD	ISSUE PRICE	FINISH	MS-65 NC
2010	Beijing International Coin Exposition	500	N/A	BU	75.
2011	World's Money Fair Berlin	500	N/A	BU	75.

COMMEMORATIVE CANADIAN COIN AND MEDAL SETS, 2011.

These sets contain six coins: 1¢, 10¢, 25¢, 50¢, $1.00 $2.00, plus a copper medallion.

DATE	DESCRIPTION	QUANTITY SOLD	ISSUE PRICE	FINISH	MS-65 NC
2011	Royal Canadian Numismatic Association Convention	500	N/A	Uncirculated	75.
2011	American Numismatic Association	500	N/A	Uncirculated	75.
2011	Beijing International Coin Exposition	500	N/A	Uncirculated	75.

COMMEMORATIVE CANADIAN COIN AND TOKEN SET, 2012.

This set contains six coins: 1¢, 5¢, 10¢, 25¢, $1.00, $2.00 plus a nickel token commemorating the World Money Fair, Berlin, Germany.

DATE	DESCRIPTION	QUANTITY SOLD	ISSUE PRICE	FINISH	MS-65 NC
2012	World Money Fair, Berlin, Germany	500	N/A	Uncirculated	75.

COMMEMORATIVE CANADIAN COIN AND MEDAL SETS, 2012.

These sets contains six coins: 1¢, 5¢, 10¢, 25¢, $1.00 and $2.00 (coins with security devices), plus a nickel medallion commemorating each venue.

DATE	DESCRIPTION	QUANTITY SOLD	ISSUE PRICE	FINISH	MS-65 NC
2012	Royal Canadian Numismatic Association, Calgary	217	N/A	Circulation	75.
2012	American Numismatic Association, Philadelphia	97	N/A	Circulation	100.
2012	Beijing International Stamp and Coin Exposition, Beijing, China	500	N/A	Circulation	75.

COMMEMORATIVE COIN AND MEDAL SETS, 2013.

These set contains five coins: 5¢, 10¢, 25¢, $1.00 and $2.00 (the $1 and $2 coins have security devices) plus a nickel medallion commemorating each venue.

DATE	DESCRIPTION	QUANTITY SOLD	ISSUE PRICE	FINISH	MS-65 NC
2013	World Money Fair, Berlin, Germany	500	N/A	Circulation	75.
2013	Royal Canadian Numismatic Association, Winnipeg	667	19.95	Circulation	75.
2013	American Numismatic Association, Chicago	500	19.95	Circulation	75.
2013	Beijing International Stamp and Coin Exposition, Beijing, China	499	19.95	Circulation	75.

SEVEN COIN NICKEL CUSTOM SETS, 1971-1975

The custom set contains one coin of each denomination, with an extra cent to show the obverse. The finish of the coins is identical to the corresponding year of brilliant uncirculated, brilliant relief on a brilliant background.

Cases: 1971:   Coins in black vinyl-covered case with Canada's coat of arms and the word "CANADA" stamped in gold on the top.
1972-1973:   As 1971, except the outer case is red.
1974-1975:   As 1971, except the outer case is maroon.

1973 Large Bust

1973 Large Bust

1973 Small Bust

1973 Small Bust

1973 Custom Set

DATE	DESCRIPTION	QUANTITY SOLD	ISSUE PRICE	FINISH	MS-65 NC
1971		33,517	6.50	BU	10.
1972		38,198	6.50	BU	10.
1973	Large Bust 25¢	49,376	6.50	BU	280.
1973	Small Bust 25¢	Included	6.50	BU	10.
1974		44,296	8.00	BU	10.
1975		36,581	8.00	BU	10.

SPECIMEN SETS, 1970-2019

SIX COIN NICKEL SPECIMEN SET, 1970

In 1968 the Royal Canadian Mint began to study the feasibility of offering for sale six-coin specimen sets to the public. The 1967 specimen set was extremely successful and opened the way for expanded offerings. Trial cases were prepared and a small number of specimen nickel and bronze coins of the years 1968 and 1969 were struck. These coins were not made available to the public.

In 1970 the Royal Canadian Mint provided special specimen sets to Prime Minister Pierre Trudeau for presentation purposes during his trip to China that year. A quantity of specimen sets in narrow cases were made up. After Trudeau's trip, some of these sets were sold to the public for $13 each. The total quantity of 1970 specimen sets issued in Canada is believed to be fewer than 1,000 and the only way 1970 specimen coins were available was in these sets. When the Mint made specimen sets available to the public starting in 1971, they were housed in larger, seven-coin cases. These sets are listed under prestige sets 1971-1980 on page 523.

In the early 1970's empty narrow specimen cases became available. The coins that could be housed in them were taken from prestige sets of the year.

Finish: Specimen, Brilliant relief on brilliant background

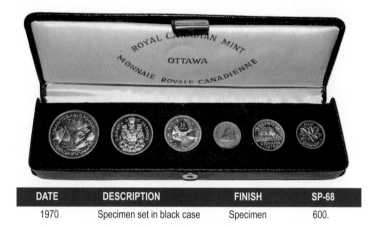

DATE	DESCRIPTION	FINISH	SP-68
1970	Specimen set in black case	Specimen	600.

SEVEN COIN NICKEL CUSTOM SPECIMEN SETS, 1976-1980

With the end of the 1976 Montreal Olympic Coin program, and with a new numismatic production facility now in place, the Mint staff turned their attention to improving the quality of their numismatic product line. The quality of the custom sets was upgraded to specimen. The packaging remained constant except for the modifications listed below.

Finish: Specimen, Brilliant relief on a parallel lined background
Cases: **1976-1978:** Coins in maroon vinyl-covered case with Canada's coat of arms and the word "CANADA" stamped in gold on the top.
  1979-1980: As 1977, except a gold maple leaf replaces the coat of arms and "CANADA"

DATE	DESCRIPTION	QUANTITY SOLD	ISSUE PRICE	FINISH	SP-68
1976 DJ	Voyageur	28,162	8.15	Specimen	10.
1977 AJ, SWL	Voyageur	44,198	8.15	Specimen	10.
1977 DJ, FWL	Voyageur	Included	8.15	Specimen	30.
1977 DJ, SWL	Voyageur	Included	8.15	Specimen	10.
1978 SJ 50¢	Voyageur	41,000	8.75	Specimen	10.
1978 RJ 50¢	Voyageur	Included	8.75	Specimen	22.
1979	Voyageur	31,174	10.75	Specimen	10.
1980	Voyageur	41,447	12.50	Specimen	10.

SIX COIN NICKEL SPECIMEN SETS, 1981-1996

1981 saw the first officially stated issue of specimen coinage. The package was redesigned, and the coins were marketed as being of specimen quality. The number of coins in the set was reduced to six. The finish on the coins from 1981 to 1995 was brilliant relief on a brilliant background, and in 1996 was changed to brilliant relief against parallel lined background.

Finish: **1981-1995:**   Specimen, Brilliant relief on a brilliant background
          1996:   Specimen, Brilliant relief on a parallel lined background
Cases: **1981-1987:**   Blue leatherette, booklet type (103 mm x 141 mm), inside a hinged blue plastic frame housing, six encapsulated coins. All enclosed in a silver box.
          1988-1996:   Blue leatherette, wallet type, (96 mm x 153 mm) silver stamped mint crest, inside clear plastic frame with blue plastic insert. All enclosed in a silver sleeve.

1992 Specimen Set

DATE	DESCRIPTION	QUANTITY SOLD	ISSUE PRICE	FINISH	SP-68
1981	Voyageur	71,300	10.00	Specimen	12.
1982	Voyageur	62,298	11.50	Specimen	12.
1983	Voyageur	60,329	12.75	Specimen	12.
1984	Voyageur	60,030	12.95	Specimen	12.
1985	Voyageur	61,533	12.95	Specimen	12.
1986	Voyageur	67,152	12.95	Specimen	12.
1987	Voyageur	74,441	14.00	Specimen	12.
1988	Loon	70,205	14.00	Specimen	12.
1989	Loon	66,855	16.95	Specimen	14.
1990	Loon	76,611	17.95	Specimen	14.
1991	Loon	68,552	17.95	Specimen	26.
1992 (1967-)	Loon	78,328	18.95	Specimen	20.
1993	Loon	77,351	18.95	Specimen	12.
1994	Loon	75,973	19.25	Specimen	12.
1995	Loon	77,326	19.25	Specimen	12.
1996	Loon	62,125	19.25	Specimen	24.

SEVEN COIN NICKEL SPECIMEN SETS, 1997-2000

In 1997 the two dollar coin was added to the set, raising the number of coins to seven. The set continued as specimen quality with the packaging being revised in 1998.

Finish: **1997-2000:**   Specimen, Brilliant relief on a parallel lined background
Cases: **1997:**   Blue leatherette, wallet type, (96 mm x 153 mm) silver stamped mint crest, inside clear plastic frame with blue plastic insert. All enclosed in a custom sleeve.
         1998-2000:   Green leatherette outer cover with RCM logo. All enclosed in a multicoloured box.

1997 Specimen Set

DATE	DESCRIPTION	QUANTITY SOLD	ISSUE PRICE	FINISH	SP-68
1997	Flying Loon/Bear	97,595	26.95	Specimen	30.
1998	Loon/Bear	67,697	26.95	Specimen	25.
1999	Loon/Bear	46,786	26.95	Specimen	25.
1999	Loon/Nunavut	45,104	26.95	Specimen	25.
2000	Loon/Bear	87,965	34.95	Specimen	25.
2000	Loon/Bears	Included	34.95	Specimen	25.

SIX OR SEVEN COIN MULTI-PLY PLATED STEEL SPECIMEN SETS, 2001-2019

The 2002 specimen set is a double anniversary set issued to commemorate the Golden Jubilee of Queen Elizabeth II, and the 15th anniversary of the Loon dollar coin which was introduced in 1987. This is the only set which contains the "Family of Loons" one dollar coin.

The 2004 issue carries the new uncrowned effigy of Queen Elizabeth II, by Susanna Blunt. In 2006 only the $2 coin carried the double date (1996-2006) which commemorated the tenth anniversary of the "Toonie".

From 2007 to 2009 all coins that comprise the specimen set carried the Royal Canadian Mint logo, but in 2010 the logo was discontinued.

In 2010 the finish used on specimen coinage was changed. The earlier finish, in use since 1996, was a variety of that used by the Bullion Department on their maple leaf coinage. However, this finish was surfacing on giftware coinage, so it is thought the time had arrived to again make specimen set coinage a distinct finish, brilliant relief on the obverse portrait and reverse design, with a frosted relief of the legends and date, all on a lined matte background.

The one dollar "Bird Series" that began in 1997 with the Flying Loon was continued to 2014 with the Ferruginous Hawk. For design illustrations of these coins see pages 121-122.

In 2012 production of the one cent coin was discontinued, bringing the number of coins in the specimen set to six.

Finish: **2001-2009:** Specimen, Brilliant relief on a raised lined background.
2010-2019: Specimen, Brilliant relief on obverse portrait and reverse design, frosted relief on legends and date, all on a laser lined background

Cases: Maroon leatherette display case, RCM Logo, black insert encased in clear plastic black shipping box.

DATE	DESCRIPTION	NO. OF COINS	RCM ITEM #	QUANTITY SOLD	ISSUE PRICE	FINISH	SP-68
2001P	Loon	7	N/A	54,613	39.95	Specimen	25.
2002P (1952-)	Loon Family	7	N/A	67,672	39.95	Specimen	30.
2003P	Loon	7	N/A	41,640	39.95	Specimen	25.
2004P	Canada Goose	7	N/A	46,493	44.95	Specimen	40.
2005P	Tufted Puffin	7	N/A	39,818	39.95	Specimen	45.
2006P	Snowy Owl	7	N/A	39,935	44.95	Specimen	45.
2007	Trumpeter Swan	7	6260107	27,056	45.95	Specimen	55.
2008	Common Eider	7	6260108	21,227	45.95	Specimen	45.
2009	Great Blue Heron	7	103608	21,677	47.95	Specimen	55.
2010	Northern Harrier	7	105794	21,111	49.95	Specimen	55.
2011	Great Grey Owl	7	111265	25,665	49.95	Specimen	55.
2012 (1987)	Loon with Chicks	7	116582	34,975	49.95	Specimen	50.
2013	Blue-Winged Teal	6	121282	28,884	49.95	Specimen	50.
2014	Ferruginous Hawk	6	127671	24,381	49.95	Specimen	50.
2015	Blue Jay	6	133241	22,739	49.95	Specimen	55.
2016	Tundra Swan	6	149524	21,565	49.95	Specimen	55.
2017	Snow Goose	6	156169	30,000	51.95	Specimen	50
2018	Burrowing Owl	6	164602	30,000	51.95	Specimen	52.
2019	Pileated Woodpecker	6	170696	30,000	49.95	Specimen	50.

Note: 1. The Loon Family design of 2002 commemorates the fifteenth anniversary of the $1.00 loon coin.
2. The ten cent coins contained in the 2007 specimen sets are the Small, Far Logo obverse / Curved 7 reverse variety.
3. The Loon Mother and Chicks design of 2012 commemorates the 25th anniversary of the $1.00 loon coin.

SPECIAL NOTE ON FINISHES

It is very important to understand the different finishes the Royal Canadian Mint uses on their various issues. These finishes are altered from time-to-time as the Mint develops new products.

For example, the brilliant relief against a parallel lined background finish first used on bullion coins was carried forward in 1996 to be used on the coins contained in the specimen set.

In 2006 this finish was used on giftware coins such as the twenty-five cent coin issued to celebrate the 80th birthday of Queen Elizabeth II.

In 2010 a new specimen finish, brilliant relief against a laser-lined background, was used for the coins contained in the specimen set. There are now two different specimen finishes being utilised on Canadian coinage.

Circulation and Brilliant Uncirculated (proof-like) finishes are another very confusing mixture of finishes, see pages xvi-xvii for a further explanation.

SPECIAL EDITION SPECIMEN SETS, 1967 and 2010-2015

100TH ANNIVERSARY OF CONFEDERATION, 1867-1967

In 1967 the Royal Canadian Mint produced two special cased coin sets to mark the 100th anniversary of Confederation. The silver medallion set in the red leather-covered case contained one each of the 1¢ to $1 (Proof-like finish) and a sterling silver medallion designed and modelled by Thomas Shingles. The gold presentation set contained a $20 gold coin and one each of the 1¢ to $1, all of specimen finish. This set was housed in a black leather presentation case.

DATE	DESCRIPTION	QUANTITY SOLD	ISSUE PRICE	FINISH	GRADE	PRICE
1967	Medallion	72,463	12.00	Proof-like	PL-65	70.
1967	Gold	337,687	40.00	Specimen	SP-68	1,000.

SPECIAL EDITION "YOUNG WILDLIFE" SPECIMEN SETS, 2010-2015

The two-dollar "YoungWildlife Series" that began in 2010 with Two Lynx Kittens was continued to 2015 with the Baby Racoons. For design illustrations of these coins see page 142.

A "finish" ten cent mule is found in the 2010 Lynx Specimen Set. The coin has an obverse with a brilliant relief on a raised lined background (2009 finish), and a reverse with a brilliant relief on the legend and date, with a lined matte finish background (2010 finish).

TEN CENT "FINISH" MULE

10¢ Obverse with
2009 Specimen Finish

10¢ Reverse with
2010 Specimen Finish

Finish: Specimen, Brilliant relief on obverse portrait and revere design, frosted relief on legends and date, all on a laser lined background
Case of Issue: Maroon leatherette clam style case, RCM logo, 6- or 7-hole black insert in clear plastic, multicoloured box.

DATE	DESCRIPTION	NO. OF COINS	RCM ITEM #	QUANTITY SOLD	ISSUE PRICE	FINISH	SP-68	SP-69
2010	$2 Two Lynx Kittens	7	107118	14,790	49.95	Specimen	70.	—
2010	'Finish' Mule ten cent coin	7	N/A	Included	49.95	Specimen	300.	—
2011	$2 Elk Calf	7	112456	13,899	49.95	Specimen	70.	—
2012	$2 Wolf Cubs	7	116619	14,968	49.95	Specimen	60.	—
2013	$2 Black Bear Cubs	6	123462	17,218	49.95	Specimen	50.	—
2014	$2 Baby Rabbits	6	130292	11,886	49.95	Specimen	50.	—
2015	$2 Baby Racoons	6	143341	8,504	49.95	Specimen	50.	

SPECIAL EDITION "CANADIAN ARCTIC EXPEDITION" SPECIMEN SET, 2013

This set contains a specimen silver dollar commemorating the 100th anniversary of the Canadian Arctic Expedition.

DATE	DESCRIPTION	NO. OF COINS	RCM ITEM #	QUANTITY SOLD	ISSUE PRICE	FINISH	SP-68	SP-69
2013	Specimen Silver Dollar Set	7	127214	9,787	99.95	Specimen	90.	—

PRESTIGE SETS, 1971-1980

SEVEN COIN PRESTIGE SETS, 1971-1980

When it was first introduced in 1971, the prestige set (double dollar set) contained two nickel dollars, with the second nickel dollar being used to display the obverse. This was also true for the 1972 set; however, from 1973 on the second nickel dollar was replaced with a silver dollar. The coins in the prestige sets were of specimen quality until 1980, and proof quality thereafter.

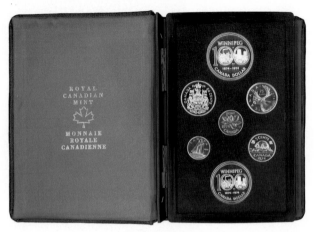

1974 Prestige Set

Finish: **1971-1980:** Specimen, Brilliant relief on a brilliant background

Cases: **1971-1973:** Crest of Canada; black leather, book type with clasp. Red satin inside red flocked 7-hole stationary display - coloured flocked jackets.

1974-1978: Crest of Canada; black leather, book type with clasp. Red satin inside, hinged black plastic 7-hole display, encapsulated coins - coloured flocked jackets.

1979-1980: Maple Leaf; black cardboard box, book type with clasp. Red satin inside, hinged black plastic 7-hole display, encapsulated coins - coloured flocked jackets.

DATE	DESCRIPTION	RCM ITEM #	QUANTITY SOLD	ISSUE PRICE	FINISH	SP-68
1971	B.C./B.C.	N/A	66,860	12.00	Specimen	20.
1972	Voyageur/Voyageur	N/A	36,349	12.00	Specimen	45.
1973 LB 25¢	P.E.I./R.C.M.P.	N/A	119,891	12.00	Specimen	280.
1973 SB 25¢	P.E.I./R.C.M.P.	N/A	Included	12.00	Specimen	25.
1974	Winnipeg/Winnipeg	N/A	85,230	15.00	Specimen	25.
1974 DYT3	Winnipeg/Winnipeg	N/A	Included	15.00	Specimen	800.
1975	Voyageur/Calgary	N/A	97,263	15.00	Specimen	25.
1976	Voyageur/Parliament	N/A	87,744	16.00	Specimen	25.
1977	Voyageur/Jubilee	N/A	142,577	16.00	Specimen	25.
1977 SWL	Voyageur/Jubilee	N/A	Included	16.00	Specimen	30.
1978 SJ	Voyageur/Edmonton	N/A	147,000	16.50	Specimen	25.
1978 RJ	Voyageur/Edmonton	N/A	Included	16.50	Specimen	35.
1979	Voyageur/Griffon	N/A	155,698	18.50	Specimen	25.
1980	Voyageur/Polar Bear	N/A	162,875	36.00	Specimen	25.

Note: For images of the large bust (LB) and small bust (SB) twenty-five cent varieties of 1973, see page 519
For an image of the 1974 nickel dollar, double yoke type 3 variety, see page 494.
For an image of the 1977 nickel dollar, short water line (SWL) variety, see page 495.
For and image of the 1978 fifty cent, square jewels (SJ) and round jewels (RJ) varieties, see page 495.

PROOF SETS, 1981-2019

PROOF SETS, 1981-1995.

SEVEN STANDARD COINS

With the product reorganization in 1981, the standard coins of the Prestige Set were converted to Proof finish.

Finish: **1981-1995:**   Proof, Frosted relief against a mirror background

Cases: **1981-1985:**   Maple Leaf; black cardboard box, book type with clasp. Red satin inside, hinged black plastic 7-hole display, coloured flocked jackets.

1986-1995:   Maple leaf; black plastic box, wallet type. Red satin inside, hinged black plastic 7-hole display, encapsulated coins

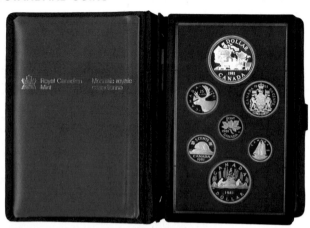

DATE	DESCRIPTION	RCM ITEM #	QUANTITY SOLD	ISSUE PRICE	FINISH	PR-68
1981	Voyageur/Train	N/A	199,000	36.00	Proof	25.
1982	Voyageur/Skull	N/A	180,908	36.00	Proof	25.
1983	Voyageur/Games	N/A	166,779	36.00	Proof	25.
1984	Voyageur/Toronto	N/A	161,602	40.00	Proof	25.
1985	Voyageur/Parks	N/A	153,950	40.00	Proof	25.
1986	Voyageur/Vancouver	N/A	176,224	40.00	Proof	25.
1987	Voyageur/Davis Strait	N/A	175,686	43.00	Proof	25.
1988	Loon/Ironworks	N/A	175,259	43.00	Proof	25.
1989	Loon/MacKenzie	N/A	154,693	46.95	Proof	25.
1990	Loon/Kelsey	N/A	158,068	48.00	Proof	25.
1991	Loon/Frontenac	N/A	131,888	48.00	Proof	50.
1992	Loon/Stagecoach	N/A	147,061	49.75	Proof	35.
1993	Loon/Hockey	N/A	143,065	49.75	Proof	35.
1994	Loon/Dogsled Team	N/A	104,485	50.75	Proof	35.
1995	Loon/Hudson's Bay	N/A	101,560	50.75	Proof	35.

PROOF SET, 1996.

SEVEN COIN SET WITH FOUR STERLING SILVER COINS

Beginning in 1996, the five, ten, twenty-five and fifty cent coins were struck on sterling silver planchets (92.5% Ag and 7.5% Cu). The one cent, and both the nickel and silver dollars were of standard specifications.

Finish: Proof, Frosted relief against a mirror background

Case of Issue: Maple Leaf logo; black leatherette wallet type case. Red satin inside, hinged black plastic 7-hole display, encapsulated coins

DATE	DESCRIPTION	RCM ITEM #	QUANTITY SOLD	ISSUE PRICE	FINISH	PR-68
1996	Loon/McIntosh	N/A	112,835	66.25	Proof	55.

EIGHT COIN SET WITH FIVE STERLING SILVER COINS 1997-2012

In 1997 the two dollar coin was added to the set, raising the total to eight coins. The two dollar coin, following the practice established in 1996, was made of sterling silver with a gold-plated centre. The one cent coin up to and including 2003, was not of the multi-ply plated steel, but of bronze composition.

Mid-year 2003 the tiara portrait of Elizabeth II, which had been in use since 1990, was replaced with the new uncrowned portrait by Susanna Blunt. The first Proof set with the new portrait was dated 2004.

The 2005 Proof set was the first set to feature a commemorative dollar selectively gold plated on the reverse and rim.

In 2012, for the first time two variations of the Proof set were issued: a standard Proof set where all coins are struck in their standard circulation alloys, and a premium fine silver Proof set where all coins are struck in 99.99% pure silver.

1997 Proof Set

1998 Proof Set

Finish: 1997-2012: Proof, frosted relief against a mirror background

Case of Issue: 1997: Maple Leaf logo; black leather wallet type case. Red satin inside, hinged black plastic 7-hole display, encapsulated coins

1998-2003: Mint logo; dark green leather wallet style case, black plastic 8-hole insert, encapsulated coins, green flocked interior; four-colour outer box

2004-2012: Mint logo; maroon leather wallet style case, black plastic 8-hole insert, encapsulated coins, black flocked interior; black outer box

DATE	DESCRIPTION	RCM ITEM #	QUANTITY SOLD	ISSUE PRICE	FINISH	PR-69
1997	Loon/Hockey/Polar Bear	N/A	113,647	79.95	Proof	65.
1997	CNA Edition signed Cournoyer / Ferguson	N/A	N/A	N/A	Proof	80.
1997	ANA Edition, signed Gilbert / Park	N/A	N/A	N/A	Proof	80.
1998	Loon/R.C.M.P./Polar Bear	N/A	93,632	79.95	Proof	65.
1999	Loon/Juan Perez/Polar Bear	N/A	95,113	79.95	Proof	65.
2000	Loon/Discovery/Polar Bear	N/A	90,921	79.95	Proof	65.
2001	Loon/Ballet/Polar Bear	N/A	74,194	81.95	Proof	65.
2001	ANA Edition	N/A	750	69.95	Proof	80.
2001	CNA Edition	N/A	N/A	89.95	Proof	80.
2002 (1952-)	Loon/Queen Elizabeth II/Polar Bear	N/A	65,315	81.95	Proof	65.
2002 (1952-)	ANA Edition	N/A	500	69.95	Proof	80.
2003	Loon/Cobalt/Polar Bear	N/A	62,007	81.95	Proof	65.
2003	ANA Edition	N/A	500	74.95	Proof	80.
2004	Loon/French Settlement/Polar Bear	N/A	57,614	83.92	Proof	65.
2004	ANA Edition	N/A	500	74.95	Proof	80.
2004	CNA Edition	N/A	250	74.95	Proof	80.
2005	Loon/Flag (gold plated) /Polar Bear	N/A	63,562	81.95	Proof	75.
2005	CNA Edition	N/A	197	74.95	Proof	90.
2006 (1996-)	Loon/Victoria Cross (gold plated) /Polar Bear	N/A	53,822	84.95	Proof	80.
2006	CNA Edition	N/A	200	84.95	Proof	90.
2007	Loon/Thayendanegea (gold plated)/Polar Bear	6260007	37,413	89.95	Proof	80.
2008	Loon/Quebec City (gold plated)/Polar Bear	6260008	38,630	89.95	Proof	80.
2009	Loon/First Flight (gold plated)/Polar Bear	103749	27,549	99.95	Proof	90.
2009	RCNA Edition	N/A	200	99.95	Proof	100.
2010	Loon/Corvette (gold plated)/Polar Bear	105793	32,342	109.95	Proof	90.
2011 (1911-)	Loon/Parks (gold plated)/Canada/Bear	111244	32,910	114.95	Proof	90.
2012 (1812-)	Loon/War of 1812/Polar Bear	117680	27,254	99.95	Proof	90.

Note: The ten cent coins contained in the 2007 proof sets are the Small, Far Logo obverse / Curved 7 reverse variety.

PREMIUM PROOF SETS, 2012-2019

With the one cent coin being phased out in 2012, the number of coins contained in the Premium Proof sets is now reduced to seven. Each coin contained in these sets is struck on a fine silver planchet.

2012 Premium Proof Set

2018 Premium Proof Set

Finish: **2012-2019:** Proof, frosted relief against a mirror background

Case of Issue: **2012:** Mint logo; black genuine leather case with black plastic 8-hole insert, encapsulated coins, black flocked interior, black outer box

2013-2018: Mint logo; black genuine leather case with black plastic 7-hole insert, encapsulated coins, black flocked interior, black outer box

2019: Mint logo; book-style packaging with removable lens and serialized certificate, CD lens concept with genuine leather outer cover and black beauty box

DATE	DESCRIPTION	RCM ITEM #	QUANTITY SOLD	ISSUE PRICE	FINISH	PR-69
2012 (1812-)	Loon/War of 1812 (gold plated)/Polar Bear	116689	19,789	224.95	Proof	170.
2013	100th Anniv. Canadian Arctic Expedition	121827	20,338	229.95	Proof	180.
2013	100th Anniv. Canadian Arctic Expedition, RCNA Edition	N/A	427	229.95	Proof	250.
2014	100th Anniv. Declaration First World War	128624	13,416	229.95	Proof	200.
2015	50th Anniv. of the Canadian Flag	133233	14,006	229.95	Proof	230.
2016	150th Anniv. of the Transatlantic Cable	151180	9,211	229.95	Proof	230.
2017	150th Anniv. of Canadian Confederation	154940	8,017	234.95	Proof	235.
2017	150h Anniv. Our Home and Native Land	158348	15,000	229.95	Proof	250.
2018	240th Anniv. Captain Cook at Nootka Sound	164786	15,000	234.95	Proof	235.
2019	75th Anniv. of D-Day	170630	15,000	234.95	Proof	235.

PROOF SETS, 2014-2019

Again, in 2014 two varieties of proof sets were issued. This set contains seven proof coins struck on the standard alloys.

Finish: **2014-2018:** Proof, frosted relief against a mirror background

Case of Issue: **2014-2017:** Mint logo; maroon leatherette case with black plastic 7-hole insert, encapsulated coins, black interior, black outer box

2018: Mint logo; book-style packaging with removable lens and serialized certificate, CD lens concept

DATE	DESCRIPTION	RCM ITEM #	QUANTITY SOLD	ISSUE PRICE	FINISH	PR-69
2014	100th Anniv. Declaration of First World War	130504	11,251	99.95	Proof	100.
2015	50th Anniv. of the Canadian Flag	145709	20,000	99.95	Proof	100.
2016	150th Anniv. of the Transatlantic Cable	151850	12,500	99.95	Proof	100.
2017	150th Anniv. Our Home and Native Land	159428	25,000	99.95	Proof	110.
2018	240th Anniv. Captain Cook at Nootka Sound	165601	15,000	104.95	Proof	105.
2019	Classic Canadian Coins – Colourised	168501	7,000	199.95	Proof	200.

SPECIAL ISSUE PROOF SETS, 1994-2011

SPECIAL LIMITED EDITION PROOF SETS, 1994-1995

First issued in 1994, these Proof sets were limited to 50,000. They contained the silver commemorative dollar, along with the bronze/nickel commemorative of the year. The other five coins are the same as contained in the Proof set of that year.

Finish: Proof, frosted relief against a mirror background
Case of Issue: Burgundy display case, wallet type, dated on spine with year of issue. Interior: White satin with brown plastic display frame
- burgundy plastic box. Over time, the colour of the case and box fades.

DATE	DESCRIPTION	RCM ITEM #	QUANTITY SOLD	ISSUE PRICE	FINISH	PR-69
1994	Remembrance/Dog Team Patrol	N/A	49,222	59.50	Proof	40.
1995	Peacekeeping/Hudson's Bay	N/A	49,802	66.95	Proof	40.

90th ANNIVERSARY OF THE ROYAL CANADIAN MINT, 1908-1998

Issued to commemorate the 90th Anniversary of the Royal Canadian Mint, this five-coin set features the same reverse designs as the original 1908 coins, except for the double date 1908-1998. The set was issued in two finishes, matte and mirror proof. The matte one cent coin does not carry the country of origin, "Canada." This error was corrected on the mirror proof cent.

Designers:
Obv.: Dora de Pédery-Hunt
Rev.: Ago Aarand

Engravers:
Obv.: Dora de Pédery-Hunt
Rev.: 1¢ – G. W. DeSaulles
5¢, 10¢, 25¢, 50¢ –
W. H. J. Blakemore

1¢ Matte Issue
Without CANADA

1¢ Mirror Issue
With CANADA

Finish: Proof, matte or mirror
Case of Issue: Burgundy leather clam style case, RCM Mint logo, white lining, five-hole plastic insert, COA
Matte set with bronze logo on case. Mirror set with nickel logo on the case

COIN	COMPOSITION	WEIGHT	DIAMETER	EDGE	DIE AXIS
1¢	92.5% Ag, 7.5% Cu, copper plated	5.90	25.30	Plain	↑↑
5¢	92.5% Ag, 7.5% Cu	1.30	15.25	Reeded	↑↑
10¢	92.5% Ag, 7.5% Cu	2.32	17.90	Reeded	↑↑
25¢	92.5% Ag, 7.5% Cu	5.89	23.50	Reeded	↑↑
50¢	92.5% Ag, 7.5% Cu	11.80	29.60	Reeded	↑↑

DATE	DESCRIPTION	QUANTITY SOLD	ISSUE PRICE	FINISH	PR-69
1998 (1908-)	Without "CANADA" on 1¢	24,893	99.00	Matte proof	60.
1998 (1908-)	With "CANADA" on 1¢	18,376	99.00	Mirror proof	60.

SPECIAL LIMITED EDITION PROOF SETS, 2002-2003

The Special Edition Proof Set for 1952-2002 contains the 2002 commemorative dollar (22kt gold plated), the two-dollar coin with a 24kt gold plated inner core, and the 2002 fifty-cent commemorative coin. The remaining coins in the set are as the regular issue.

The coins in the Special Edition Proof Set for 1953-2003, carry the laureate portrait of Queen Elizabeth II which was first issued in 1953. This set commemorates Queen Elizabeth II's Coronation in 1953, and her Jubilee in 2003, with the double date 1953-2003.

Finish: Proof, frosted relief against a mirror background

DATE	DESCRIPTION	RCM ITEM #	QUANTITY SOLD	ISSUE PRICE	FINISH	PR-69
2002 (1952-)	Accession, Gold Plated $1 coin	N/A	33,490	99.95	Proof	80.
2003 (1953-)	Coronation	N/A	21,537	99.95	Proof	90.

PREMIUM GIFT BABY AND WEDDING, STERLING SILVER PROOF SETS, 2006-2008

This set contains a commemorative sterling silver loon dollar and a commemorative medallion; the remaining coins are the regular Proof set issue.

2006 Premium Gift Baby Proof Set

2007 Premium Gift Wedding Proof Set

Finish: Proof, frosted relief, against mirror background   **Case of Issue:**   Leatherette folder

DATE	DESCRIPTION	RCM ITEM #	QUANTITY SOLD	ISSUE PRICE	FINISH	PR-69
2006	Sterling Silver Loon, Lullaby Loonie, Teddy Bear Medallion	N/A	3,863	79.95	Proof	200.
2007	Sterling Silver "Gold Plated Rattle", Baby Medallion	6260017	1,911	89.95	Proof	900.
2007	Sterling Silver Loon, Wedding Medallion	6260018	849	89.95	Proof	900.
2008	Sterling Silver Loon, Baby Medallion	100614	1,168	99.95	Proof	225.
2008	Sterling Silver Loon, Wedding Medallion	100615	508	99.95	Proof	800.

SPECIAL LIMITED EDITION PROOF SET, 2010

Canada's first circulating silver dollar was introduced in 1935 featuring Emanuel Hahn's classic Voyageur design. This special edition Proof set, with four other coins carrying the 1935 design commemorates the 75th anniversary of our famous dollar.

Finish: Proof
Case of Issue: Maple wood display case

DATE	DESCRIPTION	RCM ITEM #	QUANTITY SOLD	ISSUE PRICE	FINISH	PR-69
2010 (1935-)	75th Anniv. of the Voyageur Dollar	111020	4,996	159.95	Proof	230.

SPECIAL LIMITED EDITION PROOF SET, 1911-2011

This set was Issued to commemorate the 100th Anniversary of the striking of the 1911 silver dollars.

Designers and Engravers:
    Obv.:   Sir E. B. MacKennal
    Rev.:   1¢, 5¢, 10¢, 25¢, 50¢ –
            Original design by L. C. Wyon,
            Modified by W. H. J. Blakemore

Finish: Proof
Case of Issue: Cherry wood box

DATE	DESCRIPTION	RCM ITEM #	QUANTITY SOLD	ISSUE PRICE	FINISH	PR-69
2011 (1911-)	100th Anniv. of the 1911 Silver Dollar	114121	5,952	179.95	Proof	250.

SPECIAL ISSUE COIN SETS, 2017-2019

ROYAL CANADIAN MINT COIN LORE SERIES, 2017-2019

ROYAL CANADIAN MINT COIN LORE: THE FORGOTTEN 1927 DESIGNS – 3-COIN SET, 2017.

In 1927, three circulation coin designs were chosen to commemorate Confederation's Diamond Jubilee; alas, they never made it onto a single coin. Ninety years later, the RCM re-visited some of Canada's coin lore, to issue this three-coin set, which artfully bridges the past and Canada 150.

Common Obverse	1 Cent Obv.: E.B. MacKennal Rev.: Gustav Hahan	5 Cents Obv.: E.B. MacKennal Rev.: J.E.H. MacDonald	25 Cents Obv.: E.B. MacKennal Rev.: J.E.H. MacDonald

Designers:		**Engravers:**	
Obv.:	See illustrations	Obv.:	See illustrations
Rev.:	See reverse illustrations	Rev.:	See Illustrations
Composition:	99.99% au		
Silver content:	14.7 g, 0.473 (per set)		
Weight:	31.39 g (per coin)	**Edge:**	Reeded
Diameter:	38 mm	**Die Axis:**	↑↑
Thickness:	N/A	**Finish:**	Reverse Proof
Case of Issue:	Maroon clamshell with standard black beauty box. COA.		

DATE	DESCRIPTION	RCM ITEM #	MINTAGE	ISSUE PRICE	FINISH	PR-69
2017	The Forgotten 1927 Designs - 3-Coin Set	160230	5,500	269.95	Reverse Proof	250.

ROYAL CANADIAN MINT COIN LORE: THE COINS THAT NEVER WERE – 3-COIN SET, 2018.

In 1936 Emanuel Hahn submitted several concepts for new circulation coinage, but most were set aside. Now, some of Hahn's "coins that never were" are featured in a three-coin tribute set.

Common Obverse	5 Cents – Caribou	25 Cents - Polar Bear	25 Cents - Goose

Designers:		**Engravers:**	
Obv.:	Susanna Blunt	Obv.:	Susan Taylor
Rev.:	Emanuel Otto Hahn		
Composition:	99.99% Ag		
Silver content:	31.39 g, 1.01 tr oz		
Weight:	31.39 g	**Edge:**	Reeded
Diameter:	38 mm	**Die Axis:**	↑↑
Thickness:	N/A	**Finish:**	Reverse Proof
Case of Issue:	Standard maroon clamshell with black beauty box, COA.		

DATE	DESCRIPTION	RCM ITEM #	MINTAGE	ISSUE PRICE	FINISH	PR-69
2018	The Coins That Never Were – 3-Coin Set	164563	5,500	269.95	Reverse Proof	270.

ROYAL CANADIAN MINT COIN LORE: BACK TO CONCEPT – 2-COIN SET, 2019.

This set features an early take on two classic coin designs: Emanuel Hahn's Voyageur dollar (1935) and "caribou" 25 cents (1937). The images may look familiar, but the all-new sculpts are based solely on the artist's preliminary pencil sketches, which are preserved in the National Currency Collection - Bank of Canada.

Common Obverse	Twenty-Five Cent	Dollar

Designers:

		Engravers:	
Obv.:	T.H. Paget	Rev.:	Emaneul Hahn
Composition:	99.99% Ag	**Silver content:**	62.69 g, 2.016 tr. oz.
Weight:	62.69 g	**Edge:**	Reeded
Diameter:	50 mm	**Die Axis:**	↑↑
Thickness:	N/A	**Finish:**	Proof
Case of Issue:	Black clamshell with black beauty box..		

DATE	DESCRIPTION	RCM ITEM #	MINTAGE	ISSUE PRICE	FINISH	PR-69
2019	Back to Concept – 2-Coin Set	170962	1,750	359.95	Proof	360.

BENEATH THY SHINING SKIES – 3-COIN SET, 2018.

Coming together to form the flag of Canada, three irregular-shaped coins present a rich narrative that is the story of a nation, from pre-Confederation to today and beyond.

$25 Left	$10 Centre	$25 Right

	$25 Left	$10 Centre	$25 Right

Designers and Engravers:

Obv.:	Susanna Blunt, Susan Taylor			
Rev.:	Rebecca Yanovskaya			
Composition:	99.99% Ag			
Silver content:		47.34 g, 1.522 tr. oz.	15.67 g, 0.50 tr. oz.	47.34 g, 1.522 tr. oz.
Weight:		47.34 g	15.67 g	47.34 g
Diameter:		49.80 mm x 28.60 mm	39.6 mm x 38 mm	49.80 mm x 28.60 mm
Thickness:	N/A			
Edge:	Plain			
Die Axis:	↑↑			
Finish:	Proof			
Case of Issue:	Black clamshell with black beauty box, COA.			

DATE	DESCRIPTION	RCM ITEM #	MINTAGE	ISSUE PRICE	FINISH	PR-69
2018	Beneath Thy Shining Skies – 3-Coin Set	165900	3,000	399.95	Proof	400.

BEFORE CONFEDERATION: COLONIAL CURRENCY OF THE ATLANTIC PROVINCES – 4-COIN SET, 2018.

Before Confederation, the provinces of Atlantic Canada were separate British North American colonies, each with their own particular cultural character and even their own coins - a fact that adds a fascinating diversity to Canada's coin history.

Prince Edward Island Obverse	Newfoundland Obverse	New Brunswick & Nova Scotia Obverse

Nova Scotia 1¢	Prince Edward Island 1¢	Newfoundland 5¢	New Brunswick 1¢

Designers and Engravers:

		Nova Scotia	Prince Edward Island	Newfoundland	New Brunswick
Obv.:	Susanna Blunt, Susan Taylor				
Rev.:	L.C. Wyon				
Composition:	99.99% Ag				
Silver content:		62.69 g, 2.016 tr. oz	31.93 g, 1.023 tr. oz	15.87 g, 0.510 tr. oz	7.96 g, 0.256 tr. oz
Weight:		62.69 g	31.83 g	15.87 g	7.96 g
Diameter:		50 mm	40 mm	34 mm	27 mm
Thickness:	N/A				
Edge:	Reeded				
Die Axis:	↑↑				
Finish:	Antique				
Case of Issue:	Standard maroon clamshell with black beauty box, COA.				

DATE	DESCRIPTION	RCM ITEM #	MINTAGE	ISSUE PRICE	FINISH	PR-69
2018	Before Confederation: Colonial Currency of the Atlantic Provinces – 4-Coin Set	166904	3,000	389.95	Antique	390.

HERALDIC EMBLEMS OF CANADA – 14-COIN SET, 2018.

Each province and territory is emblematically represented on one of thirteen 25-cent coins that bear coloured arms, while our national armorial bearings, the Arms of Canada, has a special place of honour on the larger-sized $5 coin.

Designers and Engravers:

Obv.:	Susanna Blunt, Susan Taylor
Rev.:	RCM Staff

Composition: 99.99% Ag

	25-cents	$5
Silver content:	6 g, 0.193 tr. oz.	15.87 g, 0.51 tr. oz.
Weight:	6 g	15.87 g
Diameter:	23.88 mm	34 mm
Edge:	Reeded	
Die Axis:	↑↑	
Finish:	Reverse Proof	
Case of Issue:	Graphic-wrapped box with protective sleeve, COA.	

DATE	DESCRIPTION	RCM ITEM #	MINTAGE	ISSUE PRICE	FINISH	PR-69
2018	Heraldic Emblems of Canada – 14-Coin Set	168747	4,000	399.95	Reverse Proof	400.

STATE-OF-THE-ART – 4-COIN SET, 2018.

The 2018 State-of-the-Art set is an elite sampling of cutting-edge technologies and innovations that help set out coins apart. This is the first set to feature one coin from each business line — numismatics, bullion, Canadian and foreign circulation — all proudly struck at RCM facilities.

1936 10-Cent Dot

Silver Maple Leaf Bullion

$2 Canadian Circulation

Fiji 50-Cent Circulation

Designers and Engravers:	**1936 Dot 10¢**	**Silver Maple Leaf Bullion**	**$2 Canadian Circulation**	**Fiji 50¢ Circulation**
Obv.:	Sir E.B. MacKennal	Susanna Blunt	Susanna Blunt	RCM Staff
Rev.:	W.H.J. Blakemore	RCM Staff	Timothy Hsia	RCM Staff
Composition:	99.99% Ag	99.99% Ag	99.99% Ag	99.99% Ag
Silver content:	62.67 g, 2.015 tr. oz	31.11 g, 1.00 tr. oz	6.99 g, 0.224 tr. oz	6.5 g, 0.209 tr. oz
Weight:	62.67 g	31.11 g	6.99 g	6.5 g
Diameter:	54 mm	38 mm	28 mm	26.5 mm
Edge:	Plain	Plain	Plain	Plain
Die Axis:	↑↑	↑↑	↑↑	↑↑
Finish:	Proof	Proof	Proof	Proof
Case of Issue:	Graphic-wrapped box with protective sleetve, COA.			

DATE	DESCRIPTION	RCM ITEM #	MINTAGE	ISSUE PRICE	FINISH	PR-69
2018	State-of-the-Art – 4-Coin Set	170249	4,500	234.95	Proof	240.

WINGS OF HOPE – 3-COIN SET, 2019.

This three-coin set consists of two rectangular wafers and a maple-shaped coin that come together to form Canada's flag.

$25 Left	$10 Centre	$25 Right

Designers and Engravers:

Obv.:   Susanna Blunt, Susan Taylor
Rev.:   David Caesar
Composition: 99.99% Ag

	$25 Left	$10 Centre	$25 Right
Silver content:	47.34 g, 1.522 tr. oz.	15.67 g, 0.50 tr. oz.	47.34 g, 1.522 tr. oz.
Weight:	47.34 g	15.67 g	47.34 g
Diameter:	49.80 mm x 28.60 mm	39.6 mm x 38 mm	49.80 mm x 28.60 mm

Edge:	Plain	**Die Axis:**	↑↑
Finish:	Proof	**Case of Issue:**	Black clamshell with black beauty box, COA.

DATE	DESCRIPTION	RCM ITEM #	MINTAGE	ISSUE PRICE	FINISH	PR-69
2019	Wings Of Hope	170260	1,000	389.95	Proof	390.

THE CANADIAN MAPLE MASTERS COLLECTION – 5-COIN SET, 2019.

This premium collection takes the classic fractional set in a new dirction: instead of offering a 1 oz. coin with smaller fractional sizes, the set begins with a 1 oz. ($20) and ends with a stunning kilo coin ($250).

Designers and Engravers:

Obv.:   Susanna Blunt, Susan Taylor
Rev.:   Steve Hepburn
Composition: 99.99% Ag

	$20	$30	$50	$125	$250
Silver content:	31.39 g, 1.01 tr. oz	62.69 g, 2.02 tr. oz	157.6 g, 5.07 tr. oz	503 g, 16.17 tr. oz	1,006 g, 32.35 tr. oz.
Weight:	31.39 g	62,69 g	157.6 g	503 g	1,006 g
Diameter:	38 mm	50 mm	62.25 mm	85.45 mm	102.1 mm

Edge:	Reeded	**Die Axis:**	↑↑
Finish:	Proof	**Case of Issue:**	Wood case with black beauty box, COA.

DATE	DESCRIPTION	RCM ITEM #	MINTAGE	ISSUE PRICE	FINISH	PR-69
2019	The Canadian Maple Masters Collection – 5-Coin Set	171729	350	3,999.95	Proof	4,000.

PROOF GOLD SET

YEAR OF THE DRAGON, 2012.

The reverse design on these coins features a mythical water dragon surrounded by lotus flowers and clouds of good fortune, the Chinese lunar symbol for the year 2012.

Obverse

Physical and chemical specifications:

Denomination:	$50	$20	$10	$5
Weight (oz):	1.0	0.5	0.25	0.1
Diameter (mm):	30.0	25.0	20.0	16.0
Thickness (mm):	N/A	N/A	N/A	N/A
Composition:	99.99% Au			
Gold content:				
Grams	31.15	15.59	7.8	3.13
Troy ounces	1.00	0.50	0.25	0.10
Edge:	Reeded			
Die Axis:	↑↑			
Finish:	Proof			
Case of Issue:	Gold silk-covered case, black suede four-hole insert, encapsulated, COA			

$50 **$20** **$10** **$5**

Designers:
Obv.: Susanna Blunt
Rev.: Susan Taylor

Engravers:
Rev.: Three Degrees Creative Group Inc.
Rev.: Cecily Mok

DATE	DESCRIPTION	RCM ITEM #	QUANTITY SOLD	ISSUE PRICE	FINISH	PR-69	PR-70
2012	Year of the Dragon	119159	357	5,499.95	Proof	5,500.	—

PROOF PLATINUM SETS

In 1990 the Royal Canadian Mint entered the luxury market for high quality collector coins. While the proof platinum sets are scarce their value is linked to the market price of platinum. The value of these sets is based on a Canadian market price of $1,540. for platinum as of April 23rd, 2014.

CANADIAN WILDLIFE SERIES, 1990-1994.

1990-1994 Obverse

Physical and chemical specifications:

Denomination:	$300	$150	$75	$30
Weight (oz):	1.0	0.5	0.25	0.1
Diameter (mm):	30.0	25.0	20.0	16.0
Thickness (mm):	2.6	2.12	1.65	1.08
Composition:	99.95% Pt			
Platinum content:				
Grams	31.1	15.55	7.75	3.1
Troy ounces	1.0	0.5	0.25	0.1
Edge:	Reeded			
Die Axis:	↑↑			
Finish:	Proof			
Case of Issue:	1992-1994: Walnut case, black suede four hole insert, encapsulated, COA			

POLAR BEARS PLATINUM SET 1990.

Canada's "Monarch of the North" has been transferred by Robert Bateman from the sparkling Arctic environment to the gleaming surfaces of pure platinum coins.

$300	**$150**	**$75**	**$30**

Designers:
Obv.:　Dora de Pédery-Hunt
Rev.:　Robert Bateman

Engravers:
Obv.:　Dora de Pédery-Hunt
Rev.:　$300 - Terry Smith
$150 - William Woodruff
$ 75 - Ago Aarand
$ 30 - Sheldon Beveridge

DATE	DESCRIPTION	QUANTITY SOLD	ISSUE PRICE	FINISH	PR-68	PR-69
1990	Polar Bears, Set of 4 coins	2,629	1,990.00	Proof	3,300.	—

SNOWY OWLS PLATINUM SET 1991.

This is the second set in the series of Proof platinum coins dedicated to Canadian wildlife.

$300	**$150**	**$75**	**$30**

Designers:
Obv.:　Dora de Pédery-Hunt
Rev.:　Glen Loates

Engravers:
Obv.:　Dora de Pédery-Hunt
Rev.:　$300 - Sheldon Beveridge
$150 - Ago Aarand
$ 75 - Terry Smith
$ 30 - William Woodruff

DATE	DESCRIPTION	QUANTITY SOLD	ISSUE PRICE	FINISH	PR-68	PR-69
1991	Snowy Owls, Set of 4 coins	1,164	1,990.00	Proof	3,300.	—

COUGARS PLATINUM SET 1992.

This is the third set in the series of Proof platinum coins dedicated to Canadian wildlife.

| $300 | $150 | $75 | $30 |

Designers:
Obv.:   Dora de Pédery-Hunt
Rev.:   George McLean
Engravers:
Obv.:   Dora de Pédery-Hunt
Rev.: $300 - Ago Aarand,
        Cosme Saffioti
        $150 - Susan Taylor
        $ 75 - Sheldon Beveridge
        $ 30 - Ago Aarand

DATE	DESCRIPTION	QUANTITY SOLD	ISSUE PRICE	FINISH	PR-69	PR-70
1992	Cougars, Set of 4 coins	1,081	1,955.00	Proof	3,300.	—

ARCTIC FOXES PLATINUM SET 1993.

This is the fourth set in the series of Proof platinum coins dedicated to Canadian wildlife.

| $300 | $150 | $75 | $30 |

Designers:
Obv.:   Dora de Pédery-Hunt
Rev.:   Claudio D'Angelo
Engravers:
Obv.:   Dora de Pédery-Hunt
Rev.: $300 - Susan Taylor
        $150 - Sheldon Beveridge
        $ 75 - Ago Aarand
        $ 30 - Ago Aarand

DATE	DESCRIPTION	QUANTITY SOLD	ISSUE PRICE	FINISH	PR-69	PR-70
1993	Arctic Foxes, Set of 4 coins	1,033	1,955.00	Proof	3,300.	—

SEA OTTERS PLATINUM SET 1994.

This is the fifth and last set in the series of Proof platinum coins dedicated to Canadian wildlife.

| $300 | $150 | $75 | $30 |

Designers:
Obv.:   Dora de Pédery-Hunt
Rev.:   Ron S. Parker
Engravers:
Obv.:   Dora de Pédery-Hunt
Rev.: $300 - Sheldon Beveridge
        $150 - William Woodruff
        $ 75 - Terry Smith
        $ 30 - Susan Taylor

DATE	DESCRIPTION	QUANTITY SOLD	ISSUE PRICE	FINISH	PR-69	PR-70
1994	Sea Otters, Set of 4 coins	766	1,995.00	Proof	3,300.	—

ENDANGERED WILDLIFE SERIES, 1995-2004

Specifications: See page 536
Case of Issue:
1/10 oz coin: Leather display case, encapsulated coin
½ oz coin: Mahogany case, encapsulated coin
Set, 4 coins: Mahogany case, inside green satin, coins individually encapsulated

CANADA LYNX PLATINUM SET, 1995.

This is the first set in the series of Proof platinum coins commemorating Canada's endangered wildlife.

$300 $150 $75 $30

Designers:
Obv.:   Dora de Pédery-Hunt
Rev.:   Michael Dumas
Engravers:
Obv.:   Dora de Pédery-Hunt
Rev.: $300 - Susan Taylor
$150 - Cosme Saffioti
$ 75 - Stan Witten
$ 30 - Ago Aarand

DATE	DESCRIPTION	QUANTITY SOLD	ISSUE PRICE	FINISH	PR-68	PR-69
1995	30 Dollars	620	179.95	Proof	200.	—.
1995	150 Dollars	226	599.95	Proof	800.	—
1995	Canada Lynx, Set of 4 coins	682	1,950.00	Proof	3,300.	—

PEREGRINE FALCON PLATINUM SET, 1996.

This is the second set in the series of Proof platinum coins commemorating Canada's endangered wildlife.

$300 $150 $75 $30

Designers:
Obv.:   Dora de Pédery-Hunt
Rev.:   Dwayne Harty
Engravers:
Obv.:   Dora de Pédery-Hunt
Rev.: $300 - Sheldon Beveridge
$150 - Stan Witten
$ 75 - Cosme Saffioti
$ 30 - Ago Aarand

DATE	DESCRIPTION	QUANTITY SOLD	ISSUE PRICE	FINISH	PR-68	PR-69
1996	30 Dollars	910	179.95	Proof	200.	—
1996	150 Dollars	196	599.95	Proof	800.	—
1996	Peregrine Falcon, Set of 4 coins	675	2,095.95	Proof	3,300.	—

WOOD BISON PLATINUM SET, 1997.

This is the third set in the series of Proof platinum coins commemorating Canada's endangered wildlife.

Designers:

Obv.:	Dora de Pédery-Hunt
Rev.:	Chris Bacon

Engravers:

Obv.:	Dora de Pédery-Hunt
Rev.:	$300 - Sheldon Beveridge
	$150 - William Woodruff
	$ 75 - Stan Witten
	$ 30 - Ago Aarand

$300	$150	$75	$30

DATE	DESCRIPTION	QUANTITY SOLD	ISSUE PRICE	FINISH	PR-68	PR-69
1997	30 Dollars	469	179.95	Proof	200.	—
1997	150 Dollars	116	599.95	Proof	800.	—
1997	Wood Bison, Set of 4 coins	413	1,950.00	Proof	3,300.	—

GREY WOLF PLATINUM SET, 1998.

This is the fourth set in the series of Proof platinum coins commemorating Canada's endangered wildlife.

Designers:

Obv.:	Dora de Pédery-Hunt
Rev.:	Kerri Burnett

Engravers:

Obv.:	Dora de Pédery-Hunt
Rev.:	$300 - Sheldon Beveridge
	$150 - Cosme Saffioti
	$ 75 - William Woodruff
	$ 30 - A. Aarand, J. Osio

$300	$150	$75	$30

DATE	DESCRIPTION	QUANTITY SOLD	ISSUE PRICE	FINISH	PR-68	PR-69
1998	30 Dollars	664	179.95	Proof	200.	—
1998	150 Dollars	194	599.95	Proof	800.	—
1998	Grey Wolf, Set of 4 coins	661	2,095.00	Proof	3,300	—

MUSKOX PLATINUM SET, 1999.

This is the fifth set in the series of Proof platinum coins commemorating Canada's endangered wildlife.

Designers:

Obv.:	Dora de Pédery-Hunt
Rev.:	Mark Hobson

Engravers:

Obv.:	Dora de Pédery-Hunt
Rev.:	$300 -William Woodruff
	$150 - Stan Witten
	$ 75 - Cosme Saffioti
	$ 30 - Sheldon Beveridge

$300	$150	$75	$30

DATE	DESCRIPTION	QUANTITY SOLD	ISSUE PRICE	FINISH	PR-68	PR-69
1999	30 Dollars	999	179.95	Proof	200.	—
1999	Muskox, Set of 4 coins	495	2,095.95	Proof	3,300.	—

PRONGHORN PLATINUM SET, 2000.

This is the sixth set in the series of Proof platinum coins commemorating Canada's endangered wildlife.

$300	$150	$75	$30

Designers:
Obv.:	Dora de Pédery-Hunt
Rev.:	Mark Hobson

Engravers:
Obv.:	Dora de Pédery-Hunt
Rev.:	$300 - José Osio
	$150 - Susan Taylor
	$ 75 - Stan Witten
	$ 30 - William Woodruff

DATE	DESCRIPTION	QUANTITY SOLD	ISSUE PRICE	FINISH	PR-69	PR-70
2000	Pronghorn, Set of 4 coins	599	2,095.95	Proof	3,300.	—

HARLEQUIN DUCK PLATINUM SET, 2001.

This is the seventh set in the series of Proof platinum coins commemorating Canada's endangered wildlife.

$300	$150	$75	$30

Designers:
Obv.:	Dora de Pédery-Hunt
Rev.:	C. Saffioti, S. Taylor
	S. Witten

Engravers:
Obv.:	Dora de Pédery-Hunt
Rev.:	$300 - Stan Witten
	$150 - Susan Taylor
	$ 75 - Cosme Saffioti
	$ 30 - Susan Taylor

DATE	DESCRIPTION	QUANTITY SOLD	ISSUE PRICE	FINISH	PR-69	PR-70
2001	Harlequin Duck, Set of 4 coins	448	2,395.95	Proof	3,300.	—

GREAT BLUE HERON PLATINUM SET, 2002.

This is the eighth set in the series of Proof platinum coins commemorating Canada's endangered wildlife.

$300	$150	$75	$30

Designers:
Obv.:	Dora de Pédery-Hunt
Rev.:	John-Luc Grondin

Engravers:
Obv.:	Dora de Pédery-Hunt
Rev.:	$300 - Stan Witten
	$150 - Susan Taylor
	$ 75 - Stan Witten
	$ 30 - José Osio

DATE	DESCRIPTION	QUANTITY SOLD	ISSUE PRICE	FINISH	PR-69	PR-70
2002	Great Blue Heron, Set of 4 coins	344	2,495.95	Proof	3,300.	—

ATLANTIC WALRUS PLATINUM SET, 2003.
This is the ninth set in the series of Proof platinum coins commemorating Canada's endangered wildlife.

| $300 | $150 | $75 | $30 |

Designers:
Obv.:	Dora de Pédery-Hunt
Rev.:	Pierre Leduc

Engravers:
Obv.:	Dora de Pédery-Hunt
Rev.:	$300 - Susan Taylor
	$150 - José Osio
	$ 75 - Stan Witten
	$ 30 - Stan Witten

DATE	DESCRIPTION	QUANTITY SOLD	ISSUE PRICE	FINISH	PR-69	PR-70
2003	Atlantic Walrus, Set of 4 coins	365	2,995.95	Proof	3,300.	—

GRIZZLY BEAR PLATINUM SET, 2004.
This is the tenth and final set in the Endangered Wildlife Proof platinum series, and it commemorates Canada's Great Grizzly bears.

| $300 | $150 | $75 | $30 |

Designers:
Obv.:	Susanna Blunt
Rev.:	Kerri Burnett

Engravers:
Obv.:	Susan Taylor
Rev.:	$300 - José Osio
	$150 - José Osio
	$ 75 - José Osio
	$ 30 - José Osio

DATE	DESCRIPTION	QUANTITY SOLD	ISSUE PRICE	FINISH	PR-69	PR-70
2004	Grizzly Bear, Set of 4 coins	380	2,995.95	Proof	3,300.	—

MAPLE LEAF BULLION COINS
GOLD MAPLE LEAF COINS

INTRODUCTION

In 1979 the Canadian Government introduced a gold bullion coin to compete with similar coins issued by other countries (such as the Krugerrand of South Africa). From 1979 to 1981 only the 50-dollar coin (Maple Leaf) in the one troy ounce size was produced. The Maple Leaf during this period was issued with a gold fineness of .999. During November 1982 the range of the gold Maple Leaf bullion coins being offered was expanded to three sizes. Now included in the offering were the five dollar or 1/10 maple and the ten dollar or ¼ maple. With the addition of the two fractional Maple Leafs all sizes were upgraded in gold content to .9999 fine. July of 1986 saw the offering range expanded once again to include the 20 dollar or ½ maple. All four coins are produced from .9999 fine gold and are legal tender coinage of Canada. In 1988 the Royal Canadian Mint, again expanding their bullion program, introduced five new coins; four platinum (1/10, ¼, ½ and one maple) and one silver (one maple). In 1990 the reverse hub of the one ounce gold Maple Leaf was re-engraved, enhancing veins in the maple leaf design. Other changes included a more slender stem on the maple leaf and wider spacing of the letters in the legend "Fine Gold 1 oz Or Pur." In 1993 the Royal Canadian Mint added to the series of bullion coin by issuing a 1/20 of an ounce ($1.00) size in gold and platinum. Again in 1994 the $2.00 denomination was added to the bullion coin series (1/15 of an ounce) in both platinum and gold. The $2.00 - 1/15 Maple denomination was discontinued in 1995.

The original finish developed by the Mint in 1979 for the Maple Leaf Gold Program was "The Bullion Finish," a brilliant relief on a parallel lined background.

FINISHES USED ON MAPLE LEAF COINS

Bullion:	1979-2014	Brilliant relief against a parallel lined background
	2015-2018	Satin relief against a radial lined background
		Coloured
		Hologram
Specimen:		Brilliant relief on a satin background (Reverse proof)
		Coloured
		Hologram
Proof:		Frosted relief against a mirror background
		Coloured
		Hologram

PRIVY AND SECURITY MARKS ON BULLION COINS

The year 1999 marked the 20th anniversary of the Maple Leaf program. To commemorate this event a privy mark was incorporated into the reverse design of all regular issue Maple Leafs.

A special issue of maple leafs was produced for January 1st, 2000. These were given a double date, 1999-2000, and a Fireworks privy mark.

To celebrate the millennium year the privy mark added to all maple leaf denominations was "Fireworks" above the numerals 2000.

Beginning in 2013, a new security mark was added to the design of the one ounce gold maple leaf. The security mark consists of a textured maple leaf micro-engraved with a laser on a small area on the reverse of the coin. In the centre of this mark is another maple leaf containing a lasered two-digit number. The two-digit number indicates the year of issue and will change annually.

In 2015, as a security feature, a series of background radial lines was introduced.

1999
20 YEARS ANS

1999-2000
Fireworks

2000
Fireworks 2000

2013-2018
Security Mark

GOLD MAPLE LEAF SPECIFICATIONS

CHARACTERISTICS	.50¢ = 1/25 oz	$1 =1/20 oz	$2 = 1/15 oz	$5 = 1/10 oz	$10 = 1/4 oz	$20 = 1/2 oz	$50 = 1 oz
Fineness (1979-1982)	—	—	—	—	—	—	99.90%
Fineness (1982 to date)	99.99%	99.99%	99.99%	99.99%	99.99%	99.99%	99.99%
Weight (grams)	1.244	1.555	2.074	3.110	7.776	15.552	31.1035
Diameter (mm)	13.92	14.1	15.0	16.0	20.0	25.0	30.0
Thickness (mm)	0.63	0.92	0.98	1.22	1.70	2.23	2.93
Edge	Reeded	Reeded	Reeded	Reeded	Reeded	Reeded	Reeded
Die Axis	↑↑	↑↑	↑↑	↑↑	↑↑	↑↑	↑↑
Finish	Bullion	Bullion	Bullion	Bullion	Bullion	Bullion	Bullion

GOLD MAPLE LEAF OBVERSES 1979-2019

Tiara Portrait 1979-1989	Royal Diademed Portrait 1990-2003	Uncrowned Portrait 2004-2014	Uncrowned Portrait Radial Lines 2015-2016	Uncrowned Portrait 150 & Maple Leaf 2015-2019

GOLD MAPLE LEAF REVERSES 1979-2019

.999 Fine 1979-1982	.9999 Fine 1983-1989	.9999 Fine 1990-2013 Re-engraved Leaf

 .9999 Fine
Security Mark
2013-2014

 .9999 Fine
Security Mark
Radial Lines
2015-2019

		Designers:	Engravers:
Obv.:	1979-1989	Arnold Machin	Walter Ott
	1990-2003	Dora de Pédery-Hunt	Dora de Pédery-Hunt
	2004-2014	Susanna Blunt	Susan Taylor
	2015	Susanna Blunt	Susan Taylor
Rev.:	1979-1982	Walter Ott	RCM Staff
	1983-1989	Walter Ott	RCM Staff
	1990-2013	Walter Ott	RCM Staff
	2013-2014	Walter Ott	RCM Staff
	2015-2019	Walter Ott	RCM Staff

GOLD MAPLE LEAF COINS

BULLION ISSUES

FINISH: 1979-2014 – Brilliant relief against a parallel lined background

2015-2017 – Satin relief against a radial lined background. The lines, which emanate from the centre and radiate outwards into the rim, are precisely machined with a specific width and pitch to create a light refracting pattern

MINTAGES: The production (quantity minted) of regular issue gold maple leaf bullion coins is on a demand basis. As coins are ordered by the distributors, they are struck and shipped by the Mint.

PRICING: Buying and selling prices are based on the interday spot price of bullion plus a small percentage premium for the striking and handling. The smaller the unit the larger the percentage premium charged on buying; however, in later selling the premium could very well disappear.

			QUANTITIES SOLD			
DATE	50¢ = 1/31.1 oz.	$1 = 1/20 oz	$5 = 1/10 oz	$10 = 1/4 oz	$20 = 1/2 oz	$50 = 1 oz
1979	–	N/I	N/I	N/I	N/I	1,000,000
1980	–	N/I	N/I	N/I	N/I	1,215,000
1981	–	N/I	N/I	N/I	N/I	863,000
1982	–	N/I	184,000	246,000	N/I	883,000
1983	–	N/I	224,000	130,000	N/I	695,000
1984	–	N/I	226,000	355,200	N/I	1,098,000
1985	–	N/I	476,000	607,200	N/I	1,747,500
1986	–	N/I	483,000	879,200	386,400	1,093,500
1987	–	N/I	459,000	376,800	332,800	978,000
1988	–	N/I	412,000	380,000	521,600	800,500
1989	–	N/I	539,000	328,800	259,200	856,000
1990	–	N/I	476,000	253,600	174,400	815,000
1991	–	N/I	322,000	166,400	96,200	290,000
1992	–	N/I	384,000	179,600	116,000	368,900
1993	–	37,080	248,630	158,452	99,492	321,413
1994	–	78,860	313,150	148,792	104,766	180,357
1995	–	85,920	294,890	127,596	103,162	208,729
1996	–	56,520	179,220	89,148	66,246	143,682
1997	–	59,720	188,540	98,104	63,354	478,211
1998	–	44,260	301,940	85,472	65,366	593,704
1999	–	62,820	709,920	98,928	64,760	627,067
1999-2000	–	Included	Included	Included	Included	Included
2000	–	31,280	52,970	31,688	24,404	86,375
2001	–	20,720	63,470	35,168	26,556	138,878
2002	–	17,140	45,020	42,940	28,706	344,883
2003	–	3,890	26,940	23,228	23,470	194,631
2004	–	9,880	33,480	18,296	13,160	253,978
2005	–	10,220	30,380	25,748	20,052	281,647
2006	–	19,340	40,960	25,964	21,138	209,937
2007	–	17,900	21,300	17,004	13,476	189,462
2008	–	15,740	38,510	34,368	28,782	710,718
2009	–	39,020	227,670	71,268	54,506	1,011,235
2010	–	9,000	111,160	41,628	34,302	1,036,832
2011	–	19,320	81,280	36,164	31,536	1,107,974
2012	–	12,400	95,700	129,156	28,594	712,193
2013	–	12,940	64,700	173,084	43,706	1,050,564
2014	–	N/A	N/A	N/A	N/A	N/A
2015	N/A	N/A	N/A	N/A	N/A	N/A
2016	N/A	N/A	N/A	N/A	N/A	N/A
2017	N/A	N/A	N/A	N/A	N/A	N/A

Note: N/I denotes Not Issued.

GOLD MAPLE LEAF SPECIAL ISSUES

SPECIAL ISSUE SINGLES

TWO DOLLAR GOLD COINS

TWO DOLLARS (1/15 OUNCE), BULLION ISSUE, 1994.

Issued 1994 as a new addition to the line of bullion coins offered by the Royal Canadian Mint, the two dollar (1/15 troy ounce) coin was not a success and was discontinued in 1995. It is a one-year type, and for this reason listed separately.

Actual Size

Designers and Engravers:

Obv.:	Dora de Pédery-Hunt
Rev.:	Walter Ott, RCM Staff
Composition:	99.99% Au
Gold content:	2.074 g, 0.067 tr oz
Weight:	2.074 g
Diameter:	13.9 mm
Thickness:	0.6 mm
Case of Issue:	Mylar pouch

Edge:	Reeded
Die Axis:	↑↑
Finish:	Bullion

DATE	DESCRIPTION	RCM ITEM #	QUANTITY SOLD	ISSUE PRICE	FINISH	MS-65	MS-66
1994	$2 (1/15 oz), Bullion Issue	N/A	3,540	BV	Bullion	400.	—

FIVE DOLLAR GOLD COINS

FIVE DOLLARS (1/10 OUNCE), MAPLE LEAF FOREVER, 2012.

The maple leaf has been a national symbol of Canada for almost 300 years. The sugar maple is an important member of the northeastern Canadian Boreal forest. Its sap produces some of the world's purest and finest maple syrup.

Actual Size

Designers and Engravers:

Obv.:	Susanna Blunt, Susan Taylor
Rev.:	Luc Normandin, Steven Stewart
Composition:	99.99% Au
Gold content:	3.13 g, 0.1 tr oz
Weight:	3.13 g
Diameter:	16.0 mm
Thickness:	1.0 mm
Case of Issue:	Maroon leatherette clam style case, black flock insert, encapsulated coin(s), COA

Edge:	Reeded
Die Axis:	↑↑
Finish:	Proof

DATE	DESCRIPTION	RCM ITEM #	QUANTITY SOLD	ISSUE PRICE	FINISH	MS-65	MS-66
2012	$5 (1/10 oz), Maple Leaf Forever	118426	4,373	229.95	Proof	230.	—

TEN DOLLAR GOLD COINS

TEN DOLLARS, MAPLE LEAVES WITH HER MAJESTY QUEEN ELIZABETH II COINAGE EFFIGIES SERIES, 2014-2016.
Featuring Canadian maple leaves on the reverse, this series commemorates the coinage effigies of Her Majesty Queen Elizabeth II.

| 1953 Portrait | 2014 | 1965 Portrait | 2015 |
| Des.: M. Gillick | Maple Leaves | Des.: A. Machin | Maple Leaves |

Actual Size

| 1990 Portrait | 2015 | 2003 Portrait | 2016 |
| Des.: Celia Godkin | Maple Leaves | Des.: Susanna Blunt | Maple Leaves |

Designers:		**Engravers:**	
Obv.:	See reverse illustrations	Obv.:	RCM Staff
Rev.:	Celia Godkin	Rev.:	RCM Staff
Composition:	99.99% Au		
Gold content:	7.8 g, 0.25 tr oz		
Weight:	7.8 g	**Edge:**	Reeded
Diameter:	20.00 mm	**Die Axis:**	↑↑
Thickness:	N/A	**Finish:**	Reverse Proof
Case of Issue:	Maroon leatherette clam style case, black flocked insert, encapsulated coin, COA, black box		

DATE	DESCRIPTION	RCM ITEM #	QUANTITY SOLD	ISSUE PRICE	FINISH	MS-65	MS-66
2014	Maple Leaves with Queen Elizabeth II Effigy (1953)	140588	1,375	649.95	Proof	600.	—
2015	Maple Leaves with Queen Elizabeth II Effigy (1965)	141805	958	649.95	Proof	600.	—
2015	Maple Leaves with Queen Elizabeth II Effigy (1990)	142766	678	649.95	Proof	600.	—
2016	Maple Leaves with Queen Elizabeth II Effigy (2003)	147613	1,000	649.95	Proof	600.	—

FIFTY DOLLAR GOLD COINS

FIFTY DOLLARS (1 ounce), 10TH ANNIVERSARY OF THE MAPLE LEAF BULLION COINS, 1989.

To commemorate the 10th anniversary of the maple leaf bullion coin program in 1989 the Royal Canadian Mint issued a series of proof quality silver, gold and platinum coins individually and in sets. The single coins and sets were packaged in solid maple wood presentation cases with brown velvet liners.

Designers and Engravers:

Obv.:	Arnold Machin, Walter Ott
Rev.:	Walter Ott, RCM Staff
Composition:	99.99% Au
Gold content:	31.10 g, 1.0 tr oz
Weight:	31.1035 g, 1oz
Diameter:	30.0 mm
Thickness:	2.9 mm
Case of Issue:	Maple wood case, brown velvet liner, encapsulated coin, COA

	Edge:	Reeded
	Die Axis:	↑↑
	Finish:	Proof

DATE	DESCRIPTION	RCM ITEM #	QUANTITY SOLD	ISSUE PRICE	FINISH	MS-65	MS-66
1989	$50 (1 oz) 10th Anniv. of Maple Leaf Coins	N/A	6,817	N/A	Proof	2,100.	—

FIFTY DOLLARS (1 ounce), 125TH ANNIVERSARY OF THE R.C.M.P. 1997.

In 1997 the Royal Canadian Mint issued a $50.00 gold (1 oz .9999 fine) coin with a guaranteed value of U.S. $310.00 in effect until January 1st, 2000. Since that date the coin has traded at the market price of gold bullion.

Designer:	Ago Aarand
Engraver:	Stan Witten
Composition:	99.99% Au
Gold content:	31.10 g, 1.0 tr oz
Weight:	31.1035 g, 1 oz
Diameter:	30.0 mm
Thickness:	3.3 mm
Finish:	Bullion
Case of Issue:	Black card folder

	Edge:	Plain, 10-sided
	Die Axis:	↑↑

DATE	DESCRIPTION	RCM ITEM #	QUANTITY SOLD	ISSUE PRICE	FINISH	MS-65	MS-66
1997	$50 (1 oz) 125th Anniv. R.C.M.P.	N/A	12,913	310. USF	Bullion	2,000.	—

FIFTY DOLLARS (1 ounce), 25TH ANNIVERSARY OF THE GOLD MAPLE LEAF COIN, 2004.

In 2004 a special commemorative design for the one ounce maple celebrating Canada's 25 years as a world leader in bullion coin production was issued at the A.N.A. World's Fair of Money.

Designers and Engravers:

Obv.:	Susanna Blunt, Susan Taylor
Rev.:	Cosme Saffioti, Christie Paquet
Composition:	99.99% Au
Gold content:	31.10 g, 1.0 tr oz
Weight:	31.1035 g, 1 oz
Diameter:	30.0 mm
Thickness:	2.9 mm
Finish:	Bullion
Case of Issue:	Mylar pouch

	Edge:	Reeded
	Die Axis:	↑↑

DATE	DESCRIPTION	RCM ITEM #	QUANTITY SOLD	ISSUE PRICE	FINISH	MS-65	MS-66
2004	$50 (1 oz) 25th Anniv. Gold Maple Leaf	N/A	10,000	BV	Bullion	2,000.	—

FIFTY DOLLARS (1 ounce), TEST MAPLE LEAF, FIVE 9'S GOLD, 2005.

This was a production test for "five 9's" fineness of the one ounce maple leaf. Of the six hundred pieces which were produced, two hundred were melted, and four hundred were released sealed in Mylar pouches.

Designers and Engravers:

Obv.:	Susanna Blunt, Susan Taylor		
Rev.:	Walter Ott, RCM Staff		
Composition:	99.999% Au		
Gold content:	31.10 g, 1.0 tr oz		
Weight:	31.1035 g, 1 oz	Edge:	Reeded
Diameter:	30.0 mm	Die Axis:	↑↑
Thickness:	2.9 mm	Finish:	Bullion
Case of Issue:	Mylar pouch		

DATE	DESCRIPTION	RCM ITEM #	QUANTITY SOLD	ISSUE PRICE	FINISH	MS-65	MS-66
2005	$50 (1 oz) .99999, Pattern	N/A	400	BV	Bullion	2,700.	—

FIFTY DOLLARS (1 ounce), MAPLE LEAF, 2012.

This coin was issued to commemorate the fifth anniversary of the striking of the one million dollar maple leaf coin in 2007.

Designers and Engravers:

Obv.:	Susanna Blunt, Susan Taylor		
Rev.:	Walter Ott, RCM Staff		
Composition:	99.999% Au		
Gold content:	31.16 g, 1.0 tr oz		
Weight:	31.16 g, 1 oz	Edge:	Reeded
Diameter:	30.0 mm	Die Axis:	↑↑
Thickness:	2.9 mm		
Finish:	Reverse Proof		
Case of Issue:	Maroon leatherette clam style case, black flock insert, encapsulated coin, COA		

DATE	DESCRIPTION	RCM ITEM #	QUANTITY SOLD	ISSUE PRICE	FINISH	MS-65	MS-66
2012	$50 (1 oz) 99.999% gold	N/A	543	BV	Bullion	2,000.	—

FIFTY DOLLARS (1 OUNCE), BULLION REPLICA MAPLE LEAF, 2014.

This is a premium-struck one ounce gold maple leaf issued to celebrate the success of the gold maple leaf which was introduced in 1979.

Designers and Engravers:

Obv.:	Susanna Blunt, Susan Taylor		
Rev.:	Walter Ott, RCM Staff		
Composition:	99.99% Au		
Gold content:	31.16 g, 1.0 tr oz		
Weight:	31.16 g, 1 oz		
Diameter:	30.0 mm	Edge:	Reeded
Thickness:	2.9 mm	Die Axis:	↑↑
Finish:	Reverse Proof		
Case of Issue:	Maroon leatherette clam style case, black flock insert, encapsulated coin, COA		

DATE	DESCRIPTION	RCM ITEM #	QUANTITY SOLD	ISSUE PRICE	FINISH	MS-65	MS-66
2014	$50 (1 oz) Bullion Replica Maple Leaf	129486	268	2,699.95	Proof	2,200.	—

NOTE TO COLLECTORS

When the initials N.I.I. appear in the pricing table it indicates the coin was part of a set issued by the Royal Canadian Mint, and not issued individually. Coin designs that are found only in sets offered by the Royal Canadian Mint are listed individually by denomination, and date in Volume Two.

SP-68 / PR-69	This price is based on the item still being in the original package as sold by the Mint.
SP-69 / PR-70	This price is based on the item being graded by a reputable third-party grading company.

TWO HUNDRED DOLLAR GOLD COINS

TWO HUNDRED DOLLARS (1 ounce), MAPLE LEAF, FIVE 9'S GOLD, 2007-2012.

Testing was continued of the five 9's gold concept first started in 2005. However, the test coins were now offered to the numismatic market. The issue of 2007 was offered with and without a privy mark.

| 2007 Common Obverse | 2008, 2009, 2012 Obverse | 2011 Obverse | 2007 Des./Engr.: Stan Witten | 2007, Privy Mark Des./Engr.: Stan Witten |

| 2008 Reverse Des.: G. E. Kruger-Gray Engr.: RCM Staff | 2009 Reverse Des.: Walter Ott Engr.: RCM Staff | 2011 Reverse Des./Engr.: Stan Witten | 2012 Reverse Des./Engr.: Stan Witten |

Designers:
Obv.: Susanna Blunt
Rev.: See reverse illustrations
Composition: 99.999% Au
Gold content: 31.1 g, 1.0 tr oz
Weight: 31.1035 g, 1 oz
Diameter: 30.0 mm
Thickness: 2.8 mm
Case of Issue: 2007-2009, 2012: Maroon clam style case, black flocked insert, encapsulated maple leaf, COA
2011: Credit card capsule

Engravers:
Obv.: Susan Taylor
Rev.: See reverse illustrations
Edge: 2007: Plain
2008-2012: Interrupted serrations
Die Axis: ↑↑
Finish: Bullion

DATE	DESCRIPTION	RCM ITEM #	QUANTITY SOLD	ISSUE PRICE	FINISH	MS-65	MS-66
2007	$200 (1 oz) 99.999% gold	N/A	30,848	BV	Bullion	2,000.	—
2007	$200 (1 oz) 99.999% gold, with Privy Mark	N/A	500.	1,899.95	Bullion	2,500.	—
2008	$200 (1 oz) 99.999% gold	N/A	27,476	BV	Bullion	2,000.	—
2009	$200 (1 oz) 99.999% gold	N/A	13,765	BV	Bullion	2,000.	—
2011	$200 (1 oz) 99.999% gold	N/A	N/A	BV	Bullion	2,000.	—
2012	$200 (1 oz) 99.999% gold	N/A	N/A	BV	Bullion	2,000.	—

TWO HUNDRED DOLLARS, MAPLE LEAF REFLECTION, 2015.

Designers and Engravers:
Obv.: Susanna Blunt, Susan Taylor
Rev.: Lilyane Coulombe
Composition: 99.99% Au
Gold content: 31.16 g. 1.0 tr oz
Weight: 31.16 g
Diameter: 30.0 mm
Thickness: N/A
Case of Issue: Maroon leatherette clam style case, black flocked insert, encapsulated coin, COA

Edge: Reeded
Die Axis: ↑↑
Finish: Proof

DATE	DESCRIPTION	RCM ITEM #	QUANTITY SOLD	ISSUE PRICE	FINISH	MS-65	MS-66
2015	Maple Leaf Reflection	142759	350	2,699.95	Proof	2,600.	—

TWO HUNDRED DOLLARS, 3-COIN SET, ALLURING MAPLE LEAVES OF FALL, 2015.

| Common Obverse | Spring | Summer | Fall |

Designers
  Obv.: Susanna Blunt
  Rev.: Michelle Grant
Composition: 99.99% Au
Gold content: 31.16 g, 1.0 tr oz
Weight: 31.16 g
Diameter: 30.0 mm
Thickness: N/A
Case of Issue: Presented in a maple wood case with a full colour custom beatuy box, COA.

Engravers:
  Obv.: Susan Taylor
  Rev.: RCM Staff

Edge: Reeded
Die Axis: ↑↑
Finish: Proof, with colour

DATE	DESCRIPTION	RCM ITEM #	QUANTITY SOLD	ISSUE PRICE	FINISH	MS-65	MS-66
2015	Alluring Maple Leaves of Fall, 3-Coin Set	147514	108	8,000.00	Proof	8,000.	—

TWO HUNDRED DOLLARS, A HISTORIC REIGN, 2015.

Designers and Engravers:
  Obv.: Susanna Blunt, Susan Taylor
  Rev.: Cathy Bursey Sabourin
Composition: 99.99% Au
Gold content: 31.16g. 1.0 tr oz
Weight: 31.16 g   **Edge:** Reeded
Diameter: 30.0 mm   **Die Axis:** ↑↑
Thickness: N/A   **Finish:** Proof
Case of Issue: Red wooden box with black beauty box, encapsulated coin, COA

DATE	DESCRIPTION	RCM ITEM #	QUANTITY SOLD	ISSUE PRICE	FINISH	MS-65	MS-66
2015	A Historic Reign	146599	266	2,699.95	Proof	2,600.	—

TWO HUNDRED DOLLARS, CANADA 150: ICONIC MAPLE LEAF, 2017.

Designers and Engravers:
  Obv.: Susanna Blunt, Susan Taylor
  Rev.: RCM Staff
Composition: 99.99% Au
Gold content: 31.16g. 1.0 tr oz
Weight: 31.16 g   **Edge:** Interrupted reeding
Diameter: 30.0 mm   **Die Axis:** ↑↑
Thickness: N/A   **Finish:** Matte Proof
Case of Issue: Red wooden box with black beauty box, encapsulated coin, COA

DATE	DESCRIPTION	RCM ITEM #	QUANTITY SOLD	ISSUE PRICE	FINISH	MS-65	MS-66
2017	Canada 150: Iconic Maple Leaf	157231	469	2,849.95	Matte Proof	2,850.	—

TWO HUNDRED DOLLARS, GML CANADA 150, 2017.

First issued in 1979, the Gold Maple Leaf (GML) bullion coin is highly valued by collectors and investors worldwide for its outstanding combination of superior craftsmanship, purity and design.

Designers and Engravers:

Obv.:	Susanna Blunt, Susan Taylor		
Rev.:	RCM Staff		
Composition:	99.999% Au		
Gold content:	31.16 g. 1.00 tr oz		
Weight:	31.16 g	Edge:	Reeded
Diameter:	30.0 mm	Die Axis:	↑↑
Thickness:	N/A	Finish:	Reverse Proof
Case of Issue:	Maroom clamshell with black beauty box, COA		

DATE	DESCRIPTION	RCM ITEM #	QUANTITY SOLD	ISSUE PRICE	FINISH	MS-65	MS-66
2017	GML Canada 150	162360	500	2,849.95	Reverse Proof	2,850.	—

TWO HUNDRED DOLLARS, 30TH ANNIVERSARY OF THE SML, 2018.

The year 2018 marks the 30th anniversary of the iconic Silver Maple Leaf bullion coin – the standard against which other silver bullion coins are measured. This very special numismatic release includes an RCM first: incuse-struck images on both sides of this pure gold coin.

Designers and Engravers:

Obv.:	Susanna Blunt, Susan Taylor		
Rev.:	RCM Staff		
Composition:	99.999% Au		
Gold content:	31.6 g. 1.02 tr oz		
Weight:	31.6 g	Edge:	Interrupted reeding
Diameter:	30 mm	Die Axis:	↑↑
Thickness:	N/A	Finish:	Reverse Proof
Case of Issue:	Maroom clamshell with black beauty box, COA		

DATE	DESCRIPTION	RCM ITEM #	MINTAGE	ISSUE PRICE	FINISH	MS-65	MS-66
2018	30th Anniversary of the SML	166862	500	2,899.95	Reverse Proof	2,900	—

TWO HUNDRED DOLLARS, 30TH ANNIVERSARY OF THE SML, 2018.

This exquisite tribute "lifts" the bullion coin's iconic maple leaf off its engraved reverse and gently deposits it here as a 3D design element

Designers and Engravers:

Obv.:	Susanna Blunt, Susan Taylor		
Rev.:	RCM Staff		
Composition:	99.99% Au; 99.9% Ag (silver maple leaf)		
Gold content:	31.6 g. 1.02 tr oz; 1.9 g 0.061 tr oz		
Weight:	31.6 g + 1.9 g	Edge:	Reeded
Diameter:	30 mm	Die Axis:	↑↑
Thickness:	N/A	Finish:	Reverse Proof
Case of Issue:	Custom wood case with black beauty box, COA		

DATE	DESCRIPTION	RCM ITEM #	MINTAGE	ISSUE PRICE	FINISH	MS-65	MS-66
2018	30th Anniversary of the SML	166153	375	2,899.95	Reverse Proof	2,900	—

TWO HUNDRED DOLLARS, 40TH ANNIVERSARY OF THE GML, 2019.

This coin commemorates the 40th year of the Gold Maple Leaf bullion coin's production.

Designers and Engravers:

Obv.:	Susanna Blunt, Susan Taylor		
Rev.:	RCM Staff		
Composition:	99.999% Au		
Gold content:	31.16 g. 1.02 tr oz		
Weight:	31.16 g	Edge:	Interrupted reeding
Diameter:	30 mm	Die Axis:	↑↑
Thickness:	N/A	Finish:	Reverse Proof
Case of Issue:	Maroon clamshell with black beauty box, COA		

DATE	DESCRIPTION	RCM ITEM #	MINTAGE	ISSUE PRICE	FINISH	MS-65	MS-66
2019	40th Anniversary of the GML	169481	350	2,899.95	Reverse Proof	2,900	—

FIVE HUNDRED DOLLAR GOLD COINS

FIVE HUNDRED DOLLARS, MAPLE LEAF FOREVER, 2012, 2015-2019.

2012, 2019 Obverse

2015-2018 Obverse

2012 Designer: Luc Normandin

2015
Designer: Lisa Thomson-Kahn

2016 Designer: Celia Godkin

2017 Designer: Margaret Best

2018 Designer: Stan Witten

2019 Designer: RCM Staff

Designers		**Engravers:**	
Obv.:	Susanna Blunt	Obv.:	Susan Taylor
Rev.:	See illustrations		
Composition:	99.99% Au		
Gold content:	156.05 g, 5.03 tr oz		
Weight:	156.05 g	**Edge:**	Plain
Diameter:	60 mm	**Die Axis:**	↑↑
Thickness:	N/A	**Finish:**	Proof
Case of Issue:	Red lacquered wooden box, black flocked insert, encapsulated coin, COA		

DATE	DESCRIPTION	RCM ITEM #	QUANTITY SOLD	ISSUE PRICE	FINISH	PR-69	PR-70
2012	Maple Leaf Forever	119160	146	11,999.95	Proof	12,500.	—
2015	Maple Leaves	148861	97	12,000.00	Proof	12,000.	—
2016	Maple Leaves	153825	99	12,500.00	Proof	12,500.	—
2017	Maple Leaves	161375	99	12,999.95	Proof	13,000.	—
2018	Maple Leaves	165093	99	12,999.95	Proof	13,000.	—
2019	Gold Maple Leaf	172464	99	12,999.95	Proof	13,000.	—

TWO THOUSAND FIVE HUNDRED DOLLAR GOLD COINS

TWO THOUSAND FIVE HUNDRED DOLLARS, MAPLE LEAF FOREVER, 2011-2012.

Common Obverse (except for date)	**2011** Designer: Debbie Adams Engraver: Konrad Wachelko	**2012** Designer: Luc Normandin Engraver: RCM Staff

Designers:
　　Obv.:　　Susanna Blunt
　　Rev.:　　See reverse illustrations
Composition:　　99.99% Au
Gold content:　　1000.0 g, 32.15 tr oz
Weight:　　1,000.0 g (1 kilo)
Diameter:　　101.6 mm
Thickness:　　N/A
Case of Issue:　　2011:　Black clam style case, black insert, encapsulated coin, COA
　　　　　　　　　　　2012:　Maple wood case, black flocked insert, encapsulated coin, COA

Engravers:
　　Obv.:　　Susan Taylor
　　Rev.:　　See reverse illustrations

Edge:　　Plain
Die Axis:　　↑↑
Finish:　　Proof

DATE	DESCRIPTION	RCM ITEM #	QUANTITY SOLD	ISSUE PRICE	FINISH	PR-69	PR-70
2011	Maple Leaf Forever	114844	35	69,000.	Proof	69,000.	—.
2012	Maple Leaf Forever	117499	20	69,000.	Proof	69,000.	—.

Note:　See also pages 473-480 for other $2,500 gold coins. Coins illustrated smaller than actual size.

TWO THOUSAND FIVE HUNDRED DOLLARS, 40TH ANNIVERSARY OF THE GML, 2019.

The year 2018 marks the 30th anniversary of the iconic Silver Maple Leaf bullion coin – the standard against which other silver bullion coins are measured. This very special numismatic release includes an RCM first: incuse-struck images on both sides of this pure gold coin.

Designers and Engravers:
　　Obv.:　　Susanna Blunt, Susan Taylor
　　Rev.:　　Walter Ott
Composition:　　99.99% Au
Gold content:　　1006.1 g. 32.35 tr oz
Weight:　　1006.1 g　　**Edge:**　　Reeded
Diameter:　　101.6 mm　　**Die Axis:**　　↑↑
Thickness:　　N/A　　**Finish:**　　Radial Lines
Case of Issue:　　Premium wooden case
　　　　　　　　　　　with black beauty box, COA

DATE	DESCRIPTION	RCM ITEM #	MINTAGE	ISSUE PRICE	FINISH	MS-65	MS-66
2019	40th Anniversary of the GML	170425	20	75,000	Radial Lines	75,000.	—

ONE MILLION DOLLAR GOLD COIN

This coin was issued May 3, 2007, as a promotional item for a new line of five 9's (99.999% fine gold) maple leaf gold coins. The million-dollar gold coin, being the largest and heaviest minted, attracted buyers from all over the world. The Canadian Mint received orders for five coins. The 3,215 troy ounce coin is produced by casting, engraving and hand polishing. The reverse design of the million-dollar maple leaf coin is very similar to the five dollar (2006) coloured silver maple, see page 590.

Designers:		**Engravers:**	
Obv.:	Susanna Blunt	Obv.:	Stan Witten
Rev.:	Stan Witten	Rev.:	Stan Witten
Composition:	99.999% Au		
Gold content:	100 kilos, 3,215 tr oz		
Weight:	100 kilos	**Edge:**	Plain
Diameter:	53.0 cm	**Die Axis:**	↑↑
Thickness:	N/A	**Finish:**	Bullion

DATE	DESCRIPTION	QUANTITY SOLD	ISSUE PRICE	FINISH	MS-65	MS-66
2007	One Million Dollar Coin, 3,215 tr oz	4	BV	Bullion	—	—

Note: 1.   The last recorded sale of this coin was $4,300,250. at auction on June 25th, 2010. It was auctioned by Dorotheum of Vienna, Austria, at their headquarters.

2.   Coin illustrated smaller than actual size.

GOLD MAPLE LEAF SPECIAL ISSUES
SPECIAL ISSUE SETS

10TH ANNIVERSARY OF THE GOLD MAPLE LEAF COIN, 1979-1989.

The 3-coin sets detailed below were issued for the 10th anniversary of the Maple Leaf bullion program.

THREE-COIN SET
(1 OZ GOLD, SILVER AND PLATINUM MAPLE LEAFS)

THREE-COIN SET
(1 OZ SILVER, 1/10 OZ GOLD & PLATINUM MAPLE LEAFS)

1 oz Gold
Maple Leaf

1 oz Silver
Maple Leaf

1 oz Platinum
Maple Leaf

1 oz Silver Maple Leaf

1/10 oz Gold
Maple Leaf

1/10 oz
Platinum
Leaf

Designers:		Engravers:
Obv.:	Arnold Machin	Obv.: Walter Ott
Rev.:	Walter Ott	Rev.: RCM Staff

Specifications: Gold: See page 543; Platinum: See page 562; Silver: See page 568
Finish: Proof
Case of Issue: Maple wood presentation box, black flocked insert, encapsulated coin, COA

DATE	DESCRIPTION	QUANTITY SOLD	ISSUE PRICE	FINISH	PR-68	PR-69
1979-1989	3-Coin Set: 1 oz gold, 1 oz silver, 1 oz platinum	3,966	1,795.00	Proof	3,450.	—
1979-1989	3-Coin Set: 1/10 oz gold, 1/10 oz platinum, 1 oz silver	10,000	195.00	Proof	450.	—

TEN DOLLAR GOLD AND FIVE DOLLAR SILVER PIEDFORT MAPLE LEAF SET, 2010.

Ten
Dollars
Gold

Five
Dollars
Silver

Designers:		Engravers:
Obv.:	Susanna Blunt	Rev.: Susan Taylor
Rev.:	RCM Staff	Rev.: RCM Staff

	$10 Gold	$5 Silver
Composition:	99.999% Au	99.99% Ag
Gold/Silver content:	6.25 g, 0.20 tr oz	31.39 g, 1.01 tr oz
Weight:	6.25 g	31.39 g
Diameter:	15.9 mm	34.0 mm
Thickness:	1.9 mm	4.0 mm

Edge:	Reeded	**Edge:**	Reeded
Die Axis:	↑↑	**Die Axis:**	↑↑
Finish:	Bullion	**Finish:**	Bullion

Case of Issue: Maroon leatherette clam style case, black flock insert, encapsulated coin(s), COA

DATE	DESCRIPTION	RCM ITEM #	QUANTITY SOLD	ISSUE PRICE	FINISH	MS-65	MS-66
2010	$10 Gold and $5 Silver, Piedfort Set	111055	1,264	679.95	Bullion	600.	—

GOLD FRACTIONAL SETS

2012 5TH ANNIVERSARY OF THE ROYAL CANADIAN MINT MILLION DOLLAR COIN - 5 COIN SET.

The one ounce coin in this set features five 99999s with an edge containing interrupted serrations.

2012 Obverse

Des.: Susanna Blunt
Engr.: Susan Taylor

2012 Reverse

Des.: Stan Witten
Engr.: Stan Witten

2013 25TH ANNIVERSARY OF THE FRACTIONAL SET - 4 COIN SET (1oz - 99.99%)

The one ounce coin in this set features four 9999s with a reeded edge.

2013 Obverse

Des.: Susanna Blunt
Engr.: Susan Taylor

2013 Reverse

Des.: Claudio D'Angelo
Engr.: Konrad Wachelko

2014 INCUSED FRACTIONAL SET - 4 COIN SET (1oz - 99.99%)

The one ounce coin in this set features four 9999s with a reeded edge.

2014 Obverse

Des.: Susanna Blunt
Engr.: Susan Taylor

2014 Reverse

Des.: Pierre Leduc
Engr.: RCM Staff

SPECIFICATIONS

Specifications:	See page 510	
Gold content:	2012 Set:	1.90 tr oz
	2013-2014 Set:	1.40 tr oz
Finish:	2012:	Proof
	2013-2014:	Reverse Proof
Case of Issue:	2012-2014:	Canadian maple wood case, black flocked insert, encapsulated coins, COA, black sleeve

DATE	DESCRIPTION	RCM ITEM #	QUANTITY SOLD	ISSUE PRICE	FINISH	PR-69	PR-70
2012	Set of 5 coins (1, 1/2, 1/4, 1/10, 1/20, 1/25 oz)	116890	543	3,999.95	Proof	3,500.	—
2013	Set of 4 coins (1, 1/4, 1/10, 1/20 oz)	120673	730	3,899.95	Rev. Proof	4,000.	—
2014	Set of 4 coins (1, 1/4, 1/10, 1/20 oz)	128188	552	3,999.95	Rev. Proof	4,000.	—

GOLD MAPLE LEAF FRACTIONAL SET - 4 COIN SET, 2015.

Each reverse design in this set is different. The design depicts a falling maple leaf as it flutters to the ground. Each one ounce coin is edge lettered with a serialized number.

Designers:		**Engravers:**	
Obv:	Susanna Blunt	Obv.:	Susan Taylor
Rev.:	Lilyane Coulombe	Rev.:	RCM Staff
Specifications:	See page 543	**Gold Content:**	1.40 tr oz
Finish:	Reverse Proof		
Case of Issue:	Red lacquered box, black flocked insert, encapsulated coins, COA		

DATE	DESCRIPTION	RCM ITEM #	MINTAGE	ISSUE PRICE	FINISH	MS-65	MS-66
2015	Set of 4 coins (1, 1/4, 1/10, 1/20 oz)	130937	181	3,999.95	Proof	4,000.	—

GOLD MAPLE LEAF FRACTIONAL SET - A HISTORIC REIGN, 2016.

This magnificent set of gold coins pays tribute to Her Majesty Queen Elizabeth II, Queen of Canada, as the longest reigning Sovereign in modern Canadian history. Each reverse design in this set is different. The design depicts a falling maple leaf as it flutters to the ground. Each one ounce coin is edge lettered with a serialized number.

Designers:		**Engravers:**	
Obv:	Susanna Blunt	Obv.:	1 oz. Susan Taylor
Rev.:	Celia Godkin		1/4 oz. Mary Gillick
Specifications:	See page 543		1/10 oz. Arnold Machin
			1/20 oz. Dora de Pédery-Hunt
		Gold Content:	1.40 tr oz
		Finish:	Reverse Proof
		Case of Issue:	Red lacquered box, black flocked insert, encapsulated coins, COA

DATE	DESCRIPTION	RCM ITEM #	MINTAGE	ISSUE PRICE	FINISH	MS-65	MS-66
2016	Set of 4 coins (1, 1/4, 1/10, 1/20 oz)	153859	599	3,999.95	Proof	4,000.	—

GOLD MAPLE LEAF FRACTIONAL SET
- A CELEBRATION OF CANADA GOLD FRACTIONAL, 2017.

The British North America Act of 1867 is a key marker for Canadian history, for it represents the momentous birth of a national. Tommemorate the historic 150th anniversary odf the Confederatin, the Royal Canadian Mint celebrates the journey of a nation that is proud, strong and free, with a commemorative franctional set feating a beloved national emblem: the maple leaf.

Designers:		**Engravers:**	
Obv:	Susanna Blunt	Obv.:	Susan Taylor
Rev.:	Lisa Thomson-Khan		
Specifications:	See page 543	**Gold Content:**	1.40 tr oz
Finish:	Reverse Proof		
Case of Issue:	Custom-shaped maple wood case, COA		

DATE	DESCRIPTION	RCM ITEM #	MINTAGE	ISSUE PRICE	FINISH	MS-65	MS-66
2017	Set of 4 coins (1, 1/4, 1/10, 1/20 oz)	153859	577	3,999.95	Proof	4,000.	—

GOLD MAPLE LEAF FRACTIONAL SET - THE MAPLE LEAF, 2018.

Maple leaves of all sizes possess the rare ability to stir powerful feelings of pride in Canadians. This iconic emblem of Canada takes centre stage in a .99999 pure gold fractional set—the first of its kind—that stands as a superbly crafted tribute to a timeless symbol of the land and its people.

Designers:		Engravers:	
Obv:	Susanna Blunt	Obv.:	Susan Taylor
Rev.:	Caren Heine		
Specifications:	See page 543		
Gold Content:	1.40 tr oz	**Finish:**	Reverse Proof
Case of Issue:	Custom-shaped maple wood case, COA		

DATE	DESCRIPTION	RCM ITEM #	MINTAGE	ISSUE PRICE	FINISH	MS-65	MS-66
2018	Set of 4 coins (1, 1/4, 1/10, 1/20 oz)	161361	600	4,219.95	Reverse Proof	4,220.	—

GOLD MAPLE LEAF FRACTIONAL SET
- 40TH ANNIVERSARY OF THE GOLD MAPLE LEAF, 2019.

First issued in 1979, our Gold Maple Leaf (GML) remains one of the most sought-after bullion coins of its kind — one that is coveted by investors and cherished by collectors worldwide.

Designers:		Engravers:	
Obv:	Arnold Machin	Obv.:	Susan Taylor
Rev.:	Nathalie Lagacé		
Specifications:	See page 543		
Gold Content:	1.40 tr oz	**Finish:**	Reverse Proof
Case of Issue:	Custom-shaped maple wood case, COA		

DATE	DESCRIPTION	RCM ITEM #	MINTAGE	ISSUE PRICE	FINISH	MS-65	MS-66
2019	Set of 4 coins (1, 1/4, 1/10, 1/20 oz)	167285	600	4,219.95	Reverse Proof	4,220.	—

GOLD FRACTIONAL SETS WITH PRIVY MARKS

GOLD MAPLE LEAF PRIVY MARK SET, 2001.

Each of the five coins in this set carries the bow of a Viking ship as a privy mark. The maples in this set are: 1 oz, ½oz, ¼oz, 1/10 oz, and 1/20 oz.

2001 Viking Privy Mark

Designers:		Engravers:	
Obv.:	Dora de Pédery-Hunt	Obv.:	Dora de Pédery-Hunt
Rev.:	Walter Ott	Rev.:	RCM Staff
Specifications:	See page 543		
Gold content:	1.90 tr oz	**Finish:**	Specimen (reverse proof)
Case of Issue:	Red mahogany wooden case, black insert, encapsulated coins, green velour with metal trim box.		

DATE	DESCRIPTION	PRIVY MARK	QUANTITY SOLD	ISSUE PRICE	FINISH	SP-68	SP-69
2001	Set of 5 coins (1, 1/2, 1/4, 1/10, 1/20 oz)	Viking	850	N/A	Specimen	3,500.	—

100TH ANNIVERSARY OF THE ROYAL CANADIAN MINT REFINERY, 1911-2011.

100 Years/ans Privy Mark

Each of the four coins in this set carries the 100 YEARS/ANS privy mark. The maples in this set are: 1 oz, ¼oz, 1/10 oz and 1/20 oz. This set includes a bronze medallion commemorating The Mint refinery.

Designers:		**Engravers:**	
Obv.:	Dora de Pédery-Hunt	Obv.:	Dora de Pédery-Hunt
Rev.:	Walter Ott	Rev.:	RCM Staff
Specifications:	See page 543		
Gold Content:	1.40 tr oz		
Finish:	Specimen (reverse proof)		
Case of Issue:	Red mahogany wooden case, black insert, encapsulated coins, green velour with metal trim box.		

DATE	DESCRIPTION	PRIVY MARK	RCM ITEM #	QUANTITY SOLD	ISSUE PRICE	FINISH	SP-68	SP-69
2011	Set of 4 coins (1, 1/4, 1/10, 1/20 oz)	100 Years/ans	11678	479	N/A	Specimen	2,700.	—

COLOURED FRACTIONAL SET WITH PRIVY MARK

20TH ANNIVERSARY OF THE MAPLE LEAF PROGRAM, 1979-1999.

1979-1999 Privy Mark

This limited edition five-coin set, (1 oz, ½ oz, ¼ oz, 1/10 oz and 1/20 oz) struck by the Royal Canadian Mint and coloured in Balerna, Switzerland, was issued with a mintage of 500. They are the first coloured Canadian coins.

Designers:		**Engravers:**	
Obv.:	Dora de Pédery-Hunt	Obv.:	Dora de Pédery-Hunt
Rev.:	Walter Ott	Rev.:	RCM Staff
Specifications:	See page 543	**Finish:**	Bullion, Coloured
Gold Content:	1.90 tr oz		
Case of Issue:	Wooden maple display case, black leatherette sleeve, black flocked insert, encapsulated coins, COA, red and gold outer box.		

DATE	DESCRIPTION	PRIVY MARK	QUANTITY SOLD	ISSUE PRICE	FINISH	SP-68	SP-69
1999	Set of 5 coins (1, 1/2, 1/4, 1/10, 1/20 oz)	20 Years / ans	500	N/A	Bullion	3,800.	—

Note: For the Vancouver 2010 Winter Olympic Coloured Set see page 599.

BIMETALLIC FRACTIONAL SET WITH PRIVY MARK

25TH ANNIVERSARY OF THE GOLD MAPLE LEAF, 1979-2004.

25 YEARS / ANS Privy Mark

To celebrate 25 years as an international standard in bullion coins, a new bimetallic maple leaf set was issued. The six-coin set is the first to include the 1/25 oz maple leaf denomination. Each coin is double-dated 1979-2004, and the 1 ounce coin features a 25-year commemorative privy mark.

Designers and Engravers:	RCM Staff
Specifications:	See page 560
Gold Content:	1.90 tr oz
Silver Content:	0.06 tr oz
Finish:	Bullion
Case of Issue:	Black leather presentation case, black velour insert, encapsulated coins, COA

DATE	DESCRIPTION	PRIVY MARK	QUANTITY SOLD	ISSUE PRICE	FINISH	SP-68	SP-69
2004 (1979-)	Set of 6 coins	25 Years / ans	801	2,495.95	Bullion	3,800.	—

BIMETALLIC MAPLE LEAF SPECIFICATIONS

CHARACTERISTICS	.50¢ = 1/25 oz	$1 =1/20 oz	$5 = 1/10 oz	$10 = 1/4 oz	$20 = 1/2 oz	$50 = 1 oz
Composition						
Ring - fine silver	99.99%	99.99%	99.99%	99.99%	99.99%	99.99%
Core - fine gold	99.99%	99.99%	99.99%	99.99%	99.99%	99.99%
Weight (grams)	1.27	1.581	3.136	7.802	15.589	31.65
Diameter (mm)	16.0	18.03	20.0	25.0	30.0	36.07
Thickness (mm)	N/A	N/A	N/A	N/A	N/A	N/A
Edge	Plain	Plain	Plain	Plain	Plain	Plain
Die Axis	↑↑	↑↑	↑↑	↑↑	↑↑	↑↑

GOLD MAPLE LEAFS HOLOGRAM ISSUES

HOLOGRAM SINGLES AND SETS

TEN DOLLARS (¼ ounce), GOLD MAPLE LEAF HOLOGRAM, 2001.

A distinctive maple leaf design appears as a high resolution dot matrix hologram, which is struck directly into the coin.

Designers:
Obv.: Susanna Blunt
Rev.: Walter Ott
Composition: 99.99% Au
Gold content: 7.775 g, 0.25 tr oz
Weight: 7.776 g
Diameter: 20.0 mm
Thickness: 1.7 mm
Case of Issue: Wooden presentation case

Engravers:
Obv.: Susan Taylor
Rev.: RCM Staff

Edge: Reeded
Die Axis: ↑↑
Finish: Specimen
(reverse proof), Hologram

DATE	DESCRIPTION	QUANTITY SOLD	ISSUE PRICE	FINISH	SP-68	SP-69
2001	$10 (¼ oz)	14,614	195.00	Specimen	500.	—

GOLD MAPLE LEAF HOLOGRAM SETS 1999, 2001 AND 2009.

The Hologram gold maple leaf set of 1999 was the first official issue of hologram coins in Canada. The five coins in this set are: 1 oz, 1/2 oz, 1/4 oz, 1/10 oz and 1/20 oz. All coins carry identical designs.

The 2009 thirtieth anniversary hologram set was issued with four coins: 1 oz, ¼ oz, 1/10 oz and 1/20 oz maples.

2001
Obv. $50 (1 oz)

2001
Rev. $50 (1 oz)

Designers and Engravers:
Obv.: Dora de Pédery-Hunt
Rev.: Walter Ott, RCM Staff
Specifications: See page 543
Gold Content: 1999, 2001: 1.90 tr oz
2009: 1.40 tr oz
Finish: Bullion, Hologram
Case of Issue: Presentation case

DATE	DESCRIPTION	QUANTITY SOLD	ISSUE PRICE	FINISH	MS-65	MS-66
1999	20th Anniversary, Set of 5 coins (1, ½, ¼, 1/10, 1/20 oz)	500	1,995.00	Bullion	3,800.	—
2001	Set of 5 coins	600	1,995.00	Bullion	3,800.	—
2009	30th Anniversary, Set of 4 coins (1, ¼, 1/10, 1/20 oz)	739	N/A	Bullion	3,200.	—

GOLD MAPLE LEAFS WITH PRIVY MARKS

PRIVY MARK SINGLES

GOLD MAPLE LEAF PRIVY MARKS.

In 1997, the Royal Canadian Mint began adding privy marks to specific gold maple leaf denominations to commemorate special events. These privy mark maples were commissioned by different organizations and struck by the Royal Canadian Mint.

$5 — 1/10 oz Maple Leaf Privy Marks

| 1997 $5 | 1998 $5 |
| Family | Eagles |

$10 — ¼ oz Maple Leaf Privy Marks

2000 $10	2001 $10	2005 $10	2005-2006 $10
Expo	Basle Coin Fair	Liberation	M7 Privy Mark
Hannover		Royal Dutch Mint	

DATE	DENOMINATION	CASE OF ISSUE	QUANTITY SOLD	ISSUE PRICE	FINISH	SP-68	SP-69
1997	$5, Family (1/10 oz)	Plastic case	100,730	N/A	Specimen	250.	—
1998	$5, Eagles (1/10 oz)	Plastic case	51,440	N/A	Specimen	250.	—
2000	$10, Expo (¼ oz)	N/A	1,000	N/A	Specimen	550.	—.
2001	$10, Basle (¼ oz)	N/A	750	N/A	Specimen	700.	—
2005	$10, Liberation (¼ oz)	N/A	500	€299	Specimen	550.	—
2005	$10, M7 (¼ oz)	Wooden display case	600	N/A	Specimen	550.	—
2006	$10, M7 (¼ oz)	Mylar pouch	1,093	N/A	Specimen	550.	—

PLATINUM MAPLE LEAF COINS
BULLION ISSUES

Obverse 1988-1989	Obverse 1990-1999	Obverse 2009-2015	Platinum Maple Leaf Reverse

Designers:	See page 543	Engravers:	See page 543
Finish:	Bullion	Case of Issue:	Mylar pouch

PLATINUM MAPLE LEAF SPECIFICATIONS

CHARACTERISTICS	$1 =1/20 oz	$2 = 1/15 oz	$5 = 1/10 oz	$10 = 1/4 oz	$20 = 1/2 oz	$50 = 1 oz
Fineness	99.95%	99.95%	99.95%	99.95%	99.95%	99.95%
Weight (grams)	1.555	2.074	3.110	7.776	15.552	31.1035
Diameter (mm)	14.1	15.0	16.0	20.0	25.0	30.0
Thickness (mm)	0.92	0.94	1.01	1.5	2.02	2.52
Edge	Reeded	Reeded	Reeded	Reeded	Reeded	Reeded
Die Axis	↑↑	↑↑	↑↑	↑↑	↑↑	↑↑

MINTAGES

The production of platinum maple leafs was on an order basis, unlike the production of coinage for circulation where the Mint will anticipate the number of coins required to fulfill the needs of the economy. Maple leafs are not struck unless ordered.

DATE	QUANTITIES SOLD				
	$1 =1/20 oz	$5 = 1/10 oz	$10 = 1/4 oz	$20 = 1/2 oz	$50 = 1 oz
1988	N/I	46,000	87,200	23,600	26,000
1989	N/I	18,000	3,200	4,800	10,000
1990	N/I	9,000	1,600	2,600	31,900
1991	N/I	13,000	7,200	5,600	31,900
1992	N/I	16,000	11,600	12,800	40,500
1993	2,120	14,020	8,048	6,022	17,666
1994	4,260	19,190	9,456	6,710	36,245
1995	460	8,940	6,524	6,308	25,829
1996	1,640	8,820	6,160	5,490	62,273
1997	1,340	7,050	4,552	3,990	25,480
1998	2,000	5,710	3,816	5,486	10,403
1999	4,000	4,080	2,092	788	3,248
2009	N/I	N/I	N/I	N/I	33,000
2011	N/I	N/I	N/I	N/I	5,000
2012	N/I	N/I	N/I	N/I	34,600
2013	N/I	N/I	N/I	N/I	19,349
2014	N/I	N/I	N/I	N/I	N/A
2015	N/I	N/I	N/I	N/I	N/A

PRICING

Buying and selling prices are based on the interday spot price of platinum plus a small percentage premium for striking and handling. The smaller the unit the larger the percentage premium charged on buying; however, in later selling the premium could very well disappear.

Note: 1. No platinum bullion coins were produced from 2000 to 2008, or in 2010.
2. N/I indicates Not Issued.

ONE AND TWO DOLLAR PLATINUM MAPLE LEAF COINS

TWO DOLLAR (1/15 ounce) BULLION ISSUE, 1994, AND ONE DOLLAR (1/20 OUNCE), 1995.

Issued 1994 as a new addition to the line of bullion coins offered by the Royal Canadian Mint, the two dollar (1/15 troy ounce) coin was not a success and was discontinued in 1995. It is a one-year type and for this reason is popular.

The 1995 one dollar (1/20 ounce) has an extremely small mintage of 460 coins. Even so, the slightest demand will affect the price without regard for the market price of platinum.

Designers and Engravers:
    See page 543
Specifications: See page 562
Finish: Bullion
Case of Issue: Mylar pouch

1994 Obv.	1994 Rev.	1995 Obv.	1995 Rev.
$2 (1/15 oz)	$2 (1/15 oz)	$1 (1/20 oz)	$1 (1/20 oz)

DATE	DESCRIPTION	QUANTITY SOLD	ISSUE PRICE	FINISH	MS-65	MS-66
1994	$2 (1/15 oz), Bullion Issue	600	BV	Bullion	800.	—
1995	$1 (1/20 oz), Bullion Issue	460	BV	Bullion	1,100.	—

THREE HUNDRED DOLLAR PLATINUM MAPLE LEAF COINS

THREE HUNDRED DOLLARS (1 ounce), PLATINUM MAPLE LEAF ISSUES, 2012-2019.

Designers:		**Engravers:**	
Obv.:	See obverse illustrations	Obv.:	See obverse illustrations
Rev.:	See reverse illustrations	Rev.:	See reverse illustrations
Composition:	99.95% Pt, Selectively gold plated	**Thickness:**	2.5 mm
Platinum content:	31.15 g, 1.00 tr oz	**Die Axis:**	↑↑
Weight:	31.15 g	**Edge:**	Reeded
Diameter:	30.0 mm	**Finish:**	Proof

Case of Issue: (A) 2007-2015:   Maroon leatherette clam style case, black flocked insert, encapsulated coin, COA
            (B) 2014:   Red wood lacquered case, black flocked insert, encapsulated coin, COA (Maple Leaf Forever)

2012 Obverse	**2013 Obverse**	**Obverse 2014-2015**	**Obverse 2016-2019**
Des.: Susanna Blunt	Des.: Arnold Machin	Des.: Susanna Blunt	Des.: Susanna Blunt
Obv.: Susan Taylor	Engr.: RCM Staff	Engr.: Susan Taylor	Engr.: Susan Taylor

2012 Maple Leaf Forever	**2013 25th Anniv. of the**	**2014 Maple Leaf Forever**	**2015 Maple Leaf Forever**
Des.: Luc Normandin	**Platinum Maple Leaf**	Des.: Lilyane Couloumbe	Des.: M. Grant
Engr.: José Osio	Des.: Jean-Louis Sirois	Engr.: RCM Staff	Engr.: RCM Staff
	Cecily Mok		

2016 Maple Leaf Forever	**2017 Maple Leaf Forever**	**2018 Maple Leaf Forever**	**2019 Maple Leaf Forever**
Des.: Lilyane Coulombe	Des.: Margaret Best	Des.: Pierre Leduc	Des.: Celia godkin
Engr.: RCM Staff	Engr.: RCM Staff	Engr.: RCM Staff	Engr.: RCM Staff

DATE	DESCRIPTION	RCM ITEM #	MINTAGE	ISSUE PRICE	FINISH	PR-68	PR-69
2012	Maple Leaf Forever	117507	250	2,999.95	Proof	2,600.	—
2013	25th Anniv. Platinum ML, Sel. gold plated	122151	250	2,999.95	Proof	2,600.	—
2014	Maple Leaf Forever	132493	250	2,999.95	Proof	3,000.	—
2015	Maple Leaf Forever, Sel. gold plated	142601	250	2,999.95	Proof	3,000.	—
2016	Maple Leaf Forever	151979	246	2,999.95	Proof	3,000.	—
2017	Maple Leaf Forever	159183	250	3,099.95	Proof	3,100.	—
2018	Maple Leaf Forever, Sel. gold plated	164577	250	3,099.95	Reverse Proof	3,100.	—
2019	Maple Leaf Forever	172117	250	3,099.95	Reverse Proof	3,100.	—

PLATINUM MAPLE LEAF SPECIAL ISSUES

FRACTIONAL SETS

10TH ANNIVERSARY OF MAPLE LEAF BULLION COINS, 1989.

This four-coin proof platinum set was issued to commemorate the 10th anniversary of the first maple leaf coins issued in 1979.

Designers and Engravers:
Obv.: Arnold Machin, Walter Ott
Rev.: Walter Ott
Case of Issue: Wooden maple presentation case, black flocked insert, encapsulated coin, COA

Specifications: See page 562
Platinum Content: 1.85 tr oz
Finish: Proof

DATE	DESCRIPTION	QUANTITY SOLD	ISSUE PRICE	FINISH	PR-68	PR-69
1989	Set of 4 coins (1 oz, ½ oz, ¼ oz, 1/10 oz)	1,999	1,995.	Proof	3,100.	—

POLAR BEAR ISSUE, 1999.

In 1999 the Royal Canadian Mint issued a special set of platinum Maple Leafs at the request of a distributor, MTB Bank. They are legal tender coins issued in five denominations with the same specifications as the bullion issues but with a polar bear reverse design. The reverse design is a modification of the two-dollar polar bear reverse by Brent Townsend.

Designers and Engravers:
Obv.: Dora de Pédery-Hunt
Rev.: Brent Townsend, Ago Aarand
Specifications: See page 530
Platinum Content: 1.90 tr oz
Finish: Bullion, Brilliant relief against a parallel lined background
Case of Issue: N/A

DATE	DESCRIPTION	QUANTITY SOLD	ISSUE PRICE	FINISH	MS-65	MS-66
1999	Set of 5 coins (1, ½, ¼, 1/10, 1/20 oz)	500	N/A	Bullion	3,100.	—

HOLOGRAM SET

PLATINUM MAPLE LEAF PROOF HOLOGRAM FIVE-COIN SET, 2002.

In this set the distinctive maple leaf appears as a high-resolution dot matrix hologram which has been struck directly onto regular issues of each of the five coins. The five coins are struck with the same specifications and denominations as the regular issues of 1988-1999.

Designers and Engravers:
Obv.: Dora de Pédery-Hunt
Rev.: RCM Staff
Specifications: See page 589
Finish: Specimen (reverse proof), Brilliant relief on a satin background, Hologram
Case of Issue: Red mahogany wooden case, black insert, encapsulated coins, green velour.

DATE	DESCRIPTION	QUANTITY SOLD	ISSUE PRICE	FINISH	SP-68	SP-69
2002	Set of 5 coins (1, ½, ¼, 1/10, 1/20 oz)	500	2,895.95	Specimen	3,100.	—

PLATINUM FRACTIONAL SETS

A ROYAL WEDDING ANNIVERSARY, 2017.

On November 20, 2017 Her Majesty Queen Elizabeth II and The Duke of Edinburgh will celebrate their 70th wedding anniversary, an impressive milestone that is all the more remarkable for a royal couple that has been in the spotlight from the moment they met. Their wedding in 1947 was Britain's first major event after the war, and people everywhere embraced the occasion. Now, the world stands in awe once again at the steadfast devotion they have shown as the monarchy navigated years of unprecedented social and technological change—an extraordinary journey celebrated with this incomparable set of platinum coins!

Designers:		**Engravers:**	
Obv:	Susanna Blunt	Obv.:	Susan Taylor
Rev.:	Marie-Élaine Cusson		
Specifications:	See page 562	**Platinum Content:**	1.85 tr oz
Finish:	Reverse Proof		
Case of Issue:	Wooden maple presentation case, black flocked insert, encapsulated coins, COA		

DATE	DESCRIPTION	RCM ITEM #	MINTAGE	ISSUE PRICE	FINISH	PR-68	PR-69
2017	Set of 4 coins (1 oz, ½ oz, ¼ oz, 1/10 oz)	163236	600	4,999.95	Reverse Proof	5,000.	—

30TH ANNIVERSARY OF THE PLATINUM MAPLE LEAF.

Each coin in this 30th anniversary set shares the same precisely engraved design of not one but *three* iconic maple leaves, which are carefully arranged to sympbolize three decades of history that are forever preserved in 99.95% pure platinum.

Designers:		**Engravers:**	
Obv:	Susanna Blunt	Obv.:	Susan Taylor
Rev.:	Jesse Koreck		
Specifications:	See page 562	**Platinum Content:**	1.85 tr oz
Finish:	Reverse Proof		
Case of Issue:	Wooden maple presentation case, black flocked insert, encapsulated coins, COA		

DATE	DESCRIPTION	RCM ITEM #	MINTAGE	ISSUE PRICE	FINISH	PR-68	PR-69
2018	Set of 4 coins (1 oz, ½ oz, ¼ oz, 1/10 oz)	169210	400	4,999.95	Reverse Proof	5,000.	—

PALLADIUM MAPLE LEAF COINS

BULLION ISSUES

FIFTY DOLLARS (1 ounce), PALLADIUM MAPLE LEAF, 2005-2010.

Designers and Engravers:

Obv.:	Susanna Blunt, Susan Taylor
Rev.:	Walter Ott, RCM Staff
Composition:	99.95% Pd
Platinum content:	31.1 g, 1.0 tr oz
Weight:	31.1035 g
Diameter:	30.0 mm
Thickness:	2.9 mm
Finish:	Bullion
Case of Issue:	Mylar pouch

	Edge:	Reeded
	Die Axis:	↑↑

DATE	DESCRIPTION	QUANTITY SOLD	ISSUE PRICE	FINISH	MS-65	MS-66
2005	$50 (1 oz) 99.99%	62,919	BV	Bullion	1,000.	—
2006	$50 (1 oz)	68,707	BV	Bullion	1,000.	—
2007	$50 (1 oz)	15,415	BV	Bullion	1,000.	—
2008	$50 (1 oz)	9,694	BV	Bullion	1,000.	—
2009	$50 (1 oz)	40,000	BV	Bullion	1,000.	—
2010	$50 (1 oz)	25,000	BV	Bullion	1,000.	—

Note: No palladium maple leafs have been produced since 2010.

SPECIAL ISSUES

EXPERIMENTAL FINISH TEST PALLADIUM MAPLES, 2005.

In 2005 the Royal Canadian Mint conducted tests on palladium planchets. Planchets with the Royal Canadian Mint logo A were finished outside mint facilities, and planchets with the Royal Canadian Mint logo B were finished inside the Mint. Test results showed little variation in the manufacture, resulting in the internal planchets being used in the production of palladium maple leafs.

Reverse
Privy Mark "A"

Privy Mark "A"

Reverse
Privy Mark "B"

Privy Mark "B"

Designers:		
Obv.:	Susanna Blunt
Rev.:	Walter Ott
Composition:	99.95% Pd
Platinum content:	31.1 g, 1.0 tr oz
Weight:	31.1035 g
Diameter:	30.0 mm
Finish:	Bullion, Brilliant relief against a parallel lined background

Engravers:	
Obv.:	Susan Taylor
Rev.:	RCM Staff
Thickness:	2.9 mm
Edge:	Reeded
Die Axis:	↑↑

DATE	DESCRIPTION	QUANTITY SOLD	ISSUE PRICE	FINISH	MS-65	MS-66
2005	Royal Mint Privy Mark "A"	146	1,300.00	Bullion	2,500.	—
2005	Royal Mint Privy Mark "B"	144	1,300.00	Bullion	2,500.	—

SILVER MAPLE LEAF COINS

BULLION ISSUES

The first silver one ounce maple leaf was issued in 1988. The design is a continuation of that first conceived for the gold maples in 1979. The 1999-2000, and the 2000-dated silver maple leaf $5.00 coins carry the fireworks privy mark for 1999-2000, and the millennium privy mark for 2000.

Midway through 2013 a security mark (privy) was added to the reverse of the maple leaf. This security mark is a laser etched maple leaf, and within that leaf another smaller leaf which contains two digits representing the year of striking.

The finish used on the silver maple leaf was changed in 2014. The new finish is a series of radial lines originating at the centre and flowing out to the rim. This complex feature is part of the advanced visual security.

Numerous decals have been placed on $5 maple leafs, they were not issued by the Royal Canandian Mint.

SILVER MAPLE LEAF SPECIFICATIONS

CHARACTERISTICS	$1 =1/20 oz	$2 = 1/10 oz	$3 = 1/4 oz	$4 = 1/2 oz	$5 = 1 oz
Fineness	99.99%	99.99%	99.99%	99.99%	99.99%
Weight (grams)	1.555	3.11	7.776	15.552	31.1035
Diameter (mm)	16.0	20.0	27.0	34.0	38.0
Thickness (mm)	1.1	1.3	1.8	2.1	3.15
Edge	Reeded	Reeded	Reeded	Reeded	Reeded
Die Axis	↑↑	↑↑	↑↑	↑↑	↑↑

FIVE DOLLAR OR ONE OUNCE MAPLES

OBVERSES 1988-2019

Tiara Portrait
1988-1989

Royal Diademed Portrait
1990-2003

Uncrowned Portrait
2004-2013

Obverse
Without Radial Lines
2014

Obverse
With Radial Lines
2014-2019

REVERSES 1988-2019

Reverse
1988-2014
Reverse

With Security Device
With Radial Lines
2014-2019

All maple leafs dated
1999-2000
"Fireworks"

All maple leafs dated
2000
"Fireworks 2000"

Security Mark
Inner leaf with 14
date of production
radial lined
background

Designers and Engravers:

1988-1989:	Obv.:	Arnold Machin, Walter Ott	Rev.:	Walter Ott, R.C.M. Staff
1989-2003:	Obv.:	Dora de Pédery Hunt	Rev.:	Walter Ott, R.C.M. Staff
2004-2019:	Obv.:	Susanna Blunt, Susan Taylor	Rev.:	Walter Ott, R.C.M. Staff

Finish:
1988-2014: Bullion, Brilliant relief against a parallel lined background
2014-2019: Brilliant relief against a radial lined background

Case of Issue:
1988-2008: Single coin sealed in clear Mylar pouch
2009-2019: Plastic tubes of 25 coin

Pricing: Please remember that silver maple leaf prices are linked to the price of silver and may be priced higher, or lower, than prices shown depending on market conditions. Unlike gold and platinum maple leafs, silver leafs do experience a collector demand which will result in price differentials between dates. The price is affected by the total mintage and the pattern of distribution during year of issue.

SILVER MAPLE LEAF SPECIFICATIONS

DATE	PRIVY MARKS	QUANTITY SOLD	ISSUE PRICE	FINISH	MS-65	MS-66	MS-67
1988		1,062,000	BV	Bullion	35.	45.	—
1989		3,332,200	BV	Bullion	35.	45.	—
1990		1,708,800	BV	Bullion	35.	45.	—
1991		644,300	BV	Bullion	35.	45.	—
1992		343,800	BV	Bullion	35.	45.	—
1993		889,946	BV	Bullion	35.	45.	—
1994		1,133,900	BV	Bullion	40.	50.	—
1995		326,244	BV	Bullion	40.	50.	—
1996		250,445	BV	Bullion	60.	70.	—
1997		100,970	BV	Bullion	60.	70.	—
1998		591,359	BV	Bullion	35.	45.	—
1999		1,229,442	BV	Bullion	35.	45.	—
1999-2000	Fireworks	Included	BV	Bullion	40.	50.	—
2000	Fireworks 2000	403,652	BV	Bullion	40.	50.	—
2001		398,563	BV	Bullion	35.	50.	—
2002		576,196	BV	Bullion	35.	50.	—
2003		684,750	BV	Bullion	35.	45.	—
2004		680,925	BV	Bullion	35.	45.	—
2005		955,694	BV	Bullion	35.	45.	—
2006		2,464,727	BV	Bullion	35.	45.	—
2007		3,526,052	BV	Bullion	32.	40.	—
2008		7,909,161	BV	Bullion	32.	40.	—
2009		9,727,592	BV	Bullion	30.	40.	—
2010		17,799,992	BV	Bullion	30.	40.	—
2011		23,129,966	BV	Bullion	30.	40	—
2012		18,132,297	BV	Bullion	28.	40	—
2013		28,222,061	BV	Bullion	26.	35.	—
2013	Security	Included	BV	Bullion	26.	35.	—
2014	Security, Without Radial Lines	N/A	BV	Bullion	26.	35.	—
2014-2019	Security, With Radial Lines	N/A	BV	Bullion	26.	35.	—

NOTES FOR COLLECTORS

1 Silver maple leafs are priced based on the world market price for silver, plus a small premium on the day the transaction takes place. Premiums will vary depending on the size of the transaction.

2. The packaging of silver maple leafs changed in 2009 from single coins in mylar pouches to twenty-five coins packaged in plastic tubes. In 2010 the silver maple leafs were available again in mylar pouches or plastic tubes of twenty-five.

3. The silver maple leafs listed in the table above are priced at a silver market value of $23.00 Cdn. an ounce. Market changes, up or down, from $23.00 will necessitate a price revision.

4. Coins that are scratched, toned, or impaired will command a lower price.

SILVER MAPLE LEAF SPECIAL ISSUES: SINGLES
FIVE DOLLAR SILVER MAPLE LEAF COINS

FIVE DOLLARS (1 ounce), 10TH ANNIVERSARY OF MAPLE LEAF BULLION COINS, 1989.

Issued in 1989 in Proof finish to commemorate the 10th anniversary of the introduction of the maple leaf in 1979.

Designers and Engravers:

Obv.:	Arnold Machin
Rev.:	Walter Ott, RCM Staff
Composition:	99.99% Ag
Weight:	31.1035 g, 1 tr oz
Diameter:	38.0 mm
Thickness:	3.2 mm
Edge:	Reeded
Die Axis:	↑↑
Finish:	Proof
Case of Issue:	Maple wood presentation box, black flocked insert, encapsulated coins, COA, outer maple leaf printed box.

DATE	DESCRIPTION	QUANTITY SOLD	ISSUE PRICE	FINISH	PR-68	PR-69
1989	$5 (1 oz), 10th Anniv. Maple Leaf coins	29,999	39.00	Proof	75.	—

FIVE DOLLARS (1 ounce), 20TH ANNIVERSARY OF THE SILVER MAPLE LEAF, 1988-2008.

This bullion coin was issued to commemorate the 20th anniversary of the silver maple leaf which was introduced in 1988.

Designers and Engravers:

Obv.:	Arnold Machin
Rev.:	RCM Staff
Composition:	99.99% Ag, Selectively gold plated
Weight:	31.3035 g, 1 tr oz
Diameter:	38.0 mm
Thickness:	3.2 mm
Edge:	Reeded
Die Axis:	↑↑
Finish:	Bullion
Case of Issue:	Maroon leatherette clam style case, black flocked insert, encapsulated coin, COA

DATE	DESCRIPTION	RCM ITEM #	QUANTITY SOLD	ISSUE PRICE	FINISH	MS-65	MS-66	MS-67
2008	$5 (1 oz), 20th Anniv. of the Silver Maple Leaf	104188	9,998	74.95	Bullion	80.	—	—

VANCOUVER 2010 OLYMPIC GAMES

FIVE DOLLARS (1 ounce), VANCOUVER 2010 WINTER OLYMPIC GAMES, 2008-2010.

A $50 gold version of these coins were also issued (see page 434).

2008 Common Obverse	2008 Maple Leaf and Vancouver 2010 Olympic Logo	2009 Thunderbird

2009-2010 Common Obverse (Except for date)	2010 Hockey Player

Designers:
Obv.: Susanna Blunt
Rev.: 2008, 2010: RCM Staff
2009: Xwa lac tun (Ricky Harry)
Composition: 99.99% Ag
Silver content: 31.1035 g, 1 tr oz
Weight: 31.1035 g
Diameter: 38.0 mm
Finish:
1. Bullion
2. Bullion, Selectively gold plated
3. Bullion, Gilt
Case of Issue: Singly: Mylar pouch
Coloured Set: Maple wood box, black flocked insert, encapsulated coins, COA

Engravers:
Obv.: Susan Taylor
Rev.: 2008 and 2010: Stan Witten
2009: Marcos Hallam

Edge: Reeded
Die Axis: ↑↑
Thickness: 3.2 mm

DATE	DESCRIPTION	QUANTITY SOLD	ISSUE PRICE	FINISH	MS-65	MS-66	MS-67
2008	$5 (1oz) 2010 Logo	937,839	BV	Bullion	35.	40.	—
2008	$5 (1oz) 2010 Logo, Selectively gold plated	N/A	N.I.I.	Bullion	90.	110.	*
2009	$5 (1oz) Thunderbird	569,048	BV	Bullion	35.	40.	—
2009	$5 (1oz) Thunderbird, Selectively gold plated	N/A	N.I.I.	Bullion	90.	110.	*
2010	$5 (1oz) Hockey Player	79,278	BV	Bullion	35.	40.	—
2010	$5 (1oz) Hockey Player, Selectively gold plated	N/A	N.I.I.	Bullion	90.	110.	*
2010	$5 (1oz) Hockey Player, Gold plated	N/A	71.95	Bullion	65.	90.	—
—	Set of 3 coins, Selectively gold plated	4,000	199.95	Bullion	265.	*	*

Note: 1. Images illustrated smaller than actual size.
2. The mintages reported are for the total number of pieces struck that year. There is no breakdown by design reported. Total mintage for the three designs 1,586,165.

FIVE DOLLARS (1 ounce), PIEDFORT MAPLE LEAF, 2010.

This five-dollar silver Piedfort maple leaf was issued singly, or as part of the Piedfort Maple Leaf Set. The set, which consists of a ten-dollar gold and a five-dollar silver coin, is listed on page 555.

Designers and Engravers:

Obv.:	Susanna Blunt, Susan Taylor
Rev.:	RCM Staff
Composition:	99.99% Ag
Silver content:	31.39 g, 1.01 tr. oz
Weight:	31.39 g
Diameter:	34.0 mm
Thickness:	4.0 mm
Case of Issue:	Maroon leatherette clam style case, black flock insert, encapsulated coin, COA

Edge:	Reeded
Die Axis:	↑↑
Finish:	Bullion

DATE	DESCRIPTION	RCM ITEM #	QUANTITY SOLD	ISSUE PRICE	FINISH	PR-69	PR-70
2010	$5 (1 oz), Silver Piedfort Maple Leaf	111055	6,843	79.95	Bullion	80.	—

FIVE DOLLARS (1 ounce), 25TH ANNIVERSARY OF THE SILVER MAPLE LEAF, 2013.

This selectively gold plated silver maple leaf was issued to celebrate 25 years of the Royal Canadian Mint's silver maple leaf.

Designers and Engravers:

Obv.:	Susanna Blunt, Susan Taylor
Rev.:	Jean-Louis Sirois, Cecily Mok
Composition:	99.99% Ag, Selectively gold plated
Silver content:	31.10 g, 1.00 tr. oz
Weight:	31.10 g
Diameter:	38.0 mm
Thickness:	3.0 mm
Case of Issue:	Maroon leatherette clam style case, black flock insert, encapsulated coin, COA

Edge:	Reeded
Die Axis:	↑↑
Finish:	Proof

DATE	DESCRIPTION	RCM ITEM #	QUANTITY SOLD	ISSUE PRICE	FINISH	PR-69	PR-70
2013	$5 (1 oz), 25th Anniv. of the SML	122196	9,966	109.95	Proof	80.	—

FIVE DOLLARS (1 ounce), PIEDFORT, 25TH ANNIVERSARY OF THE SILVER MAPLE LEAF, 2013.

This Piedfort silver maple leaf was issued to celebrate 25 years of the Royal Canadian Mint's silver maple leaf.

Designers and Engravers:

Obv.:	Susanna Blunt, Susan Taylor
Rev.:	Jean-Louis Sirois, RCM Staff
Composition:	99.99% Ag
Silver content:	31.39 g, 1.01 tr oz
Weight:	31.39 g
Diameter:	34.0 mm
Thickness:	3.8 mm
Case of Issue:	Maroon leatherette clam style case, black flock insert, encapsulated coin, COA

Edge:	Reeded
Die Axis:	↑↑
Finish:	Proof

DATE	DESCRIPTION	RCM ITEM #	QUANTITY SOLD	ISSUE PRICE	FINISH	PR-69	PR-70
2013	$5 (1 oz), Piedfort 25th Anniv. of SML	126804	9,978	99.95	Proof	75.	—

FIVE DOLLARS (1 ounce), 25TH ANNIVERSARY OF THE SILVER MAPLE LEAF, 2013.

This silver maple leaf was issued to celebrate 25 years of the Royal Canadian Mint's silver maple leaf program.

Designers and Engravers:

Obv.:	Susanna Blunt, Susan Taylor
Rev.:	RCM Staff
Composition:	99.99% Ag
Silver content:	31.2 g, 1.9 tr oz
Weight:	31.2 g
Diameter:	38.0 mm
Thickness:	3.25 mm
Case of Issue:	Tubes of 25, or sealed thermotron film

Edge:	Reeded
Die Axis:	↑↑
Finish:	Bullion

DATE	DESCRIPTION	RCM ITEM #	QUANTITY SOLD	ISSUE PRICE	FINISH	PR-69	PR-70
2013	$5 (1 oz), 25th Anniv. of SML	N/A	N/A	BV	Bullion	35.	—

FIVE DOLLARS (1 ounce), BULLION REPLICA SILVER MAPLE LEAF, 2014.

Designers and Engravers:

Obv.:	Susanna Blunt, Susan Taylor
Rev.:	RCM Staff

Composition: 99.99% Ag
Silver content: 31.1 g, 1.0 tr oz

Weight:	31.1 g	**Edge:**	Reeded
Diameter:	38.0 mm	**Die Axis:**	↑↑
Thickness:	3.3 mm	**Finish:**	Reverse Proof

Case of Issue: Maroon leatherette clam style case, black flock insert, encapsulated coin, COA

DATE	DESCRIPTION	RCM ITEM #	QUANTITY SOLD	ISSUE PRICE	FINISH	PR-69	PR-70
2014	$5 (1 oz), Replica Silver ML	129468	8,095	79.95	Rev. Proof	60.	—

30TH ANNIVERSARY OF THE SILVER MAPLE LEAF

FIVE DOLLARS, 2-COIN SET 30TH ANNIVERSARY OF THE SML, 2018.

Unchanged since the very first issue in 1988, the solitary maple leaf that adorns the Silver Maple Leaf (SML) coin is widely regarded as a symbol for unparalleled artistry, craftsmanship and value.

Obverse – Modified Proof	Reverse - Modified Proof	Obverse - Modified Reverse Proof	Reverse - Modified Reverse Proof

Designers:

Obv.:	Susanna Blunt
Rev.:	RCM Staff

Composition: 99.99% Ag
Silver content: 31.39, 1.0 tr oz
Weight: 31.39 g,
Diameter: 38.0 mm
Thickness: N/A
Case of Issue: Maroon clamshell with black beauty box, COA

Engravers:

Obv.:	Susan Taylor

Edge: Reeded
Die Axis: ↑↑
Finish: Modified Proof & Modified Reverse Proof

DATE	DESCRIPTION	RCM ITEM #	MINTAGE	ISSUE PRICE	FINISH	69	70
2018	2-Coin Set 30th Anniversary of the SML	164145	5,000	189.95	Modified Proof & Modified Reverse Proof	190.	—
2018	$5 (1 oz.) 30th Anniversary of the SML	N/A	N/A	BV	Bullion	35.	—
2018	$5 (1 oz.) Incuse	N/A	250,000	BV	Bullion	30.	—
2019	$5 (1 oz.) Incuse	N/A	250,000	BV	Bullion	30.	—

EIGHT DOLLAR SILVER MAPLE LEAF COINS

EIGHT DOLLARS (1½ ounce), CANADIAN MAPLE LEAF: THE SUPERLEAF, 2015.

This coin features a radial line finish first used in the 2014 Maple Leaf.

Designers and Engravers:

Obv.:	Susanna Blunt, Susan Taylor		
Rev.:	Stan Witten, RCM Staff		
Composition:	99.99% Ag		
Silver content:	46.65 g, 1.5 tr oz		
Weight:	46.65 g	Edge:	Reeded
Diameter:	38.0 mm	Die Axis:	↑↑
Thickness:	3.2 mm		
Finish:	Bullion, Radial lines		
Case of Issue:	Plastic tubes		

DATE	DESCRIPTION	QUANTITY SOLD	ISSUE PRICE	FINISH	MS-65	MS-66
2015	$8 (1½ oz), The Superleaf	N/A	BV	Bullion	50.	—
2016	$8 (1½ oz), The Superleaf	N/A	BV	Bullion	45.	—
2017	$8 (1½ oz), The Superleaf	N/A	BV	Bullion	45.	—

TEN DOLLAR SILVER MAPLE LEAF COINS

TEN DOLLARS (½ ounce), MAPLE LEAF FOREVER, 2011.

The design on the reverse of this maple leaf coin commemorates the three maple leaf design that has graced Canada's one cent coin since 1937.

Designers, and Engravers:

Obv.:	Susanna Blunt, Susan Taylor		
Rev.:	Debbie Adams, Konrad Wachelko		
Composition:	99.99% Ag		
Silver content:	15.87 g, 0.5 tr oz		
Weight:	15.87 g	Edge:	Reeded
Diameter:	34.0 mm	Die Axis:	↑↑
Thickness:	2.0 mm	Finish:	Specimen
Case of Issue:	Maroon leatherette clam style case, black insert, encapsulated coin, COA		

DATE	DESCRIPTION	RCM ITEM #	QUANTITY SOLD	ISSUE PRICE	FINISH	SP-68	SP-69
2011	$10 (½ oz) Maple Leaf Forever	116513	41,712	34.95	Specimen	22.	—

TEN DOLLARS (½ ounce), MAPLE LEAF FOREVER, 2012.

Designers, and Engravers:

Obv.:	Susanna Blunt, Susan Taylor		
Rev.:	Luc Normandin		
Composition:	99.99% Ag		
Silver content:	15.87 g, 0.5 tr oz		
Weight:	15.87 g	Edge:	Reeded
Diameter:	34.0 mm	Die Axis:	↑↑
Thickness:	2.1 mm	Finish:	Specimen
Case of Issue:	Black card envelope with green maple leaf design, encapsulated coin, COA, black card coin holder		

DATE	DESCRIPTION	RCM ITEM #	QUANTITY SOLD	ISSUE PRICE	FINISH	SP-68	SP-69
2012	$10 (½ oz) Maple Leaf Forever	117243	29,173	34.95	Specimen	28.	—

Note: Identical designs are utilized on the $500 gold coin (page 552) and the $300 platinum maple leaf (page 562) for 2012.

THE MAPLE LEAF 2013-2017

TEN DOLLARS, MAPLE LEAF, 2013-2017.

Designers:		Engravers:	
Obv.:	Susanna Blunt	Obv.:	Susan Taylor
Rev.:	See illustrations	Rev.:	See illustrations

	2013-2014	**2015-2017**
Compostion:	99.99% Ag	99.99% Ag
Silver content:	16.1 g, 0.517 tr oz	15.85 g, 0.5 tr oz
Weight:	16.1 g	15.87 g

Diameter:	34.0 mm	Edge:	Reeded
Thickness:	2.1 mm	Die Axis:	↑↑
Finish:	Specimen		
Case of Issue:	Maroon leatherette clam style case, black flocked insert, encapsulated coin, COA		

Common Obverse

2013
Designer: Pierre Leduc
Engraver: Eric Boyer

2014
Designer: Pierre Leduc
Engraver: RCM Staff

2015
Designer: Celia Godkin
Engraver: RCM Staff

2016
Designer: Donna Kriekle
Engraver: RCM Staff

2017
Designer: Pierre Leduc
Engraver: RCM Staff

DATE	DESCRIPTION	RCM ITEM #	QUANTITY SOLD	ISSUE PRICE	FINISH	SP-68	SP-69
2013	Maple Leaf	123685	5,101	39.95	Specimen	35.	—
2014	Maple Leaf	130512	8,732	39.95	Specimen	35.	—
2015	Maple Leaf	140838	24,577	29.95	Specimen	30.	—
2016	Maple Leaf	154436	29,776	29.95	Specimen	30	—
2017	Maple Leaf	156296	2,520	29.95	Specimen	35.	—

TEN DOLLARS, CANADA 150 ICONIC MAPLE LEAF, 2017.

Designers and Engravers:			
Obv.:	Susanna Blunt		
Rev.:	RCM Staff		
Composition:	99.99% Ag,		
Silver content:	15.87 g, 0.510 tr oz		
Weight:	62.69 g	Edge:	Reeded
Diameter:	50 mm	Die Axis: ↑↑	
Thickness:	N/A	Finish:	Matte Proof
Case of Issue:	Maroon clamshell with black beauty box.		

DATE	DESCRIPTION	RCM ITEM #	QUANTITY SOLD	ISSUE PRICE	FINISH	PR-69	PR-70
2017	Canada 150 Iconic Maple Leaf	159185	5,179	169.95	Matte Proof	200	—

TEN DOLLARS, SML TRIBUTE TO 30 YEARS, 2018.

Unchanged since the very first issue in 1988, the solitary maple leaf that adorns the Silver Maple Leaf (SML) coin is widely rgarded as a symbol for unparalleled artistry, craftsmanship and value.

Designers and Engravers:

Obv.:	Susanna Blunt, Susan Taylor
Rev.:	RCM Staff

Composition:	99.99% Ag, Selective gold plating		
Silver content:	62.69 g, 2.02 tr oz		
Weight:	62.69 g	Edge:	Reeded
Diameter:	38.0 mm	Die Axis:	↑↑
Thickness:	N/A	Finish:	Modified Proof
Case of Issue:	Maroon clamshell with black beauty box, COA.		

DATE	DESCRIPTION	RCM ITEM #	MINTAGE	ISSUE PRICE	FINISH	PR-69	PR-70
2018	SML Tribute to 30 Years	163661	6,000	194.95	Modified PR	200.	—

TEN DOLLARS, MAPLE LEAVES, 2018.

Designers and Engravers:

Obv.:	Susanna Blunt, Susan Taylor
Rev.:	Celia Godkin

Composition:	99.99% Ag		
Silver content:	15.87 g, 0.510 tr oz		
Weight:	15.87 g	Edge:	Reeded
Diameter:	34 mm	Die Axis:	↑↑
Thickness:	N/A	Finish:	Specimen
Case of Issue:	Folder with removable capsule.		

DATE	DESCRIPTION	RCM ITEM #	MINTAGE	ISSUE PRICE	FINISH	SP-68	SP-69
2018	Maple Leaves	164889	W.S.L.	34.95	Specimen	35.	—

TEN DOLLARS, MAPLE LEAVES, 2019.

Designers and Engravers:

Obv.:	Susanna Blunt, Susan Taylor
Rev.:	Pierre Leduc

Composition:	99.99% Ag		
Silver content:	15.87 g, 0.510 tr oz		
Weight:	15.87 g	Edge:	Reeded
Diameter:	34 mm	Die Axis:	↑↑
Thickness:	N/A	Finish:	Specimen
Case of Issue:	Maroon clamshell with custom beauty box..		

DATE	DESCRIPTION	RCM ITEM #	MINTAGE	ISSUE PRICE	FINISH	SP-68	SP-69
2019	Maple Leaves	170288	35,000	34.95	Specimen	35.	—

TEN DOLLARS, SILVER MAPLE LEAF (LIMITED EDITION), 2019.

A 30th anniversary tribute to the Silver Maple Leaf (SML), this 2 oz. fine silver piece has the added distinction of being the first black rhodium-plated SML every issued by the RCM.

Designers and Engravers:

Obv.:	Susanna Blunt, Susan Taylor
Rev.:	Walter Ott

Composition:	99.99% Ag		
Silver content:	62.69 g, 2.02 tr oz		
Weight:	62.69 g	Edge:	Reeded
Diameter:	34 mm	Die Axis:	↑↑
Thickness:	N/A	Finish:	Matte Proof
Case of Issue:	Maroon clamshell with custom beauty box..		

DATE	DESCRIPTION	RCM ITEM #	MINTAGE	ISSUE PRICE	FINISH	PR-69	PR-70
2019	Silver Maple Leaf (Limited Edition)	169174	4,000	199.95	Matte Proof	200.	—

TWENTY DOLLAR SILVER MAPLE LEAF COINS

TWENTY DOLLARS (1 OUNCE), MAPLE LEAVES, GLOW-IN-THE-DARK, 2014.

Featuring autumnal colours of the sugar maple tree when viewed in light, the coin transforms to a glow-in-the-dark single maple leaf when viewed in the dark.

Designers and Engravers:

Obv.:	Susanna Blunt, Susan Taylor
Rev.:	C. Godkin, RCM Staff
Composition:	99.99% Ag, Glow-in-the-dark
Silver content:	31.39 g, 1.01 tr oz
Weight:	31.39 g	**Edge:**	Reeded
Diameter:	38.0 mm	**Die Axis:** ↑↑
Thickness:	N/A	**Finish:**	Proof
Case of Issue:	Maroon leatherette clam style case, black flocked insert, encapsulated coin, COA, custom box

DATE	DESCRIPTION	RCM ITEM #	MINTAGE	ISSUE PRICE	FINISH	PR-69	PR-70
2014	Maple Leaves (1 oz)	140455	7,492	104.95	Proof	100.	—

TWENTY DOLLARS, 30TH ANNIVERSARY OF THE SILVER MAPLE LEAF (INCUSE), 2018.

The year 2018 marks the 30th anniversary of our iconic Silver Maple Leaf (SML) bullion coin — the standard against which other silver bullion coins are measured. This very special numismatic release includes a RCM first: incuse-struck images on both sides of the coin, as well as edge lettering, with the number "30" flanked on both sides by a maple leaf.

Designers and Engravers:

Obv.:	Susanna Blunt, Susan Taylor
Rev.:	RCM Staff
Composition:	99.99% Ag
Silver content:	31.39 g, 1.01 tr oz
Weight:	31.39 g	**Edge:**	Interruped reeding
Diameter:	38 mm	**Die Axis:** ↑↑
Thickness:	N/A	**Finish:**	Reverse Proof
Case of Issue:	Maroon clamshell with black beauty box, COA

DATE	DESCRIPTION	RCM ITEM #	MINTAGE	ISSUE PRICE	FINISH	PR-69	PR-70
2018	30th Anniversary of the Silver Maple Leaf (SML)	166223	6,500	104.95	Reverse Proof	110.	—

TWENTY DOLLARS, 30TH ANNIVERSARY OF THE SILVER MAPLE LEAF (SHAPED), 2018.

The Royal Canadian Mint proudly celebrates 30 years of an icon with a maple leaf-shaped tribute to the Silver Maple Leaf (SML) bullion coin.

Designers and Engravers:

Obv.:	Susanna Blunt, Susan Taylor
Rev.:	RCM staff
Composition:	99.99% Ag,
Silver content:	31.5 g, 1.01 tr oz
Weight:	31.5 g	**Edge:**	Plain
Diameter:	42 mm x 43 mm	**Die Axis:** ↑↑
Thickness:	N/A	**Finish:**	Proof
Case of Issue:	Maroon clamshell with black beauty box, COA

DATE	DESCRIPTION	RCM ITEM #	MINTAGE	ISSUE PRICE	FINISH	SP-68	SP-69
2018	30th Anniversary of the SML	164965	6,000	159.95	Proof	160.	—

TWENTY DOLLARS, 40TH ANNIVERSARY OF THE GOLD MAPLE LEAF, 2019.

This coin commemorates the 40th year of the Gold Maple Leaf bullion coin's production. This unique coin also features 40th anniversary edge lettering, and selective gold plating on the iconic maple leaf to resemble the Gold Maple Leaf.

Designers and Engravers:

Obv.:	Susanna Blunt, Susan Taylor
Rev.:	RCM Staff

Composition: 99.99% Ag
Silver content: 31.39 g, 1.01 tr oz
Weight: 31.39 g
Diameter: 38 mm
Thickness: N/A
Case of Issue: Maroon clamshell with black beauty box, COA

Edge: Interruped reeding
Die Axis: ↑↑
Finish: Reverse Proof

DATE	DESCRIPTION	RCM ITEM #	MINTAGE	ISSUE PRICE	FINISH	PR-69	PR-70
2019	40th Anniversary of the Gold Maple Leaf (GML)	169886	5,000	104.95	Reverse Proof	105.	—

FIFTY DOLLAR SILVER MAPLE LEAF COINS

FIFTY DOLLARS (10 ounces), 10TH ANNIVERSARY OF THE SILVER MAPLE LEAF, 1998.

In 1998 the Royal Canadian Mint issued the 10-ounce silver maple leaf in celebration of the 10th anniversary of the silver maple leaf bullion coin. The coin is accompanied by a sterling silver plaque of authenticity.

Designers:

Obv.:	Dora de Pédery-Hunt
Rev.:	RCM Staff

Composition: 99.99% Ag
Silver content: 311.0 g, 10.0 tr oz
Weight: 311.04 g, 10.0 tr oz
Diameter: 65.0 mm
Thickness: 11.0 mm
Case of Issue: Black leather case with silver "Royal Canadian Mint" plaque, black flocked lining, encapsulated coin, Sterling silver certificate of authenticity

Engravers:

Obv.:	Dora de Pédery-Hunt
Rev.:	RCM Staff

Edge: Lettered, 10th Anniversary 10e Anniversaire
Die Axis: ↑↑
Finish: Reverse proof
Nominal Value: $50.00

DATE	DESCRIPTION	QUANTITY SOLD	ISSUE PRICE	FINISH	PR-68	PR-69
1998	$50 (10 oz), 10th Anniv. Silver Maple Leaf	13,533	200.00	Proof	600.	—

Note: Coin illustrated smaller than actual size.

FIFTY DOLLARS (5 ounces), 25TH ANNIVERSARY OF THE SILVER MAPLE LEAF, 2013.

These coins were issued to commemorate the striking of the first silver maple leaf in 1988.

Common Obverse

2013
25th Anniv. of the Silver Maple Leaf
Des.: Arnold Nogy Eng.: Steven Stewart

2013
25th Anniv. of the Silver Maple Leaf
Des.: Jean Louis Sirois Eng.: RCM Staff

Designers:		**Engravers:**
Obv.:	Susanna Blunt	Obv.: Susan Taylor
Rev.:	See reverse illustrations	
Composition:	99.99% Ag	**Silver content:** 157.6 g, 5.0 tr oz
Weight:	157.6 g, 5.0 tr oz	**Edge:** Reeded
Diameter:	65.0 mm	**Die Axis:** ↑↑
Thickness:	N/A	**Finish:** See reverse illustrations
Case of Issue:	(A) Lacquered red wooden case, black lining, encapsulated coin, COA	
	(B) Maroon leatherette clam style case black flocked insert, encapsulated coin, COA, custom beauty box	

DATE	DESCRIPTION	RCM ITEM #	QUANTITY SOLD	ISSUE PRICE	FINISH	PR-69	PR-70
2013 (1988)	$50 (5 oz), 25th Anniv. SML	123520	2,525	499.95	Rev. Proof	500.	—
2013 (1988)	$50 (5 oz) 25th Anniv. SML, Selectively gold plated	127099	1,900	549.95	Matte Proof	500.	—

FIFTY DOLLARS, 30TH ANNIVERSARY OF THE SML, 2018.

The year 2018 marks the 30th anniversary of the iconic Silver Maple Leaf bullion coin – the standard against which other silver bullion coins are measured.

Designers and Engravers:		
Obv.:	Susanna Blunt, Susan Taylor	
Rev.:	Walter Ott	
Composition:	99.99% Ag,	
Silver content:	94.4 g, 30.4 tr oz	
Weight:	94.4 g	**Edge:** Interruped reeding
Diameter:	55 mm	**Die Axis:** ↑↑
Thickness:	N/A	**Finish:** Reverse Proof
Case of Issue:	Maroom clamshell with black beauty box, COA.	

DATE	DESCRIPTION	RCM ITEM #	MINTAGE	ISSUE PRICE	FINISH	PR-69	PR-70
2018	30th Anniversary of the SML	167223	3,000	299.95	Rev. Proof	300.	—

FIFTY DOLLARS, 40TH ANNIVERSARY OF THE GML, 2019.

Designers and Engravers:		
Obv.:	Susanna Blunt, Susan Taylor	
Rev.:	Walter Ott	
Composition:	99.99% Ag	
Silver content:	94.4 g, 3.04 tr oz	
Weight:	94.4 g	**Edge:** Interruped reeding
Diameter:	55 mm	**Die Axis:** ↑↑
Thickness:	N/A	**Finish:** Reverse Proof
Case of Issue:	Maroon clamshell with black beauty box, COA	

DATE	DESCRIPTION	RCM ITEM #	MINTAGE	ISSUE PRICE	FINISH	PR-69	PR-70
2019	40th Anniversary of the GML	169864	2,000	299.95	Reverse Proof	300.	—

TWO HUNDRED FIFTY DOLLAR SILVER MAPLE LEAF COINS

TWO HUNDRED FIFTY DOLLARS (kilogram), MAPLE LEAF FOREVER, 2011-2012.

The reverse design was inspired by the spirit of the maple leaves seen on the one cent coin used since 1937.

Common Obverse (Except date)	2011 Maple Leaf Forever Des.: Debbie Adams Engr.: Konrad Wachelko	2012 Maple Leaf Forever Des.: Luc Normandin Engr.: RCM Staff

\Designers:

Obv.:	Susanna Blunt		Engravers:	
Rev.:	See reverse illustrations		Obv.:	Susan Taylor
Composition:	99.99% Ag		Rev.:	See reverse illustrations
Silver content:	1,000.0 g, 32.151 tr oz		Thickness:	13.2 mm
Weight:	1,000.0 g (1 kilo)		Edge:	2011: Plain 2012: Reeded
Diameter:	101.8 mm		Die Axis:	↑↑
			Finish:	Proof
Case of Issue:	2011: Black display case, black flocked insert, encapsulated coin, COA			
	2012: Canadian maple wood box, black flocked insert, encapsulated coin, COA, custom sleeve			

DATE	DESCRIPTION	RCM ITEM #	QUANTITY SOLD	ISSUE PRICE	FINISH	PR-69	PR-70
2011	Maple Leaf Forever	114842	997	2,195.95	Proof	2,000.	—
2012	Maple Leaf Forever	117494	934	2,249.95	Proof	2,000.	—

Note: 1. Identical designs are utilized on the $2,500 gold (maple leaf) coins for 2011 and 2012, see page 553.
2. Coins illustrated smaller than actual size.

TWO HUNDRED FIFTY DOLLARS (kilogram), MAPLE LEAF FOREVER, 2013.

Designers and Engravers:

Obv.:	Susanna Blunt, Susan Taylor
Rev.:	Emily Damstra
Composition:	99.99% Ag
Silver content:	1,000.0 g, 32.151 tr oz
Weight:	1,000.0 g (1 kilo) Edge: Reeded
Diameter:	102.1 mm Die Axis: ↑↑
Thickness:	12.5 mm
Finish:	Proof, Selectively gold plated
Case of Issue:	Maple wood box, black flocked insert, encapsulated coin, COA

DATE	DESCRIPTION	RCM ITEM #	QUANTITY SOLD	ISSUE PRICE	FINISH	PR-69	PR-70
2013	Maple Leaf Forever, Selectively gold plated	123179	596	2,299.95	Proof	2,000.	—

SILVER MAPLE LEAFS WITH PRIVY MARKS
SINGLES

FIVE DOLLARS (1 ounce), SILVER MAPLE LEAFS WITH PRIVY MARKS, 1998-2018.

Beginning in 1998 the Royal Canadian Mint started a special issue of the $5.00 - 1 oz silver Maple Leafs. Privy marks were added to the reverses, commemorating special events for each year. For Designers and Engravers see page 569 and for Specifications see page 568.

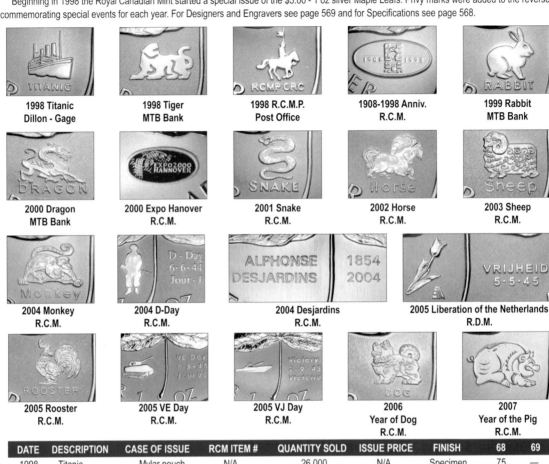

1998 Titanic Dillon - Gage	1998 Tiger MTB Bank	1998 R.C.M.P. Post Office	1908-1998 Anniv. R.C.M.	1999 Rabbit MTB Bank
2000 Dragon MTB Bank	2000 Expo Hanover R.C.M.	2001 Snake R.C.M.	2002 Horse R.C.M.	2003 Sheep R.C.M.
2004 Monkey R.C.M.	2004 D-Day R.C.M.	2004 Desjardins R.C.M.	2005 Liberation of the Netherlands R.D.M.	
2005 Rooster R.C.M.	2005 VE Day R.C.M.	2005 VJ Day R.C.M.	2006 Year of Dog R.C.M.	2007 Year of the Pig R.C.M.

DATE	DESCRIPTION	CASE OF ISSUE	RCM ITEM #	QUANTITY SOLD	ISSUE PRICE	FINISH	68	69
1998	Titanic	Mylar pouch	N/A	26,000	N/A	Specimen	75.	—
1998	Tiger	Mylar pouch	N/A	25,000	N/A	Specimen	55.	—
1998	R.C.M.P.	Mylar pouch	N/A	25,000	N/A	Specimen	70.	—
1998	90th Anniv.	Mylar pouch	N/A	13,025	N/A	Specimen	55.	—
1999	Rabbit	Mylar pouch	N/A	25,000	N/A	Specimen	55.	—
2000	Dragon	Mylar pouch	N/A	25,000	N/A	Specimen	60.	—
2000	Expo	Mylar pouch	N/A	15,000	N/A	Specimen	90.	—
2001	Snake	Mylar pouch	N/A	25,000	N/A	Specimen	55.	—
2002	Horse	Mylar pouch	N/A	25,000	N/A	Specimen	55.	—
2003	Sheep	Mylar pouch	N/A	25,000	N/A	Specimen	55.	—
2004	Monkey	Mylar pouch	N/A	25,000	N/A	Specimen	55.	—
2004	D-Day	Red display	N/A	11,698	39.95	Specimen	70.	—
2004	Desjardins	Red display	N/A	15,000	39.95	Bullion	70.	—
2005	Rooster	Mylar pouch	N/A	15,000	24.95	Specimen	50.	—
2005	Liberation	Mylar pouch	N/A	3,500	€45.95	Specimen	160.	—
2005	VE Day	Mylar pouch	N/A	6,998	49.95	Specimen	80.	—
2005	VJ Day	Mylar pouch	N/A	6,998	49.95	Specimen	80.	—
2006	Year of the Dog	Mylar pouch	N/A	10,000	24.95	Specimen	55.	—
2007	Year of the Pig	Mylar pouch	N/A	8,000	29.95	Specimen	55.	—

FIVE DOLLARS (1 ounce), SILVER MAPLE LEAFS WITH PRIVY MARKS, 1998-2018, (cont.).

2007, 2008, 2009
Fabulous 12

2008
Year of the Rat
R.C.M.

2008
Brandenburg Gate

2009
Year of the Ox
R.C.M.

2009
Tower Bridge

2012
Tower of Pisa

2010-2018
Fabulous 15

2012
Titanic 100th Anniv.

2012
Year of the Dragon

2013
Year of the Snake

2014
World Money Fair

2014
Year of the Horse

2014
A.N.A.
Chicago

2014
Dual Horse

2015
Year of the Ram

2015
Heart
Rosland Capital
Fisher House

2015
E=mc2

2015
A.N.A. Chicago
Tulip

DATE	DESCRIPTION	CASE OF ISSUE	RCM ITEM #	QUANTITY SOLD	ISSUE PRICE	FINISH	68	69
2007	Fabulous 12	Mylar pouch	N/A	5,000	39.95	Specimen	90.	—
2008	Fabulous 12	Mylar pouch	N/A	5,000	N/A	Specimen	130.	—
2008	Year of the Rat	Mylar pouch	N/A	8,000	24.95	Specimen	55.	—
2008	Brandenburg Gate	Mylar pouch	N/A	50,000	39.95	Bullion	60.	—
2009	Year of the Ox	Mylar pouch	N/A	8,000	23.95	Specimen	55.	—
2009	Tower Bridge	Mylar pouch	N/A	75,000	34.95	Bullion	60.	—
2009	Fabulous 12	Mylar pouch	N/A	5,000	N/A	Specimen	110.	—
2010	Fabulous 15	Plastic case	N/A	5,000	44.95	Specimen	110.	—
2011	Fabulous 15	Plastic case	N/A	5,000	44.95	Specimen	170.	—
2012	Leaning Tower of Pisa	Mylar pouch	N/A	50,000	N/A	Bullion	60.	—
2012	Fabulous 15	Mylar pouch	N/A	10,000	N/A	Bullion	75.	—
2012	Titanic 100th Anniversary	Mylar pouch	N/A	25,000	N/A	Specimen	50.	—
2012	Year of the Dragon	Mylar pouch	N/A	25,000	N/A	Specimen	50.	—
2013	Fabulous 15	Mylar pouch	125489	10,000	55.95	Bullion	75.	—
2013	Year of the Snake	Display box	N/A	N/A	N/A	Specimen	45.	—
2014	World Money Fair, Berlin	Display box	129449	7,429	100.00	Bullion	100.	—
2014	Year of the Horse	Mylar pouch	N/A	N/A	32.75	Specimen	45.	—
2014	American Numismatic Society	Display box	130570	7,452	100.00	Proof	90.	—
2014	Fabulous 15	Mylar pouch	131684	10,000	59.95	Bullion	60.	—
2014	Dual Horse, Horse & Hieroglyphic	Display box	N/A	1,000	N/A	Bullion	—	—
2015	Year of the Ram	Plastic case	N/A	N/A	25.00	Specimen	35.	—
2015	Heart	Capsule	N/A	25,000	N/A	Bullion	200.	—
2015	E=mc2	Mylar pouch	N/A	50,000	35.00	Proof	50.	—
2015	A.N.A. Chicago	Display box	148094	5,000	79.95	Bullion	85.	—
2015	Fabulous 15	Capsule	N/A	N/A	N/A	Bullion	—	—

FIVE DOLLARS (1 ounce), SILVER MAPLE LEAFS WITH PRIVY MARKS, 1998-2018, (cont.).

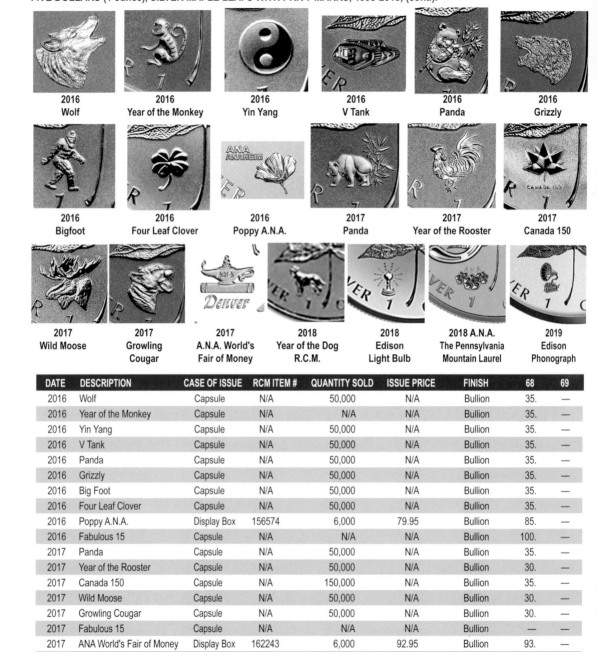

2016 Wolf	2016 Year of the Monkey	2016 Yin Yang	2016 V Tank	2016 Panda	2016 Grizzly
2016 Bigfoot	2016 Four Leaf Clover	2016 Poppy A.N.A.	2017 Panda	2017 Year of the Rooster	2017 Canada 150
2017 Wild Moose	2017 Growling Cougar	2017 A.N.A. World's Fair of Money	2018 Year of the Dog R.C.M.	2018 Edison Light Bulb	2018 A.N.A. The Pennsylvania Mountain Laurel	2019 Edison Phonograph

DATE	DESCRIPTION	CASE OF ISSUE	RCM ITEM #	QUANTITY SOLD	ISSUE PRICE	FINISH	68	69
2016	Wolf	Capsule	N/A	50,000	N/A	Bullion	35.	—
2016	Year of the Monkey	Capsule	N/A	N/A	N/A	Bullion	35.	—
2016	Yin Yang	Capsule	N/A	50,000	N/A	Bullion	35.	—
2016	V Tank	Capsule	N/A	50,000	N/A	Bullion	35.	—
2016	Panda	Capsule	N/A	50,000	N/A	Bullion	35.	—
2016	Grizzly	Capsule	N/A	50,000	N/A	Bullion	35.	—
2016	Big Foot	Capsule	N/A	50,000	N/A	Bullion	35.	—
2016	Four Leaf Clover	Capsule	N/A	50,000	N/A	Bullion	35.	—
2016	Poppy A.N.A.	Display Box	156574	6,000	79.95	Bullion	85.	—
2016	Fabulous 15	Capsule	N/A	N/A	N/A	Bullion	100.	—
2017	Panda	Capsule	N/A	50,000	N/A	Bullion	35.	—
2017	Year of the Rooster	Capsule	N/A	50,000	N/A	Bullion	30.	—
2017	Canada 150	Capsule	N/A	150,000	N/A	Bullion	35.	—
2017	Wild Moose	Capsule	N/A	50,000	N/A	Bullion	30.	—
2017	Growling Cougar	Capsule	N/A	50,000	N/A	Bullion	30.	—
2017	Fabulous 15	Capsule	N/A	N/A	N/A	Bullion	—	—
2017	ANA World's Fair of Money	Display Box	162243	6,000	92.95	Bullion	93.	—
2018	Fabulous 15	Capsule	N/A	N/A	N/A	Bullion	—	—
2018	Year of the Dog	Capsule	N/A	N/A	BV	Bullion	35.	—
2018	Edison Light Bulb	Capsule	N/A	N/A	BV	Bullion	35.	—
2018	ANA World's Fair of Money	Display Box	169286	6,000	89.95	Bullion	90.	—
2019	Edison Phonograph	Capsule	N/A	N/A	BV	Bullion	35.	—

Pricing has not been established for the Fabulous 15 coins for 2015, 2017 and 2018 due to lack of information.

SPECIAL PRIVY MARK SET

FIVE DOLLARS (1 OUNCE), SILVER MAPLE LEAFS, ZODIAC PRIVY MARK SET, 2004.

This special zodiak privy mark set was issued by the Royal Canandian Mint. Of the 25,000 sets issued five thousand were boxed and sold as a packaged set with ceritficates of authenticity and sold by Universal Coins of Ottawa.

Aries	Taurus	Gemini	Cancer	Leo	Virgo
Libra	Scorpio	Sagittarius	Capricorn	Aquarius	Pisces

Designers:		**Engravers:**	
Obv.:	Susanna Blunt	Obv.:	Susan Taylor
Rev.:	RCM Staff	Rev.:	José Osio
Composition:	99.99% Ag	**Thickness:**	3.2 mm
Weight:	31.1035 g, 1 tr oz	**Edge:**	Reeded
Diameter:	38.0 mm	**Die Axis:**	↑↑
Finish:	Specimen (reverse proof)		
Case of Issue:	Singly: Mylar pouch		
	Set: Red 12-hole case		

DATE	DESCRIPTION	RCM ITEM #	QUANTITY SOLD	ISSUE PRICE	FINISH	SP-68	SP-69
2004	Set of 12 coins	N/A	25,000	368.88	Specimen	575.	*
2004	Single coin	N/A	Included	39.95	Specimen	55.	—

NOTES

1. A specimen finish on a bullion coin is also known as a reverse proof – a brilliant relief on a matte or satin background.
2. The method of packaging may vary from the normal mylar pouch to red or black flocked clam style cases, depending on the distributor.
3. The maple leaf coins which carry either an "F12" or "F15" privy mark commemorate the winning coin design at the Berlin Money Fair for the year which they are dated.

SILVER MAPLE LEAF FRACTIONAL SETS

15TH ANNIVERSARY OF THE SILVER MAPLE (HOLOGRAM SET), 2003.

These maple leaf coins were struck to commemorate the 15th anniversary of the silver maple leaf, 1988-2003. This five-coin set contains two new denominations for Canadian coinage, a $3 and a $4 coin. All coins are struck with a maple leaf hologram.

Designers and Engravers:

Obv.:	Dora de Pédery-Hunt
Rev.:	RCM Staff
Specifications:	See page 568
Silver content:	1.90 tr oz
Finish:	Bullion, Hologram
Case of Issue:	Red wooden case, black flocked insert, encapsulated coin, COA, silver outer box

DATE	DESCRIPTION	RCM ITEM #	QUANTITY SOLD	ISSUE PRICE	FINISH	MS-66	MS-67
2003	Set of 5 coins (1, ½, ¼, 1/10, 1/20 oz)	N/A	28,947	149.95	Bullion	150.	—

ROYAL CANADIAN MINT LOGO SET, 2004.

Each coin in this set carries the Royal Canadian Mint logo on each coin.

Designers and Engravers:

Obv.:	Susanna Blunt, Susan Taylor
Rev.:	RCM Staff
Specifications:	See page 568
Silver content:	1.90 tr oz
Finish:	Specimen (reverse proof)
Case of Issue:	Dark blue leatherette clam style case, black insert, encapsulated coin, COA, silver sleeve

DATE	DESCRIPTION	RCM ITEM #	QUANTITY SOLD	ISSUE PRICE	FINISH	SP-68	SP-69
2004	Set of 5 coins (1, ½, ¼, 1/10, 1/20 oz)	N/A	13,859	99.95	Specimen	120.	—

SILVER MAPLE LEAF 25TH ANNIVERSARY FRACTIONAL SET, 2013.

This set was issued to commemorate the twenty-fifth anniversary of the Silver Maple Leaf bullion coin first issued in 1988.

Designers and Engravers:

Obv.:	Susanna Blunt, Matt Bowen
Rev.:	Arnold Nogy, Steven Stewart
Specifications:	See page 568
Silver content:	1.90 tr oz
Finish:	Reverse Proof
Case of Issue:	Maroon leatherette clam style case, black flocked insert, encapsulated coins, COA

DATE	DESCRIPTION	RCM ITEM #	QUANTITY SOLD	ISSUE PRICE	FINISH	PR-69	PR-70
2013 (1998-)	Set of 5 coins (1, 1/2, 1/4, 1/10, 1/20 oz)	120674	9,993	199.95	Proof	225.	—

SILVER MAPLE LEAF FRACTIONAL SET, 2014.

Designers and Engravers:

Obv.:	Susanna Blunt, Matt Bowen
Rev.:	Arnold Nogy, RCM Staff
Specifications:	See page 568
Silver content:	1.90 tr oz
Finish:	Reverse Proof, Selectively gold plated
Case of Issue:	Maroon leatherette clam style case, black flocked insert, encapsulated coins, COA

DATE	DESCRIPTION	RCM ITEM #	QUANTITY SOLD	ISSUE PRICE	FINISH	PR-69	PR-70
2014	Set of 5 coins (1, ½, ¼, 1/10, 1/20 oz)	127913	9,997	249.95	Proof	225.	—

SILVER SUGAR MAPLE LEAF FRACTIONAL SET, 2015.

The one ounce coin features a rich translucent red enamel. All coins are struck with an incuse design.

Designers and Engravers:

Obv.:	Susanna Blunt, Matt Bowen
Rev.:	Lilyane Coulombe, RCM Staff
Specifications:	See page 568
Silver content:	1.90 tr oz
Finish:	Reverse Proof
Case of Issue:	Maroon leatherette clam style case, black flocked insert, encapsulated coins, COA

DATE	DESCRIPTION	RCM ITEM #	QUANTITY SOLD	ISSUE PRICE	FINISH	PR-69	PR-70
2015	Set of 5 coins (1, ½, ¼, 1/10, 1/20 oz)	140483	834	224.95	Proof	225.	—

SILVER MAPLE LEAF FRACTIONAL SET: A HISTORIC REIGN, 2016.

The one-ounce coin in the set features the edge lettering: "LONGEST REIGNING SOVEREIGN".

Designers and Engravers:

Obv.:	Susanna Blunt, Susan Taylor
Rev.:	Donna Kriekle
Specifications:	See page 568
Silver content:	1.90 tr oz
Finish:	Reverse Proof
Case of Issue:	Maroon leatherette clam style case, black flocked insert, encapsulated coins, COA

DATE	DESCRIPTION	RCM ITEM #	QUANTITY SOLD	ISSUE PRICE	FINISH	PR-69	PR-70
2016	Set of 5 coins (1, ½, ¼, 1/10, 1/20 oz)	146734	7,297	224.95	Proof	200.	—

SILVER MAPLE LEAF FRACTIONAL SET:
MAPLE LEAF TRIBUTE, 2017.

A unique design celebrating Canada's most cherished national symbol and a commemorative double-date (1867-2017) to highlight this historic year.

Designers and Engravers:

Obv.:	Susanna Blunt, Susan Taylor
Rev.:	Stan Witten
Specifications:	See page 568
Silver content:	1.90 tr oz
Finish:	Reverse Proof
Case of Issue:	Maroon leatherette clam style case, black flocked insert, encapsulated coins, COA

DATE	DESCRIPTION	RCM ITEM #	QUANTITY SOLD	ISSUE PRICE	FINISH	PR-69	PR-70
2017	Set of 4 coins (1, ½, ¼, 1/10 oz)	161790	5,500	199.95	Reverse Proof	200.	—

SILVER MAPLE LEAF FRACTIONAL SET:
A BICENTENNIAL CELEBRATION, 2019.

The 2019 fine silver fractional set commemorates the bicentennial of the birth of Queen Victoria while highlighting Canada's natural heritage on the reverse, where blue rhodium plating (a first) adds a special splash of colour to the 1 oz. piece..

Designers and Engravers:

Obv.:	Susanna Blunt, Susan Taylor
Rev.:	Julius Csotonyi
Specifications:	See page 568
Silver content:	1.90 tr oz
Finish:	Reverse Proof
Case of Issue:	Maroon leatherette clam style case, black flocked insert, encapsulated coins, COA

DATE	DESCRIPTION	RCM ITEM #	QUANTITY SOLD	ISSUE PRICE	FINISH	PR-69	PR-70
2019	Set of 4 coins (1, ½, ¼, 1/10 oz)	167586	6,500	224.95	Reverse Proof	225.	—

SILVER MAPLE LEAFS WITH COLOUR

SINGLE COINS

FIVE DOLLARS (1 OUNCE), SILVER MAPLE LEAFS, COLOURED COIN SERIES, 2001-2007.

| 2001-2003 Obverse
Designer and Engraver:
Dora de Pédery-Hunt | 2001 Autumn
Designer: Debbie Adams
Engraver: W. Woodruff | 2002 Spring
Designer and Engraver:
William Woodruff | 2003 Summer
Designer and Engraver:
Stan Witten |

| 2004-2007 Obverse
Designer: Susanna Blunt
Engraver: Susan Taylor | 2004 Winter
Designer and Engraver:
Stan Witten | 2005 Bigleaf Maple
Designer and Engraver:
Stan Witten | 2006 Silver Maple
Designer and Engraver:
Stan Witten |

2007 Sugar Maple
Designer and Engraver:
Stan Witten

Designers and Engravers: See obverse and reverse illustrations
Specifications: See page 568
Finish: Bullion, colourised
Case of Issue: 2001-2004: Dark green clam case, black flocked insert, encapsulated coin, COA
2005-2007: Maroon plastic slide case, black plastic insert, encapsulated coin, COA

DATE	DESCRIPTION	QUANTITY SOLD	ISSUE PRICE	FINISH	MS-65	MS-66
2001	Autumn	49,709	34.95	Bullion	50.	—
2002	Spring	29,509	34.95	Bullion	50.	—
2003	Summer	29,416	34.95	Bullion	50.	—
2004	Winter	26,763	34.95	Bullion	50.	—
2005	Bigleaf Maple	21,233	39.95	Bullion	60.	—
2006	Silver Maple	14,157	45.95	Bullion	60.	—
2007	Sugar Maple	11,495	49.95	Bullion	100.	—

Note: Coins illustrated smaller than actual size.

SILVER MAPLE LEAFS WITH HOLOGRAMS
SINGLE COINS

FIVE DOLLARS (1 ounce), "MAPLE OF GOOD FORTUNE" HOLOGRAM, 2001, 2003 AND 2005.

First issued in 2001, the $5 Maple Leaf coin carries a privy mark of Chinese characters, meaning Maple of Good Fortune, or Hope, as part of the hologram.

2001 Obverse

2001 Reverse

2003 Obverse

2003 Reverse

2005 Obverse

2005 Reverse

Designers:			Engravers:	
2001, 2003:	Obv.:	Dora de Pédery-Hunt	Obv.:	Dora de Pédery-Hunt
	Rev.:	RCM Staff	Rev.:	RCM Staff
2005:	Obv.:	Susanna Blunt	Obv.:	Susan Taylor
	Rev.:	RCM Staff	Rev.:	RCM Staff
Specifications:		See page 568	**Case of Issue:**	Mylar pouch
Finish:		Specimen (reverse proof), hologram		
Case of Issue:		Red clam oval case, taupe flocked insert, encapsulated coin, COA		

DATE	DESCRIPTION	QUANTITY SOLD	ISSUE PRICE	FINISH	SP-68	SP-69
2001	Good Fortune	29,817	59.99	Specimen	50.	—
2003	Good Fortune	29,731	39.99	Specimen	50.	—
2005	Good Fortune	19,888	39.95	Specimen	50.	—

SILVER MAPLE LEAFS WITH HOLOGRAMS

SINGLE COINS

FIVE DOLLARS (1 OUNCE), 15TH ANNIVERSARY OF THE ONE DOLLAR LOON, 2002.

These maple leaf coins were struck to commemorate the 15th anniversary of the one dollar loon coin issued in 1987. The reverse design on this coin depicts a male loon flapping its wings in the "Loon Dance" protecting its nest from intruders.

Designers and Engravers:
Obv.:	Dora de Pédery-Hunt
Rev.:	RCM Staff

Composition: 99.99% Ag
Weight: 31.1035 g, 1 oz
Diameter: 38.0 mm Edge: Reeded
Thickness: 3.2 mm Die Axis: ↑↑
Finish: Specimen (reverse proof), Hologram
Case of Issue: Black leatherette clam case, hunter green interior, encapsulated coin, COA

DATE	DESCRIPTION	QUANTITY SOLD	ISSUE PRICE	FINISH	SP-68	SP-69
2002	$5 (1 oz) 15th Anniv. of One Dollar Loon	29,970	39.95	Specimen	45.	—

SILVER MAPLE LEAF SETS

$5 SILVER MAPLE LEAF WITH PROOF SETS, 2001.

Three varieties of silver maples (colourised, hologram and regular) were combined with seven proof coins, 1¢ to $2, of the 2001 Proof Set to form the following Premium Proof sets:

DATE	DESCRIPTION	QUANTITY SOLD	ISSUE PRICE	ISSUER	FINISH	MARKET VALUE
2001	**Proof Set 2001.** Seven proof coins. Reverse proof hologram, silver maple leaf	3,000	150.00	RCM	PR-68 SP-66	110.
2001	**Proof Set 2001.** Seven proof coins. Reverse proof privy snake, silver maple leaf	Included	100.00	RCM	PR-69, MS-65	110.
2001	**Proof Set 2001.** Seven proof coins and a colourised 2001 silver maple leaf	Included	75.00	RCM	PR-69, MS-65	110.

SILVER MAPLE LEAF DERIVATIVES

DATE	DESCRIPTION	QUANTITY SOLD	ISSUE PRICE	ISSUER	FINISH	MARKET VALUE
1998	125th Anniv. of R.C.M.P., Silver maple with R.C.M.P. privy mark. Souvenir sheet. Dark blue presentation case. COA.Booklet	25,000	47.95	RCM, CP	SP-66	75.
2004	Sambro Island. Framed image and twenty dollar coin	N/A	249.00	RCM	PR-67	75.